Metallurgy and Metallurgical Engineering Series

ROBERT F. MEHL, *Consulting Editor*

Structure of Metals

Metallurgy and Metallurgical Engineering Series

Robert F. Mehl, *Consulting Editor*

Michael B. Bever, *Associate Consulting Editor*

STRUCTURE OF METALS

Crystallographic Methods, Principles, and Data

Charles S. Barrett, Ph.D.

Professor, Institute for the Study of Metals
University of Chicago

SECOND EDITION

New York   Toronto   London

McGRAW-HILL BOOK COMPANY, Inc.

1952

PREFACE TO THE SECOND EDITION

The general plan of the first edition has been retained throughout this revision. Much significant research has been published in the interval between editions, and the discussions and treatments of the previous edition have been expanded accordingly. Extensive revision has been made of the sections concerning dislocations, imperfections, creep, structures of solid and liquid metals and alloys, textures and transformations. As before, many references have been given not only to original articles but to detailed summaries of research data, symposia, advanced textbooks, and other references that should prove helpful in bridging the gap between this book and a literature that has become very extensive.

Grateful acknowledgment is made to the many coworkers in the Institute for the Study of Metals at the University of Chicago, and elsewhere, who have critically reviewed portions of the manuscript, and to my wife who has contributed much time to the project. Permission to reproduce various illustrations has kindly been given by authors and publishers: Fig. 15/I is from W. L. Bragg, "The Crystalline State," The Macmillan Company; Fig. 20/I is from R. W. James, "X-ray Crystallography," E. P. Dutton & Co., Inc.; Figs. 4/XI and 5/XI are from W. Hume-Rothery, "Structure of Metals," The Institute of Metals; Figs. 3/V, 4/V, and 10/VII are from R. W. G. Wyckoff, "The Structure of Crystals," Reinhold Publishing Corporation; Figs. 9/III, 16/XI, and 17/XI are from G. L. Clark, "Applied X-rays," McGraw-Hill Book Company, Inc.; Figs. 11/VI, 12/VI, 13/VI, and 11/VII are from W. P. Davey, "A Study of Crystal Structure and Its Applications," McGraw-Hill Book Company, Inc.; and Figs. 9, 11 to 13, 16 to 20 of Chap. IV, and Fig. I/X are from the "Metals Handbook," American Society for Metals. A number of prints have kindly been furnished by investigators and manufacturers; references to these and to the source of illustrations and data from the technical journals are given in the text.

CHARLES S. BARRETT

BIRMINGHAM, ENGLAND
May, 1952

PREFACE TO THE FIRST EDITION

This book is intended to serve both as a text and as a reference book. The portions intended for classroom use have been written for courses in crystallography, particularly the courses offered to students of metallurgy. It is primarily intended for graduate courses, but a number of chapters are at a level appropriate for advanced undergraduate courses in applied X-rays, crystallography, and physical metallurgy (Chaps. I to IV, IX to XI, XIII). In an effort to make the book more readable, certain advanced topics on X-ray diffraction and various tables of data have been placed in appendixes, and laboratory manipulations that would not interest the general reader have been printed in smaller type.

The first four chapters of this book explain the fundamentals of crystal lattices and projections, and the general principles of the diffraction of X-rays from crystals. Chapters V to VII cover the technique of X-ray diffraction, presenting the operating details of the methods that are in common use. Several chapters are included on the applications of X-ray diffraction in the field of physical metallurgy, covering techniques for determining constitution diagrams, identifying unknown materials, determining crystal structures, determining the orientation of single crystals, detecting and analyzing preferred orientations, and measuring stresses.

One chapter is devoted to electron diffraction, its metallurgical uses, and the precautions to be observed in interpreting electron diffraction data. The electron microscope receives only a brief mention because at the time the manuscript was written the metallographic technique for this instrument was still being rapidly developed and, except for particle-size determinations, the instrument had not yet achieved the status of a widely accepted tool in metallographic or crystallographic research.

The last half of the book is devoted to the results of research and contains extensive reviews of fields that are of current interest. In assembling these summaries, an effort has been made to include an adequate number of references to the literature, to cover thoroughly the subjects that have not been extensively reviewed in readily available publications, and to maintain a critical but unbiased attitude toward the data and conclusions that are reviewed. The subjects treated include the following: principles governing the crystal structure of metals and alloys; superlattices and their effect on properties; imperfections in

vii

crystals; the structure of liquid metals; the processes of slip, twinning, and fracture and modern theories of these processes, including the current "dislocation theory"; the effects of cold work and annealing on the structure of metals, including the effects on diffraction patterns of static and fatigue stressing, rolling, grinding, and polishing; the results of X-ray studies of internal stresses; preferred orientations resulting from cold work, hot work, recrystallization, freezing, electrodeposition, evaporation, and sputtering; directionality in commercial products and in single crystals and its relation to crystal orientation.

The author is indebted to many colleagues and graduate students who have assisted directly and indirectly in the preparation of this book. He particularly wishes to thank Dr. R. F. Mehl, head of theDepartment of Metallurgy and director of the Metals Research Laboratory at Carnegie Institute of Technology, who guided the organization of the courses out of which the book evolved, encouraged publication of the material, and offered valuable criticisms of the manuscript.

CHARLES S. BARRETT

PITTSBURGH, PA.
June, 1943

CONTENTS

CHAPTER I

THE FUNDAMENTALS OF CRYSTALLOGRAPHY

A crystal consists of atoms arranged in a pattern that repeats periodically in three dimensions. The regular repetition of the unit of structure in a crystal is analogous to a pattern of wallpaper. The design of the wallpaper consists of a fundamental unit of the design placed in parallel fashion at each point of a two-dimensional lattice; the structure of a crystal consists of a unit of structure—an atom or group of atoms—placed in parallel fashion at each point of a three-dimensional lattice.

Crystallinity is completely absent in a *gas*, owing to the kinetic and random motion of the atoms, but in a *liquid* the velocity of atomic movement is less, and some tendency to take a regular arrangement is apparent. If an instantaneous photograph of a liquid could be taken that would show the individual atoms, it would disclose several clusters in which the atoms have the close packing characteristic of the crystalline state. These clusters are potential nuclei of the solid phase, but above the melting point they are unable to maintain their close-packed near-crystalline arrangement against the severe thermal agitation of the atoms of which they are composed and the bombardment of the impinging atoms. In some substances the liquid arrangement may be frozen in by rapid cooling, and the material hardens into the *glassy state* and is a supercooled liquid. The vitreous state acquired in this way then persists until the atoms are given an opportunity to rearrange themselves; annealing below the melting point permits a glass to crystallize (devitrify) and become a true solid.

Molten metals do not supercool to the glassy state, but it is possible to produce an amorphous or nearly amorphous condition in many metals by deposition under certain conditions. Bridgman has also succeeded in disrupting almost completely the crystallinity of certain metals by extreme amounts of twisting, and there is some evidence from electron diffraction that polished layers on metals are amorphous. The individual crystals in a polycrystalline aggregate may have any size from macroscopic dimensions down to a few atoms. Obviously, there can be no regular repetition in the atomic pattern if the grain size is of the order of one structural unit, and so the crystallinity would really be zero at the lower limit of grain size. It is thus inconsistent to speak of the crystal structure of a glass or of an amorphous body, even though a fundamental configuration can be found in it, for there is no periodicity to the configura-

1

tion. Intermediate degrees of crystallinity are possible as the grain size increases above this lower limit.

Carbon and various organic and inorganic substances may exist in semicrystalline states that possess periodicity in only one or two dimensions but lack it in others. The *mesomorphic state* possessed by certain long-chain organic substances (also called "liquid crystals") affords examples of various intermediate types of regularity. Among metallic crystals and others it is not unusual to find deviations from perfection that consist of occasional atoms being absent from the array, atoms or layers of atoms being displaced from their regular positions, and atoms being replaced more or less at random by atoms of a different kind; but it is logical to discuss ideal crystals first before taking up these deviations.

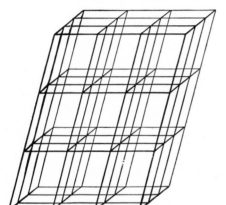

FIG. 1. A space lattice.

Space-lattices and Crystal Systems.[1] The atomic array in a crystal is conveniently described with respect to a three-dimensional net of straight lines. Imagine a lattice of lines, as in Fig. 1, dividing space into equal-sized parallelepipeds which stand side by side with all faces in contact so as to fill space with no voids. The intersections of the lines are points of a space-lattice. These points are of fundamental importance in descriptions of crystals, for they may be the positions occupied by atoms in crystals—as they are in the common metals—or they may be points about which several atoms are clustered. Since parallelepipeds of many different shapes can be drawn through the points of a space-lattice to partition the crystal into cells, the manner in which the network of reference lines is drawn is arbitrary. They need not be drawn so that lattice points lie only at the corners of the unit cells; in fact, it is found more convenient to describe some crystals with respect to cells in which points lie not only at cell corners but also at cell centers or at the centers of cell faces.

The important characteristic of a space-lattice is that *every point of a space-lattice has identical surroundings*. The grouping of lattice points about any given point is identical with the grouping about any other lattice point in the lattice. If it were possible for a tiny observer to hop

---

[1] The space-lattices are also called "translation groups" because there are certain movements—"primitive translations"—which by repetition will lead from one lattice point to any other. Space-lattices are also referred to as "Bravais lattices."

about on the lattice points, he would be unable to distinguish one from another, for the rows and planes of points near each point would be identical; and if he wandered among the atoms of a solid metal or a chemical compound, he would find the outlook from any lattice point just like that from any other.

There are 14 space-lattices. No more than 14 ways can be found in which points can be arranged in space so that each point has identical surroundings. There are, of course, many more than 14 ways in which actual crystals may be built up of atoms piled together; *i.e.*, there are a great many *crystal structures*. However, each of the structures consists of some fundamental pattern repeated at each point of a space-lattice. The schemes of repetition, the *space-lattices*, are very limited in number while the possible *crystal structures* are almost unlimited. Not infrequently the term "lattice" has been loosely used as a synonym for "structure," a practice that is incorrect and likely to be confusing.

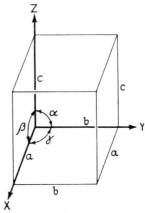

FIG. 2. Crystal axes.

To specify a given arrangement of points in a space-lattice or of atoms in a structure, it is customary to give their coordinates with respect to a set of coordinate axes chosen with an origin at one of the lattice points. Cubic crystals, for example, are referred to a cubic set of axes, three axes of equal length that stand perpendicular to one another and that form three edges of a cube. Each space-lattice has some convenient set of axes that is conventionally used with it, some axes being equal in length and others unequal, some standing at right angles and others not. Seven different *systems of axes* are used in crystallography, each possessing certain characteristics as to equality of angles and equality of lengths. These are the basis of the seven *crystal systems* employed, for instance, in the classification of minerals. Referring to Fig. 2, the lengths of the three axes of a system are a, b, and c, respectively; the angles are α, β, and γ, with the angle α opposite the a axis, etc.[1] The crystal systems are listed in Table I, together with their axial lengths, angles, and some examples of crystals belonging to each classification. When a crystal structure is determined, definite values are found for the axial lengths and angles; different substances crystallizing in a given system will have different values for these variables.

[1] It is customary to use axes oriented as in Fig. 2 in crystal drawings, with the c axis vertical.

The network of lines through the points of a space-lattice, as in Fig. 1, divides it into parallelepipeds called *unit cells*. Each unit cell in a space-lattice is identical in size, shape, and orientation with every other. It is the fundamental building block of the structure. The crystal is constructed by stacking identical unit cells face to face in perfect alignment

TABLE I. THE CRYSTAL SYSTEMS

(In this table $\neq$ means "not necessarily equal to, and generally different from")

System	Axes and interaxial angles	Examples
Triclinic	Three axes not at right angles, of any lengths $a \neq b \neq c$ $\alpha \neq \beta \neq \gamma \neq 90°$	K_2CrO_7
Monoclinic	Three axes, one pair not at right angles, of any lengths $a \neq b \neq c$ $\alpha = \gamma = 90° \neq \beta$	β-S $CaSO_4 \cdot 2H_2O$ (gypsum)
Orthorhombic (rhombic)	Three axes at right angles; all unequal $a \neq b \neq c$ $\alpha = \beta = \gamma = 90°$	α-S Ga Fe_3C (cementite)
Tetragonal	Three axes at right angles; two equal $a = b \neq c$ $\alpha = \beta = \gamma = 90°$	β-Sn (white) TiO_2
Cubic	Three axes at right angles; all equal $a = b = c$ $\alpha = \beta = \gamma = 90°$	Cu, Ag, Au Fe NaCl
Hexagonal	Three axes coplanar at 120°, equal Fourth axis at right angles to these $a_1 = a_2 = a_2 \neq c$ (or $a_1 = b \neq c$) $\alpha = \beta = 90°, \gamma = 120°$	Zn, Cd NiAs
Rhombohedral (trigonal)	Three axes equally inclined, not at right angles; all equal $a = b = c$ $\alpha = \beta = \gamma \neq 90°$	As, Sb, Bi Calcite

in three dimensions. Each face of a unit cell is a parallelogram (Fig. 2); the cell is a parallelepiped with the axes a, b, and c as edges. In the hexagonal system, two axes, a_1 and a_2, are equal in length and are at 120° to each other. These two, together with the c axis that stands 90° to each, form the edges of the unit cell; there is also a third axis, a_3, that is coplanar with a_1 and a_2 and 120° from each, which is used when one wishes to show the full symmetry of the lattice.

Unit cells are drawn with lattice points at all corners. Unit cells in some lattices are drawn so as to have lattice points at the center of certain faces or at the center of volume in addition to the points at the corners.

This is done as a matter of convenience so that the symmetry of the unit cell will be more closely that of the crystal. It is customary to specify the positions of the points in a unit cell by means of *lattice coordinates,* in which each coordinate is a fraction of the axial length, a, b, or c, in the direction of the coordinate. The origin of coordinates is taken at the corner of a cell. A point at any other cell corner then has coordinates m,

TABLE II. THE SPACE-LATTICES

System	Space-lattice	Hermann-Mauguin symbol	Schoenflies symbol
Triclinic	Simple	P	Γ_{tr}
Monoclinic	Simple	P	Γ_m
	Base-centered*	C	$\Gamma_{m'}$
Orthorhombic	Simple	P	Γ_o
	Base-centered*	C	$\Gamma_{o'}$
	Face-centered	F	$\Gamma_{o''}$
	Body-centered	I	$\Gamma_{o'''}$
Tetragonal	Simple	P	Γ_t
	Body-centered	I	$\Gamma_{t'}$
Hexagonal	Simple	P (or C)†	Γ_h
Rhombohedral	Simple	R	Γ_{rh}
Cubic	Simple	P	Γ_c
	Face-centered	F	$\Gamma_{c'}$
	Body-centered	I	$\Gamma_{c''}$

* The face that has a lattice point in its center may be chosen as the c face (the XY plane) denoted by the symbol C, or the a or b face denoted by A or B, since the choice of axes is arbitrary and does not alter the actual translations of the lattice.

† The symbol C may be used for hexagonal crystals since they may be regarded as base-centered orthorhombic.

n, p, where these numbers are all integers. All points at the centers of unit cells have coordinates $m + \frac{1}{2}$, $n + \frac{1}{2}$, $p + \frac{1}{2}$, and in the cell at the origin this central point is at $\frac{1}{2}\frac{1}{2}\frac{1}{2}$. Points at the center of the c face (the face containing the a and b axes) have coordinates $m + \frac{1}{2}$, $n + \frac{1}{2}$, p; in the cell at the origin this point is at $\frac{1}{2}\frac{1}{2}0$. The other face-centered positions are $\frac{1}{2}0\frac{1}{2}$ and $0\frac{1}{2}\frac{1}{2}$. Some writers enclose coordinates in double square brackets thus: [[mnp]].

The 14 space-lattices are pictured in Fig. 3 and listed in Table II, together with standard notations for them.

It will be noted that one space-lattice in each system is a "simple" one in that it has lattice points only at the corners. In the newer notation

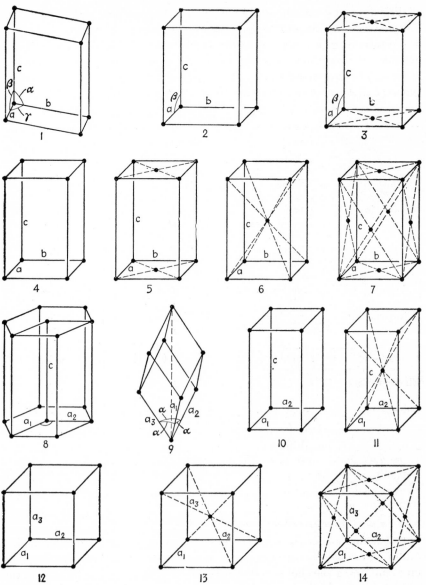

FIG. 3. The 14 space lattices illustrated by a unit cell of each: (1) triclinic, simple; (2) monoclinic, simple; (3) monoclinic, base centered; (4) orthorhombic, simple; (5) orthorhombic, base centered; (6) orthorhombic, body centered; (7) orthorhombic, face centered; (8) hexagonal; (9) rhombohedral; (10) tetragonal, simple; (11) tetragonal, body centered; (12) cubic, simple; (13) cubic, body centered; (14) cubic, face centered.

all these, except the rhombohedral, are given the symbol *P*, meaning "primitive." In the monoclinic system there is also a base-centered cell, in the tetragonal a body-centered, in the orthorhombic all types, and in the cubic all types save the base-centered.

It might be supposed that a face-centered tetragonal lattice should be added to this list, since such an arrangement fulfills the requirements for a space-lattice. If one makes a sketch of this arrangement, however, it will become clear that with a different choice of axes the lattice may be described as a body-centered tetragonal lattice and thus it is not different

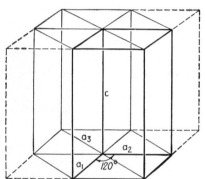

Fig. 4. Relation of the unit cell in the hexagonal system (heavy lines) to a prism with hexagonal symmetry.

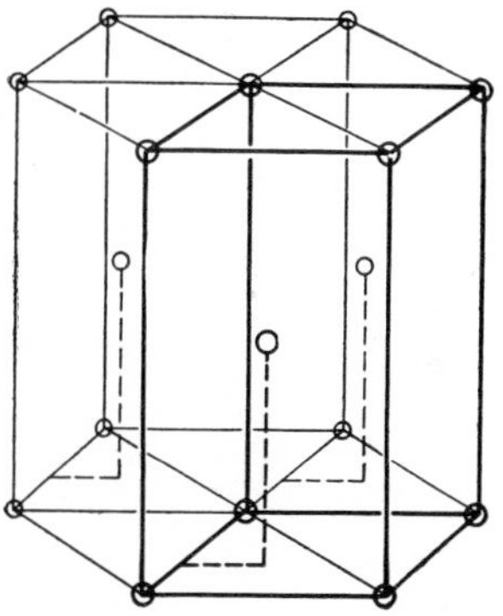

Fig. 5. The close-packed hexagonal structure.

from one of those listed. Similarly, it is unnecessary to list a base-centered tetragonal lattice for it is equivalent to a *P* lattice; other examples of equivalency are not difficult to find.

The hexagonal unit cell is drawn as a parallelepiped having edges parallel to a_1, a_2, and c, the heavier lines in Fig. 4. It is thus constructed like all the others, and it is not immediately apparent from the unit cell why it is called hexagonal. But if a number of these cells are packed together with axes parallel to one another, as in a space-lattice, a hexagonal prism can be carved out of them as shown in Fig. 4. This prism will contain two whole unit cells and two halves and is in no sense a true unit cell itself, for a parallel repetition of it will not build up the extended lattice.

A common crystal structure among the metals is the *close-packed hexagonal structure* possessed by zinc, cadmium, and magnesium. In this structure the coordinates of atom positions are 000 and $\frac{2}{3}\frac{1}{3}\frac{1}{2}$, as shown in Fig. 5. A study of the drawing will reveal that the atom positions in this structure do not constitute a space-lattice, since the surroundings of the interior atom are not identical with those of the corner atoms. The actual space-lattice is *simple hexagonal* with a *pair* of atoms $(000; \frac{2}{3}\frac{1}{3}\frac{1}{2})$ associated with each lattice point.

Miller Indices. It is necessary to have a system of notation for the faces of a crystal, and for the planes within a crystal or a space-lattice, that will specify *orientation* without giving *position* in space. Miller indices are universally used for this purpose. These indices are based on the intercepts of a plane with the three crystal axes (three edges of the unit cell). The intercepts are measured in terms of the dimensions of the unit cell, which are the unit distances along the three axes, and not in centimeters. For example, a plane that cuts the X axis at a distance from the

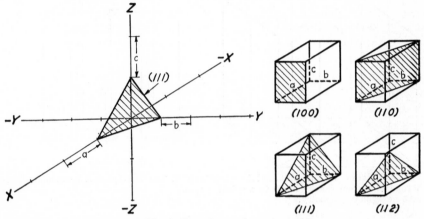

Fig. 6. Miller indices of some important planes.

origin equal to half the a dimension of the cell is said to have the X intercept $\frac{1}{2}$; and if it cuts the Y axis at $\frac{1}{2}b$, its Y intercept is $\frac{1}{2}$, regardless of the relative sizes of a and b. If a plane is parallel to an axis, it intersects it at infinity. To determine the Miller indices of a plane, the following steps may be taken:[1]

1. Find the intercepts on the three axes in multiples or fractions of the unit distances on each axis.

2. Take the reciprocals of these numbers.

3. Reduce to the three smallest integers having the same ratio.

4. Enclose in parentheses, (hkl).

Thus the plane shown cutting the axes in Fig. 6 has intercepts 1, 1, 1 and

---

[1] An equivalent way to derive the indices is as follows: Draw parallel planes through all points of the lattice. Count the number of these planes that are crossed in going from one lattice point to the next, first in going along the a axis, next in going along b, and finally in going along c; these three numbers are the required indices. (See Fig. 10, p. 12, for examples.)

therefore indices (111). A plane that has intercepts 2, ∞, and 1 has reciprocal intercepts $\frac{1}{2}$, 0, 1 and Miller indices (102). The figure shows some of the most important planes in relation to the unit cell, but it should be remembered that planes parallel to the crosshatched ones have the same indices. If a plane cuts any axis (*e.g.*, the X axis) on the negative side of the origin, the corresponding index will be negative and is indicated by placing a minus sign above the index: $(\bar{h}kl)$.

Parentheses, (hkl), around Miller indices signify a single plane or set of parallel planes. Curly brackets (braces) signify planes of a "form"— those which are equivalent in the crystal—such as the cube faces of a cubic crystal: $\{100\} = (100) + (010) + (001) + (\bar{1}00) + (0\bar{1}0) + (00\bar{1})$.

The *indices of a direction* are derived in a different way. Consider a point at the origin of coordinates which must be moved in a given direction by means of motion parallel to the three crystal axes. Suppose the desired motion can be accomplished by going along the X axis a distance u times the unit distance a, along the Y axis a distance v times the unit distance b, and along the Z axis a distance w times the unit distance c. If u, v, and w are the smallest integers that will accomplish the desired motion, they are the indices of the direction and are written with square brackets, $[uvw]$.

Examples: The X axis has indices [100], the Y axis [010], and the Z axis [001]; a face diagonal of the XY face of the unit cell has indices [110], and a body diagonal of the cell has indices [111]. Negative indices occur if any of the translations are in the negative directions of the axes; for example, the $-X$ direction has indices [$\bar{1}$00]. A full set of equivalent directions (directions of a form) are indicated by carets: $<uvw>$.

It should be noted that reciprocals are not used in computing indices of a direction. A frequent source of error is to assume that a direction will always be perpendicular to a plane having the same indices. This happens to be true for all planes in the cubic system but is not true in general for other systems.[1]

Hexagonal Indices. Indices based on the three axes a_1, a_2, and c are generally used for hexagonal crystals but are open to the objection that equivalent planes do not have similar indices. For instance, the planes (100) and ($\bar{1}$10) are both "prism planes of type I"[2] and are equivalent. The same objection applies to the indices of directions. For these reasons some crystallographers have preferred to use four indices, which are determined in the way the usual three are, except that attention is given to all

[1] Indices of a direction may be described as the lattice "coordinates" of a point on a line in the given direction through the origin. When the coordinates are lowest integers, this is equivalent to the definition in the text above.

[2] The use of this nomenclature is decreasing.

four axes, a_1, a_2, a_3, and c.[1] When reciprocal intercepts of a plane on all four axes are found and reduced to smallest integers, the indices will be of the type $(hkil)$, where the first three indices will always be related by the equation

$$i = -(h + k)$$

Since the third index is always completely determined by the first two, it is not necessary to write it down, and the abbreviated style $(hk \cdot l)$ may be used in which the third index is replaced by a dot. With this system equivalent planes are obtained by interchanges of position and sign of the first three indices; for example, the "prism planes of type I" are $(1\bar{1}00)$, $(10\bar{1}0)$, $(0\bar{1}10)$, $(\bar{1}100)$, $(\bar{1}010)$, and $(01\bar{1}0)$. Similarly, "prism planes of type II" are the planes having indices of the type $(11\bar{2}0)$. Examples will be seen in Fig. 7.

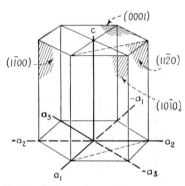

Fig. 7. Indices of some planes in a hexagonal crystal.

Direction indices in this system are translations parallel to each of the *four* axes that will cause motion in the required direction. These translations must be reduced to smallest integers and must be chosen so that *the third index is the negative of the sum of the first two*. In Fig. 8 these translations are illustrated as arrows (vectors) laid parallel to the axes, and both kinds of indices are given for the principal directions. The "secondary" axes a_1, a_2, and a_3 (occasionally called "digonal axes of type I," when there is a twofold axis of symmetry in this direction) are the directions of close-packed rows of atoms in the close-packed hexagonal structure. "Tertiary" axes, of the type $[10\bar{1}0]$, have also been called "digonal axes of type II."

Transformations of Indices. It is frequently desirable to change from one set of axes to another and to transform the indices of a crystallographic plane accordingly. This presents no problem when changing the indices of planes of hexagonal crystals from three to four, for the index i in the notation $(hkil)$ is always given by the equation $i = -(h + k)$. To transform from four to three requires dropping the third index, i.

A direction in the hexagonal system may be written with either three

---

[1] The three and four indices discussed here, based on hexagonal axes, are "Miller-Bravais indices." Another system can be used, which is based on rhombohedral axes, called "Miller indices" by most crystallographers, but best referred to as "rhombohedral indices" to avoid confusion. Further confusion may arise in rhombohedral crystals if it is not clear what distances have been chosen as unit cell edges: a set of axes may be chosen, each of which is half the face diagonal of another set.

or four indices, as explained in the previous section, and $[UVW]$ in the one case will have the indices $[uvtw]$ in the other if[1]

$$U = u - t \qquad\qquad V = v - t \qquad\qquad W = w$$
$$u = \tfrac{1}{3}(2U - V) \qquad v = \tfrac{1}{3}(2V - U) \qquad t = -(u + v) \qquad w = W$$

Some crystals can be described on the basis of either hexagonal or rhombohedral axes. If the $(10\bar{1}1)$ plane in the hexagonal cell is made the

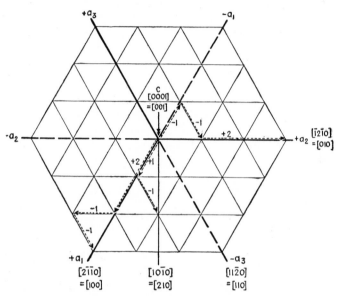

FIG. 8. Indices of directions in the hexagonal system. Three- and four-indices systems are both illustrated; the former is gaining in popularity. Close-packed rows of atoms in close-packed hexagonal metals are along a_1, a_2, a_3, the "secondary" axes. The "primary" axis c is normal to the plane of the drawing.

(100) face of the rhombohedral cell, then any plane $(hkil)$ in the hexagonal system will be the plane (HKL) in the rhombohedral system if

$$H = 2h + k + l \quad K = k - h + l \qquad\qquad L = -2k - h + l$$
$$h = \tfrac{1}{3}(H - K) \quad k = \tfrac{1}{3}(K - L) \quad i = \tfrac{1}{3}(L - H) \quad l = \tfrac{1}{3}(H + K + L)$$

[1] These relations may be derived by considering the vector, $\mathbf{R}$, in the given direction, which is the vector sum of the components along the crystal axes as follows:

$$\mathbf{R} = u\mathbf{a}_1 + v\mathbf{a}_2 + t\mathbf{a}_3 + w\mathbf{c}$$
$$\mathbf{R} = U\mathbf{a}_1 + V\mathbf{a}_2 + W\mathbf{c}$$

Since the three vectors $\mathbf{a}_1$, $\mathbf{a}_2$, and $\mathbf{a}_3$ build an equilateral triangle, it follows that

$$\mathbf{a}_3 = -(\mathbf{a}_1 + \mathbf{a}_2)$$

which, together with the expressions for $\mathbf{R}$ and the relation $t = -(u + v)$, gives the relations $U = u - t$, etc. For a comprehensive treatment of transformation of indices see M. J. Buerger, "X-ray Crystallography," Wiley, New York, 1942.

In the hexagonal system it is sometimes useful to refer planes to axes at right angles, *orthohexagonal axes*. These define a unit cell, shown in Fig. 9, which is actually orthorhombic and for which the indices of a plane (pqr) are related to hexagonal indices for the same plane $(hkil)$ by the relations

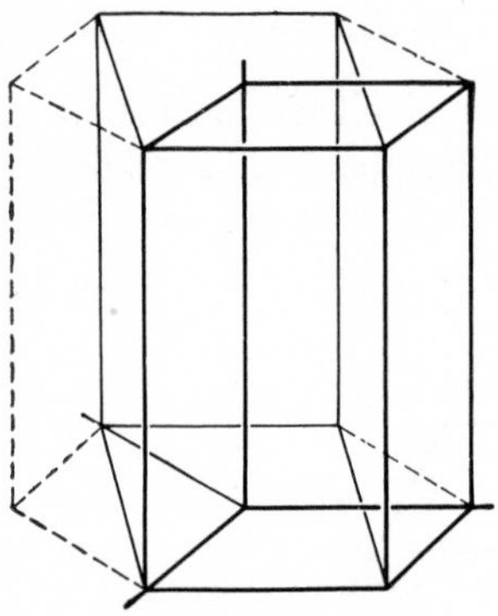

$$p = k + 2h \qquad q = k \qquad r = l$$
$$h = \tfrac{1}{2}(p - q) \qquad k = q$$
$$i = -(h + k) \qquad l = r$$

FIG. 9. Relation of the simple hexagonal cell (heavy lines) to the orthohexagonal cell (light full lines) and the hexagonal prism.

Law of Rational Indices. Figure 10 represents a single plane of a lattice, say the plane containing the X and Y axes. Many sets of parallel planes extend through the lattice in different directions, and a number are indicated in the figure by parallel lines with different orientations. If all the planes indicated are parallel to the Z axis, their indices will be as given on the drawing. Each complete set of parallel planes will pass through every point on the lattice, and, as a consequence of this, the set of planes that is most widely spaced will contain the fewest planes; each plane of this set will be more

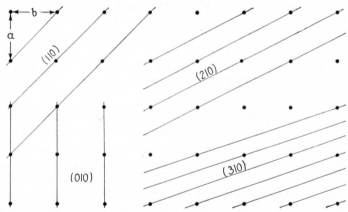

FIG. 10. Sketch of different sets of planes in a lattice, showing interplanar spacings which decrease in the sequence (010), (110), (210), (310).

densely studded with lattice points than planes of any other set. Planes listed in the order of decreasing spacing will be in the order of decreasing numbers of lattice points per plane.

In the natural growth of crystals it is the planes that are densely packed with lattice points that tend to become the crystal faces. Consideration of the example in Fig. 10 or of a three-dimensional model will show that these are always planes of low indices.   Hence it is an empirical law—the law of rational indices—that the commonly occurring crystal faces have indices that are small whole numbers.   These are usually 1, 2, or 3 and rarely exceed 6.   This law can be considered the result of a tendency for crystal faces to be relatively closely packed layers of atoms, for atoms or groups of atoms are located on lattice points.[1]

Zones and Zone Axes; Crystal Geometry.   Certain sets of crystal planes meet along a line or along parallel lines.   For example, the vertical sides of a hexagonal prism intersect along lines that are parallel to the c axis.   Such planes are known as planes of a zone, and the direction of their intersection is the zone axis.   Any two nonparallel planes will intersect and will thus be planes of a zone, for which their line of intersection is the zone axis; but the important zones in a crystal will be those to which many different sets of planes belong.   On the surface of a crystal the faces of a zone form a belt around the crystal; and, by placing the crystal on the graduated circle of a goniometer with the zone axis parallel to the goniometer axis, the angles between all faces of the zone can be measured directly on the circle.   Zones are also useful in interpreting X-ray diffraction patterns and in making projections of a crystal.

There are simple rules governing the Miller indices of planes of a zone, given in Appendix III, which are a great convenience to crystallographers. They apply to all crystal systems.   For example, the plane (hkl) belongs to the zone $[uvw]$ (*i.e.*, is parallel to $[uvw]$) if $hu + kv + lw = 0$.

Formulas are given in Appendix III for computing spacings between planes and along crystallographic directions, angles between planes and directions, and unit-cell volumes—quantities that are useful in X-ray work and in various crystallographic problems.

Symmetry Classes and Point Groups.   A crystal possesses definite symmetry in the arrangement of its external faces, if the faces are developed, and also in the value of its physical properties in different directions, such as its thermal expansion, elastic moduli, and optical constants.   The nature of the symmetry revealed by measurements of these features is the basis of the classification of the crystals into 32 symmetry classes.   These can be understood best if one dissects the total symmetry of a crystal into simple fundamental symmetry elements, which when grouped together at a point within the crystal combine to yield the total symmetry of the

[1] The word "tendency" is used because growth shapes are not always made up of planes of the simplest indices; they are, however, the planes with small rates of thickening and rapid rates of lateral spreading.   Impurities alter the relative growth rates of crystal faces when they are adsorbed.   The rate of change of temperature and the occurrence of temperature cycling also modify crystal habit.   An introduction to morphology will be found in C. W. Bunn, "Chemical Cyrstallography," Oxford, New York, 1945.

crystal. A group of symmetry elements at a point constitutes a point group, and the 32 possible point groups in crystallography define the symmetry of the 32 classes of crystal symmetry.

A symmetry element describes the fact that certain operations, like rotation of half a turn about a certain axis, will bring the crystal into a position indistinguishable from its former one, *i.e.*, bring it into coincidence with itself. In this connection it is the tilt—the orientation—of the crystal faces or of the atomic planes within the crystal that is important, and not the size and shape of the faces and planes, for their size and shape are matters of accidents of growth and subsequent handling, while the orientation of the faces and internal planes is a consequence of the

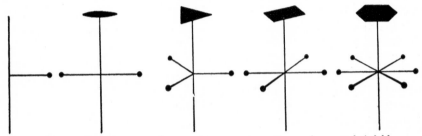

Fig. 11. Rotation axes of symmetry, one-, two-, three-, four-, and sixfold.

regular and symmetrical arrangement of atoms inside the crystal. To describe the symmetry of the arrangement of faces, however, we may assume an ideal crystal in which all equivalent faces are equally developed.

When this ideal crystal can be brought into self-coincidence (into an equivalent position) by a rotation around an axis, it is said to possess a *rotation axis* of symmetry. The symmetry elements of this kind that have been found to occur in crystals are onefold, twofold, threefold, fourfold, and sixfold axes, which bring about self-coincidence by the operations, respectively, of a full turn, a half turn, a third turn, a fourth turn, and a sixth turn about the rotation axis. A square is an example of a figure having fourfold rotation axis, the axis standing perpendicular to the plane of the square and passing through its center. A regular pentagon, similarly, has a fivefold rotation axis, but this symmetry axis does not occur in crystals, nor does an axis of greater multiplicity than 6. The onefold axis represents, of course, no symmetry at all. Each rotation axis is indicated in Fig. 11 as a vertical line; the symmetry is indicated by a geometrical figure at the top and a group of points at the ends of arms extending out from the axis.

If a plane can be drawn through the center of a crystal so that one half of the crystal is the reflection of the other half in this plane, the crystal possesses a *plane of symmetry*. Figure 12 illustrates this symmetry where the point A' is produced from the point A by the operation of reflection in the plane as if in a mirror.

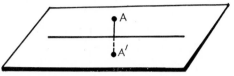

Fɪɢ. 12. Plane of symmetry.

A crystal has a *center of symmetry* if to every point on one side of the crystal there is a corresponding point on the opposite side of the crystal that is located an equal distance from the center and on the same line through the center. This is illustrated in Fig. 13, where the operation of the center of symmetry at O produces the point A' from the point A, with AOA' a straight line and $OA = OA'$; it is an operation of inversion through point O.

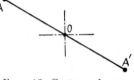

Fɪɢ. 13. Center of symmetry.

A crystal has a *rotation-inversion axis* if it is brought into self-coincidence by a combined rotation and inversion. The operation is indicated in Fig. 14, which shows a twofold rotation-inversion axis standing vertically with its center at O, operating on the

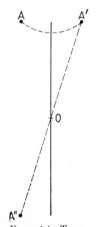

Fɪɢ. 14. Two-fold rotation-in-version axis.

point A by rotating it 180° into the intermediate position A' and then inverting it through the center to the point A''. It will be seen that the points A and A'' in this figure have a plane of symmetry between them, the plane standing perpendicular to the axis and passing through point O; so it follows that the twofold rotation-inversion axis is exactly equivalent to a reflection plane of symmetry. A similar construction will show that a onefold rotation-inversion axis is equivalent to a center of symmetry. Crystals can possess one-, two-, three-, four-, and sixfold rotation-inversion axes. The copper mineral, calcopyrite ($CuFeS_2$), is a common example of a crystal with a fourfold rotation-inversion axis. In Fig. 15 this axis is in a vertical position.

The symmetry elements that have been enumerated above—axes, planes, centers, and inversion axes—occur singly and in groups in crystals and define their external symmetry, the symmetry of faces, and of physical properties. They are known as the *macroscopic symmetry elements* (to distinguish them from certain others having to do only with the microscopic internal structure). Some classes of crystals have the symmetry of a single rotation axis,

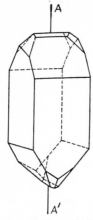

FIG. 15. Crystal of calcopyrite having a vertical fourfold rotation-inversion axis. (*Bragg.*)

others have the symmetry of several rotation axes that intersect at a point, and many crystals have the symmetry of a complex group of symmetry elements all of which intersect at a point.

Several notations have been devised for the 32 symmetry classes, but crystallographers have agreed to adopt the *Hermann-Mauguin* symbols. In the Schoenflies system, widely used in the past, the symbols are C, S, D, V, T, and O, with certain subscripts, C_2, for example, standing for the "cyclic" class having only a twofold rotation axis of symmetry, C_{3h} denoting the class having a threefold rotation axis and a reflection plane, and D_2 or V denoting the "dihedral" class having three twofold axes at right angles. In the Hermann-Mauguin notation, the point group is merely a brief list of symmetry elements associated with three important crystallographic directions. The macroscopic symmetry elements in this notation are as follows:

Element	Hermann-Mauguin Symbol
1-, 2-, 3-, 4-, and 6-fold rotation axes	1, 2, 3, 4, and 6
Plane of symmetry	m (for "mirror" plane)
Axes of rotation-inversion*	$\bar{1}$, $\bar{2}$, $\bar{3}$, $\bar{4}$, and $\bar{6}$
Center of symmetry	$\bar{1}$ (equivalent to 1-fold rotation-inversion)

* Several inversion axes are equivalent to other elements: $\bar{1}$ is equivalent to a center, $\bar{2}$ to m, $\bar{3}$ to 3 together with a center, $\bar{6}$ to 3 normal to m.

The 32 crystal classes are divided among the seven crystal systems in such a way that each system has a certain minimum of symmetry elements, as follows:

Triclinic: None
Monoclinic: A single 2-fold rotation axis or a single plane
Orthorhombic: Two perpendicular planes or three mutually perpendicular 2-fold axes of rotation
Tetragonal: A single 4-fold axis of rotation or of rotation-inversion
Rhombohedral: A single 3-fold axis of rotation or of rotation-inversion
Hexagonal: A single 6-fold axis of rotation or of rotation-inversion
Cubic: Four 3-fold rotation axes (along cube diagonals)

These elements may coexist with others, but they are sufficient to identify the system to which any crystal belongs.[1] In each system there are several classes differing from one another; thus in the triclinic system

[1] The rhombohedral classes are included with the hexagonal classes by some crystallographers, forming a system containing 12 classes, and making a total of six systems. The preferred practice with regard to this question and other controversial or arbitrary matters will be to follow the agreements reached by committees of the International Union of Crystallography as printed in the latest edition of the International Tables.

there is a class having no symmetry, and a second class having only a center of symmetry. Some classes of crystals contain axes of symmetry that are different at their two ends. The opposite ends of such *polar axes* show different physical properties—for example, they may develop electric charges of opposite sign when heated (*pyroelectricity*) or when mechanically stressed (*piezoelectricity*).

When a crystal is built up of atoms located only at the corners of unit cells, the crystal will have the highest symmetry possible in its system, and this will also be true if the crystal has highly symmetrical groups of atoms at the lattice points. But if a low-symmetry group of atoms surrounds each lattice point, the symmetry of the crystal will be reduced. Thus, it is possible for several classes of symmetry to exist in a single system.

The importance of the point groups is not limited solely to morphology and other macroscopic studies, for the point groups describe the symmetry of the group of atoms (or of molecules) that surrounds each lattice point in a crystal. Clearly, the symmetry of the atomic grouping around an individual lattice point must be consistent with the sym-

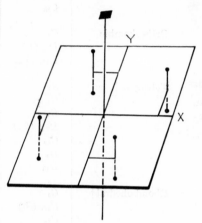

Fig. 16. Symmetry elements of class C_{4h}—$4/m$ (fourfold axis normal to a plane of symmetry).

metry of the lattice points as seen from any one of the points. For example, one would not expect to find a molecule having a threefold axis of symmetry to be located at lattice points of a tetragonal crystal where the lattice symmetry always involves axes of fourfold symmetry (4 or $\bar{4}$); similarly, if a molecule normally having sixfold symmetry were placed at each lattice point of a space-lattice having only threefold symmetry, one would expect to find that the molecules were distorted into lower symmetry, perhaps threefold, by the less symmetrical interatomic forces.

There is no need to discuss in detail all the 32 individual classes. These are listed briefly in Table III together with the notations commonly used to designate them and to indicate their symmetry elements.[1]

As an introduction to these tabulations one of the classes of lower symmetry will be mentioned, the one whose elements are sketched in Fig. 16, possessing a vertical fourfold axis and a horizontal plane of

[1] "International Tabellen zur Bestimmung von Kristallstrukturen," Bornträger, Berlin, 1935. R. W. G. Wyckoff, "The Structure of Crystals," pp. 41–44, Chemical Catalog, New York, 1931. W. H. Zachariasen, "Theory of X-ray Diffraction in Crystals," Wiley, New York, 1945.

TABLE III. THE 32 SYMMETRY CLASSES AND THEIR SYMBOLS*

System	Schoenflies symbol	Hermann-Mauguin symbol	
		Full	Abbreviated
Triclinic	C_1	1	1
	C_i, (S_2)	$\bar{1}$	$\bar{1}$
Monoclinic	C_s, (C_{1h})	m	m
	C_2	2	2
	C_{2h}	$2/m$	$2/m$
Orthorhombic	C_{2v}	$2mm$	mm
	D_2, (V)	222	222
	D_{2h}, (V_h)	$2/m\ 2/m\ 2/m$	mmm
Tetragonal	S_4	$\bar{4}$	$\bar{4}$
	C_4	4	4
	C_{4h}	$4/m$	$4/m$
	D_{2d}, (V_d)	$\bar{4}2m$	$\bar{4}2m$
	C_{4v}	$4mm$	$4mm$
	D_4	422	42
	D_{4h}	$4/m\ 2/m\ 2/m$	$4/mmm$
Rhombohedral†	C_3	3	3
	C_{3i}, (S_6)	$\bar{3}$	$\bar{3}$
	C_{3v}	$3m$	$3m$
	D_3	32	32
	D_{3d}	$\bar{3}\ 2/m$	$\bar{3}m$
Hexagonal	C_{3h}	$\bar{6}$	$\bar{6}$
	C_6	6	6
	C_{6h}	$6/m$	$6/m$
	D_{3h}	$\bar{6}2m$	$\bar{6}2m$
	C_{6v}	$6mm$	$6mm$
	D_6	622	62
	D_{6h}	$6/m\ 2/m\ 2/m$	$6/mmm$
Cubic	T	23	23
	T_h	$2/m\ \bar{3}$	$m3$
	T_d	$\bar{4}3m$	$\bar{4}3m$
	O	432	43
	O_h	$4/m\ \bar{3}\ 2/m$	$m3m$

* In the Hermann-Mauguin notation the symmetry axes parallel to and the symmetry planes perpendicular to each of the "principal" directions in the crystal are named in order. When there is both an axis parallel to and a plane normal to a given direction, these are indicated as a fraction; thus $6/m$ means a sixfold rotation axis standing perpendicular to a plane of symmetry, while $\bar{4}$ means only a fourfold rotary inversion axis.

† Rhombohedral ("trigonal") is grouped with hexagonal in some classifications.

symmetry. The symmetry in Schoenflies notation is C_{4h} and in the Hermann-Mauguin notation $4/m$. The figure shows a set of points which come into coincidence by the operation of the symmetry elements—the *equivalent points*. If the origin in this figure is placed at one of the points of a space-lattice, the equivalent points are possible locations for equivalent atoms in a crystal. The coordinates of one of these points, referred to the X, Y, and Z axes of the tetragonal system to which this point group belongs, may be chosen at random and are written in the general form xyz. The coordinates of all the other equivalent points are then written in terms of these three coordinates; thus $\bar{y}x\bar{z}$ refers to the point whose coordinate along the X axis is $-y$, along the Y axis is x, and along the Z axis is $-z$, respectively. The full list of equivalent points for this class is as follows: xyz, $\bar{y}xz$, $\bar{x}\bar{y}z$, $y\bar{x}z$, $\bar{x}\bar{y}\bar{z}$, $y\bar{x}\bar{z}$, $xy\bar{z}$, $\bar{y}x\bar{z}$.

The different crystallographic forms and the number of equivalent faces in each form can be derived from these equivalent points[1] (since the points can be taken as the intercepts of the planes) and are listed in crystallographers' tables. In the example chosen, $(C_{4h} - 4/m)$, there is a form containing the two planes (001) and (00$\bar{1}$), and another containing faces whose indices are (hk0), ($\bar{h}\bar{k}$0), ($k\bar{h}$0), and ($\bar{k}h$0); these are "special" forms, containing fewer equivalent faces than the "general" form $\{hkl\}$, which has all indices unequal and different from zero. The equivalent faces of $\{hkl\}$ are (hkl), ($\bar{h}\bar{k}l$), ($\bar{h}\bar{k}\bar{l}$), ($hk\bar{l}$), ($k\bar{h}l$), ($\bar{k}hl$), ($\bar{k}h\bar{l}$), ($k\bar{h}\bar{l}$). The more complete tables also list the symmetry properties possessed by each face of the crystal; for example, in our illustration the faces (001) and (00$\bar{1}$) each have the symmetry of a fourfold rotation axis. This is, therefore, the symmetry which would be expected in etch pits or other crystallographic markings on these faces.

Names have been assigned to the various forms and are occasionally encountered in current literature. *Pinacoids* are forms consisting simply of two parallel faces. *Prisms* are forms with faces parallel to one axis, usually the principal, or vertical, axis (the Z axis in the above illustration). *Domes* have faces parallel to one (horizontal) axis and intersecting the other two. *Pyramids* have faces intersecting all three axes.

Space Groups. The preceding section discusses the symmetry of the external faces of crystals and of their anisotropic physical properties; this permits a classification of all crystals into 32 *crystal classes*, which are divided among the 7 *systems*. The symmetry of each of these classes is described by macroscopic symmetry elements grouped at a point, termed a *point group*. It may also be described by a group of *equivalent points* that can be written in the form xyz, $\bar{x}\bar{y}\bar{z}$, etc. The operation of all the symmetry elements of the point group upon any one of the equivalent

[1] R. W. G. Wyckoff, "The Structure of Crystals," Chemical Catalog, New York. 1931.

points will produce all the others. We now consider another classification of crystals that has become of primary importance since the advent of X-ray analysis of crystals, a classification that specifies the total symmetry of the arrangement of *atoms* in a crystal.

A *space group* is an array of symmetry elements in three dimensions on a space lattice. Just as a point group is a group of symmetry elements at a *point*, a space group is a group in *space*. Each element of symmetry has a specific location in a unit cell as well as a specific direction with respect to the axes of the cell, and each unit cell in the crystal has an identical array of symmetry elements within it. The elements are always arranged so that the operation of any one of them brings all others into self-coincidence, and thus they may be said to be self-consistent. The group of symmetry elements at and around every lattice point is identical throughout a crystal.

A large number of the possible space groups consist simply of point groups placed at the points of the 14 space-lattices. This procedure, however, does not produce all possible space groups, for there are certain symmetry elements possible in a space group that are not possible in a point group; these are commonly termed the *microscopic symmetry elements* since they involve translations through distances of the order of a few angstrom units. Every self-consistent arrangement of all macroscopic and microscopic symmetry elements in space leads to a total of 230 space groups, to one or more of which every crystal must belong.

The symmetry elements of a space group, operating on a point located at random in a unit cell of the lattice, will produce a set of *equivalent points* in the cell. In an actual crystal, if an atom is located at one of these equivalent points, identical atoms should be found at each of the other equivalent points. The complete tabulation of coordinates of equivalent points in all the space groups is thus of great convenience to crystallographers when they are determining complex crystal structures, for it is a *description of all possible atomic groupings in crystals.*[1]

Consider as an example the space group derived by placing a center of symmetry at the lattice points of the simple triclinic space-lattice. The lattice is represented by a unit cell in Fig. 17a; a center of symmetry is indicated by a small circle at the origin which turns a point A into a point A', the former having coordinates xyz, the latter $\bar{x}\bar{y}\bar{z}$, where x, y, and z may be any fractions of the axial lengths, a, b, and c. The translations of the lattice produce symmetry centers and pairs of equivalent points identical with A and A' at all other points of the space-lattice, as will be seen from Fig. 17b.

It will be seen by studying this figure that additional symmetry ele-

---

[1] These statements refer, as mentioned earlier, to crystals free from strains, imperfections, and disorders.

ments are to be found in this arrangement of equivalent points, for the full symmetry includes symmetry centers at the mid-points of each edge and of each face of the unit cell, as well as one at the center of the cell. The coordinates xyz of an equivalent point are always expressed as fractions of the axial lengths a, b, and c; these fractions may have any value whatever without altering the symmetry properties of the group of points derived from it by the operation of the symmetry elements of the space groups. The value of the coordinates does alter the *number* of

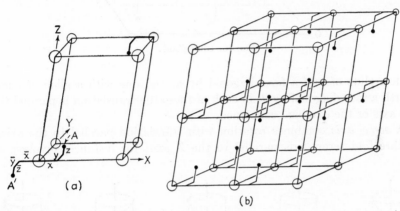

Fig. 17. The space group $C_1{}^1$—$P\bar{1}$. (a) Unit cell with center of symmetry at 000 indicated by open circle. Points xyz and $\bar{x}\bar{y}\bar{z}$ are equivalent. (b) Showing repetition of unit cell in the crystal. Additional symmetry elements are present but are not indicated on the drawing.

equivalent points in special cases, however, for if a point is located on an axis of symmetry it is obvious that no new equivalent points will be produced by the operation of rotation around the axis. Similarly, in the example of Fig. 17a, if the point A lies at the special position 000, where a center of symmetry is located, all the equivalent points will be at the corners of the unit cells, and there will be only half as many as for the general position.

Glide Planes and Screw Axes. In the point groups the operation of a symmetry element located at the origin on a point xyz will always produce equivalent points that are equidistant from the origin; but in the space groups it is possible to have symmetry elements in which a translation is involved, and equivalent points will consequently be at different distances from the origin.

A *glide plane* combines a reflection plane with a translation parallel to the plane so that the structure is brought into coincidence by reflection across the plane and simultaneous movement along the plane a specified distance. This is illustrated in Fig. 18, where the point A' is produced from point *A* by the action of glide plane *GG*. In the different kinds of glide planes the translations are half the axial lengths, half the face diagonals, or one-fourth the face diagonals.

In the Hermann-Mauguin notation glide planes with a glide of $a/2$, $b/2$, and $c/2$ are represented by the symbols a, b, and c, respectively, one

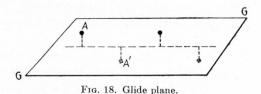

FIG. 18. Glide plane.

with a glide of half a face diagonal by n, and one with a glide of one-fourth a face diagonal by d; in each of these the translation is parallel to the axis or the diagonal concerned.

A *screw axis* combines rotation with translation parallel to the axis. A threefold screw axis parallel to the *Z* axis, for instance, involves a

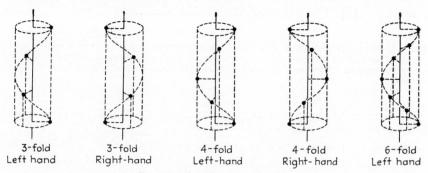

| 3-fold | 3-fold | 4-fold | 4-fold | 6-fold |
| Left hand | Right-hand | Left-hand | Right-hand | Left hand |

FIG. 19. Example of screw axes.

rotation of one-third turn around *Z* and a translation of one-third the axial length *c*, as indicated in Fig. 19. An *n*-fold screw axis combines a rotation of $2\pi/n$ with a translation parallel to the axis amounting to a certain fraction of the distance between lattice points in the direction of the axis; the translation is one-half this distance for a twofold screw axis, one-third in the case of a threefold, one-fourth or one-half in the case of a fourfold, and one-sixth, one-third, or one-half in the case of a sixfold. Several of these axes can be either right-handed or left-handed, since the equivalent points are on spirals that advance as either a right-handed or a left-handed screw (see Fig. 19). The following table lists the screw axes and their Hermann-Mauguin symbols.

Symbol	Multiplicity	Translation	Nature
2_1	2-fold	1/2	
3_1	3-fold	1/3	Right-handed
3_2	3-fold	1/3	Left-handed
4_1	4-fold	1/4	Right-handed
4_2	4-fold	1/2	Includes rotation axis 2
4_3	4-fold	1/4	Left-handed
6_1	6-fold	1/6	Right-handed
6_2	6-fold	1/3	Right-handed
6_3	6-fold	1/2	Includes rotation axis 3
6_4	6-fold	1/3	Left-handed
6_5	6-fold	1/6	Left-handed

As far as the *external* symmetry of crystals is concerned, glide planes cannot be distinguished from reflection planes, nor can screw axes be distinguished from rotation axes of the same multiplicity.   For example, the orthorhombic crystal class having three mutually perpendicular twofold axes, V—222, has a number of possible internal arrangements of twofold rotation and screw axes, leading to different space groups pictured in Fig. 20.   While the internal structures of the crystals belonging to these space

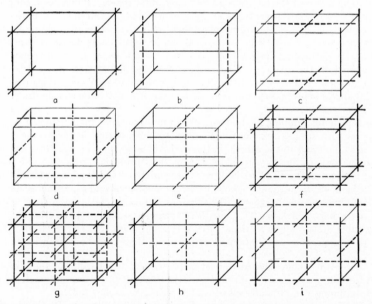

Fig. 20. Space groups of Class D_2—222, of the orthorhombic system, showing ¼ of unit cell of each.   Dashed and heavy lines are 2_1 and 2 axes, respectively.   (Other portions of unit cell are similar to these.)   (*James.*)

groups are all different, their macroscopic symmetry properties are identical.

Space-group Notation. The symmetry elements of each of the 230 space groups have been tabulated many times.[1] The content of space-group tables will be illustrated with reference to Fig. 20c. The notation for this space group is D_2^3—$P2_12_12$, the symbol in front of the dash being the Schoenflies and the second the newer Hermann-Mauguin symbol, which has now been universally adopted by international agreement. In the older system the symbol for the point group is retained as the symbol for all space groups belonging thereto, and a superscript is added to designate the serial number of the space group belonging to that particular point group; the one under discussion is thus the third space group of the point group D_2. The symbols in the newer notation indicate the type of lattice (in this case simple, since the letter P is used) and the symmetry elements associated with the principal crystallographic directions (here twofold screw axes parallel to two of the principal axes and a twofold rotation axis parallel to the third). The object of the international committee in urging the simultaneous and eventually the exclusive use of the new notation was to provide a shorthand from which all the symmetry properties of a space group would be self-evident.

Rules that must be kept in mind for an understanding of this notation are as follows:[2]

The designation of the lattice is given by a capital letter. P denotes a simple lattice, A or B or C a lattice centered on the a, b, or c face (*i.e.*, a cell of a C lattice has a point $\frac{1}{2}\frac{1}{2}0$ equivalent to the corner point 000), and F a lattice centered on all faces.

In this system of notation, cells are chosen so as to be as nearly rectangular as possible, the hexagonal lattice being denoted by the letter C (an orthohexagonal cell centered on the c face with $a:b = 1:\sqrt{3}$) or by the letter H if a cell is chosen having an axial ratio $a:b = \sqrt{3}:1$. The simple rhombohedral cell having equal axes at equal angles is given a special symbol, R, since it is not conveniently drawn using rectangular axes.

The remaining symbols in the space-group notation give the symmetry elements associated with special directions in the crystals. These are: in the monoclinic system the axis normal to the others; in the orthorhombic system the three mutually perpendicular axes; in the tetragonal system the "principal" axis (the one parallel to the fourfold axis), the "secondary" axis, and the "tertiary" axis 90° from the principal and 45° from the secondary; in the rhombohedral and hexagonal systems the principal axis (the one parallel to the three- or sixfold axis), the secondary axis, and the tertiary axis, which lies 90° from the principal and 30° from the secondary; and in the cubic system the directions [001], [111], and [110]. The symbols for rotation axes, screw axes, or axes of rotary inversion along these directions are written in the

---

[1] R. W. G. Wyckoff, The Analytical Expression of the Results of the Theory of Space Groups, *Carnegie Inst. Wash. Pub.* 318, 1922, 1930. "International Tabellen zur Bestimmung von Kristallstrukturen," Bornträger, Berlin, 1935.

[2] The system is presented in detail in "International Tabellen zur Bestimmung von Kristallstrukturen," Bornträger, Berlin, 1935; and in *Z. Krist.*, vol. 79, p. 495, 1931.

symbol, as are also the symbols for the reflection planes and glide planes that stand perpendicular to the directions. If two symmetry elements belong to one direction, their two symbols may be combined as a fraction; $2/m$ thus denotes a twofold axis normal to a reflection plane. Only the necessary minima of symmetry elements are given, for the remainder follow as a consequence of those given.

Example: The space group $O_h^5 - Fm3m$ is based on a face-centered lattice and has reflection planes normal to [100] and [110] with threefold axes along the secondary axes [111], an arrangement possible only in the cubic system. It should be mentioned that the crystal axes sometimes can be chosen in different ways with respect to the symmetry elements; these different orientations are distinguished from one another in the notation, and a normal, or standard, orientation is chosen from the various possible ones and is used in space-group tables.

Tables of Equivalent Points. The equivalent points in each space group are listed in tables in such a way as to show clearly the number of equivalent points belonging to each set (the "multiplicity") and thus the number of equivalent atoms that could be located at these points in a crystal. For the example we are considering (Fig. 20c), the points that lie on no symmetry elements form a set of four equivalent points known as the "general" set, while two sets of "special" point positions are possible in which the points lie on rotation axes; the sets are labeled (a), (b), and (c) for convenience in working with the tables. The information is tabulated as follows:

EQUIVALENT POINT POSITIONS OF SPACE GROUP $D_2^3 - P2_12_12$

Multiplicity	Set	
2:	(a)	$0\,0\,z;\ \tfrac{1}{2}\tfrac{1}{2}\bar{z}$
	(b)	$0\,\tfrac{1}{2}\,z;\ \tfrac{1}{2}0\,\bar{z}$
4:	(c)	$xyz;\ \bar{x}\bar{y}\bar{z};\ \tfrac{1}{2}+x,\tfrac{1}{2}-y,\bar{z};\ \tfrac{1}{2}-x,\tfrac{1}{2}+y,\bar{z}$

CHAPTER II
THE STEREOGRAPHIC PROJECTION

Mineralogists have used the stereographic projection for many years in the description of symmetry classes and crystal planes, for it presents an accurate, easily understood plot of angular relations in crystals with all unessential features eliminated (such as the accidentally determined size and shape of crystal faces).   Metallurgists are making use of the stereographic projection to a steadily increasing extent.   In physics and physical metallurgy the projection is much used for the analysis of markings appearing on polished grains, such as slip lines, twins, cracks, structures formed by precipitation, magnetic powder patterns, and etch pits.   Data from certain types of X-ray photograms are most conveniently analyzed by its use, particularly those for determining the orientation of single crystals or the preferred orientation of grains in an aggregate.   Calculations of the angular relationships involved in tilting or cutting a crystal parallel to a certain crystallographic plane or in reflecting X-rays from a certain plane are rapidly carried out.   It has been adopted almost universally to the exclusion of other methods by those studying the deformation of metallic crystals, except where the accuracy required is greater than a few tenths of a degree.   Any directional property in a crystal or polycrystalline material can be shown on a stereographic projection; examples are the modulus of elasticity and the yield point.

Reference Sphere and Its Stereographic Projection.   Crystallographic planes, axes, and angles are conveniently represented on a sphere, known as the reference sphere or polar sphere.   The crystal is assumed to be very small compared with the sphere and to be located exactly at the center of the sphere.   Planes on the crystal can then be represented by extending them until they intersect the sphere, as in Fig. 1, where the plane F intersects the sphere along the circle M.   The crystal is assumed to be so small that each of these planes passes through the center of the sphere; this results in the plane's intersecting the sphere in a circle of maximum diameter—a great circle.   If all planes of the crystal are projected upon the sphere in this manner, it will be found that the great circles intersect each other at the same angles as do the planes of the crystal and so exhibit without distortion all the angular relations of the crystal.

Crystal planes can also be represented on the reference sphere by erecting perpendiculars to the planes.   These plane normals are made to pass through the center of the sphere and to pierce the spherical surface at a point known as the pole of the plane. This is illustrated in Fig. 1, where the plane *F* and its pole *P* are shown. The array of poles on the sphere, forming a *pole figure*, represents the orientation of the crystal planes without, of course, indicating the size and shape of the crystal planes. The angle between any two planes is equal to the angle between their poles and is the number of degrees between the poles measured on a great circle through them, as indicated in Fig. 2.

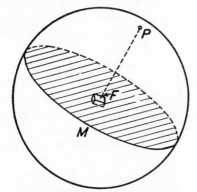

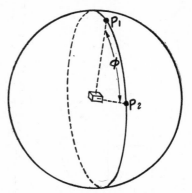

FIG. 1. Projection of crystal plane upon reference sphere. Plane *F* represented on sphere by great circle *M* or pole *P*.

FIG. 2. Angle ϕ between poles P_1 and P_2 is measured on great circle through poles.

The applications discussed in this chapter can be carried through by using the spherical projection just described, but in practice it is usually more convenient to use a map of the sphere, so that all the work can be done on flat sheets of paper. The stereographic projection is one of the methods—and generally the most satisfactory one—by which the sphere may be mapped without distorting the angular relations between planes or poles.

In Fig. 3 it will be seen that there is a simple relation between the sphere and its stereographic projection. If the sphere is transparent and a source of light is located *at a point on its surface*, the markings on the surface of the sphere will be projected as shadows upon a plane erected as shown. The plane is perpendicular to the diameter of the sphere that passes through the light source. The pattern made by the shadows is a stereographic projection of the sphere; the point P' is the stereographic projection of the pole *P*. The distance of the plane ("projection plane") from the sphere is immaterial, for changing the distance will merely change the magnification of the map and will not alter the geometrical relations (in fact, the plane is frequently considered as passing through the center of the sphere).

Obviously, only the hemisphere opposite the source of light will project within the *basic circle* shown in the figure. The hemisphere containing the source of light will project outside the basic circle and extend to infinity. It is possible, however, to represent the whole sphere within the basic circle if two projections are superimposed, the one for the left-hand hemisphere constructed as in Fig. 3 and the one for the right-hand hemisphere constructed by having the light source on the left and the screen on the right. The same basic circle is used for both projections, and the points on one hemisphere are distinguished from those on the other by some notation such as plus and minus signs.

Projection of Great and Small Circles. Let us consider how great circles and small circles inscribed on the sphere will appear on the projection (Fig. 4a). Any great circle that passes through the point N will project to form a straight line passing diametrically through the basic circle on the projection; thus $SPNS$ projects to EE. That this is true will be seen from the fact that the great circle $SPNS$ and its projection EE are in fact lines of intersection of a plane with the sphere and projection plane, respectively. If the great circle is graduated in degrees, its projection EE will be a scale of stereographically projected degree points[1] and will be useful for reading angular distances on the projection; it is shown with 5° graduations in Fig. 4b.

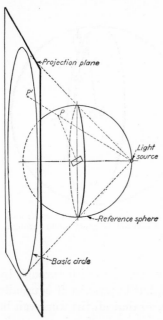

FIG. 3. Stereographic projection. Pole P of crystallographic plane projects to P' on projection plane.

A small circle inscribed about a point such as P (Fig. 4a) that lies on the great circle $SPNS$ will cut the great circle at two points, each of which is $\phi°$ from P. The point P will project to P'. The bundle of projection lines for the small circle will form an elliptical cone with its apex at S, and the cone will intersect the plane in a true circle of which the center is on the line EE, either inside or outside the basic circle. The point P' will not be at the center of area of this projected circle but will lie on the line EE at a point distant an equal number of *stereographically projected* degrees from all points of the projected circle. The scale of projected degrees enables the size of the projected circle to be determined quickly, as indicated in Fig. 4b: the scale EE is laid diametrically across the basic circle so as to pass through P'; then two points are laid down at a distance

[1] S. L. Penfield, *Am. J. Sci.*, vol. 11, pp. 1, 115, 1901.

of $\phi°$ from P' in each direction, and a circle, centered on EE, is drawn through the two points thus located. (In Fig. 4b, $\phi = 30°$ and the center of area on the projected circle is at C.)

If the radius of the small circle about P is increased, it finally becomes a great circle. Since this great circle does not pass through the point N, its projection will not be a straight line. It will be a circle with a large

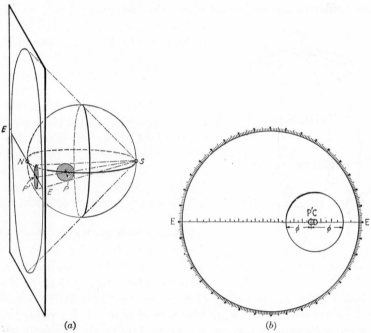

(a)   (b)

Fig. 4. Stereographic projection of small circle. Projection of great circle through N is EE; projection of small circle (shaded) is circle having center displaced from P', which is the projection of P.

radius having its center on an extension of EE; it will cut the basic circle at two diametrically opposite points, and it will cut the line EE at the point 90° from P'. Its position and radius will thereby be uniquely determined.

Ruled Globe and Stereographic Nets. A ruled globe is useful in crystallographic work, just as it is in geography, and the method of ruling is the same in both cases. Great circles are drawn through the north and south poles of the sphere for meridians, connecting all points of equal longitude. Another set of circles is drawn concentric with the north and south poles to connect points of equal latitude. (Since they have diameters less than the great circles, these are *small circles*.) A globe ruled with latitude and longitude lines is shown in Fig. 5.

If the net of latitude and longitude lines on the reference sphere is projected upon a plane, it will form a stereographic net much resembling the rulings of the globe in appearance. When the north-south axis of the sphere is *parallel to the projection plane*, the latitude and longitude lines form the stereographic net of Fig. 6, frequently referred to as a *Wulff net*. The meridians extend from top to bottom, the latitude lines from side to side (compare with Fig. 5). If, on the other hand, the north-south axis is perpendicular to the projection plane, the net of Fig. 7 will be formed, which is known as the *polar net* or *equatorial net*. In this case the meridians radiate from the pole in the center, and the latitude lines are concentric circles.

The nets reproduced here are graduated in intervals of 2°. Larger nets of greater precision have been published repeatedly.[1] Nets of reasonable size will enable problems to be solved with an error of a degree or at best a few tenths of a degree; for greater precision it is necessary to resort to mathematical analysis.

Rotation with the Nets. For the solution of crystallographic problems on a ruled globe it is necessary to use a device similar or equivalent to the one

FIG. 5. Ruled globe. Projections of this form the stereographic nets of Figs. 6 and 7.

sketched in Fig. 8, consisting of a transparent cap fitting accurately over the globe but free to rotate with respect to it. Poles marked on the cap, such as P_1 and P_2, may be studied with reference to the underlying net of latitude and longitude lines. Rotating this cap about the north-south axis of the globe will cause each point on the cap to move along a circle of constant latitude on the globe, as shown, and in so doing each

[1] An accurate stereographic net, 15¾ in. diameter, of the type reproduced in Fig. 6, was engraved by Admiral Sigsbee for the Hydrographic Office of the United States Navy, known as *H.O. Miscellaneous* 7736. Nets are sold by Ward's Natural Science Establishment, Inc., Rochester, N.Y. (10 cm diameter, also Penfield protractors, Fisher protractors, etc.) and by the University of Chicago Bookstore, University of Chicago, Chicago, Ill. (10 cm and 18 cm diameter; Fisher protractors). Reproductions appear in the following references: F. Rinne, "Einführung in die kristallographische Formenlehre," Leipzig, 1922 (12 cm); H. E. Boeke, "Die Anwendung der stereographischen Projektion bei kirstallographischen Untersuchungszeichnung," Bornträger, Berlin, 1914 (14 cm); B. Gossner, "Kristallberechnung und Kristallzeichnung," Leipzig and Berlin, 1914 (20 cm); G. Wulff, *Z. Krist.*, vol. 36, p. 1, 1902 (20 cm); F. Rinne, *Z. Krist.*, vol. 65, p. 83, 1927 (10 cm); D. Jerome Fisher, *Bull. Am. Assoc. Petroleum Geol.*, vol. 22, p. 1261, 1938. Various stereographic and X-ray charts are sold by The Institute of Physics, London, England.

point will cross the same number of meridians; *i.e.*, each point will retain its latitude, and each will alter its longitude equally.

An exactly analogous rotation may be carried out with stereographic nets. A transparent sheet of tracing paper replaces the transparent spherical cap, and the stereographic net laid under the paper replaces the ruled globe. An array of poles on the tracing paper is rotated with

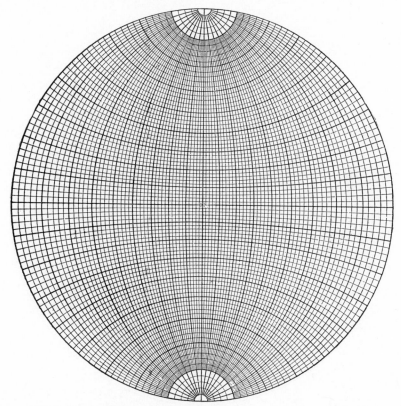

Fig. 6. Stereographic net, Wulff or meridional type, with 2° graduations.

respect to the net by moving each point along the latitude line that passes through it, counting off along that line the required difference in longitude. With the Wulff net of Fig. 6, the poles shift to the right or left, whereas with the polar net of Fig. 7 they rotate about the center.

A greater freedom of rotation is possible with the cap-and-globe device than with the nets, for the axis of rotation in the former case can be chosen at random while in the latter rotation must always be done about the north-south axis of a net. It is possible, however, to rotate first about the axis of one net and then about the axis of the other and by thus combining rotations to effect a rotation about an axis inclined to both. In this way, rotations of *any* amount about *any* axis, whatever its inclination to the projection, can be made. The method amounts to resolving the rotation into components; one component is rotation about the axis parallel to the plane of the paper and is carried out by the Wulff net, and the other component is rotation about the axis normal to the paper and is accomplished by using the polar net.

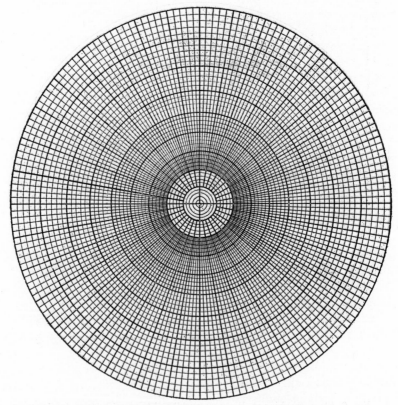

Fig. 7. Polar stereographic net with 2° graduations.

In practice, rotation about an inclined axis can be accomplished without transferring the tracing paper from one net to the other, for obviously the circular rotation with the polar net can be performed simply by rotating the tracing paper about a pin at the center of its basic circle. Rotations of both types can be carried out conveniently with the tracing paper lying on the Wulff net and free to swing about a central pin.

Angle Measurement. As has been stated in connection with Fig. 2, the angle between two points on a sphere is the number of degrees separating them on the great circle through them. The angle can be read on the spherical-cap and ruled-globe apparatus by so rotating the cap that the two points are made to lie on the same meridian of the globe, for all meridians are great circles (they all pass through two diametrically opposite points—the north and south poles). With the two points on the same meridian the angle between them is their difference in latitude, directly read with the help of the latitude lines ruled on the globe. Angles are measured with a sterographic net in exactly the same way by bringing the points to the same meridian of the sterographic net and counting their difference in latitude. Any two points can be brought to the same meridian merely by rotating them a certain amount about the center (swinging the tracing paper about the central pin of a Wulff net).

The most frequent source of error in students' work with the projection comes from misunderstanding or forgetting this principle, that *the angle between two points is equal to their difference in latitude only when they lie on the same meridian.* It is also true, of course, that the angle between two points is equal to their difference in *longitude* when, and only when, they lie on the *equator*, the equator of the Wulff net then serving as the scale of projected degrees that was mentioned earlier.

FIG. 8. Ruled globe with transparent cap. Rotation of cap about NS axis moves P_1 to P_1' and P_2 to P_2'.

The operation of angle measurement described above is, of course, identical whether the points on the projection represent poles of crystallographic planes, crystallographic directions, or points on a sphere.

When planes appear in a stereographic projection as great circles, like the circle M of Fig. 1, it is easy to plot the poles of the planes and then to measure the angle between the poles. To plot the projection of pole P (Fig. 1) it is necessary merely to turn the tracing paper about the central pin in a Wulff net until the projection of great circle M falls on a meridian of the Wulff net; then the point on the equator 90° from that meridian is the pole P of the plane.

Properties of Stereographic Projection. Elaborate treatises have been written on the properties and uses of the stereographic projection for crystallographic work,[1] and the reader is referred to these for details not

[1] S. L. Penfield, *Am. J. Sci.*, vol. 11, pp. 1, 115, 1901; vol. 14, p. 249, 1902; *Z. Krist.*, vol. 35, p. 1, 1902. E. Boeke, "Die Anwendung der stereographische Projektion bei kristallographischen Untersuchungen," Bornträger, Berlin, 1911. F. E. Wright, *J. Optical Soc. Am.*, vol. 20, p. 529, 1930; *Am. Mineral.*, vol. 14, p. 251, 1929. A. Hutchinson, *Z. Krist.*, vol. 46, p. 225, 1909. D. Jerome Fisher, A New Projection Protractor, *J. Geol.*, vol. 49, pp. 292, 419, 1941 (reprints are sold by University of Chicago Bookstore, Chicago, Ill.).

mentioned in the present discussion and for mathematical proofs. We may summarize as follows some very useful properties of the projection:

1. The reference sphere is projected as it would appear to the eye at a point on the spherical surface; hence it is a "perspective projection." It is also the "shadow projection" when a source of light is on the sphere, as has been discussed above.

2. Small circles on the sphere appear as circles on the projection; however, the centers of these circles on the sphere will not project to the center of the area of the projected circles but will be displaced radially an amount sufficient to correspond to equal *angular* distances from the center to all points on the circumference.

3. Great circles on the sphere appear on the projection as circles cutting the basic circle at two diametrically opposite points; a great circle lying in a plane perpendicular to the projection plane becomes a diameter on the projection, while great circles in inclined positions on the sphere may be made to coincide with one of the meridians of a Wulff net.

4. Angles between points are measurable and may be read as a difference of latitude on a net so rotated as to give the points the same longitude. The *linear* distance on the projection representing 1° of arc varies from the center to the basic circle by a factor of 2.

5. The projection is angle true; the angle between intersecting planes equals the angle at which the projection of the planes intersect. (However, see page 33 for a more suitable method of determining the angle.)

6. Angular relations between points on the projection remain unchanged by rotation of the points about the axis of a stereographic net as described earlier (page 30).

7. Half of a sphere is projected within a basic circle; the other half is projected on a plane of infinite extent but is more conveniently projected within the basic circle and distinguished from the first by some notation.

Standard Projections of Crystals. A stereographic projection of the poles of all the important planes in a crystal is indispensable in metallographic studies. When such a projection is prepared with a plane of low indices as the plane of projection, it is called a standard projection. Figure 9 is a simple example representing a cubic crystal with a cube face parallel to the projection plane; the X and Y axes of the crystal lie in the projection plane so that the poles of the planes (100) and (010), respectively, are on the basic circle, and the Z axis is normal to the plane of projection so that the pole of the plane (001) is at the center of this circle. The plot is constructed by calculating the angles between the poles and crystallographic axes and laying off these angles by the aid of the stereographic net. The process is much shortened by using the symmetry properties of the crystal; further short cuts are possible by using zonal relations—by locating poles through the intersections of zone circles. The more important zone circles are shown in the projection.

Tables of angles that may be used for plotting standard projections have been published for many crystals and are particularly useful for cubic crystals, since the angles are identical for all crystals of the cubic system. A convenient list of the angles between different planes of two different indices (HKL) and (hkl) for cubic crystals is given in Table IV.[1]

The principal planes of the cubic system are plotted in Fig. 10. Standard projections with other planes as the projection plane can be derived from this by rotation with a net.

In the *cubic* system a standard projection of poles of planes also serves as a standard projection of crystallographic directions of similar indices, for in this system the direction $[hkl]$ is perpendicular to the plane (hkl) for all values of the indices h, k, and l.

Each different hexagonal metal requires its own standard projection, for the angles depend on the axial ratio in the crystal. A projection for zinc is given in Fig. 11.

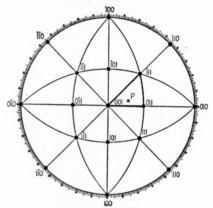

Fig. 9. Standard projection of cubic crystal. Unit stereographic triangle which contains specimen axis P, is outlined.

Orientation of Single-crystal Wires and Disks. The orientations of single-crystal wires, rods, or disks are conveniently represented using a stereographic projection. It is customary to plot the position of the axis of the specimen on a standard projection of the crystal. The specimen axis appears on the projection as a point such as P, Fig. 9, at the required angular distances from the axes of the crystal. It is not necessary, however, to draw the whole standard projection before plotting the axis in it, for the axis may just as well be referred to the three neighboring poles of (100), (110), and (111) planes. If poles of these three types are joined by great circles, there results (for the cubic system) a pattern of 24 equivalent triangles, one of which is outlined with heavy lines in Fig. 9, and it is common practice to draw only one of these triangles or two adjacent triangles before plotting the specimen orientation.

[1] R. M. Bozorth, *Phys. Rev.*, vol. 26, p. 390, 1925. Coordinates for poles in cubic standard projections have been tabulated extensively by W. May in *Koninkl. Nederland. Akad. Wetenschap. Proc.*, vol. 50, p. 626, 1947; and for hexagonal Mg, Zn, and Cd by E. I. Salkovitz, *Trans. AIME*, vol. 189, p. 64, 1951.

TABLE IV.   ANGLES BETWEEN CRYSTALLOGRAPHIC PLANES (AND BETWEEN CRYSTALLOGRAPHIC DIRECTIONS) IN CRYSTALS OF THE CUBIC SYSTEM

{HKL}	{hkl}	Values of angles between HKL and hkl planes (or directions)						
100	100	0°	90°					
	110	45°	90°					
	111	54°44′						
	210	26°34′	63°26′	90°				
	211	35°16′	65°54′					
	221	48°11′	70°32′					
	310	18°26′	71°34′	90°				
	311	25°14′	72°27′					
	320	33°41′	56°19′	90°				
	321	36°42′	57°41′	74°30′				
110	110	0°	60°	90°				
	111	35°16′	90°					
	210	18°26′	50°46′	71°34′				
	211	30°	54°44′	73°13′	90°			
	221	19°28′	45°	76°22′	90°			
	310	26°34′	47°52′	63°26′	77°5′			
	311	31°29′	64°46′	90°				
	320	11°19′	53°58′	66°54′	78°41′			
	321	19°6′	40°54′	55°28′	67°48′	79°6′		
111	111	0°	70°32′					
	210	39°14′	75°2′					
	211	19°28′	61°52′	90°				
	221	15°48′	54°44′	78°54′				
	310	43°6′	68°35′					
	311	29°30′	58°31′	79°59′				
	320	36°49′	80°47′					
	321	22°12′	51°53′	72°1′	90°			
210	210	0°	36°52′	53°8′	66°25′	78°28′	90°	
	211	24°6′	43°5′	56°47′	79°29′	90°		
	221	26°34′	41°49′	53°24′	63°26′	72°39′	90°	
	310	8°8′	31°57′	45°	64°54′	73°34′	81°52′	
	311	19°17′	47°36′	66°8′	82°15′			
	320	7°7′	29°45′	41°55′	60°15′	68°9′	75°38′	82°53′
	321	17°1′	33°13′	53°18′	61°26′	68°59′	83°8′	90°
211	211	0°	33°33′	48°11′	60°	70°32′	80°24′	
	221	17°43′	35°16′	47°7′	65°54′	74°12′	82°12′	
	310	25°21′	49°48′	58°55′	75°2′	82°35′		
	311	10°1′	42°24′	60°30′	75°45′	90°		
	320	25°4′	37°37′	55°33′	63°5′	83°30′		
	321	10°54′	29°12′	40°12′	49°6′	56°56′		
		70°54′	77°24′	83°44′	90°			
221	221	0°	27°16′	38°57′	63°37′	83°37′	90°	
	310	32°31′	42°27′	58°12′	65°4′	83°57′		
	311	25°14′	45°17′	59°50′	72°27′	84°14′		
	320	22°24′	42°18′	49°40′	68°18′	79°21′	84°42′	
	321	11°29′	27°1′	36°42′	57°41′	63°33′	74°30′	
		79°44′	84°53′					
310	310	0°	25°51′	36°52′	53°8′	72°33′	84°16′	90°
	311	17°33′	40°17′	55°6′	67°35′	79°1′	90°	
	320	15°15′	37°52′	58°15′	74°45′	79°54′		
	321	21°37′	32°19′	40°29′	47°28′	53°44′	59°32′	
		65°		85°9′	90°			
311	311	0°	35°6′	50°29′	62°58′	84°47′		
	320	23°6′	41°11′	54°10′	65°17′	75°28′	85°12′	
	321	14°46′	36°19′	49°52′	61°5′	71°12′	80°44′	
320	320	0°	22°37′	46°11′	62°31′	67°23′	72°5′	90°
	321	15°30′	27°11′	35°23′	48°9′	53°37′	58°45′	68°15′
		72°45′	77°9′	85°45′	90°			
321	321	0°	21°47′	31°	38°13′	44°25′	50°	60°
		64°37′	69°4′	73°24′	81°47′	85°54′		

It is easy to show by means of a projection of this sort (using one triangle or sometimes two adjacent ones) how the orientation of the lattice changes during deformation of the crystal, for deformation causes a certain rotation of the axis with respect to the lattice and causes the point P (Fig. 9) to move along a definite path on the standard projection.[1]   It

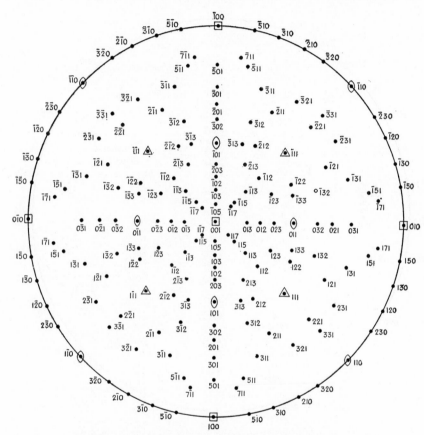

Fɪɢ. 10. Standard (001) projection for cubic crystals.

will be noted that plotting the specimen axis in this way leaves unspecified the orientation of the lattice with respect to rotation around the specimen axis, but in many problems this is unimportant, for example, in tensile tests of a wire.   A number of investigators have made use of this kind of plot to show the variation of physical properties with lattice orientation; measurements of a physical property of a wire can be written beside the

[1] G. I. Taylor and C. F. Elam, *Proc. Roy. Soc.* (*London*), vol. A102, p. 643, 1923; vol. A108, p. 28, 1925.   G. I. Taylor, *Proc. Roy. Soc.* (*London*), vol. A116, p. 16, 1927. H. J. Gough, Edgar Marburg Lecture, *ASTM, Proc.*, vol. 33, pt. 2, p. 3, 1933.

point representing the wire orientation, and points of equal magnitude can be joined by contours.

Applications. The combination of standard projection and stereographic net is particularly convenient for analyzing the crystallographic features of the deformation of crystals by slip, twinning, and cleavage or

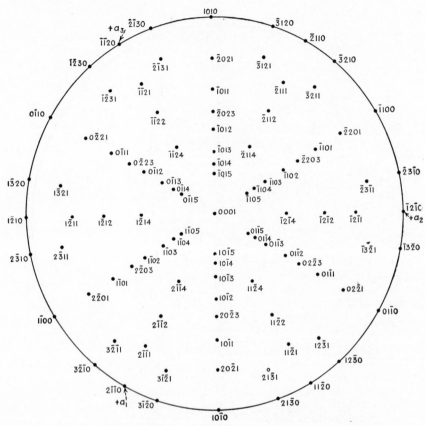

FIG. 11. Standard (0001) projection for zinc (hexagonal, $c/a = 1.86$).

the growth habits of crystals precipitated within a crystal, forming a Widmanstätten pattern. Such studies deal with the orientation of planes in space, the angles between these planes, and the intersections of these planes with one another, matters readily visualized and handled on the stereographic projection.[1] To aid the beginner it is desirable to list the more common problems and to give the operations by which they are graphically solved, but it should be borne in mind that as soon as one is accustomed to think clearly of the sphere and its "picture," the stereographic net, these operations become self-evident.

[1] C. S. Barrett, *Trans. AIME*, vol. 124, p. 29, 1937.

Obviously, the solutions are independent of the choice of projection plane and are applicable to problems in pure spherical trigonometry; but, to make the operations more easily understood, we shall present some typical applications in considerable detail. We shall speak of polished surfaces of specimens and of traces of crystallographic planes in these surfaces (lines of intersection), and we shall generally consider the projection plane to lie in one of the surfaces.

1. ORIENTATION OF PLANES CAUSING A GIVEN TRACE IN A SURFACE. Let us consider the stereographic projection of a polished surface containing the trace of a crystal plane, the projection being made on a sheet of paper laid parallel to the polished

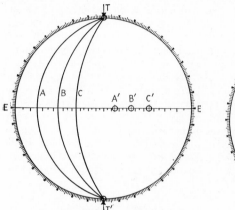

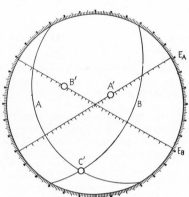

FIG. 12. Planes A, B, C, with poles A', B', C', and all other poles along EE' intersect projection plane in trace TT'.

FIG. 13. Planes A and B, with poles A' and B', intersect along direction C'.

surface. The surface will then be represented on the paper by the basic circle, and markings on the surface will be plotted as points on the circumference of this basic circle. A trace in the surface that runs lengthwise of the page ("vertically") will be plotted in the projection as the diametrically opposite points T and T' at the top and bottom of the basic circle (Fig. 12). A trace in any other direction in the surface would be plotted similarly, as the end points of a diameter parallel to the given direction.

To find the planes that would intersect the surface in the direction TT', the points TT' are superimposed on the N and S poles of a Wulff net. It will then be seen that all the meridans of the net—such as the meridians A, B, and C of Fig. 12—are projections of the required planes, since they intersect the basic circle at T and T'. Similarly, any other plane whose pole lies on the equator of the Wulff net will intersect the surface in the direction of the NS axis.

Conversely, if the pole of a plane is given, such as A', its trace in the projection plane is readily found. The transparent sheet on which the pole is plotted is laid on a Wulff net and turned until the pole falls on the equator, in which position the required trace will be parallel to the NS axis of the net.

2. TRACE OF ONE PLANE IN ANOTHER WHEN BOTH ARE INCLINED TO THE PROJECTION PLANE. Given two poles A' and B' (Fig. 13), the planes A and B are first

plotted. This is accomplished for A by rotating the projection over a Wulff net so that the pole A' lies on the equator E_A and then tracing on the projection the meridian lying at 90° to the pole A'. The operation is repeated for the second pole, B', with the net turned so that its equator is in the position E_B. The point of intersection, C',

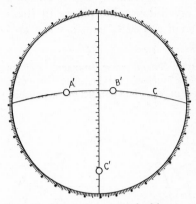

of the two planes thus plotted is the projection of the required line of intersection of the planes.

3. DIRECTION NORMAL TO TWO GIVEN DIRECTIONS (OR ZONE AXIS OF TWO PLANES WHOSE POLES ARE GIVEN). Referring again to Fig. 13, let us assume that the directions A' and B' are given and that the direction normal to both is required. The projection is rotated over a Wulff net until both A' and B' lie on the same meridian, as in Fig. 14; then the point C' on the equator and 90° from this meridian is the projection of the required direction. If A' and B' are poles of planes, C is the zone circle and C' is their zone axis.

FIG. 14. Alternative method of locating C', which is normal to A' and B'.

4. DETERMINATION OF ORIENTATION OF PLANE FROM ITS TRACES IN TWO SURFACES. The surfaces are first plotted on the projection as in Figs. 15a and 15b, one surface lying in the plane of projection and forming the basic circle A of Fig. 15b, the other surface, B, coinciding with the meridian of the stereographic net that lies ϕ from the first about the axis NS. (To draw this meridian the net is rotated so that the direction NS is parallel to the line of intersection of the

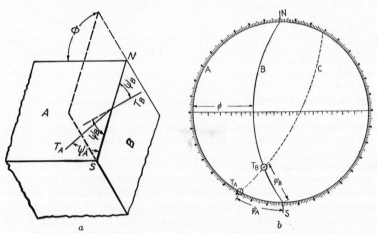

FIG. 15. Determination of orientation of plane from its traces in two surfaces. Traces are T_A and T_B in surfaces A and B, respectively. Plane causing these is C.

two surfaces.) On the planes A and B thus plotted in Fig. 15b are then located the points T_A and T_B, which represent the directions of the traces in the two surfaces, respectively; they will lie at angles laid off from the edge NS to correspond with the angles on the specimen, the angles being measured as differences of latitude, ψ_A and ψ_B, on the stereographic net. The traces T_A and T_B having been plotted, the plane that causes them can be drawn by rotating the net so that some single meridian of the net will pass through both points; this meridian (the dashed circle C in the figure) is then the projection of the required plane.

5. DETERMINATION OF CRYSTAL ORIENTATION FROM TRACES OF $\{hkl\}$ PLANES WHEN h, k, AND l, ARE KNOWN. (a) *Traces in One Surface Only.* On tracing paper a basic circle is drawn representing the specimen surface; through this circle are drawn diameters perpendicular to the directions of traces seen on the specimen surface. These diameters are then the loci of all poles capable of forming the traces. A standard projection on a transparent sheet of all poles of the given form $\{hkl\}$ is then superimposed on this plot and on a Wulff net, and a pin is put centrally through all three sheets. By trial the relative position of the three sheets is found in which each pole of the standard projection may be rotated into coincidence with one of the diameters by the same amount of rotation about the axis of the net. This position of the sheets is illustrated in Fig. 16, in which appear the $\{111\}$ trace normals (diameters), the $\{111\}$ poles of the standard projection (○), and the position of these poles on the trace normals after the rotation with the net (●). This final array of poles (●) describes an orientation of the crystal consistent with the observed traces; it may not be, however, the only consistent orientation. In fact, if traces on only one surface are studied, the crystal may have the orientation shown or a mirror image of this orientation in the plane of projection, the poles lying in either of the hemispheres.

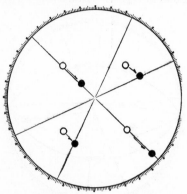

FIG. 16. Orientation of cubic crystal determined from traces of $\{111\}$ planes. Indicated on projection are normals to traces (diameters); $\{111\}$ poles of standard projection (○); $\{111\}$ poles in orientation explaining traces (●).

The example in Fig. 16 is an orientation determination in which a method of this sort was necessary, for the crystal in which the traces originated had decomposed. (The traces were formed by decomposition of a gamma-iron crystal into alpha-iron crystals which formed lamellae on $\{111\}$ planes.[1])

5. (b) *Traces in Two Surfaces.* The solution is more direct and rigorous if traces can be followed from one surface around the edge to the other surface, thus eliminating any uncertainty as to the proper pairing of traces on the two surfaces. If this is possible, the first operation is to plot the orientation of each plane by method 4 above. The poles thus plotted give the crystal orientation. If the orientations of other poles of the same crystal are required, they may be obtained by rotation of the standard projection, as in the previous method—the plotted poles on one sheet and the standard projection on another being rotated with respect to the net until a difference of $\phi°$ of longitude and no difference of latitude exists between each $\{hkl\}$ pole of the standard and a corresponding plotted pole. Rotation of $\phi°$ then puts any pole of the standard into its proper position in the plot.

When the pairing of traces on the two surfaces is uncertain, it is necessary to make a plot of poles for all possible pairings. Among this array of poles there will be one or

---

[1] R. F. Mehl and D. W. Smith, *Trans. AIME*, vol. 113, p. 203, 1934. In this work, traces on two surfaces were used, but for simplicity the author has shown in the present chapter the data from only one surface.

more groupings having the angular relations appropriate for {*hkl*} planes, and these may be singled out from the whole number by trial rotations of the {*hkl*} poles of the standard, possible solutions being those for which $\phi°$ rotation about the net axis brings the standard poles into coincidence with the sets of plotted poles.

6. Determining Indices of Set of Planes Causing Traces on One or More Surfaces. (*a*) *Crystal Orientation Unknown.* The poles of the planes (or of all possible planes in cases of uncertain pairing) are plotted as in the preceding problem. Trial rotations are then performed, using different sets of standard projection poles, until a set is brought into coincidence with the plotted poles. For example, traces on two polished surfaces were found to be consistent with {111} planes by the analysis shown in Fig. 17.[1] Normals to traces on the plane of projection appear in this figure as diameters, while normals to traces on a second plane of polish appear as great circles. The dots are poles of {111} planes that have been rotated from a standard projection in such a way as to lie at or near the intersections of diameters and circles and that are therefore capable of explaining the traces in both surfaces.

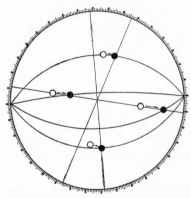

Fig. 17. Orientation of cubic crystal determined from traces on two surfaces. Normals to traces are full lines; standard projection {111} poles (○); {111} poles in orientation explaining traces (●).

The procedure in this problem is laborious and leads to uncertain results unless traces are measured on two surfaces and unless the planes are of low indices. It is frequently possible to save labor by noting the number of different directions of traces on each surface, for in this way certain planes may be eliminated from further consideration. If, for example, a single crystal of a cubic metal exhibits more than three directions of traces, the {100} planes alone could not be responsible; if more than four directions are found, neither {100} nor {111} planes alone could have produced them; if more than six directions, neither {100}, nor {111}, nor {110}, etc. Numerous applications of this principle have been made, particularly in Widmanstätten studies, both for determining the indices of planes and for excluding planes of certain indices.

6.(*b*) *Crystal Orientation Known.* If X-ray data or other observations have already given the orientation of a crystal, a standard projection of all likely planes can be rotated to their positions for this crystal orientation. By the methods presented above, the traces that each set of planes will make in the plane of polish may then be plotted. The coincidence of predicted and observed traces will then single out the sets of planes best able to explain the data.[2]

7. Representation of Symmetry Classes. To represent one of the symmetry classes of crystals by a projection, points may be plotted that represent poles of a plane having general (not special) indices. Let poles be represented by filled circles when they lie in one hemisphere, and by open circles when they lie in the other, and let the positions of symmetry axes be indicated by small geometrical figures. Some

[1] R. F. Mehl and C. S. Barrett, *Trans. AIME*, vol. 93, p. 78, 1931.

[2] When traces are available on a single surface, it is best to rotate into one stereographic triangle all arcs of the great circles representing trace normals. The arcs then intersect at the standard projection pole that accounts for all the traces. J. S. Bowles, *Trans. AIME*, vol. 189, p. 44, 1951.

of the crystal classes of the tetragonal system then appear as shown in the stereo-graphic projections of Fig. 18. Referring to the last drawing at the right, it will be seen that, given one twofold axis in the plane of the drawing, the fourfold axis generates another at right angles to the first, and these in turn generate the symmetry indicated by the twofold axes inclined at 45°. This is the reason that the notation 422 can be shortened to 42, the necessary minimum to describe the class.

8. HOMOGENEOUS SHEARING DISTORTIONS. Distortions of a crystal in which all atom movements are in a single direction, and in which a plane of atoms remains undistorted are handled stereographically as follows.[1] All *directions* except those in the undistorted plane move along great circles that pass through the point on the projection that represents the direction of atom movement. All *planes* except the

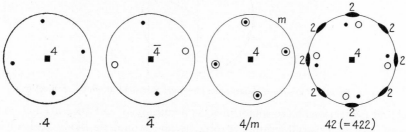

FIG. 18. Stereographic projections of four crystal classes of the tetragonal system, showing symmetry elements (squares and ellipses) and poles of a general plane {*hkl*} in one hemisphere (○) and the other (●), respectively.

planes parallel to the direction of atom movement, which are not rotated, rotate so that their poles move along great circles that pass through the pole of the undistorted plane. A special case of this class of homogeneous distortions, pure shear, has the shear plane as the undistorted, unrotated plane, and the shear direction as the direction of motion of the atoms.[2]

Other Perspective Projections. The stereographic projection is but one of a series of projections that are "perspective," *i.e.*, that represent what the eye sees when placed at a definite position with respect to the reference sphere. The eye (or a light source) placed on the *surface* of the reference sphere gives the *stereographic* projection. When it is at infinity, it gives the *orthographic* projection so widely used in mechanical drawing. And when it is at the *center* of the sphere, it gives the *gnomonic* projection. These relations are sketched in Fig. 19, which represents a section through the center of the sphere normal to the projection plane. It will be seen that the hemisphere adjacent to the projection plane is mapped within a basic circle in the case of the stereographic projection, but it extends to infinity in the case of the gnomonic. The gnomonic is accordingly less

[1] J. S. Bowles, *Acta Cryst.*, vol. 4, p. 162, 1951.

[2] An example of the stereographic treatment of pure shear is given in A. B. Greninger and A. R. Troiano, *Trans. AIME*, vol. 185, p. 590, 1949. The problem can also be handled by vector analysis (and, of course, with much greater precision); see, for example, J. S. Bowles, C. S. Barrett, and L. Guttman, *Trans. AIME*, vol. 188, p. 1478, 1950.

useful in crystallographic problems [see applications of the gnomonic to the Laue method in Chap. V]. All perspective projections have the property that the azimuthal positions around the central ray (the dot-dash line in Fig. 19) are the same on the sphere and its projection. Other

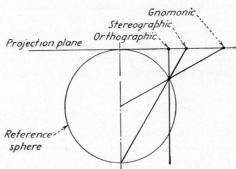

FIG. 19. Relations among orthographic, stereographic, and gnomonic projections.

related projections have sometimes been employed[1] but they are not conventional for crystallographic problems and would be likely to lead to confusion if occasionally adopted for this purpose by investigators. The reflection of X-rays from a crystal plane forms a projection on a photographic film which has been called a *reflection projection*.

[1] F. E. Wright, The Methods of Petrographic Microscopic Research, *Carnegie Inst. Wash. Pub. 158, 1911.*

CHAPTER III

X-RAYS

When Laue suggested to his assistant, Friedrich, in 1912 that X-rays should be of the right wavelength to diffract from the atoms within crystals, he started a train of experiments that has been of incalculable aid to the development of crystallography. In the hands of W. H. Bragg and his son, W. L. Bragg, X-rays were immediately put to work in the solution of crystal structures. Practically every structure determination since that time has employed X-rays; applications of X-rays to chemistry, physics, and metallurgy have been continuous.

X-rays were discovered in 1895 when Prof. W. K. Röntgen was experimenting at the University of Würzburg, Germany, with highly evacuated tubes in which cathode rays were being generated. Röntgen discovered that the impact of the cathode rays on the wall of the bulb generates an invisible, penetrating radiation which in many respects resembles light. The rays spread outward from the source in straight lines and cast sharp shadows; they darken photographic plates that have been wrapped in black paper; they excite barium platinocyanide to brilliant fluorescence; and, like ultraviolet light, they ionize air.

The interest in this discovery was tremendous, especially among the physicists, who were anxious to learn the exact relation of the rays to light, and among the technologists, who within a few months had begun to apply them to medical and industrial uses. The concentrated efforts of physicists in many laboratories disclosed additional properties of the rays analogous to the properties of light and other electromagnetic radiation: their path can be bent by refraction when passing through a substance; they can be polarized; they can be reflected from a smooth surface if the glancing angle between the beam and the surface is less than about $\frac{1}{2}°$; they can be diffracted (very slightly) by a slit, a grating, or a crystal; they can stimulate, "burn," or kill living matter, depending on dosage; they can eject electrons from an absorbing substance which becomes, in turn, an emitter of fluorescent X-rays; they are scattered by the atoms of a substance, and if the atoms are arranged in a regularly repeating pattern the scattered rays cooperate to build up diffracted rays. In addition to following the laws of wave propagation and diffraction, the rays also act as discrete particles, quanta, possessing definite energy and momentum.

When electrons are driven at high speed into the metal target of an

X-ray tube, about 2 per cent of their energy is converted into X-rays; the balance is converted into heat in the target. The distribution of the X-ray energy in the different wavelengths of the spectrum is a matter of first importance in the various methods of crystal analysis and the different techniques of industrial radiography.

The radiation consists of a continuous spectrum—radiation spread over a wide band of wavelengths—and a superimposed line spectrum of high-intensity single-wavelength components. The former corresponds to

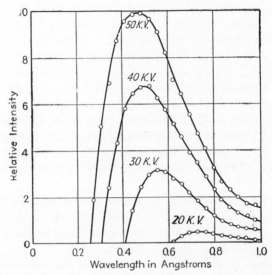

Fig. 1. Distribution of energy in the continuous X-ray spectrum of tungsten at different voltages. (*Ulrey.*)

white light and is frequently called the *white radiation*. The latter corresponds to monochromatic light; and because the wavelength of each component is characteristic of the metal emitting the rays, it is called the *characteristic radiation*. The continuous spectrum can be produced without the characteristic if the tube is operated at a low voltage, but as soon as the voltage is increased beyond a critical value the characteristic spectral lines appear in addition to the white radiation.

The Continuous Spectrum. Figure 1 shows the distribution of energy in the continuous or white radiation emitted from a tungsten-target tube operating at a series of voltages. The important features of the spectra in Fig. 1 are the abrupt ending of each spectrum at a minimum wavelength, the maximum at longer wavelengths, and the gradual decrease in intensity on the long-wavelength end of the spectrum. Increasing the operating voltage shifts both the minimum wavelength (the *short-wave-*

length limit) and the point of maximum intensity to the left and increases the intensity of all wavelengths.

The radiation originates when an electron that is moving with a high velocity encounters an atom in the target. If it converts its entire kinetic energy into X-rays at a single encounter, the frequency of the rays produced will be given by the quantum relation

$$eV = h\nu$$

where e is the charge on the electron, V the voltage applied to the tube, h a universal constant (Planck's constant), and ν the frequency of the radiation.[1] While all electrons strike the target with energy eV, only rarely are they stopped in a single encounter so as to convert their entire energy into one quantum. More frequently they dissipate their energy in a series of glancing encounters with a number of atoms and generate heat or quanta of lower frequency than the maximum. From varied encounters an entire continuous spectrum is produced which extends from the limiting frequency given in the above equation down to very low frequencies. In terms of the operating potential of the tube in volts and the wavelength of the radiation (which is equal to the velocity of light divided by the frequency) the above relation for the short-wavelength limit of the continuous spectrum is

$$\lambda_{\min} = \frac{12,430}{V} \qquad \text{angstroms}$$

If the voltage impressed on the tube is pulsating between limits or is alternating, it is the peak value and not the root-mean-square value that must be used in this formula to give the minimum wavelength. For X-ray diffraction the wavelengths used are 0.2 A or more and thus do not require potentials in excess of 60,000 volts (60 kv); but for industrial radiography much shorter waves are needed, and voltages are raised to 200, 400, and even thousands of kilovolts.

The efficiency of an X-ray tube as a generator of white radiation is greatly influenced by the metal used for the target and the voltage employed. The total energy emitted increases directly as the atomic number of the target material and roughly as the square of the applied voltage.[2] Increased emission with increasing voltage is evident in the

[1] The energy in ergs is computed using electrostatic units: in terms of ordinary volts, V, and the value of e in esu the energy is $4.80 \times 10^{-10} \times V/300$; the frequency is found by using $h = 6.62 \times 10^{-27}$, and the wavelength by the relation

$$\lambda = \frac{c}{\nu} = 3.00 \times \frac{10^{-10}}{\nu}$$

For precise values of the constants and conversion factors see Appendix IX.

[2] W. W. Nicholas finds the energy emitted is proportional to $V^{1.5}$ for high voltages and a tungsten target. (*J. Research Natl. Bur. Standards*, vol. 5, p. 853, 1930.)

curves of Fig. 1, where the area under the curves is proportional to the total energy in the continuous spectrum. The intensity at the highest

Direct
beam   Kβ₂ Kβ₁,₃ Kα

Fig. 2. Spectrum of radiation from molybdenum. Characteristic lines of the *K* series are superimposed on continuous spectrum.

point of the curve also increases rapidly with voltage; doubling the voltage may result in as much as a sixteenfold increase in the maximum intensity.

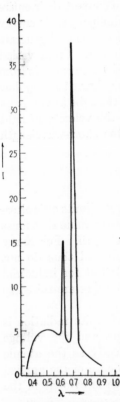

Fig. 3. Spectrum of molybdenum at 35,000 volts showing $K\alpha$ and $K\beta$ lines superimposed on continuous spectrum.

The wavelength at which the intensity is a maximum is about 1.5 times the minimum wavelength and shifts to shorter wavelengths with increasing voltages. For radiographic purposes requiring high intensities and short wavelengths it is therefore necessary to use very high voltages, not only to reduce the value of the short-wave limit, but also to shift the effective mean wavelength to the short-wave end of the spectrum; it is also necessary to use a metal of high atomic number for the target in order to increase the efficiency of the tube. Tungsten is universally chosen for the purpose because its atomic number is high (74) and because it has a high melting point and good thermal conductivity, which permits the heat arising from the impact of the electrons to flow through the target and be dissipated without melting or vaporizing the target.

The Characteristic Spectrum. In addition to the continuous spectrum, an X-ray tube operating at a sufficiently high potential will also emit a line spectrum that is characteristic of the kind of atoms in the target. The nature of the characteristic spectrum is illustrated by Fig. 2, in which a portion of the spectrum from a molybdenum target is reproduced. The sharp lines in the spectrum are classified into series (*K, L, M,* etc.) and are named with Greek letters and subscripts in accordance with their origin in the atoms of the target. The most important lines for X-ray diffraction work, the *K* series, are shown in this figure. In the order of decreasing wavelength these are the $K\alpha$ line, which is a close doublet composed of $K\alpha_2$ and

$K\alpha_1$, and a weaker $K\beta$ line, a close doublet of $K\beta_3$ and $K\beta_1$, which is rarely resolved. There is sometimes also a weak line formerly called $K\gamma$, now known as $K\beta_2$, which is also a very close (unresolved) doublet. Unless special precautions are taken to eliminate some of these lines, $K\alpha$, $K\beta$, and possibly $K\beta_2$ will appear on X-ray diffraction patterns. A plot of intensity vs. wavelength for a tube emitting the K series is shown in Fig. 3; the strong $K\alpha$ and $K\beta$ peaks appear in this plot, but the weaker $K\beta_2$ and the longer wavelength L and M lines do not.

There are a number of lines in the L series, M series, etc., particularly with the heavier elements, but these are always of longer wavelength, as illustrated in Fig. 4, and are less penetrating. They contribute to diffraction photograms only when they are emitted by very heavy atoms such

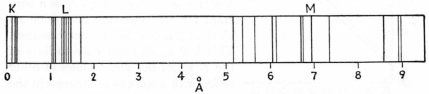

Fig. 4. Plot of K-, L-, and M-series lines of tungsten with wavelength scale below.

as tungsten and mercury, unless a special vacuum camera is used to prevent absorption in the glass of the X-ray tube and in the air surrounding it. These longer wavelength lines are of importance in chemical analysis by X-rays, but in crystal analysis they are avoided. Appendix VIII lists the strongest lines in the K and L spectra and their wavelengths.[1] The relative intensities of the lines of a series vary with atomic number, with the exception of $K\alpha_2$ and $K\alpha_1$, which are always very close to the ratio $K\alpha_2 : K\alpha_1 = 1:2$. With a molybdenum target the intensity ratio is $K\beta : K\alpha = 1:7.7$ (with the doublets unresolved); with a target of high atomic number the ratios $K\alpha_2 : K\alpha_1 : K\beta_3 + K\beta_1 : K\beta_2$ are approximately $50:100:35:15$. The relative intensities of the more intense lines of the L series in tungsten are $\alpha_2 : \alpha_1 : \beta_1 : \beta_2 : \beta_3 : \beta_4 : \gamma_1 = 12:100:52:20:8:5:9.*$

The targets most used for diffraction purposes produce $K\alpha$ rays in the wavelength range from 0.56 to 2.29 A; these are Ag, Mo, Cu, Ni, Co, Fe, and Cr. Elements of lower atomic number emit long waves that are largely absorbed in the windows of an ordinary X-ray tube, while elements heavier than these give white radiation that is too intense to be useful when only line radiation is wanted.

[1] For comprehensive lists of wavelengths of emission lines see current edition of "International Tables for Crystal Structure Determination"; also Y. Chauchois and H. Hulubei, "Longueurs d'onde des émissions X et des discontinuités d'absorption X," Hermann & Cie, Paris, 1947.

* Additional measurements are summarized in A. H. Compton and S. K. Allison, "X-rays in Theory and Experiment," pp. 638*ff*., Van Nostrand, New York, 1935.

Moseley's Law. The wavelengths of the lines in the characteristic spectra vary in a regular manner from one element to another, as was first shown by Moseley. He discovered that for corresponding lines of the spectrum, the higher the atomic number of the emitting atom, the shorter the wavelength (the higher the frequency). The quantitative relation is illustrated in Fig. 5 and is known as Moseley's law: The square root of the frequency of corresponding lines from different elements increases linearly with atomic number Z. This can be expressed by the formula

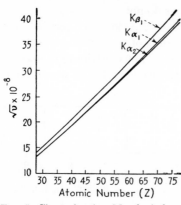

Fig. 5. Chart showing Moseley's law relating atomic number of X-ray emitter to the square root of the frequency of emission lines.

$$\sqrt{\nu} = K(Z - \sigma)$$

where ν is the frequency, K is a constant for corresponding lines from all elements, and σ is another constant. This law applies not only to lines of the K series but also to lines of other series with appropriate changes in the constants K and σ. The regular increase in frequency on the plot of one of the lines, as illustrated in Fig. 5, enables an investigator to detect missing elements of the periodic table and to identify them by means of their emission spectra when they have been discovered. Original surveys of this type disclosed gaps at the atomic numbers 43, 61, 72, 75, 85, and 87, which were later filled with newly discovered elements identified by their X-ray emission spectra. X-ray spectra are much simpler than optical spectra and are consequently much more convenient for identification work of this sort.

Origin of Characteristic Radiation and Absorption. The remarkable regularities in X-ray spectra are best understood by considering the states of energy in which an atom can exist, after the manner proposed by Bohr. In the Bohr theory an atom is capable of remaining indefinitely in a state of minimum energy unless an amount of energy is imparted to it that is capable of raising it to one of a set of higher energy states. In a higher energy state (excited state) there is no radiation or loss of energy until the atom reverts suddenly to a lower energy state. At this time, the atom throws out a unit of energy, a quantum, in the form of radiation, and the frequency of the radiation, ν, is related to the loss in energy of the atom, E, by the equation

$$h\nu = E$$

where h is Planck's constant. Since the energy states, or "levels," are discrete and sharp, the transitions between them give rise to sharp lines in the spectrum.

It will be recalled that, on the Bohr model of the atom, the charge on the central nucleus of the atom holds the electrons surrounding the nucleus in definite shells, *K, L, M,* etc. When electrons from the filament of an X-ray tube are driven into the target with sufficient energy, they eject an electron from one of these shells and thereby raise the atom to an excited state. A characteristic ray is emitted when an electron

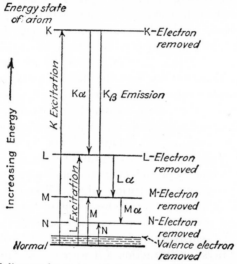

Fig. 6. Energy-level diagram for an atom (schematic). Excitation and emission processes indicated by arrows.

from an outer shell falls into the shell vacated by the ejected electron. If it is an electron from the *K* shell that has been ejected and if the *K*-shell vacancy is filled by an electron from the adjacent *L* shell, the atom will emit *Kα* radiation. If the *K*-shell vacancy is filled by an *M* electron, the *Kβ* line will be emitted. From the various atoms of the target the various lines of the *K* series will be emitted. Similarly, vacancies in the *L* shells of the atoms are filled by transitions from outer shells, and *L*-series lines are emitted.

The customary way of showing these relations on a diagram is to make a one-dimensional plot of the energy states of an atom with energy increasing vertically above the normal state (Fig. 6). Reference to this simplified figure shows that ejection of a *K* electron raises the atom to the *K* energy level; filling the *K*-shell vacancy from the *L* shell lowers the atom to the *L* energy level and produces *Kα* radiation, or filling the *K*-shell vacancy from the *M* shell lowers the atom to the *M* level and produces *Kβ* radiation. All lines of the *K* series are emitted whenever the voltage on the X-ray tube is sufficient to eject an electron from the K shell.

The same characteristic radiation is emitted from an atom if it is put into an excited state by the absorption of a quantum of X-rays, for if the quantum has sufficient energy (high enough frequency) it will eject an electron from the atom. If a beam of X-rays is passed through an absorbing substance and the rate of intensity diminution of the transmitted beam is measured as the wavelength of the constant-intensity initial beam is steadily decreased, it will be found that an abrupt change in absorption occurs when the frequency of the beam is such as to excite the atoms of the absorber. This will occur when the energy in a quantum of radiation, given by the equation $E = h\nu$, is sufficient to eject an electron from one of the shells of the absorbing atom. Thus the K absorption process results in K excitation, and the discontinuity in absorption is called the K *absorption edge*. Reference to Fig. 6 will show that the energy change for K absorption is greater than the energy change in the emission of any K series line; *i.e.*, the wavelength of the K absorption edge is less than any K emission wavelength. A similar relation holds for the various L and M absorption processes and the emission lines resulting from them. The frequency of each emission line is equal to the difference in frequency between two absorption edges. When radiation results from the excitation of an atom by the absorption of X-rays, it is known as *fluorescent radiation,* just as in the analogous case with visible light, and is composed almost exclusively of line radiation.[1] It would serve as an excellent source of rays for diffraction if it were not of such low intensity compared with other sources.

Thorough investigation of the absorption edges and emission lines for the elements has disclosed a complex array of energy levels; while there is only a single K absorption edge, there are three L absorption edges, five M absorption edges, and many N and O levels (in the heavier atoms). The complete energy-level diagram for one of the heavy elements is reproduced in Fig. 7 with the transitions marked that give rise to the X-ray emission lines.[2]

Dependence of Line Intensities on Voltage. Emission lines are not excited unless the voltage exceeds the critical value V_0 necessary to remove an electron entirely from an atom of the target. This occurs when

$$eV_0 = h\nu_a$$

where ν_a is the frequency of the absorption edge. The intensity I of a

---

[1] A. H. Compton, *Proc. Natl. Acad. Sci.*, vol. 14, p. 549, 1928.

[2] An account of the relation of X-ray spectra to atomic structure will be found in W. T. Sproull, "X-rays in Practice," McGraw-Hill, New York, 1946.

spectral line increases with voltage V, and the current through the X-ray tube i approximately according to the relation

$$I = ci(V - V_0)^n$$

where c is a proportionality constant and V_0 is the excitation voltage for the line. The value of n is slightly less than 2 if a tube is operated with constant-potential direct current and moderate voltages; *i.e.*, the intensity is nearly proportional to the square of the voltage in excess of the critical.

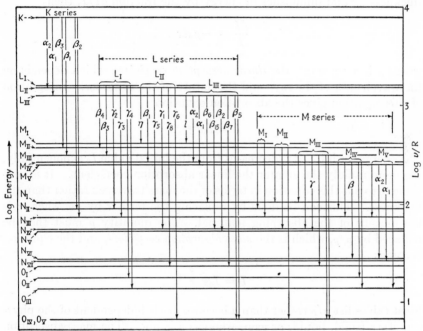

Fɪɢ. 7. Energy-level diagram for uranium atom with emission-line transitions indicated by arrows.

The exponent decreases toward unity at higher voltages, and the squared relation should be considered a good approximation only at voltages less than two or three times the excitation potential.

The critical excitation voltage for molybdenum K radiation is about 20,000 volts, but because of the relations discussed above it is advantageous to operate considerably above this voltage to obtain a line spectrum that is intense in comparison with the continuous spectrum, which is always present. Molybdenum tubes are usually operated between 35 and 60 kv, while tubes with targets similar to copper and chromium are operated near 35 kv. The ratio of line intensities to white radiation at a given voltage becomes more favorable as the atomic number decreases, since the lighter elements are inefficient generators of white radiation.

Absorption of X-rays. An X-ray beam loses intensity in traversing matter both by "true" absorption, which is a transformation from X-rays into kinetic energy of ejected electrons and atoms, and by "scattering," a transfer of radiant energy from the primary beam to scattered beams originating in the atoms of the absorbing matter. An understanding of these processes is important both in radiography and in X-ray diffraction.

Consider a monochromatic beam of X-rays penetrating a sheet of material of thickness x. If a beam of energy I traverses a thin layer of thickness dx and diminishes in energy by the fraction dI/I, then

$$\frac{dI}{I} = -\mu \, dx$$

where μ is a constant, the *linear absorption coefficient*, which depends on the wavelength of the rays and the nature of the absorber. Integration of this equation gives the absorption equation

$$I = I_0 e^{-\mu x}$$

The energy, or intensity, decreases from the initial value I_0 exponentially, the more rapidly the greater the linear absorption coefficient. It is convenient to put this equation in terms of the mass traversed rather than the thickness. This can be done by replacing the term x by ρx, where ρ is the density of the absorbing material. The quantity μ must then be replaced by μ/ρ, which is the *mass absorption coefficient*, and the equation becomes

$$I = I_0 e^{-\frac{\mu}{\rho} \cdot \rho x}$$

Most tables list μ/ρ rather than μ because μ/ρ is independent of the physical state (solid, liquid, or gas), whereas μ is not. The mass absorption coefficient of an alloy can readily be calculated from the weight percentages $w_1, w_2, \ldots$ and the values $(\mu/\rho)_1, (\mu/\rho)_2, \ldots$ for the individual elements in the alloy by the formula

$$\frac{\mu}{\rho} = \frac{w_1}{100}\left(\frac{\mu}{\rho}\right)_1 + \frac{w_2}{100}\left(\frac{\mu}{\rho}\right)_2 + \cdots$$

In the absorption formula this over-all absorption coefficient μ/ρ is multiplied by the density of the alloy and the thickness penetrated.

These absorption equations are fundamental to the practice of *radiography*. When a beam of X-rays or gamma-rays from radioactive material passes through an object, it emerges with an intensity that is dependent upon the thickness and absorption coefficient of the material it penetrates. A beam that encounters a cavity in a metal casting, forging, or weld emerges with greater intensity than a beam that encounters only sound metal.   An image of the cavity is registered on a photographic film placed behind the object, and the nature of a defect is recognized from the appearance of its image on the radiograph.

Since the loss of intensity is due to the combined effects of true absorption and scattering, μ/ρ is the sum of two separable terms, the *true absorption coefficient*, τ/ρ, and the *scattering coefficient*, σ/ρ.   The scattering term is the less important of the two and contributes a relatively small amount to the total absorption for elements of greater atomic number than iron (26).   It does not vary greatly with changes in wavelength or atomic number.

The true absorption coefficient varies markedly with wavelength and atomic number, for it depends on the efficiency of the rays in ejecting photoelectrons.   Between absorption edges, τ/ρ varies with the fourth power of the atomic number and the cube of the wavelength:

$$\frac{\tau}{\rho} = cZ^4\lambda^3$$

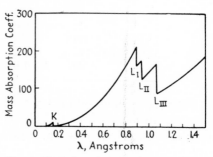

Fig. 8. Variation of absorption in platinum with wavelength, showing K and L absorption edges.

At each absorption edge there is an abrupt change in the constant c. This results from the fact that an absorption edge marks the place on the frequency scale where the radiation is just able to eject an electron from one of the electron shells.   For example, radiation of longer wavelength than the K edge cannot eject K electrons, while waves shorter than the K edge are able to do so.   Owing to the fact that true absorption predominates over scattering in all except the light elements and the very short X-ray wavelengths, the total absorption varies approximately according to the relation

$$\frac{\mu}{\rho} = cZ^4\lambda^3$$

Here again the constant changes at each absorption edge.   In the curve of μ/ρ against wavelength reproduced in Fig. 8 the absorption edges are very prominent; in most elements μ/ρ differs by a factor of about 5 on the two sides of the K absorption edge.   Appendix IV lists values of μ/ρ for a number of wavelengths frequently encountered.

It is often convenient to know for common materials the thickness that will reduce the intensity of a beam to a certain fraction of its initial value, say one-half.   The "half-value thickness" that will reduce I to $\frac{1}{2}I_0$ can be computed from the absorption equation by taking natural logarithms; this yields the equation

$$x_{\frac{1}{2}} = \frac{0.69}{\mu}$$

where $x_{\frac{1}{2}}$ is the half-value thickness in centimeters. Some values are given in Table V.

TABLE V. THICKNESS OF ABSORBER IN CENTIMETERS TO REDUCE INTENSITY TO HALF VALUE

Wavelength, A	Absorber				
	Air at 0°C, 760 mm	Cellophane	Al	Cu	Pb
0.1	...	4.3	1.6	0.21	0.016
0.7	410	0.4	0.050	0.0016	0.00044
1.5	62	0.11	0.0056	0.0016	
2.0	26	0.049	0.0025	0.00071	

Filtering. An absorbing layer may be used to render a heterogeneous beam more monochromatic. Even with white radiation this tendency can be observed, because the longer wavelength components, which are

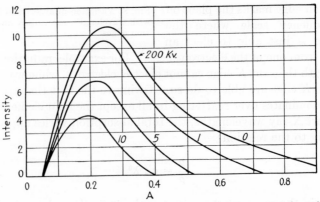

FIG. 9. Spectra showing effect of filtering X-rays from a tungsten target through 1, 5, and 10 mm of aluminum.

"softer," diminish more rapidly than the "harder" short waves, and thus the energy is concentrated in the harder components. Figure 9 illustrates the filtering of a typical continuous spectrum by aluminum sheets 1, 5, and 10 mm thick.[1] Filtering is important in medical diagnosis and

[1] George L. Clark, "Applied X-rays," 3d ed., p. 145, McGraw-Hill, New York, 1940.

therapy, for it removes the soft components, which would be completely absorbed in the outer layers of the skin and would cause severe burns.

Filtering is frequently used in diffraction work to remove unwanted components of the characteristic spectrum together with some of the white radiation. For this purpose, a β *filter* is used that consists of a sheet

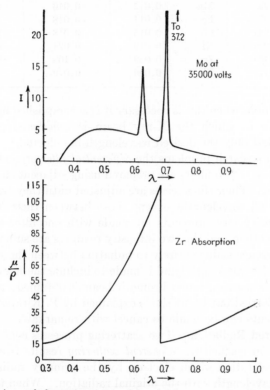

Fig. 10. Emission and absorption spectra for molybdenum target and zirconium filter.

of material relatively transparent to the $K\alpha$ and opaque to the $K\beta$ radiation. Proper choice of the atomic number of the filter makes this possible, because of the abrupt change in absorption at the K absorption edge, as illustrated in Fig. 10 for the case of a zirconium filter to be used with the molybdenum spectrum shown just above it. A β filter for any target can be chosen by referring to wavelength tables (see Appendix VIII) and picking a filter with a K edge between the $K\alpha$ and $K\beta$ emission wavelengths. Metal foils frequently used for filters are listed below.[1] The filters may be rolled foil, or (somewhat less efficiently) electrodeposits of the filter metal on aluminum foil or compounds of the metal in powder form mounted on cardboard. No filter will remove all traces of general

[1] O. S. Edwards and H. Lipson, *J. Sci. Instruments*, vol. 18, p. 131, 1941.

Target material	Filter to reduce intensity of $K\beta$ to $\frac{1}{500}K\alpha$			
	Metal	G per sq cm	Thickness, mm	Thickness, in.
Cr (24)	V	0.009	0.016	0.0006
Fe (26)	Mn	0.012	0.016	0.0006
Co (27)	Fe	0.014	0.018	0.0007
Ni (28)	Co	0.015	0.018	0.0007
Cu (29)	Ni	0.019	0.021	0.0008
Mo (42)	Zr	0.069	0.108	0.0042
Ag (47)	Rh	0.096	0.079	0.0031

and $K\beta$ radiation; when this is necessary it is accomplished by the use of a *monochromator* in which the X-ray beam is reflected from a crystal oriented so that only the desired wavelength is reflected.[1]

For certain research problems the *differential filter* originated by Ross has advantages. Two filters are prepared using adjacent elements in the periodic series. Their thicknesses are adjusted until they transmit equal intensities of all wavelengths except those between their K absorption limits. Intensity measurements are made with one filter in the beam, then with the other, and the two intensity readings are subtracted. The intensity difference is due entirely to radiation between the K absorption limits.[2] If this wavelength band is made to include the $K\alpha$ emission line from the target, a strong monochromatic beam is obtained;[3] and if careful balancing is carried out by methods explained by P. Kirkpatrick,[4] undesired components can be made to cancel with remarkable accuracy.

The Scattered Radiation. Two scattering processes contribute to the total absorption coefficient. *Coherent scattering* results from the back-and-forth acceleration of an electron by the primary radiation and is identical in wavelength with the original radiation. When this coherent radiation from the electrons of one atom is superimposed on the rays from

---

[1] Cleavage faces of sodium chloride may be used, for example, or for more intense reflections, pentaerythritol (I. Fankuchen, *Nature*, vol. 139, p. 193, 1937) or urea nitrate (K. Lonsdale, *Proc. Roy. Soc. (London)*, vol. A177, p. 272, 1941). A bent crystal of quartz is highly efficient if a slight angular convergence of the rays can be tolerated (see also Chap. VII,). A component with a wavelength half that of the desired wavelength comes through the ordinary crystal monochromator and can be avoided only by lowering the tube voltage sufficiently, or by using a crystal with negligible reflecting power in a second-order reflection, such as fluorite (111 reflection) or β-alumina (0002 reflection) (H. Lipson, J. B. Nelson, and D A. Riley, *J. Sci. Instruments*, vol. 22, p. 184, 1945).

[2] P. A. Ross, *Phys. Rev.*, vol. 28, p. 425, 1926; *J. Optical Soc. Am.*, vol. 16, p. 433, 1928.

[3] C. S. Barrett, *Proc. Natl. Acad. Sci.*, vol. 14, p. 20, 1928.

[4] P. Kirkpatrick, *Rev. Sci. Instruments*, vol. 10, p. 186, 1939.

other atoms arranged on a space lattice, reinforcement occurs and diffracted beams are formed. A second type of scattering also occurs which is not coherent and which does not take part in diffraction; this is the *modified radiation*.

A. H. Compton showed that the modified radiation may be understood as being the result of an encounter of a quantum with a loosely bound or a free electron, the electron recoiling under the impact and the quantum being deflected with a partial loss of energy (the Compton effect). The laws of conservation of energy and of momentum govern the encounter, and it is therefore possible to derive a formula relating the angle of deflection of the quantum to the loss of energy in the encounter and thus to the increase in wavelength of the quantum. The equation giving the increase of wavelength in angstroms is

$$\Delta\lambda = \frac{h}{mc}(1 - \cos\phi)$$
$$= 0.024(1 - \cos\phi)$$

where h is Planck's constant, m is the mass of the electron, c is the velocity of light, and ϕ is the angle between the scattered ray and the original beam. The modified radiation forms a decreasing proportion of the total scattered radiation as the wavelength of the primary beam is increased and as the angle between primary beam and the direction of measurement of the scattered ray is decreased, other conditions remaining the same. In the heavier elements more of the electrons are tightly bound and contribute to the coherent rather than the modified scattering.

X-ray Tubes. A great variety of X-ray tubes is used for diffraction purposes and still others for radiography, but all are of two general types.

1. Gas Tubes. Gas tubes, in which electrons are supplied by the electrical discharge through low-pressure gas, are operated with vacuum pumps attached and are usually maintained at the proper gas pressure, near 0.01 mm of mercury, by balancing the rate of pumping against the rate of influx of air through a controlled leak, or by providing a large reservoir that is kept at operating pressure. There are two advantages of gas tubes over other types: they are the most inexpensive tubes that can be built, and they produce the purest spectra, since the target is not contaminated with materials evaporated from a hot filament. A number of suitable designs have appeared.[1]

[1] R. W. G. Wyckoff and J. B. Lagsdin, *Radiology*, vol. 15, p. 42, 1930; *Rev. Sci. Instruments*, vol. 7, p. 35, 1936. C. J. Ksanda, *Rev. Sci. Instruments*, vol. 3, p. 531, 1932. G. Hägg, *Rev. Sci. Instruments*, vol. 5, p. 117, 1934. I. Fankuchen, *Rev. Sci. Instruments*, vol. 4, p. 593, 1933. R. E. Clay, *Proc. Phys. Soc. (London)*, vol. 40, p. 221, 1928. Bulletins of American Instrument Co., Silver Spring, Md., and of Baird Associates, Cambridge, Mass.

2. ELECTRON TUBES. Electron tubes ("Coolidge tubes") utilize electrons emitted from a hot filament in a high vacuum. A demountable electron tube offers the advantages over a gas tube of better control of X-ray intensity and of focal-spot size and shape and may be operated at larger currents, usually at 20, 30, or 40 ma, the limit being set by melting or excessive pitting of the target. On the other hand, the equipment requirements are greater than for the gas tube, and there is a need for periodic cleaning of the target to avoid danger of contamination of the spectrum by tungsten L lines (and mercury L lines if a mercury pump is used). Electrostatic or electromagnetic focusing of the electron beam may be used to obtain small focal spots if desired;[1] less exact focusing is ordinarily obtained by controlling the shape of the focusing cup and the position of the filament within it when cup and filament are at the same potential.[2] It is common for focal spots to have a very uneven distribution of intensity, and for much of it to be outside the area that furnishes the rays through the slits of a diffraction camera. It is well to survey the focal spot with a pinhole camera in which the rays pass from the target through a pinhole in a lead sheet placed an inch or two in front of an X-ray film.

In addition to demountable tubes of conventional design,[3] occasional tubes have been built with rotating targets that are capable of operation at upwards of five or ten times the usual input.[4] Sealed-off tubes are manufactured in quantities for medical purposes, industrial radiography, and diffraction by a number of concerns;[5] the diffraction tubes are available in a number of target materials and are made to be quickly interchanged in the X-ray unit when a different wavelength is needed. The

[1] A. Guinier and J. Devaux, *Rev. sci.*, p. 341, 1943; *Compt. rend.*, vol. 217, p. 682, 1943. A. Guinier, "Radiocristallographie," Dunod, Paris, 1945.

[2] N. C. Breese, *Rev. Sci. Instruments*, vol. 8, p. 258, 1937. J. S. Thorp, *J. Sci. Instruments*, vol. 26, p. 201, 1949.

[3] H. Ott, *Physik. Z.*, vol. 27, p. 598, 1926. J. Eggert and E. Schiebold, "Ergebnisse der technischen Röntgenkunde," vol. I, Akademische Verlagsgesellschaft m.b.H., Leipzig, 1930. V. E. Pullin and C. Croxson, *J. Sci. Instruments*, vol. 8, p. 282, 1931. W. M. Roberds, *Rev. Sci. Instruments*, vol. 1, p. 473, 1930. E. A. Owen and G. D. Preston, *J. Sci. Instruments*, vol. 4, p. 1, 1926. L. G. Parratt, *Phys. Rev.*, vol. 41, p. 553, 1932. Bulletins of Hilger and Watts, Ltd., Hilger Division, London.

[4] A. Müller, *Brit. J. Radiology*, vol. 3, p. 127, 1930; *Proc. Roy. Soc. (London)*, vol. A117, p. 30, 1927; vol. A125, p. 507, 1929; vol. A132, p. 646, 1931. A. Müller and R. Clay, *J. Inst. Elec. Engrs. (London)*, vol. 84, p. 261, 1939. J. W. M. DuMond, B. B. Watson, and B. Hicks, *Rev. Sci. Instruments*, vol. 6, p. 183, 1935. A. Bouwers, *Physica*, vol. 10, p. 125, 1930. H. Stinzing, *Physik. Z.*, vol. 27, p. 844, 1926. W. T. Astbury and R. D. Preston, *Nature*, vol. 133, p. 460, 1934. J. E. deGraaf and W. J. Oosterkamp, *J. Sci. Instruments*, vol. 15, p. 293, 1938. I. MacArthur, *Electronic Eng.*, vol. 17, pp. 272, 317, 1944–1945.

[5] General Electric X-ray Corp., Milwaukee, Wis.; Machlett Laboratories, Inc., Springdale, Conn.; North American Phillips Co., Mt. Vernon, N.Y.

line-focus principle is used to spread out the focal spot without losing the effectiveness of a point source of radiation.

The convenience of having X-rays immediately available at the snap of a switch makes the sealed-off type a great favorite in laboratories where diffraction work is intermittent or laboratory technicians are inexperienced. Installation and maintenance costs are higher, of course, and purity of spectrum must be watched since there is danger of gradual contamination with tungsten, but the stability and constancy of operation are unmatched by other types of tubes.

Electrical Equipment for Diffraction Tubes. The elaborate high-voltage installations with rectifying and filtering circuits that are necessary for radiography are unnecessary for diffraction work unless precise

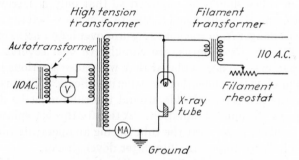

FIG. 11. A wiring diagram for self-rectifying X-ray tube.

intensity measurements are required. Many research problems need only the minimum equipment: a transformer giving 30 to 50 kv, an autotransformer to regulate the voltage, and a voltmeter, milliammeter, and filament transformer with control (Fig. 11). Both gas and electron tubes can be operated as self-rectifying units, although the use of a rectifier tube contributes to the stability and performance of both types. The essentials can be assembled at low cost from outmoded medical or dental equipment, or a complete assembly with conveniently mounted switches, controls, voltage regulators, safety devices, and meters can be purchased for diffraction work either using X-ray films or using Geiger counters.[1] Various wiring circuits are used.[2] Much care should be exercised in pro-

---

[1] General Electric X-ray Corp., Milwaukee, Wis.; North American Phillips Co.; New York, N.Y.; Picker X-ray Corp., New York, N.Y.; for manufacturers of industrial and medical X-ray equipment see Thomas's "Register of American Manufacturers" and MacRae's "Blue Book."

[2] See, for example, George L. Clark, "Applied X-rays," McGraw-Hill, New York, 1940. "Symposium on Radiography and X-ray Diffraction," American Society for Testing Materials, Philadelphia, 1936. H. M. Terrill and C. T. Ulrey, "X-ray Technology," pp. 76–98, Van Nostrand, New York, 1930. A. St. John and H. R. Isenberger, "Industrial Radiography," pp. 58–69, Wiley, New York, 1934. L. G. Sarsfield, "Electrical Engineering in Radiology," Instruments Publishing Co., Pitts-

viding safeguards against the high voltages used.   Complete enclosure of high-voltage circuits is best.

X-ray Protection.   Soft radiation of the type used for diffraction work is readily absorbed in the tissues of the body and is consequently a source of grave danger to the careless operator.   A brief exposure of the hands to the direct radiation can cause an X-ray burn that ultimately becomes very painful and may require years to heal, if it can be healed at all, and yet the operator may be conscious of no sensation at the time he is exposed or for several days thereafter.   Just as severe burns have been received from *scattered rays* by operators who avoided the direct beam but put their hands or faces in the way of the radiation scattered by some piece of apparatus they were demonstrating or adjusting.

Diffraction tubes should be mounted so that only a narrow pencil of rays emerges, and this only when a camera is in place before the opening. There is also a danger from weaker exposures over larger areas of the body, and these, like the local burns, are cumulative over several weeks.   A general dosage may be accumulated that will cause a serious lowering of the white blood count and other destructive effects.   To guard against this danger the protective shields around the tube must be designed to absorb properly the unused radiation.   A test for this is to place a piece of X-ray film in black paper near the tube during an operating time of a few days and to look for fog on the film after development.

Photographic Efficiency of X-rays.   The intensity of an X-ray beam can be measured in a variety of ways, the most common of which is by means of photography on X-ray films.   With care, most diffraction problems can be solved with photographically measured intensities of the diffracted beams, but an understanding of the laws of film darkening by X-rays is required for this work.

The density D of a photographic emulsion after exposure to X-rays and development is measured by the absorption of light in the emulsion.   If the intensity of a beam of light incident on the emulsion and transmitted through it is measured, D is given by the relation

$$D = \log_{10} \frac{\text{incident light}}{\text{transmitted light}}$$

The density is related to the exposure, which is defined as the product of the intensity of the rays striking the film and the time of exposure.   For moderate densities there is a linear relation between density and exposure, as indicated in the typical curves of Fig. 12.   The density with zero

burgh, 1936. W. T. Sproull, "X-rays in Practice," McGraw-Hill, New York, 1946. A. F. LeMieux and W. W. Beeman, *Rev. Sci. Instruments*, vol. 17, p. 130, 1946.   U. W. Arndt, *J. Sci. Instruments*, vol. 126, p. 45, 1949.

exposure is the "fog" in the emulsion, which varies with the type and age of the emulsion and the technique of development.   The most useful range of densities lies between the fog level and densities of the order of 1.0, and most X-ray films retain their linear relationship throughout this range or even further.[1]   Linearity in fast and in screenless types of commercial X-ray films is sometimes reported up to densities of 2.0 to 4.0— ranges where the films are so dark that they must be viewed with variable high-intensity viewing screens.   The contrast in the image increases with developing time,[2] varies with all factors affecting development, varies

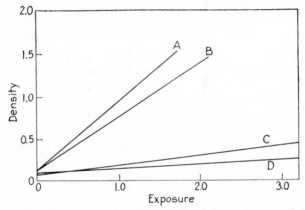

Fig. 12. Typical density vs. exposure curves for X-ray films with normal developments. *A*, high-speed type; *B*, screenless type; *C* and *D*, fine-grained slow types.

with different emulsions, and even varies with different samples of the same emulsion.   Thus a calibration curve applies strictly to a single film only.

In practice it is not usually necessary to plot the curve, for the densities to be measured can be compared directly with a graded series of densities made by known exposures on pieces of the same film and developed in an identical manner.   For example, a series of spots along one edge of the film can be exposed to weak radiation of constant intensity for periods such as 2, 4, 8, 16, 32 sec, and these can be compared by eye with the spots of unknown density on the film.   A rotating disk with sectors cut out so as to interrupt the rays for suitable fractions of each revolution can be placed in front of the film to provide the graded exposures without accurate timing.   Calibration of the film in this way is possible because film

[1] C. Gamertsfelder and N. S. Gingrich, *Rev. Sci. Instruments*, vol. 9, p. 154, 1938. G. W. Brindley and F. W. Spiers, *Phil. Mag.*, vol. 16, p. 686, 1933.   See also R. B. Wilsey and H. A. Pritchard, *J. Optical Soc. Am.*, vol. 11, p. 661, 1926; *Rev. Sci. Instruments*, vol. 12, p. 661, 1926.   With long exposure and development it is possible to get into a range where "reversal" takes place; increased exposure then *lessens* density.

[2] Contrast is defined as the slope of the characteristic curve of *D* vs. $\log_{10}$(exposure).

darkening by X-rays obeys the *reciprocity law* that exposure is proportional to intensity times time, regardless of the length of exposure and whether it is continuous or interrupted. The eye is capable of judging equal densities rather well but cannot judge density ratios; when ratios are required, the film must be measured on a densitometer or a microphotometer or compared with a graded series of exposures.

A series of spots in a diffraction pattern can be graded in intensity with sufficient precision for many purposes by the expedient of using two superimposed films in the same film holder. The rays will be absorbed a definite amount in the first film and will thus blacken the second film to a density that is a definite fraction of the density of the first film. The ratio of densities on the two films can be determined for a particular wavelength of radiation and can be used as a basis for judging approximate intensities of the entire series of spots. A pack of three or more films may also be used in this way.

To increase the speed of blackening, most X-ray films are made with an emulsion on each side of the cellulose acetate base. This must be kept in mind when using a diffraction camera in which the rays strike the film obliquely, for the records on the two sides of the film will not exactly coincide, and it may be necessary to resort to the slower single-emulsion films, or to keep the developing solution from reaching one side of a double-emulsion film. All high-speed X-ray films have large-grained emulsions; and so for applications requiring maximum detail in the image a slower, finer grained X-ray film must be substituted for the common types of screenless films.[1] Clumping of grains tends to occur when film is stored or developed at higher than normal temperatures. Almost indefinite storage is possible without deterioration at temperatures near 40°F.

When maximum detail and precision are not needed, it is possible to decrease exposure time by the use of intensifying screens placed in intimate contact with the film. For short-wavelength radiation a calcium tungstate screen will reduce exposure time for a standard X-ray film to $\frac{1}{10}$ normal, but the efficiency rapidly diminishes as the wavelength of the rays increases, and such a screen is no longer useful above 0.6 or 0.7 A; the newer zinc sulfide screens[2] continue to be effective up to a wavelength of 1.5 A or more. For Mo $K\alpha$ radiation (0.71 A) a zinc sulfide screen sold under the name Fluorazure increases the speed of standard film by a factor of 5. However, the advantages of intensifying screens have been

---

[1] Relative speeds of the different types, recommended darkroom practice, and many helpful suggestions are available in publications of the film manufacturers and need not be treated here.

[2] L. Levy and D. W. West, *Brit. J. Radiology*, vol. 8, p. 191, 1934. "Symposium on Radiography and X-ray Diffraction," p. 206, American Society for Testing Materials, Philadelphia, 1936.

much lessened by the introduction of films that even without screens compare favorably in speed with the fastest film-screen combinations. In handling films one should avoid abrasion; creasing; kinking; excessive pressure; finger marks; excessive temperature during storage or processing; incomplete developing, fixing, and washing; and water spots during drying.

Electrical Methods of X-ray Measurement A steadily increasing number of devices are becoming available for X-ray intensity measurements. Photographic films are still widely used for this purpose, since the accuracy they permit is ample for the usual type of crystal-structure determination, and they have many advantages. On the other hand, some applications require extreme accuracy, particularly the highly detailed investigations of crystal structure, and quantitative chemical analysis with X-rays. For problems such as these, various electrical methods permit intensities to be measured to within tenths of a per cent or a few per cent, an improvement by an order of magnitude over the accuracies obtained with films, which usually lie in the range 5 to 10 per cent. The efficiency in registering the incident quanta of radiation is so near 100 per cent for each of the better methods that other considerations govern the relative desirability of the methods for each application.

The *ionization chamber* consists of a container of gas in which ions are produced by the radiation to be measured, the ions being attracted by the electric field surrounding an electrode in the gas. The number of ions collecting on the electrode is measured by a sensitive electrometer or equivalent. The ions are formed by the radiation when it produces photoelectrons and recoil electrons from the atoms of the gas, each of these electrons in turn producing several hundred ions by colliding with atoms of the gas. When ionization chambers are properly operated, the ionization currents are proportional to X-ray intensity, but the extremely small currents they furnish (often of the order of 10^{-11} to 10^{-13} amp) require high-sensitivity electrometers or vacuum-tube amplifiers. In medical work they provide the standard of X-ray dosage, *viz.*, the "roentgen unit" or "r unit."[1]

The *Geiger counter* consists of a wire electrode in a cylindrical gas chamber, with a voltage on the wire sufficient to attract an electron in the

---

[1] This is the quantity of radiation that produces, by the ionization accompanying it, one esu of quantity of electricity of either sign per 0.001293 g of air. (The latter is the mass of 1 cc of dry air at 0°C and at a pressure of 760 mm of mercury.) The size of the unit may be judged from the following data: a tungsten target tube operating at 100 kv and 10 ma will provide a dosage rate of about 25 rpm at a distance of a yard from the target. The unit involves not only the intensity of the beam (expressible in ergs per square centimeter per second), but also the absorption coefficient of the air, which varies with wavelength. (*Cf.* W. T. Sproull, "X-rays in Practice," McGraw-Hill, New York, 1946.)

gas so strongly that the electron ionizes many atoms along its path. Each initial ionization event touches off a chain of ionizing events that culminates in a strong discharge through the gas. The current in the gas is then quenched and the counter is restored to normal conditions ready for the next count in a time interval of the order of 10^{-4} sec. The number of these pulses in a given time interval is a measure of the radiation intensity.

The counting rate depends on the voltage across the counter in the manner indicated in Fig. 13 when exposed to radiation of constant intensity; the counter sensitivity increases with voltage as the voltage increases beyond the threshold value a, but when the plateau $b - c$ is reached the counter sensitivity is approximately independent of voltage. A counter should be operated on this plateau of the curve and should be reconditioned or replaced if this plateau becomes too narrow.

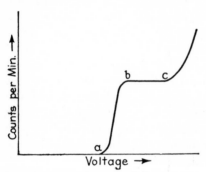

Fig. 13. Variation of Geiger-counter sensitivity with voltage. Proper operating range is from b to c.

A counter filled with an inert gas, such as argon, to which a small percentage of organic vapor or of a halogen such as chlorine is added, may have the property of quenching itself;[1] other counters are quenched by connecting them to the grid of a vacuum tube in a circuit that lowers the voltage on the wire abruptly when the pulse reaches the grid.[2] When the voltage drops below the threshold value at which collision ionization is possible the discharge ceases. It is desirable to arrange the electrical circuit and the characteristics of the counter itself so that a very short time is required for the counter to recover full sensitivity after each pulse, since the maximum number of pulses that can be counted per second is limited by this.[3] Constancy of sensitivity may be aided by a circuit that keeps the counter voltage low for a constant, controlled time sufficient to clear the counter of ions and restore full sensitivity.

To record the counting rate the pulses may be fed through pulse-equalizing circuits into a condenser shunted by a resistor, thus charging the condenser at a rate that is proportional to the number of pulses per second. At constant radiation intensity the condenser charges up until

[1] S. H. Liebson and H. Friedman, *Rev. Sci. Instruments*, vol. 19, p. 303, 1948.

[2] H. V. Neher and W. W. Harper, *Phys. Rev.*, vol. 49, p. 940, 1936. H. V. Neher and W. H. Pickering, *Phys. Rev.*, vol. 53, p. 316, 1938. E. H. Cooke, *J. Sci. Instruments*, vol. 26, p. 124, 1949. J. Strong, "Procedures in Experimental Physics," Prentice-Hall, New York, 1946. Journals on instrumentation have carried many articles on counter technology in recent years.

[3] H. G. Stever, *Phys. Rev.*, vol. 61, p. 38, 1942.

the current input to the condenser is balanced by the current draining through the resistor, at which time the voltage across the condenser measures the radiation intensity. This arrangement permits automatic recording of intensity. In another method, the pulses are counted directly. Since they occur at rates too fast to operate mechanical counters they are passed through a series of circuits in each of which the number of pulses is divided by two, the number of these scale-of-two circuits being chosen so that the pulses may be counted mechanically without missing an appreciable number.

In measuring intensities with precision it is important to calibrate the apparatus, for the response may not be linear with intensity. Calibration may be done by inserting an increasing number of identical thin metal-foil filters in a monochromatic X-ray beam before it reaches the counter and measuring the intensity passed by each group of filters. A word of caution is necessary regarding this test, however, for if the beam is not truly monochromatic—if it contains an appreciable component of half the predominating wavelength, for example, as is common with reflection from a crystal—then the absorption coefficient of the filter material changes as more filters are added. An extremely important characteristic of counter impulses is the randomness of their time distribution. Because of this it is necessary to count for appreciable time intervals in order to average out statistical variations. The probable error due to statistical fluctuations in a count involving n pulses is $0.67 \sqrt{n}$ whenever n is large.[1] It is necessary to count 4500 pulses to reduce the probable error to 1 per cent, or 450,000 to reduce it to 0.1 per cent.

The newer *proportional counters*[2] have certain advantages[3] over conventional Geiger counters and have replaced the latter in some spectrometers. Proportional counters provide pulses that are proportional in magnitude to the energy of the absorbed quantum. The pulses are fed through a narrow-width single-channel high-gain linear amplifier into a scaling circuit or recorder. The amplifier may be set to pass pulses arising from $K\alpha$ and to exclude nearly all of those from $K\beta$, from the continuous spectrum, from fluorescent rays of the specimen, and from wavelengths that are half the wavelength of the $K\alpha$. Compared with Geiger counters, proportional counters have lower background counts, negligible counting losses at high intensities, and much longer counter life. On the other hand, they require more elaborate electronic equipment, and the danger of variation in sensitivity with variation in voltages in the electronic circuits is greater.

[1] J. Strong, "Procedures in Experimental Physics," Prentice-Hall, New York, 1946.

[2] S C. Curran, J. Angus, and A. L. Cockroft, *Phil. Mag.*, vol. 40, p. 36, 1949; S. C. Curran, *Nucleonics*, vol. 1, p. 221, 1950. R. Pepinsky, *Anal. Chem.*, vol. 22, p. 1580, 1950 (abstract).

[3] A. R. Lang, *Nature*, vol. 168, p. 907, 1951. U. W. Arndt and D. P. Riley, *Proc. Phys. Soc. (London)*, vol. 65, p. 74, 1952.

The *electron multiplier* tube is a vacuum tube with a series of about 10 electrodes. It is constructed so that an electron ejected from the first electrode is swept by a potential difference of about 100 volts to the second electrode, where it ejects about four or five secondary electrons. These in turn are swept to the next electrode where similar multiplication occurs, and so on until an amplification of 10^6 to 10^9 is obtained. The intensity of a beam of X-rays may be measured by directing the beam at the first electrode and counting the number of impulses per minute, as in a Geiger counter. The impulses are said to last only 10^{-8} sec and therefore to permit higher counting rates than Geiger counters.[1] At greater beam intensities the continuous current from the tube may be measured; these are of the order of 10^4 times the currents obtained in ionization chambers. With weak X-ray beams some tests have placed the electron multiplier in an inferior position to the Geiger counter.[2,3] A *photomultiplier detector* consists of an X-ray fluorescent screen mounted on a photomultiplier tube in such a way that the fluorescent light from the screen is focused on the photocathode and ejects electrons which then are multiplied by the electron-multiplier scheme.[3] Higher efficiencies are claimed for this device than for the direct emission of photoelectrons by X-rays in the multiplier tube itself, and the device is able to handle higher intensities than the Geiger counter because at high intensities the continuous-current output can be measured. At low intensities the photomultiplier detector is comparable with the Geiger counter. *Scintillation counters* based on the same principle have employed thick crystals as the fluorescing agent, crystals being chosen that are transparent to their own fluorescent radiation, such as naphthalene and anthracene.[4] These have a high background count, which can be lowered only with special precautions.

X-rays in the Million-volt Range. The laws reviewed in this chapter apply to X-rays in the range of wavelengths used for diffraction and for moderate-voltage radiography, but not necessarily to X-rays produced with accelerating voltages of several million volts, such as those produced by a betatron. In the high-energy range, the absorption coefficient decreases with increasing voltage only up to the voltage at which a new absorption mechanism becomes the predominating one, *viz.*, absorption caused by the production of electron-positron pairs. Above this voltage, which is about 7×10^6 volts when iron is the absorber, the absorption coefficient again rises, notwithstanding the continued decrease in photoelectric absorption and Compton scattering.

[1] G. Papp and K. Sasvári, *J. Applied Phys.*, vol. 19, p. 1182, 1948. S. Rodda, *J. Sci. Instruments*, vol. 26, p. 65, 1949.

[2] A. Eisenstein and N. S. Gingrich, *Rev. Sci. Instruments*, vol. 12, p. 582, 1941.

[3] Fitz-Hugh Marshall, J. W. Coltman, and A. I. Bennett, *Rev. Sci. Instruments*, vol. 19, p. 744, 1948.

[4] H. Kallmann, *Natur u. Tech.*, July, 1947. P. R. Bell, *Phys. Rev.*, vol. 73, p.1405, 1948.

CHAPTER IV

DIFFRACTION OF X-RAYS BY CRYSTALS

This chapter presents a brief survey of the fundamental principles and the several methods by which X-rays are employed to investigate the inner structure of crystals. Simple sketches are given for each of the common types of cameras and films. Subsequent chapters are devoted to more detailed treatments of the individual methods and the techniques used in various applications.

A beam of X-rays is diffracted from a crystal when certain geometrical conditions are satisfied, which may be stated either by Bragg's law or alternatively by Laue's equations. With the aid of these relationships the positions of the diffracted beams forming the diffraction pattern can be analyzed to give the size, shape, and orientation of the unit cell. To determine the manner in which the atoms are arranged within the unit cell it is necessary to analyze the intensities of the reflected beams. This is done using the structure-factor equation, which relates the position of each atom to the intensities of all reflections. In an actual determination of crystal structure by X-rays it is often necessary to apply certain correction factors to the intensities as read from the film in order to reduce them to true intensities. The corrections are presented in Appendix I.

Scattering of X-rays by Atoms. When a beam of X-rays passes over an atom, the electric field of the beam acts upon each electron of the atom, accelerating each with a vibratory motion. Any electric charge undergoing an oscillation of this sort becomes the source of a new set of electromagnetic waves, just as the alternating electric current in the antenna of a radio transmitter sends out electromagnetic waves of radio frequency. The waves radiating out from the vibrating electrons have the same frequency and wavelength as the incident beam that is responsible for the vibration. (We are concerned in this chapter only with the coherent scattered radiation, not with the modified radiation that is altered in wavelength.) In effect, each electron subtracts a small amount of energy from the impinging beam and broadcasts it in all directions, "scatters" it. The various scattered waves from the individual electrons of an atom combine and may be treated as a single set of radiating waves which, for most purposes, can be considered as originating from a point. Actually, the difference in the nature of the scattering by a number of electrons grouped at a point and the same number distributed in a cloud around the

69

nucleus of an atom is sufficiently marked so that an analysis of the scattering gives the dimensions of the cloud and the distribution of the electrons within it.   An introduction to this type of analysis of the structure of individual atoms is given in Appendix I.

The superposition of waves scattered by individual atoms results in diffraction.   The waves that radiate from the atoms of a crystal combine in an additive way in certain directions from the crystal but annul one another in other directions, the intensity in any direction depending on whether or not the crests of the waves from each of the atoms superpose, *i.e.*, whether or not the individual scattered waves are in phase.   The

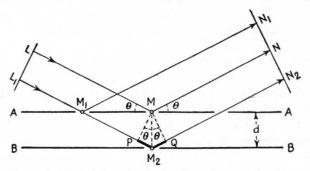

Fɪɢ. 1. Illustrating Bragg's law of reflection from planes of atoms in a crystal.

relation of the regularly repeating pattern of atoms in a crystal to the directions of the reinforced diffracted beams is given in the sections immediately following.

Bragg's Law.   Consider a set of parallel planes of atoms in a crystal, two of which are represented by the lines AA and BB in Fig. 1, and suppose a beam of monochromatic X-rays is directed at the planes in the direction LM, which makes an angle θ with the planes.   The line LL_1 is drawn to represent one of the crests in the approaching waves and is perpendicular to the direction of propagation of the waves.   As this crest reaches each of the atoms in the crystal, it generates a scattered wave crest.   We shall see that the various scattered waves reinforce in the direction MN, their crests coinciding along the line N_1N_2.   There will be a certain number of complete wavelengths in the path LMN along which a ray proceeds that is scattered by an atom at M.   Now if the ray scattered by an atom at M_1 travels the same distance (*i.e.*, if the distance $L_1M_1N_1$ is equal to LMN), then the scattered rays from the two atoms will be in phase and will reinforce each other.   It will also be true that any other atom lying anywhere in the plane AA will also reinforce the beam in this direction.   This reinforcement will take place when the incident and the scattered rays make equal angles with the atomic plane.

It is then possible to regard the plane of atoms as a mirror that is *reflecting* a portion of the X-rays at an angle of reflection equal to the angle of incidence. Let us now consider the condition for reinforcement of the waves from successive planes in the crystal that lie parallel to AA. The requirement to be met is that the difference in the length of the path for rays reflected from successive planes be equal to an integral number of wavelengths. In Fig. 1 this corresponds to the condition that the distance PM_2Q is one wavelength or a multiple of it, since PM is drawn perpendicular to LM and MQ is drawn perpendicular to MN, making the paths of the rays from L and L_1 the same except for the distance PM_2Q. It will be seen from the figure that

$$PM_2 = M_2Q = d \sin \theta$$

Thus the condition for reinforcement of all the reflected rays is

$$n\lambda = 2d \sin \theta$$

where $n = 0, 1, 2, 3$, etc., λ is the wavelength, and d is the spacing of the planes. This is Bragg's law. The integer n, which gives the number of wavelengths' difference in path for waves from successive planes, is the *order of reflection*.

The Laue Equations. Diffraction from a crystal, as indicated above, is analogous to reflection from a series of semitransparent mirrors, but it is also to be understood as diffraction from a three-dimensional grating, analogous to the diffraction of light from a one-dimensional optical grating.

If an X-ray beam is directed at a row of equally spaced atoms, as represented in Fig. 2, each atom will be a source of scattered waves spreading spherically, which reinforce in certain directions to produce the zero-, first-, second-, and higher order diffracted beams. Successive waves are indicated on the drawing by concentric arcs, which are linked together to show how the various orders are built up. The condition for reinforcement can be derived from Fig. 3, which shows the path difference for rays scattered by two adjacent atoms in the row. If the incident beam makes an angle α_0 with the row, and the diffracted beam leaves at the angle α, then the path difference is $a(\cos \alpha - \cos \alpha_0)$. This path difference must be an integral number of wavelengths if the scattered waves are to be in phase, so the following relation must hold:

$$a(\cos \alpha - \cos \alpha_0) = h\lambda$$

where h is an integer and λ is the wavelength. This equation will be satisfied by all the generators of a cone that is concentric with the line of atoms and that has the semiapex angle α. Thus for any given angle of incidence there will be a series of concentric cones surrounding the row of atoms, each cone being made up of one order of diffracted rays. A set of cones of this type is indicated in Fig. 4.

If there is a two-dimensional network of atoms with spacings a in one

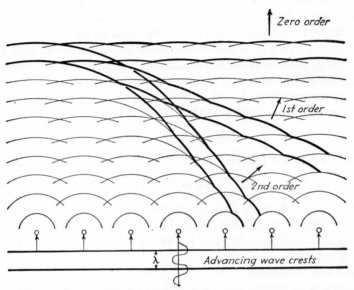

Fig. 2. Reinforcement of scattered waves producing diffracted beams in the different orders.

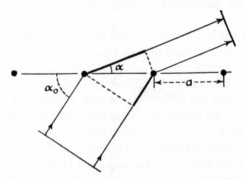

Fig. 3. Conditions for reinforcement leading to one of the Laue equations.

direction and b in another, there will be two simultaneous equations to be fulfilled for intense diffracted beams:

$$a(\cos \alpha - \cos \alpha_0) = h\lambda$$
$$b(\cos \beta - \cos \beta_0) = k\lambda$$

In these relations, α_0 and α are the angles the incident and diffracted beams make with the a rows, while β_0 and β are the corresponding angles

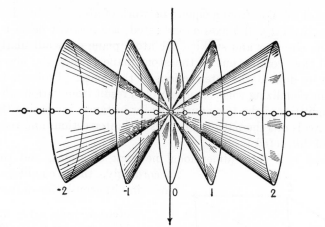

FIG. 4. Cones of diffracted beams around a row of atoms, with direction of primary beam indicated by the arrow.   Orders of diffraction indicated by numbers.

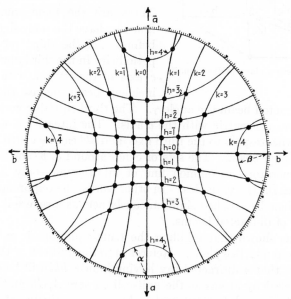

FIG. 5. Stereographic projection of diffracted beams from a two-dimensional square network.   Cones are concentric with a and b axes; intersections are strong diffracted beams.

for the b rows; h is the integer giving the order of reflection with respect to the a rows, and k is the order for the b rows.   These equations correspond to two sets of cones, a set around the a axis and another concentric with the b axis.   The most intense diffracted beams will travel out along the intersections of these two sets.   The geometry of these beams can be illustrated neatly on a stereographic projection.   The projection of Fig. 5

illustrates diffraction from a square network of atoms in the plane of the projection, with a and b axes as indicated; the incident beam is coming toward the observer and striking the atom plane perpendicularly. The diffracted rays coming out of the atom plane toward the observer are indicated by dots at the intersections of the cones. Projections of this type aid in visualizing what changes would result from various alterations in the quantities of the two equations; for instance, increasing the wavelength spreads out the pattern of cones and intersections and reduces the number of diffracted beams.

A crystal is a three-dimensional network of atoms, and there are, accordingly, three conditions to be met simultaneously for diffraction:

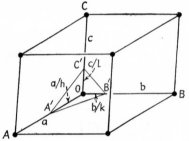

$$a(\cos \alpha - \cos \alpha_0) = h\lambda$$
$$b(\cos \beta - \cos \beta_0) = k\lambda$$
$$c(\cos \gamma - \cos \gamma_0) = l\lambda$$

These are the Laue equations; the first two have the same significance as before, and the third relates to the periodicity in the third dimension, the

Fig. 6. A reflecting plane (hkl) in a unit cell.

c axis of the crystal, with which the incident beam makes the angle γ_0 and the diffracted beam the angle γ. The third equation corresponds to a set of cones concentric with the c axis. The integer l is the order of diffraction with respect to the third axis, and hkl can be called the indices of the diffracted beam. The sets of cones around a, b, and c all have a common generator—a common line of intersection—only if there are special values for the variables. In other words, the requirement that all three equations be satisfied simultaneously acts as a severe limitation to the number of diffracted beams.

Bragg[1] has shown that fulfilling the Laue equations is equivalent to reflecting from a lattice plane. Reference to the unit cell of the lattice in Fig. 6 shows that a diffracted ray having indices hkl will be built up of waves scattered by atoms at the unit-cell corners A, B, and C, if these waves are h, k, and l wavelengths ahead, respectively, of the waves scattered by O. If we now draw a crystal plane such that its intercepts are $OA' = a/h$, $OB' = b/k$, and $OC' = c/l$, then the wave scattered by every atom on this plane $A'B'C'$ will be one wavelength ahead of the wave scattered by O. All waves scattered by the plane $A'B'C'$ will thus be in phase; this is the condition for reflection from the plane (hkl).

It is a great convenience to distinguish between *indices of a reflected*

[1] W. L. Bragg, "The Crystalline State," vol. I, p. 18, Macmillan, New York, 1934.

beam and the indices of a reflecting plane in a crystal. It will be remembered that indices of crystal planes never have a common factor. We are therefore free to use indices with a common factor to express the order of reflection, n. The first-order reflection is given the same indices as the plane. For example, the first order from (110) is written 110. The second order is written with the indices of the reflecting plane multiplied by two—220. The third order is 330, etc. To avoid confusion, the indices of the reflections are written without parentheses.

This scheme of notation for reflections is more than a mere convention, for it simplifies the interpretation of diffraction patterns. Its usefulness depends on the fact that nth-order reflection from a plane (hkl) is equivalent to first-order reflection from an imaginary set of planes spaced $1/n$th the spacing of the (hkl) planes. If the intercepts of the (hkl) plane nearest the origin are $1/h$, $1/k$, and $1/l$, then the intercepts of the first plane of the new set will be $1/nh$, $1/nk$, and $1/nl$. All reflections can be considered as first-order reflections from this new set of planes, and if their spacing is d' the Bragg equation can be simplified to

$$\lambda = 2d' \sin \theta$$

The reflecting angles are computed by the equations in the following section, in which this convention is used.

Interplanar Spacings. From the foregoing sections it is apparent that the *directions* of the diffracted beams are governed entirely by the *geometry of the lattice* (by the orientation and spacing of the planes of atoms, from the point of view of Bragg's law, or by the periodicity of the lattice in three dimensions, from the point of view of the Laue equations). In other words, the size and shape of the unit cell determine where the diffracted beams will go. The distribution of atoms within the unit cell has no effect on these directions but determines, on the other hand, the *intensities* of the diffracted beams. This will be discussed later.

Given a unit cell of known dimensions, the diffracted beams can be predicted if the various interplanar spacings, d, are computed and inserted in Bragg's law. Consider as an example a crystal composed of atoms only at the corners of simple cubic unit cells. Reference to Fig. 7 will show that the most widely spaced atomic planes are those that are spaced at intervals equal to the edge of the cell, a, which are the (100) planes. This spacing is $d_{100} = a/\sqrt{1}$. The reflected beam from these planes will have the least value of θ and will thus be least deviated by reflection. The next planes in order of spacing will be the (110) planes which bisect the face diagonal and for which $d_{110} = a/\sqrt{2}$. The third set, illustrated at the right of Fig. 7, which cuts the body diagonal into three parts, has $d_{111} = a/\sqrt{3}$.

The general rule for these spacings is

$$d_{hkl} = \frac{a}{\sqrt{h^2 + k^2 + l^2}}$$

This formula can be inserted in the Bragg equation, which can most conveniently be written in the squared form

$$\sin^2 \theta = \frac{n^2\lambda^2}{4} \cdot \frac{1}{d^2}$$

Using the convention that the nth-order reflection from a plane has

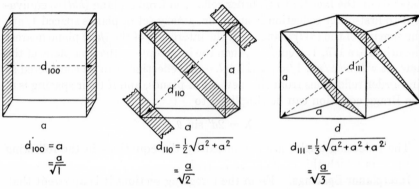

$$d_{100} = a \qquad d_{110} = \frac{1}{2}\sqrt{a^2 + a^2} \qquad d_{111} = \frac{1}{3}\sqrt{a^2 + a^2 + a^2}$$
$$= \frac{a}{\sqrt{1}} \qquad\qquad = \frac{a}{\sqrt{2}} \qquad\qquad = \frac{a}{\sqrt{3}}$$

FIG. 7. Some reflecting planes in a simple cubic lattice and their spacings.

indices that are n times the Miller indices, it is possible to predict the angles for all the possible reflections from *cubic* crystals by the formula

$$\sin^2 \theta_{hkl} = \frac{\lambda^2}{4a^2} (h^2 + k^2 + l^2)$$

The equations for the other systems can also be derived by inserting the proper spacing formulas (see Appendix III); for example,

Tetragonal

$$\sin^2 \theta = \frac{\lambda^2}{4} \left(\frac{h^2 + k^2}{a^2} + \frac{l^2}{c^2} \right)$$

Orthorhombic

$$\sin^2 \theta = \frac{\lambda^2}{4} \left(\frac{h^2}{a^2} + \frac{k^2}{b^2} + \frac{l^2}{c^2} \right)$$

Hexagonal

$$\sin^2 \theta = \frac{\lambda^2}{4} \left[\frac{4}{3} \frac{(h^2 + k^2 + hk)}{a^2} + \frac{l^2}{c^2} \right]$$

These are special cases of the more complicated formula for the triclinic lattice which involves the interaxial angles α, β, γ, as well as the axial lengths a, b, and c. These equations hold for all types of diffraction patterns and are the principal means of deciphering the patterns. For the less symmetrical crystals, however, there are so many reflections that these relations alone cannot be relied upon to unravel the patterns, and additional geometrical relations are required, which are taken up in later chapters.

Relation of Atom Arrangement to the Diffraction Pattern. The *positions* of the diffracted beams from a crystal are determined by the size and shape of the unit cell, but the *intensities* of the beams are independent of these dimensions and are affected only by the distribution of electrons within the cell. The diffracted beams are built up by the combination of the scattered rays from each of the electrons in the unit cell. (The nuclei of the atoms contribute a negligible amount to the total scattering and need not be considered.) The scattering power of an individual electron is the natural unit to which to refer all quantitative treatments of intensities; so we shall first discuss the cooperative scattering of the electrons in an atom, using the scattering from an individual electron as a unit, and then the cooperative scattering of the various atoms in the unit cell.

It is customary to use a quantity f, the *atomic scattering factor*, to express the efficiency of an atom in scattering X-rays. The atomic scattering factor is simply the ratio of the amplitude of the wave scattered by an atom to that scattered by an electron under the same conditions. In other words, since the intensity of a wave is the square of its amplitude, f^2 is the ratio of the intensity of the scattering from an atom to that from an electron. The atomic scattering factor varies with angle—an atom scatters less efficiently at large angles from the incident beam than at small. This is because the individual scattered waves from the various electrons in the atom are nearly in phase and reinforce each other for directions near the incident beam, while they are out of phase and reinforce each other less effectively at the larger angles. Values of f have been tabulated for all atoms and will be found in Appendix I. It will be noted that at small diffraction angles where reinforcement is nearly complete f is nearly equal to the atomic number.

Relation of Atom Arrangement to Diffracted Intensities. Let us now consider the intensity of the diffracted beam that results from the combination of the waves scattered by a number of atoms in a unit cell. Each atom scatters a wave of amplitude f, which is wholly or partly in phase with the waves from the other atoms of the group. Consider the atomic arrangement in Fig. 8, for example, with a beam reflecting in the first order from the planes marked A and A'. The wave from A' will therefore be one wavelength ahead of the wave from A and will reinforce it. On the other hand, the beam from the plane of atoms marked B will be one-half wavelength ahead and will be exactly out of phase; thus the reflections from alternate planes annul each other, B canceling A, etc., throughout the crystal—provided that the scattering power of plane B is equal to that of A. If the scattering powers are unequal or if B is not midway between A and A', the interference will not lead to complete annihilation of this reflection. Note also that, if the reflection is of the second order from A and A', then it will be of the first order from A and B, so that complete reinforcement will occur. Thus a body-centered lattice has 002 but not 001 reflections.

The Structure-factor Equation. To compute quantitatively the total intensity of a reflection it is necessary to sum up the waves that come from

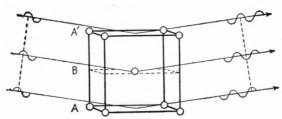

Fig. 8. Interference in 100 reflection from a body-centered cubic lattice.

all the atoms. Mathematically, this is the problem of adding sine waves of different amplitude and phase but of the same wavelength to determine the amplitude of the resultant wave. The square of this resultant amplitude is the required intensity.

The summation for the total intensity may be accomplished by inserting the coordinates and f values of each atom in the unit cell in the structure-factor formula for I, which is proportional to the square of the absolute value of the amplitude of the diffracted ray:

$$I \propto |F|^2 = [f_1 \cos 2\pi(hu_1 + kv_1 + lw_1) + f_2 \cos 2\pi(hu_2 + kv_2 + lw_2) + \cdots]^2$$
$$+ [f_1 \sin 2\pi(hu_1 + kv_1 + lw_1) + f_2 \sin 2\pi(hu_2 + kv_2 + lw_2) + \cdots]^2$$

where I is the intensity of the reflection, F is the scattering factor, $u_1v_1w_1$, $u_2v_2w_2$, etc., are the coordinates of atoms having structure factors f_1, f_2, etc., respectively, and hkl are the indices of the reflection being computed. This may be written

$$|F|^2 = \left[\sum_i f_i \cos 2\pi(hu_i + kv_i + lw_i) \right]^2 + \left[\sum_i f_i \sin 2\pi(hu_i + kv_i + lw_i) \right]^2$$

The formula applies to all crystal systems and lattices. A derivation is included in Appendix I.

We shall illustrate the use of the structure-factor equation by applying it to a body-centered lattice having identical atoms at the coordinates 000 and $\frac{1}{2}\frac{1}{2}\frac{1}{2}$ in the unit cell, as in Fig. 8. The formula for this case becomes

$$I \propto f^2 \left[\cos 2\pi \cdot 0 + \cos 2\pi \left(\frac{h}{2} + \frac{k}{2} + \frac{l}{2} \right) \right]^2$$
$$+ f^2 \left[\sin 2\pi \cdot 0 + \sin 2\pi \left(\frac{h}{2} + \frac{k}{2} + \frac{l}{2} \right) \right]^2$$

Thus

$$I \propto [1 + \cos \pi(h + k + l)]^2 + \sin^2 \pi(h + k + l)$$

and it will be seen that $I = 0$ for every reflection having $(h + k + l)$ an odd number. This is true regardless of the system to which the body-centered crystal belongs. Thus when a diffraction pattern of a crystal has been assigned indices, the absence of all reflections for which the sum $(h + k + l)$ is odd indicates a body-centered lattice, while the presence of any reflection of this type proves that the lattice is not body-centered. Other rules hold for lattices centered on one or more faces. If we apply the formula to a crystal of cesium chloride in which a cesium atom is at 000 and a chlorine atom is at $\frac{1}{2}\frac{1}{2}\frac{1}{2}$, quite a different result is obtained, for although cesium chloride resembles somewhat a body-centered cubic type of structure, the f values of the two atoms are not the same. The formula becomes

$$I \propto [f_{Cs} + f_{Cl} \cos \pi(h + k + l)]^2 + [f_{Cl} \sin \pi(h + k + l)]^2$$

and thus

$$I = c(f_{Cs} + f_{Cl})^2 \qquad \text{when } (h + k + l) \text{ is even}$$
$$I = c(f_{Cs} - f_{Cl})^2 \qquad \text{when } (h + k + l) \text{ is odd}$$

where c is a constant. There are no reflections missing in the diffraction patterns of this crystal, though the reflections that are missing in a true body-centered lattice are present in this case with very low intensity. This is illustrated in the structure of Fig. 8 when the B-plane atoms scatter less strongly than the A-plane atoms, or vice versa, and are unable to reduce the 001 reflection to zero intensity.

X-RAY DIFFRACTION METHODS

If a monochromatic beam of X-rays is directed at a single crystal, the angle of incidence may not be correct for reflection from any of its planes. To ensure that Bragg's law is satisfied it is necessary to provide a range of values of either λ or θ. The various ways of doing this form the bases of the standard methods of diffraction used in crystal analysis.

1. In the *Laue method* a single crystal is held stationary in a beam of white radiation usually from a tungsten target. The variable is provided by the range of wavelengths in the beam.

2. In the *rotating-crystal method* a single crystal is rotated (or oscillated) in a beam of monochromatic X-rays. The rotation brings different atomic planes, in turn, into reflecting position. Thus θ is the variable.

3. In the *powder method* θ is again the variable, for powdered crystalline material is placed in a monochromatic beam, and among the myriad particles with random orientations certain particles will be properly oriented to reflect from each of the possible reflecting planes.

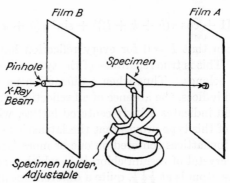

FIG. 9. Laue camera. Film *A* records the transmission pattern, or Film *B* may be substituted, for recording the back-reflection pattern.

The elements of these three methods are presented below, and a more detailed treatment of each is given in later chapters.

The Laue Method. A Laue camera (Fig. 9) consists of a pinhole system which collimates the beam into a narrow pencil of rays, a goniometer head or other device to hold the crystal in a definite orientation, and a flat film in a lightproof envelope placed to receive either the rays diffracted through the crystal or those reflected back from its surface. Each reflecting plane in the crystal reflects a portion of the beam, and the diffraction pattern (Fig. 10) is a pattern of spots that can be visualized simply as a pattern made by reflection from a number of mirrors inclined at different angles.

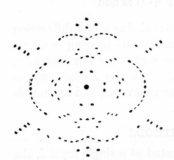

FIG. 10. A Laue pattern, transmission type, with twofold symmetry. X-ray beam parallel to a twofold axis of symmetry of an undistorted crystal.

The spots in a Laue *transmission pattern* (on a film placed at *A*, Fig. 9) are arranged on ellipses that have one end of their major axes at the central spot on the film. All spots on any one ellipse are reflections from planes of a single zone (planes parallel to a single zone axis). This characteristic can be demonstrated easily by the corresponding experiment with mirrors and a beam of light: a set of small mirrors fastened to the surface of a cylindrical rod will produce an elliptical pattern of spots on the wall— or the polished surface of the cylindrical rod will reflect an ellipse. On a

Laue *back-reflection pattern* (on a film placed at *B*, Fig. 9) these zones of spots lie on hyperbolas.

Laue patterns reflect the *symmetry* of a crystal; when the X-ray beam is directed parallel to a fourfold axis of symmetry, for example, the pattern will have fourfold symmetry about the central point and a quarter turn will bring coincidence of all the spots. Any other macroscopic symmetry element parallel to the beam will also be evident on the pattern. The method has been widely used as an aid in determining symmetry classes of crystals although it is not capable of fully establishing the symmetry.

In the relation $n\lambda = 2d \sin \theta$ each plane selects a wavelength that satisfies the equation, and as a wide range of wavelengths is present (from 0.2 A to over 2 A when a tube is operated at 65,000 volts) there may be two wavelengths reflecting from a single plane. Thus two or more different orders of reflection

Fig. 11. A Laue pattern of a distorted crystal, showing asterism.

may superimpose on a single spot. This makes the method an awkward one for determining the relative *intensities* of the reflected beams. The differing intensities of the various wavelengths in the beam as well as their differing efficiencies in blackening a photographic film are additional factors that make it difficult to measure the intensities of the

Fig. 12. A Laue pattern of undistorted polycrystalline material. Typical of recrystallized metal.

reflections. Consequently, the Laue method is not widely used for crystal-structure determination and is mainly of importance for determining symmetry and orientations of crystals. In the metallurgical field it is also useful for revealing imperfections resulting from accidents of crystal growth or from deformation. The Laue spots from perfect crystals are sharp, but those from imperfect or deformed crystals are blurred or elongated, giving the appearance known as *asterism* illustrated in Fig. 11. Asterism corresponds to the reflection of light from bent mirrors. If several grains of a polycrystalline metal are struck by the beam from the X-ray tube, their Laue patterns will superimpose, as shown in Fig. 12, and from the number of spots or their average size it is possible to estimate the grain size in the metal.

The Rotating-crystal Method. The elements of a simple rotating-crystal camera are sketched in Fig. 13. In the simpler instruments of this class the crystal is rotated continuously about an axis that is per-

pendicular to the beam of rays from the pinhole system. The diffracted
beams flash out when the angle of incidence on a certain plane is correct
for the monochromatic radiation employed. It will be seen by reference
to Fig. 13 that all planes parallel to the vertical axis of rotation will reflect
rays horizontally.

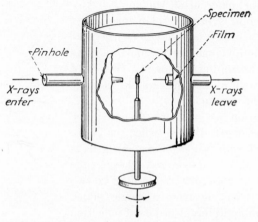

FIG. 13. Rotating crystal camera.

A cylindrical film taken from such a camera is illustrated in Fig. 14.
The reflections are arranged on *layer lines*. The spots on the central
layer line are reflections from planes whose normals are in a horizontal
plane; the spots on any other layer line are from planes that have the same
intercept on the axis of rotation. It is not difficult to assign indices to all

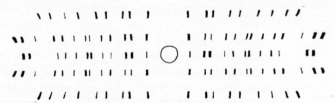

FIG. 14. Rotating crystal pattern. Axis of rotation vertical, layer lines horizontal.

of the spots if the crystal has been placed in the camera with an important
zone axis along the axis of rotation.

The *spectrometer* is used for measuring the reflecting power of single
crystals for monochromatic beams (Fig. 15). The crystal is set in a
reflecting position in the beam through slit S_1, and the reflected beam is
caught in a Geiger counter or an ionization chamber connected to an
electrometer. The intensity of reflection is measured by the ionization
produced in the chamber. A wide slit, S_2, in front of the chamber may be
used so that the whole beam is received, or a narrow slit may be used if it

is desired to plot the intensities at intervals every few minutes of arc across the reflection. The advantages of the method are the accuracy with which intensities can be determined and the fact that the reflected intensities can be referred to the intensity of the incident beam as a standard so as to yield *absolute reflecting powers* of the different planes. For the latter purpose the incident beam is rendered monochromatic by reflection from a crystal before it strikes the crystal being studied.

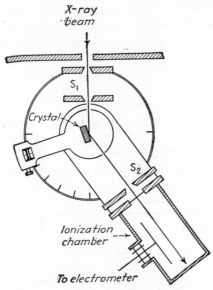

Fig. 15. X-ray spectrometer. A Geiger counter or a proportional counter frequently replaces the ionization chamber, and powdered crystals may be used instead of a single crystal.

Absolute intensities are needed only when the crystal structure is too complex to be solved by the less laborious photographic methods or when the electron distribution in an atom is to be determined.

If a plate of crystalline powder is substituted for the crystal, the spectrometer measures diffraction-line positions and intensities, line widths, and background intensities between the lines, each with precision unattainable by other methods. It has become, therefore, a very important technique in connection with the powder method discussed below.

The Powder Method. The powder method employs monochromatic radiation falling on a finely powdered specimen or a fine-grained polycrystalline specimen. The usual type of camera, sketched in Fig. 16, consists of a pinhole collimating system, a wire-shaped specimen, and a cylindrical film. A cup to catch the undiffracted beam or a tube to conduct it out of the camera prevents fogging of the film. Diffracted rays leave the specimen along the generators of cones concentric with the primary beam, each cone having a semiapex angle equal to twice the Bragg angle θ. When the film is laid out flat, it has the appearance of Fig. 17; the cones make a series of concentric rings around the central

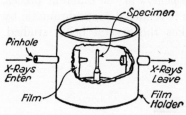

spot, and the Bragg angles can be determined quickly from the maximum diameter of these Debye rings. If $2S$ is the maximum diameter of a ring on a film of the type sketched in Fig. 17 and if R is the radial distance from specimen to film, then the angle θ in radians is $S/2R$, and in degrees the angle is 57.30 times this. If a camera

FIG. 16. Powder camera (Debye-Scherrer-Hull method).

holds a film on only one side of the central spot, it is necessary to determine the θ value by calibrating the film with the diffraction pattern from a standard substance having known diffracting angles.

Focusing cameras are also cylindrical, but are designed so that the specimen, slits, and photographic film all lie on the circumference of the cylin-

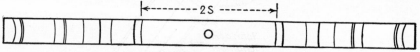

FIG. 17. Powder diffraction pattern.

der, as shown in Fig. 18. This arrangement causes diffracted rays from all parts of the specimen to focus on the film in sharp lines. Since a large area of the specimen contributes to the pattern, exposure times with focusing cameras are usually shorter than with cameras of the Debye type; they also have higher dispersion—more widely spaced lines—than Debye cameras of similar diameter.

The indices of the lines on a powder pattern are determined by trial. From the positions of the lines the spacings of the corresponding atomic planes are computed by Bragg's law, and observed spacings are compared with the spacings that would exist in unit cells of various dimensions and

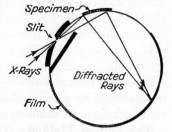

FIG. 18. Focusing camera.

angles. In the highly symmetrical crystal systems this trial procedure is relatively simple, but when there are many variable parameters, as for example in orthorhombic, monoclinic, or triclinic crystals, the procedure becomes almost hopelessly unwieldly because of the tremendous number of trials that are required.   Prediction of the lines for a given unit cell is carried out by inserting all combinations of h, k, and l in the corresponding formula for $\sin^2 \theta$ (page 76).   Effective graphical aids for shortening the procedure with cubic, hexagonal, rhombohedral, and tetragonal crystals are described in Chap. VII.   Intensities of the various lines can be measured very precisely, but only the simpler crystals can be completely determined by the powder method alone.

Powder cameras are operated with X-ray targets that emit strong characteristic radiation.   If the characteristic spectrum contains $K\beta$ as well as $K\alpha$ radiation, the diffraction pattern will contain reflections of both wavelengths, and the $K\beta$ diffraction pattern will be superimposed on the $K\alpha$.   The lines of the $K\beta$ pattern can be recognized by the following characteristics:

1. They are all single lines, whereas the $K\alpha$ pattern consists of close doublets resolved at the higher diffraction angles.

2. The $K\beta$ lines are always weaker than the $K\alpha$ lines from the same planes and may be weakened or even eliminated by a β filter.

3. The ratio of $\sin \theta$ values for $K\alpha$ and $K\beta$ radiation reflecting from a given atomic plane always equals the ratio of the wavelengths.

It is best to choose the target of the X-ray tube so that the $K\alpha$ emission line has a longer wavelength than the K absorption limit of the principal chemical elements in the specimen, for unless this is done the specimen will become a strong emitter of fluorescent radiation, which will fog the film.

Back-reflection cameras (precision cameras) make use of the fact that diffraction lines at large angles are extremely sensitive to slight changes of interplanar spacings.   If the spacing d in the equation $n\lambda = 2d \sin \theta$ is varied, it will produce variations in θ according to the relation

$$\Delta d \sin \theta + d \cos \theta \, \Delta\theta = 0$$
$$\frac{\Delta\theta}{\Delta d} = - \frac{\tan \theta}{d}$$

Therefore, as θ approaches 90°, the quantity $\Delta\theta/\Delta d$ becomes very great. The slight changes in d caused by elastic stress can be measured in a camera designed to record these high-angle lines to best advantage, and lattice alterations accompanying the change in composition of a solid solution can be determined.   With ordinary care a precision of 0.02 per cent is obtained, and with extreme care 0.003 per cent can be reached. The small cylindrical cameras of the Debye type usually yield results with an accuracy of 0.1 to 0.02 per cent.

Identification of phases by their powder patterns is an important practical use of the method.   This may be done without solving the crystal structure or assigning indices to the reflections, simply by comparing the patterns of the unknown material with patterns of known substances. The films are laid side by side or superimposed, and the similarities are observed directly. For this work, many lines should be recorded on the film, and every individual line of the pattern of the unknown must be accounted for. Identification is often possible when the specimen contains as many as three or more different substances, provided that each substance represents an appreciable fraction of the mass of the sample, for each produces its spectrum independently, and the pattern consists of superimposed spectra with relative intensities dependent on the relative amounts of the different phases present. If a series of alloys is prepared

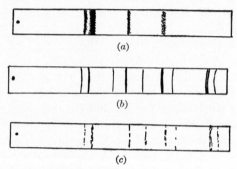

FIG. 19. (a) Pattern from cold-worked iron. Lines widened and weakened by "microscopic" internal stresses; from camera of Fig. 16, with FeKα and FeKβ radiation; increasing θ from left to right. (b) Powder pattern of annealed iron. (c) Pattern from recrystallized iron, the large unstrained grains forming spotty lines.

consisting of various compositions spaced across a binary constitutional diagram, the powder patterns will follow the alternate single and two-phase regions of the diagram. With a spectrometer the powder pattern can be scanned and recorded automatically and intensities can be read directly from the record, a great convenience in many research and industrial control problems.

Cold work, recovery and *recrystallization* are readily recognized by their effect on the patterns. Cold work is shown by a blurring of individual spots on the diffraction rings, and by broadening of the rings, especially at the higher diffraction angles. Figure 19a illustrates this for a cold-worked sample, compared with Fig. 19b for the annealed condition. Recovery from the strained condition is indicated by sharpening of the lines (Fig. 19b), and recrystallization (the growth of strain-free grains) by a spotty type of pattern indicative of large grains, sketched in Fig. 19c.

The distribution of intensity around a diffraction ring reveals the presence or absence of a *preferred orientation* of the grains. Random orientations produce rings that are uniformly black all around, while the presence of a texture is indicated by intense spots at certain points on the rings. A flat-film camera of the Laue type (Fig. 9, Film *A*), which is commonly used for this type of work, is often referred to as a *pinhole camera*. A typical pattern for highly oriented grains is illustrated in Fig. 20. Data from a series of patterns of this type, made with the sample tilted at

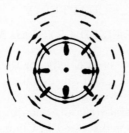

FIG. 20. Pinhole pattern of sheet steel having a preferred orientation from cold rolling (rolling direction vertical, sheet surface perpendicular to the X-ray beam).

various angles in the X-ray beam, are required for a full specification of the texture. These data may also be obtained with a spectrometer. When the data are plotted on a stereographic projection they provide a *pole figure*, which is a map showing the relative frequency of the lattice planes in different orientations.

CHAPTER V
LAUE AND FIXED-CRYSTAL METHODS

The Laue method is now used chiefly for the determination of crystal orientation and symmetry, and in metallurgical work for revealing crystalline imperfection, distortion, and recrystallization, although it was once also important in crystal-structure determination.[1] Crystal orientation by Laue photographs is discussed in Chap. IX.

As has been indicated in the preceding chapter, the Laue method requires but very simple equipment (a crystal mounted with an adjustable orientation in a beam of general radiation, and a flat film in a lightproof holder mounted normal to the beam a few centimeters from the crystal). A variety of designs is available commercially,[2] in most instances as an attachment or integral part of an X-ray goniometer that is also capable of taking rotating- or oscillating-crystal photographs—a convenient arrangement since it is frequently desirable to combine Laue studies with studies of the same crystal by other methods. A crystal may, for example, be oriented by the aid of the Laue method before being investigated by the Weissenberg method. The better Laue cameras and goniometers include a detachable combination telescope-microscope with which the sample can be aligned in the beam and oriented so that symmetrical patterns will be obtained. Pinholes of several sizes are desirable, and a small lead disk or cup in front of the film holder or fastened to it may be used to prevent fogging of the film by the central beam.

High-intensity fluorescent screens permit visual observation of Laue patterns, provided that the observer remains in darkness or deep red light for 15 to 30 min for eye adaptation. It is then possible to orient the crystal quickly to give a symmetrical pattern.[3] Care to avoid exposure of the hands and face to the scattered rays is very necessary.

[1] R. W. G. Wyckoff, "The Structure of Crystals," Chemical Catalog, New York, 1931. E. Schiebold, "Die Lauemethode," Akademische Verlagsgesellschaft, m.b.H., Leipzig, 1932.

[2] General Electric X-ray Corp., Milwaukee, Wis. Picker X-ray Corp., New York, N.Y. Charles Supper Co., Newton Center, Mass. Otto von der Heyde, Newton Highlands, Mass. Unicam Instruments (Cambridge) Ltd., Cambridge, England.

[3] The rods in the retina are responsible for vision in this range of intensities; compared with vision at normal intensities (using the cones) the rods are inferior in resolving power for detail and in ability to distinguish differences in light intensity. The screens have grain sizes that also limit the detail in the image.

Samples for the transmission Laue method are small single crystals 1 mm or less in diameter or crystals cut thin enough to transmit the beam without excessive absorption. The radiation from a tube with a tungsten target is usually employed, with operating voltages of 40 to 60 kv, but other targets (*e.g.*, molybdenum) will serve if it is remembered that with these targets there will normally be K radiation superimposed on the necessary white radiation.

Determination of Symmetry. Any rotation axes of symmetry or planes of symmetry that lie parallel to the incident beam produce corresponding

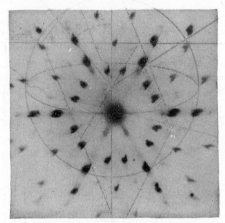

FIG. 1. Laue photograph of magnesium crystal with X-ray beam parallel to hexagonal axis.

symmetry around the center of the Laue photograph. The pattern reproduced in Fig. 1, for example, exhibits sixfold symmetry around the center because the sample was a hexagonal crystal in which the beam was directed along the hexagonal axis. Owing to the fact that the face (hkl) and the parallel face ($\overline{hkl}$) reflect to the same spot and cannot be distinguished, all crystals seem to have a center of inversion as judged by the symmetry of diffraction effects (*Friedel's law*). From Laue photographs, therefore, it is possible to distinguish only 11 different types of symmetry instead of the entire 32 classes.[1]

Assigning Indices to Spots by Gnomonic Projection. The spots in a Laue transmission photograph lie on ellipses that pass through the central point, all spots on any one ellipse being reflections from planes of one zone. The most convenient method of interpreting Laue photographs is to employ a projection that transforms these ellipses into straight lines.

---

[1] Friedel's law does not hold if the radiation has almost the same wavelength as the absorption edge of one of the atoms in a crystal. A phase change then occurs in scattering that makes it possible to distinguish (111) from ($\overline{111}$), etc., as has been demonstrated in experiments with zinc blende (ZnS).

The gnomonic projection does this and is almost universally used for the purpose. It is illustrated in Fig. 2, which represents a crystal C at the center of a reference sphere, a reflecting plane oriented as indicated by the dotted lines, and an X-ray beam reflecting from the crystal to form a Laue spot, F, on a film perpendicular to the beam. The line GC through the center of the reference sphere and normal to the reflecting plane inter-

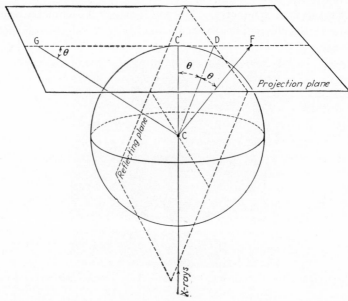

FIG. 2. Gnomonic projection of a Laue spot. Crystal at C with reflecting plane as indicated by dotted lines produces a Laue spot at F, which has its gnomonic projection at G.

sects the plane of projection at the point G, which is the gnomonic projection of the Laue spot. Thus

$$\frac{GC'}{CC'} = \frac{CC'}{C'D} = \cot \theta$$

The distance CC' is usually taken as 5 cm, and so the projection of any Laue spot is given by the relation $GC' = 5 \cot \theta$. In practice, it is convenient to construct a ruler that can be laid on the Laue photograph to locate directly the position of the gnomonic projection of any spot (Fig. 3).[1] The left side of the ruler is graduated in millimeters from the point C', which superimposes on the central point (C') of the film, and the right side is graduated to give the corresponding distances on the gnomonic projection; *i.e.*, the left side reads the distance $C'F$ of Fig. 2, and the right side reads $C'G$. If the left side is graduated directly in values of sin θ for

[1] R. W. G. Wyckoff, *Am. J. Sci.*, vol. 50, p. 317, 1920.

the spots instead of millimeters and the right side is graduated accordingly, this saves an additional computation.[1]

When the a, b, or c axis of a crystal is normal to the plane of projection, it is possible to read the indices of spots directly from the gnomonic projection. In Fig. 4, for instance, a Laue photograph of magnesium oxide (cubic) shown in the center circle is projected gnomonically. The photograph, taken with the beam parallel to the c axis, is oriented so that the a axis extends to the right. All spots for which the h index is zero lie on the central vertical line of the projection, since they belong to the zone [100]; similarly, all spots with $k = 0$ lie on the central horizontal line. The zone lines for $h = 1$, $h = 2$, $k = 1$, $k = 2$, etc., form a coordinate network of squares that are 5 cm on a side (if the projection sphere has a radius of 5 cm).* The indices of any spot can be read from this network by simply reading the two coordinates from the plot, assuming the third to be unity, and then clearing of fractions. For example, the spot R has coordinates $2, -\frac{1}{2}, 1$ and indices $4\bar{1}2$.

When the crystal axes parallel to the plane of the projection are of unequal length, the network will still be orthogonal, provided that the crystal is orthogonal, but will be rectangular instead of square. With the beam along the c axis of an orthorhombic crystal each rectangle will have the dimensions $5c/a$ in the direction of the a axis and $5c/b$ in the direction of the b axis. Similar principles hold for other orientations and other orthogonal axes. For example, if a crystal has a parallel to the beam, the network will have lines of constant k and l values that divide the projection into rectangles with sides $5a/b$ and $5a/c$. Inclined axes, as in triclinic crystals, project into parallelograms on a gnomonic projection, and so both parallelograms and rectangles are encountered with projections of monoclinic crystals.

Converging lines replace parallel lines if a crystal is not oriented with the incident beam exactly along an axis. It is often possible to tell by inspection how much a crystal must be rotated to bring it from an unsymmetrical to a symmetrical position. After the adjustment has been made,

Fig. 3. Ruler for plotting gnomonic projection of Laue spots. (*Wyckoff.*)

---

[1] M. L. Huggins, *J. Optical Soc. Am.*, vol. 14, p. 55, 1927.

* By reference to Fig. 2 it may be seen that the $(h0l)$ planes have cot $\theta = h/l$, and therefore $GC' = 5h/l$ when $CC' = 5$. The reasoning is easily extended to orthorhombic crystals.

a second photogram should then yield a symmetrical pattern and a simple gnomonic projection. As an alternate procedure, Wyckoff[1] has used a gnomonic rotation net that rotates the gnomonic projection directly and eliminates the necessity for resetting the crystal. Lonsdale[2] has published rules for indexing less symmetrical Laue patterns of cubic crystals.

Analysis of Crystal Structure from Laue Photographs. After a gnomonic projection of a Laue photograph has been made, the crystallographer frequently cannot deduce immediately the unit cell in his crystal, for

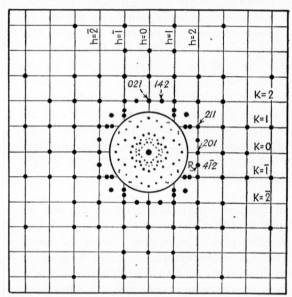

Fig. 4. Gnomonic projection of Laue photograph of MgO (cubic). Photograph is within central circle. X-ray beam parallel to c axis.

there are many cells of different size and orientation that could be chosen to account for the data. For example, in an orthorhombic crystal a unit cell could be chosen having any or all of its sides an integral multiple of the correct unit cell. The possible unit cells for other systems have been listed by Wyckoff.[3]

For each unit cell there is a new system of indices for the Laue spots. The correct unit cell among those possible is determined by measuring θ and computing the value of λ for each spot from the appropriate Bragg equation. The correct unit cell will be the one for which the calculated values of λ will range down to the short-wavelength limit of the continuous

[1] R. W. G. Wyckoff, *Am. J. Sci.*, vol. 50, p. 317, 1920.

[2] K. Lonsdale, *Acta Cryst.*, vol. 1, p. 225, 1948.

[3] R. W. G. Wyckoff, "The Structure of Crystals," 2d ed., pp. 143–145, Chemical Catalog, New York, 1931.

spectrum but will not go below this minimum wavelength. In this test one must guard against being misled by a strong absorption edge in the crystal that might introduce a false minimum wavelength, and by the superposition of different orders of reflection on a single spot.[1]

The Shapes of Laue Spots. The shapes of the spots in a Laue pattern are determined by crystal imperfection and by geometrical conditions such as the nature of the convergence or divergence of the primary beam of X-rays. It is possible for patterns of polycrystalline samples to contain spots of such a nature that they give the pattern the appearance of a preferred orientation when actually there is only a random orientation

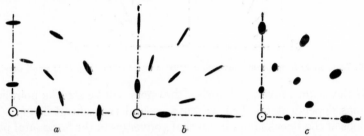

Fig. 5. Laue spot shapes. (*a*) Divergent cone of X-rays striking large crystal; (*b*) converging cone of X-rays striking large crystal; (*c*) converging cone of X-rays striking small crystal.

of crystals in the sample. It is well, therefore, to have some understanding of the shapes frequently encountered. The discussion below applies to transmission Laue photographs of perfect, nonabsorbing single crystals and polycrystalline samples.[2]

1. If the primary beam is a divergent circular cone of rays, as if it were originating at a point, and if the reflecting crystal covers the entire cone, then the spots of the Laue pattern will appear as in Fig. 5*a*. The spots will be elliptical with the minor axes of the ellipse radial. The ellipse will be smallest when the distance of the spot from the crystal is equal to the distance from the crystal to the point of origin of the conical incident beam, for the diffracted beams focus here. A small pinhole uniformly filled with rays can produce this type of pattern.

2. If the beam is a converging circular cone of rays, the spots will be elliptical, with their major axis radial, and the diffracted rays will diverge rather than come to a focus. If the crystal is large enough to fill the conical beam, the pattern will resemble Fig. 5*b*. On the other hand, if a very *small* crystal is located at the apex of a conical incident beam, the

[1] This can be minimized by operating the tube at 50 to 60 kv so that the maximum photographic effect lies between 0.48 and half this value, for then strong first- and second-order reflections cannot both be obtained from any one plane.

[2] J. Leonhardt, *Z. Krist.*, vol. 63, p. 478, 1926.

pattern will resemble Fig. 5c. The latter is very common in practice, because the individual grains of a polycrystalline specimen are so small they are effectively a point and the rays that pass a circular pinhole effectively converge to this point (*i.e.*, all rays that are reflected by that grain do so).

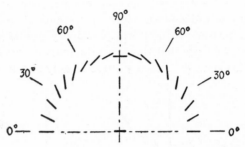

Fɪɢ. 6. Laue spots from beam converging fanwise in a horizontal plane; small crystal.

3. If the beam converges fanwise, the spots will be streaks pointed in directions dependent on their azimuth around the central beam. The directions of the streaks for a beam that converges in the horizontal plane are plotted in Fig. 6. This condition is frequently encountered when an X-ray tube is used in which the target is horizontal and the camera is placed to take a beam that is going only slightly upward from the horizontal; the focal spot may then be foreshortened into a line which fills the pinhole openings in the camera horizontally but not vertically. The effect will be noted in the polycrystalline pattern of Fig. 7, although it is partly obscured by arcs from characteristic radiation (molybdenum $K\alpha$ and $K\beta$) that cut across the streaks.

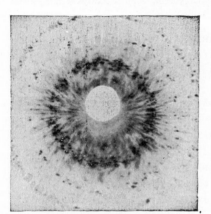

Fɪɢ. 7. X-ray photograph illustrating shapes of Fig. 9. Molybdenum tube, annealed steel samples; beam from horizontal line focus incompletely fills circular pinholes.

4. Fanwise convergence with a large crystal is similar to Fig. 6 except that the streaks are longer near the 0° azimuth than near 90°.

5. Fanwise divergence with a large crystal gives shorter streaks near 0° than near 90° and somewhat different directions of streaks from those in Fig 6.

Undesirable effects among the types listed above may be avoided by using pinholes that limit the beam to small convergence or divergence and by seeing that the pinhole system is completely filled with radiation. To test this, a fluorescent screen is placed at a considerable distance from the pinhole system. If the pinholes are properly filled with radiation, the spot on the fluorescent screen will be circular rather than elliptical.

Laue spots from imperfect or strained crystals may have distorted shapes, and internal detail. For example, a quartz plate with ground surfaces will yield Laue spots that are doublets, because most of the reflecting power lies in the two surface layers that have been altered by the grinding, and the Laue pattern is therefore equivalent to the superimposed patterns from two thin, parallel crystals located on the surfaces of the actual plate, as indicated in Fig. 8. If the quartz crystal is undergoing piezo-electric oscillation during the exposure there will be internal fine structure in the spots corresponding to the variation of reflecting power from point to point throughout the interior of the crystal, a result of the strains accompanying the vibrations.[1] Internal detail also results when natural imperfection varies throughout the crystal. When a crystal is strained so that the crystal planes are bent or

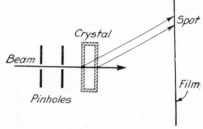

Fig. 8. A crystal with strongly reflecting surfaces (crosshatched) produces spots with strong inner and outer edges.

twisted, the Laue spots become distorted in a manner related geometrically to the distortion in the crystal. This effect, known as asterism, is discussed further in Chap. XVII. Strains and imperfections are also registered by other types of X-ray cameras to be mentioned later.

Crystal Images Formed by X-ray Reflection. Many investigators have used reflected rays to form images of the reflecting crystal. Berg[2] produced interesting images of the cleavage surface of rock salt, using a source of X-rays distant from the crystal and a photographic film quite close to the crystal and parallel to the reflecting surface. The geometrical arrangements for general radiation and for monochromatic radiation are indicated in Fig. 9. With these arrangements, each point on the surface of a perfect crystal directs a ray to a single point in the image on the film. Berg found that the reflected image became striated when a crystal was deformed, as if a local rotation of crystallites had occurred along the planes where deformation was localized, transferring the reflected X-rays from one strip of the image to another and leaving an unexposed line in the image. Some investigators have used a beam of

[1] C. S. Barrett, *Phys. Rev.*, vol. 38, p. 832, 1931. S. Nishikawa, Y. Sakisaka, and I. Sumoto, *Phys. Rev.*, vol. 38, p. 1078, 1931. C. S. Barrett and C. E. Howe, *Phys. Rev.*, vol. 39, p. 889, 1932.

[2] W. Berg, *Z. Krist.*, vol. 89, p. 286, 1934; *Naturwissenschaften*, vol. 19, p. 391, 1931.

characteristic radiation diverging from a pinhole placed near a focal spot and have placed a film parallel to the surface of the crystal on a carriage that oscillated with the crystal.[1,2] The images have been called "X-ray topographs,"[1] and "X-ray reflection micrographs."[2]

When a crystal is mounted on a goniometer and brought into reflecting position for $K\alpha$ radiation—by watching for the reflection of the character-

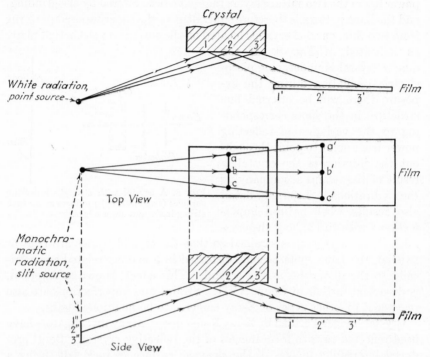

Fig. 9. Berg's two arrangements for studying the fine structure of Laue spots. Points on crystal surface 1, 2, 3, a, b, c reflect to corresponding points on film, 1′, 2′, 3′, a', b', c'.

istic radiation on a fluorescent screen—a good image of the crystal is obtained without oscillating the crystal or employing Berg's line source. The conditions for sharp detail in the reflected image are:[2] (1) a minimum distance between crystal and film, preferably under a millimeter; (2) a large distance from X-ray tube or pinhole to crystal (though any distance above a foot or so is satisfactory); (3) an X-ray tube with a target of low atomic number such as Cr, Fe, Co, or Cu; (4) a specimen surface undistorted by sawing, abrasion, or mechanical polishing; and (5) a film with a fine-grained emulsion, preferably high-resolution spectroscopic plates, the film being shielded from the direct radiation. Under these conditions,

[1] N. Wooster and W. A. Wooster, *Nature*, vol. 155, p. 786, 1945.
[2] C. S. Barrett, *Trans. AIME*, vol. 161, p. 15, 1945.

using a spectroscopic plate that has a resolving power of 1000 lines per millimeter, images are obtained that can be enlarged to useful magnifications of 100 diameters or more.[1] If a block of polycrystalline material is used instead of a single crystal, occasional grains will find themselves in reflecting position at any setting of the block, and the reflected rays leaving the surface will yield images in the manner sketched in Fig. 10. The incident beam is indicated by the arrow, the diffracted beams by the shading.

Fig. 10. Images formed by reflected rays penetrating a photographic plate placed above a polycrystalline sample. Primary beam indicated by arrow.

An example of a micrograph prepared by the reflection of cobalt characteristic radiation is given in Fig. 11 (See also Fig. 19, page 255). The micrograph is a map of the reflecting power as it varies from point to point over the reflecting surface (with very oblique incidence and soft radiation the penetration is very slight). Variations in reflecting power can be due to either variations in the orientation and spacing of the reflecting planes, or variations in "extinction" of the rays in the crystal, highly perfect regions with high extinction being low in reflecting power.

With proper choice of radiation and camera geometry it is possible to record either the variation in reflecting power from point to point over the surface of a crystal, or small variations in orientation, or both. A reflection made by characteristic radiation records both extinction and orientation variations, provided that it is a strong low-order reflection,

---

[1] Exposure times increase from a few minutes with dental X-ray films, lantern slides and other emulsions that permit enlargements of 10 or 20 diameters, up to several hours for the finest grained spectroscopic emulsions.

but if it is a weak high-order reflection it is unaffected by extinction and therefore is sensitive only to orientation effects. On the other hand, if the reflected image is a Laue spot and is formed by a component of the

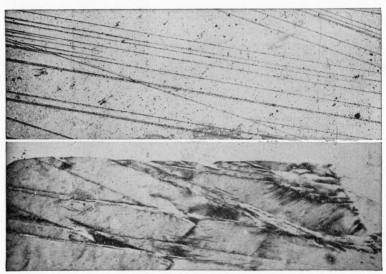

Fig. 11. X-ray reflection micrograph made by the method of Fig. 10.   Single crystal of iron containing 4 per cent silicon, containing deformation twins and slip lines.   Top, optical micrograph after polishing and etching, showing twins.   ×25.   Bottom, X-ray micrograph (different area) showing twins, slip lines, and rotated regions.   ×25.

continuous spectrum, it is unaffected by slight changes in orientation because this merely changes slightly the wavelength that is selected for reflection by the crystal, and the internal detail must be ascribed chiefly to extinction.[1]

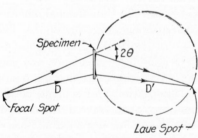

Fig. 12. Focusing condition for Laue spots. When the specimen is tangent to the focusing circle as shown, the distance D is equal to D'.

Laue spots in transmission photographs can be made very sensitive to slight orientation variations if the geometry is such that focusing occurs. Guinier and Tennevin[1] have employed a narrow focal spot (effective width 0.04 mm) and a large crystal to film distance (25 to 100 cm) in an arrangement sketched in Fig. 12, and have obtained sharp line images of aluminum crystals in which the disorientation was less than 10 seconds of arc.   These focused Laue spots are distorted into irregular smears when the reflecting crys-

[1] A. Guinier and J. Tennevin, *Compt. rend.*, vol. 226, p. 1530, 1948; *Acta Cryst.*, vol. 2, p. 133, 1949.

tals are stretched, and the smeared images coalesce into sharp lines again during annealing, when the curved reflecting planes are replaced by perfect crystal segments slightly disoriented from one another.

By using the reflection of X-rays from a cylindrically bent crystal it is possible to form a focused image of characteristic radiation of a given wavelength,[1] and this has been used by Cauchois and by Hámos as the basis for very low power X-ray microscopes.[2]

Divergent-beam Photography. When monochromatic X-rays diverge from a point source and strike a crystal placed near the source, or when the

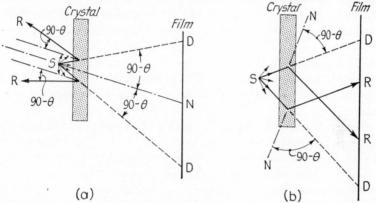

(a)   (b)

FIG. 13. Divergent-beam photography. Reflection from atomic planes will produce reflected cones, *RR*, in either the back-reflection range (sketch *a*) or forward-reflection range (sketch *b*). Reflected cones give black lines; deficiency cones, *DD*, give white lines. Position of the divergent source of rays, *S*, determines separation of black-white pair in arrangement *b*.

source lies actually within the crystal, Bragg reflection of the rays will occur in such a way that the diffracted rays form a cone. In Fig. 13*a* such a cone is represented by the rays *R, R*; this would appear on a back-reflection photograph. Since the energy in the rays *R, R* is subtracted from the beam that penetrates the crystal in the forward direction, a film in the transmission position will show a deficiency cone, *D, D* (white lines on the gray background of the film). The semiapex angle of the cones is

[1] G. Gouy, *Ann. phys.*, Ser. 9, vol. 5, p. 241, 1926 (on catoptric theory). H. H. Johann, *Z. Physik*, vol. 69, p. 185, 1931. Y. Cauchois, *Ann. phys.*, Ser. 11, vol. 1, p. 215, 1934; *Rev. optique*, vol. 29, p. 151, 1950. L. v. Hámos, *Am. Mineral.*, vol. 23, p. 215, 1938; *J. Sci. Instruments*, vol. 15, p. 87, 1938.

[2] Another variety of X-ray microscope should also be mentioned. This employs specular reflection of X-rays from curved mirrors, with the rays striking the mirrors within the critical angle of about 1°. Imperfection in the mirrors, astigmatism, and spherical aberration have limited the resolving power of these instruments so seriously that the theoretical resolving power of about 70 A has not as yet been remotely approached. (Paul Kirkpatrick and A. V. Baez, *J. Optical Soc. Am.*, vol. 38, p. 766, 1948. E. Prince, *J. Applied Phys.*, vol. 21, p. 698, 1950.)

$90 - \theta$ where θ is the Bragg angle for the reflecting plane. For planes that make a small angle with an incident ray there may be both black and white lines on a transmission film, as indicated in Fig. 13b. All cones will have their axes along the normal to a reflecting plane of atoms.

The source of radiation may be the X-rays generated by a narrow beam of electrons striking the crystal itself,[1] but it is more convenient to have fluorescent rays excited in the crystal by a beam of incident X-rays.[2] An ordinary pinhole beam in a Laue camera can be used for this. If fluorescence is not strong in the diffracting crystal, a fluorescing material can be placed in front of the crystal and irradiated with a primary beam of wavelength short enough to cause strong fluorescence. An X-ray tube of unusual design, which emits a widely diverging beam from a pinhole window, has been placed against diffracting crystals with excellent results.[3] To get good deficiency lines in transmission photographs the sample must be thick enough so that strong reflection occurs, but thin enough to permit considerable characteristic radiation to penetrate the sample.

A divergent-beam photograph contains many overlapping hyperbolas and ellipses centered about various plane normals. The indices of these lines may be determined from the symmetry of the pattern or from the apex angles of the cones. Since each cone is coaxial with a plane normal, the orientation of the plane normal can be determined from the line on the film, either by the aid of spherical trigonometry or by plotting stereographically. The angles between the normals can then be used to index the planes. (A standard projection of important planes, or a table of angles between planes aids this work.) The cone angles disclose the indices because they are dependent on the spacing of the reflecting planes causing them. A measurement of the semiapex angle of a cone, $90 - \theta$, gives the Bragg angle θ and this, in turn, leads to an identification of the plane through the interplanar spacing formula appropriate to the crystal, just as indices are assigned to the θ values read from a powder photograph.

Lattice constants can be determined from the photographs in an unusual way. The axes of the cones remain fixed along the plane normals regardless of the value of θ, but the semiapex angle depends on the spacing and the wavelength, for, by the Bragg law, $90 - \theta = \cos^{-1}(\lambda/2d)$. Consider now two cones from a pair of equivalent planes in a crystal, say the 022

[1] W. Kossel, V. Loeck, and H. Voges, *Z. Physik*, vol. 94, p. 139, 1935. H. Voges, *Ann. phys.*, vol. 27, p. 694, 1936. W. Kossel, *Ergeb. exakt. Naturw.*, vol. 16, p. 296, 1937.

[2] C. Borrmann, *Naturwissenschaften*, vol. 23, p. 591, 1935; *Ann. phys.*, vol. 27, p. 669, 1936. A. H. Geisler, J. K. Hill, and J. B. Newkirk, *J. Applied Phys.*, vol. 19, p. 1041, 1948.

[3] K. Lonsdale, *Phil. Trans. Roy. Soc. (London)*, vol. A240, p. 219, 1947. A review of many early experiments is included.

and $02\bar{2}$, which are at a known angle to each other. If the wavelength happens to be such that the cones just touch each other it is clear that the semiapex angle is exactly equal to half the angle between their axes. This would be evident from inspection of the film, and would be independent of the distance from the specimen to the film; an intersection of this kind in a cubic crystal would therefore furnish information from which the lattice constant could be determined. In practice, intersections between nonequivalent hyperbolas are also used, as well as near intersections of two or more hyperbolas, and highly precise lattice constants have been determined without precise measurements of the crystal-to-film distance.[1] Precision to about one part in 100,000 is estimated for the method. The precision is great enough so that an index-of-refraction correction must be applied to the data.[2]

Crystal imperfection strongly influences the visibility of the lines in divergent-beam photographs and must be within certain limits for the patterns to be visible at all. At one extreme are crystals so perfect that primary extinction is strong, reflecting power is low, and the lines are so fine and so faint that they cannot be distinguished from the background radiation. Lonsdale has found examples of this with diamonds (of type I), calcite, rochelle salt, ice, and many organic compounds. At the other extreme are crystals so imperfect that the cones are diffuse to the extent of being invisible against the background. The diffuseness can originate either from the range of orientation between mosaic blocks, or from a variation in lattice parameter from block to block. It should be possible to distinguish between these causes by noting whether high-order lines are blurred more than low-order lines, as they must be when parameter variation is the cause, or whether all are equally diffuse, as they must be when orientation divergence is responsible. The theory of the lines has been worked out by Laue,[3] but measurements of the intensities of the lines are not appropriate for determining reflecting power and extinction in crystals. Analogous lines occur in electron diffraction patterns, where they are known as "Kikuchi lines."

[1] W. Kossel, *Ann. phys.*, vol. 26, p. 533, 1936. H. van Bergen, *Naturwissenschaften*, vol. 25, p. 415, 1937; *Ann. phys.*, vol. 33, p. 737, 1938; vol. 39, p. 553, 1941. K. Lonsdale, *Phil. Trans. Roy. Soc. (London)*, vol. A240, p. 219, 1947.

[2] Stereographic projections have been published showing the cones for some cubic crystals and a particular wavelength, and a chart has been prepared showing the intersections and near intersections for face-centered cubic crystals with a_0 between 3.4 and 3.6 A when Co $K\alpha_1$ radiation is used. A. H. Geisler, J. K. Hill, and J. B. Newkirk, *J. Applied Phys.*, vol. 19, p. 1041, 1948.

[3] M. v. Laue, *Ann. phys.*, vol. 23, p. 705, 1935; vol. 28, p. 528, 1937; "Die Interferenzen von Röntgen und Electronstrahlen," Springer, Berlin, 1935. A summary appears in R. W. James, "The Optical Principles of the Diffraction of X-rays," G. Bell, London, 1948. James refers to the lines as "Kossel lines."

CHAPTER VI

ROTATING-CRYSTAL METHODS AND
THE RECIPROCAL LATTICE

The identification of individual reflections and the measurement of their intensities are accomplished with greater convenience and certainty by using one of the rotating-crystal methods than by any other method; consequently the rotating-crystal methods are preferred in most crystal-structure determinations. The apparatus can be very simple, as shown in Chap. IV (page 82), for it may consist merely of a rotating spindle on which a single crystal is mounted, a cylindrical film around the crystal (the axis of the cylinder coinciding with the spindle axis), and a set of pinholes to collimate the X-ray beam. It is essential to place an important zone axis of the crystal parallel to the axis of rotation, and for this purpose the apparatus should have a goniometer head that provides small angular and lateral adjustments of the crystal. A telescope and collimator are usually employed so that the small crystals (preferably 0.1 to 0.5 mm in average dimension) can be visually adjusted to a setting in which an important crystal edge lies along the axis of rotation, or planes of an important zone lie *parallel* to the axis. Optical adjustment of the crystal is often supplemented by X-ray patterns; one or two Laue photographs (preferably made on the same instrument) serve to determine the orientation of the crystal and to predict the angle through which the crystal must be turned to reach the desired setting.

An X-ray goniometer with provision for optical adjustment of the crystal and for Laue, oscillating, and rotating-crystal photographs is shown in Fig. 1. Any camera of the Weissenberg type, discussed on page 116, serves not only for the moving-film methods for which it is designed, but also for stationary-film rotation and oscillation photographs. A number of suitable designs of this type have been published,[1] the most convenient probably being that of Buerger.[2] A low-temperature camera is described by Keesom and Taconis,[3] and a high-temperature camera by Goetz and Hergenrother.[4] The construction and operation of many types of stationary-film and moving-film cameras are covered in detail in Buerger's

---

[1] K. Weissenberg, Z. Physik, vol. 23, p. 229, 1924. J. Bohm, Z. Physik, vol. 39, p. 557, 1926.

[2] M. J. Buerger, Z. Krist., vol. 94, p. 87, 1936.

[3] W. H. Keesom and K. W. Taconis, Physica, vol. 2, p. 463, 1935.

[4] A. Goetz and R. C. Hergenrother, Phys. Rev., vol. 40, p. 643, 1932.

books.[1] Several designs of X-ray goniometers are available on the market.[2]

Long-wavelength radiation, such as copper $K\alpha$ and $K\beta$, is desirable in order to gain high dispersion. It is unnecessary to employ a filter, for the $K\beta$ spots are readily recognized from their position on the film, but the characteristic radiation should be strong compared with the general radiation since the latter is not used in this method.

Interpretation of Rotation Photographs. Figure 2 is a typical rotation photograph showing prominent horizontal layer lines of spots and

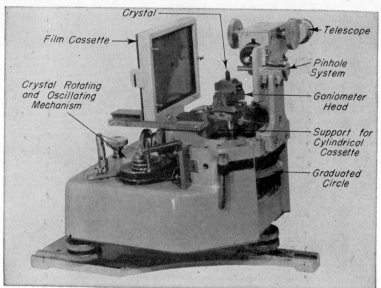

Fig. 1. An X-ray goniometer for Laue, oscillating-crystal, rotating-crystal, and powder methods. A cylindrical-film cassette may replace the flat-film cassette shown. (*Unicam Instruments, Ltd.*)

approximately vertical rows of spots (row lines). If a crystal is mounted for rotation around the a, b, or c axis, the spacings of the layer lines give immediately the spacing between lattice points in the direction of the rotation axis. This can be seen from the Laue equations, for each layer line is produced by diffracted rays forming the generators of a cone

[1] M. J. Buerger, "X-ray Crystallography," Wiley, New York, 1942; "The Photography of the Reciprocal Lattice," Murray Printing Co., Cambridge, Mass.

[2] General Electric X-ray Corp., Milwaukee, Wis.; Hilger and Watts, Hilger Division, London, England; Charles Supper Co., Newton Center, Mass.; North American Phillips Co., Inc., New York, N. Y.; Unicam Instruments (Cambridge) Ltd., Cambridge, England; Otto von der Heyde, Newton Highlands, Mass. The reader should realize that lists of manufacturers are seldom complete and that their accuracy diminishes as they age, but they are included as an aid to those unfamiliar with possible suppliers.

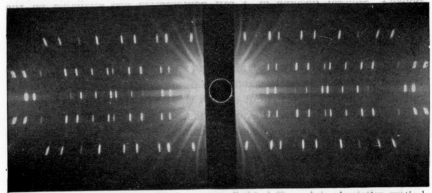

FIG. 2. Rotating crystal pattern of quartz, cylindrical film. Axis of rotation vertical. Filtered radiation. (*Warren.*)

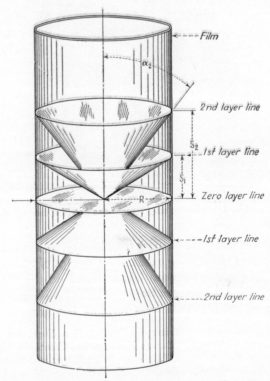

FIG. 3. Formation of layer lines from cones of diffracted rays.

coaxial with the rotation axis (Fig. 3). The cone is actually the cone along which reinforcement occurs according to one of the three Laue equations, *viz.*, the equation concerned with the periodicity along the axis of rotation. If the crystal is rotated around the *a* axis, the Laue equation that applies is

$$a(\cos \alpha - \cos \alpha_0) = h\lambda$$

and if the incident beam is perpendicular to the axis of rotation, this reduces to

$$a = \frac{h\lambda}{\cos \alpha}$$

where *a* is the identity distance along the rotation axis, α is the semiapex angle of the diffracted cone, λ is the wavelength, and *h* is an integer (the order of reflection for the cone) which is 0 for the horizontal layer line through the central spot, 1 for the first layer line above this, 2 for the second layer line, etc. Similar equations hold for rotation about any other direction in the crystal. We may therefore generalize the equation to apply to the identity distance in any direction that is chosen as the rotation axis, and if we insert the measured distance, S_n, on the film (Fig. 3) from the zero layer line to the *n*th layer line we have the formula

$$I = \frac{n\lambda}{\cos \alpha_n}$$

where α_n is determined by the relation cot $\alpha_n = S_n/R$; *R* is the radius of the cylindrical film; and *I* is the identity distance in the chosen direction.

Perhaps the greatest advantage of the rotating-crystal method is the fact that the dimensions of the unit cell can be obtained unequivocally from photographs taken with each of the unit-cell axes in turn serving as the rotation axis. With other diffraction methods it is not uncommon to derive a unit cell that is half the true unit cell in some dimension. In rotation photographs this error could be made only by overlooking entire layer lines, which is easily avoided, particularly if attention is directed to the higher order layer lines. The precision of the determinations is usually about 1 per cent and is inferior to determinations by the powder method, but it can be much improved by operating in the back-reflection region with precision cameras,[1] or by using extrapolation methods to minimize errors.[2]

Assigning Indices to Spots. Each spot on a rotation photograph satisfies not only the Laue equation discussed in the preceding section but also the two other Laue equations and consequently Bragg's law. Thus

[1] M. J. Buerger, "X-ray Crystallography," Wiley, New York, 1942.

[2] M. C. M. Farquhar and H. Lipson, *Proc. Phys. Soc. (London)*, vol. 58, p. 200, 1945. O. Weisz, W. Cochran, and W. F. Cole, *Acta Cryst.*, vol. 1, p. 83, 1948.

each spot is located on an invisible Debye ring for which the Bragg angle, θ, is given by an appropriate formula (quadratic form) on page 76. Thus, indices can be assigned to the spots by the method of calculating the θ values for all possible reflections and then comparing these calculated values with the ones read from the film by the aid of an appropriate chart.

A great advantage of the rotating-crystal method is its separation of the reflections into layer lines. Not only does this prevent some overlapping of reflections that would superimpose in powder photographs, but it makes assigning indices much easier. All planes that are parallel to the rotation axis reflect to the zero layer line. On a photograph with the a axis as the axis of rotation in the crystal these will be planes of the type $(0kl)$. Similarly planes of the type $(1kl)$ will reflect to the first layer line above the central one, $(2kl)$ to the second, $(\bar{1}kl)$ to the first one below, etc. The general rule is that reflections on the nth layer line will have indices hkl that satisfy the equation

$$hu + kv + lw = n$$

where $[uvw]$ are the indices of the axis about which the crystal is rotated.

Identifying Face-centered and Body-centered Lattices. Rotating a crystal about the direction [110] gives the identity distance in this direction. If this is compared with the a and b dimensions of the cell, it will be evident at once whether the (001) face of the unit cell has a lattice point at its center or not. Similar photographs for [011], [101], and [111] directions will disclose space lattices with a- or c-face-centered and body-centered lattices, respectively.[1]

The Reciprocal Lattice. The indexing of spots on rotation photographs is nearly always done by methods based on the reciprocal lattice, a concept originally applied to crystal diffraction by Ewald and by von Laue[2] and worked out in detail for rotation photographs by Bernal.[3] The reciprocal lattice is the best basis for the analysis of many types of X-ray and electron diffraction patterns and results in such savings in time over other methods of solving diffraction patterns that it is indispensable to the research worker. It provides an easy visualization of the orientation and reflecting power of lattice planes in a crystal and at the same time shows the spacings of these planes.

The reciprocal lattice is a lattice of points, each of which represents a reflecting plane in the crystal and each of which is given the same indices as the corresponding reflecting plane. By "reflecting planes" is meant

[1] The type of space lattice can be determined also without taking these additional photographs if indices are assigned to all spots and "characteristic absences" noted. This is discussed in Chap. VIII.

[2] P. P. Ewald, *Z. Krist.*, vol. 56, p. 129, 1921; *Physik. Z.*, vol. 14, pp. 465, 1038, 1913. M. von Laue, *Jahrb. Radioakt. u. Elektronik*, vol. 11, p. 308, 1917.

[3] J. D. Bernal, *Proc. Roy. Soc. (London)*, vol. A113, p. 117, 1926.

not only the true atomic planes with Miller indices such as (hkl), but also the fictitious planes with spacings that are submultiples of these, which give the reflections in higher orders with indices that are multiples of the Miller indices. Each reciprocal lattice point is located on a line through the origin perpendicular to the corresponding planes of the crystal and at a distance from the origin that is the reciprocal of the crystal plane spacing,[1] *i.e.*,

$$r^* = \frac{1}{d}$$

where r^* is the distance from the origin to the reciprocal lattice point and d is the spacing of the corresponding planes in the crystal, as indicated in

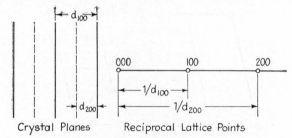

FIG. 4. Relation between crystal lattice planes and their reciprocal lattice points.

Fig. 4. By carrying out this construction for all other sets of crystal planes a three-dimensional lattice of reciprocal points is constructed representing all true and fictitious crystal planes.

The points of a reciprocal lattice always form a space lattice. If we designate the unit-cell edges in the reciprocal lattice by the starred quantities a^*, b^*, and c^*, then the relation between these axial lengths and the crystal axial lengths a, b, c, and interaxial angles α, β, and γ will be given by the following equations:

$$a^* = \frac{bc}{V} \sin \alpha \qquad \text{and is perpendicular to the } bc \text{ plane}$$

$$b^* = \frac{ac}{V} \sin \beta \qquad \text{and is perpendicular to the } ca \text{ plane}$$

$$c^* = \frac{ab}{V} \sin \gamma \qquad \text{and is perpendicular to the } ab \text{ plane}$$

where V is the volume of the unit cell in the crystal.[2]

[1] Some authors use reciprocal lattices in which $r^* = \lambda/d$, where λ is the wavelength of the radiation they are employing at the time. The convention adopted here is chosen for its clarity, simplicity, and invariance.

[2] To derive these relations consider the volume of the unit cell, V, which equals the area of the base of the cell times its altitude. In the first formula the area of the base is $bc \sin \alpha$ and the altitude is d_{100}; hence, $d_{100} = V/(bc \sin \alpha)$ and since $a^* = 1/d_{100}$ it follows that $a^* = (bc/V)(\sin \alpha)$.

Several planes of a crystal lattice are illustrated by the solid lines and filled circles of Fig. 5. The dashed lines in this figure are drawn perpendicular to these planes and contain rows of open circles, the reciprocal lattice points. Along the a^* direction in the reciprocal lattice are the points 100, 200, 300, etc., which have coordinates a^*, $2a^*$, $3a^*$, etc. These correspond to the (100) planes in the crystal, which reflect in the first, second, and third order with reflection indices 100, 200, and 300. Similarly, all other planes in the crystal are represented in the different orders by other rows of points which extend out radially from the origin in reciprocal coordinate space. Along the b^* axis lie the points 010, 020, etc., and along the negative b^* axis lie the points $0\bar{1}0$, $0\bar{2}0$, etc. All points of the

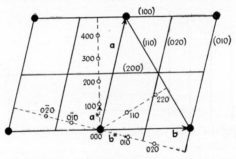

FIG. 5. A portion of a single layer of a reciprocal lattice (°) and a crystal lattice (●), for a monoclinic crystal.

reciprocal lattice have coordinates that are integral multiples of a^*, b^*, and c^*. These integral multiples are both the coordinates of the points and the indices of the points; thus the point having coordinates $1a^*$, $1b^*$, 0, which in terms of the unit axes can be written 110, has indices 110 and represents the 110 reflection.

In Fig. 5 a portion of one layer of the reciprocal lattice for a monoclinic crystal is shown; other layers will lie above and below the one shown and will have their points directly over or under these, the point $hk1$ lying above the point $hk0$ and the point $hk\bar{1}$ lying immediately under it. This will also be true for all orthogonal crystals (cubic, tetragonal, orthorhombic, orthohexagonal). A perspective view of a typical reciprocal lattice for an orthogonal crystal is shown in Fig. 6.[1]

Diffraction and the Reciprocal Lattice. A simple geometrical construction in the reciprocal lattice gives the condition that corresponds to reflection. Consider a sphere that touches the origin of the lattice and

---

[1] A reciprocal lattice is cubic for a cubic crystal, tetragonal for a tetragonal crystal (but, of course, with $c/a < 1$ if $c/a > 1$ in the crystal), orthorhombic for an orthorhombic crystal, and rhombohedral for a rhombohedral crystal. There is a sixfold axis in the reciprocal lattice parallel to the one in a hexagonal crystal, but the angle between a^* and b^* is not 120°, but 60°.

that has a radius equal to the reciprocal of the wavelength that is being used. Any crystal plane will reflect if the corresponding reciprocal

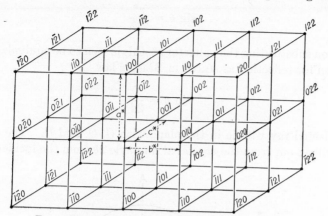

FIG. 6. Reciprocal lattice for an orthorhombic crystal.

lattice point lies on the surface of this sphere, the diameter of the sphere being always along the direction of the incident X-ray beam. This may be seen from Fig. 7, which represents a set of crystal planes at O

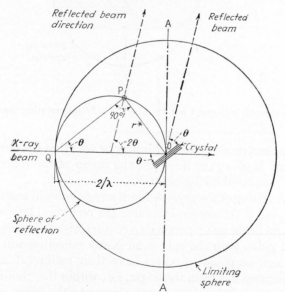

FIG. 7. Sphere of reflection in a reciprocal lattice.

having its reciprocal lattice point at P, and an incident beam along QO. The "sphere of reflection" is drawn with QO as its diameter, the distance QO being twice the radius, or $2/\lambda$ where λ is the wavelength of the incident radiation.   Now reference to the figure will show that the point P will lie on the sphere of reflection if

$$\sin\,\theta = \frac{r^*}{2/\lambda}$$

and, upon substituting the value for r^*, this is seen to be equivalent to the condition for reflection as stated in Bragg's law

$$\sin\,\theta = \frac{\lambda}{2d}$$

The reflected ray will lie in the plane with Q, O, and P.   The reflected beam will go out from the crystal at an angle 2θ from the incident beam,

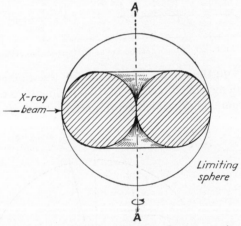

Fig. 8. Section through tore swept out by sphere of reflection rotating through reciprocal lattice.

and from the construction of Fig. 7 it may be seen that the direction of the reflected beam is along the line from the center of the reflection sphere through the reciprocal lattice point P.

At any one setting of the crystal, few if any points will touch the sphere of reflection, but if the crystal is rotated the reciprocal lattice will rotate with it and will bring many points into contact with the sphere.   At each contact of a point with the sphere an X-ray reflection will occur.   All planes that can be made to reflect have their reciprocal lattice points within the distance $2/\lambda$ from the origin, *i.e.*, within the "limiting sphere" shown.   Rotation of the crystal with respect to the beam can be represented by rotating the sphere of reflection and keeping the lattice fixed; if the axis of rotation is AA, the sphere of reflection will sweep out a tore whose cross section is shown in Fig. 8.   During a complete rotation of the crystal each point within this tore will pass through the surface of the sphere twice and will produce two reflections, one on the right and one on the left side of the rotating crystal pattern. For each point hkl that yields spots in the upper quadrants of the film there will be a corresponding point $\bar{h}\bar{k}\bar{l}$, on the opposite side of the origin, that will also pass through the sphere twice and yield similar reflections in the lower quadrants of the rotation photograph. Thus if the axis of rotation is normal to the beam, the photograph will be symmetrical about horizontal and vertical lines through the center.

Relation of the Reciprocal Lattice to the Film. Suppose the "limiting sphere" in Fig. 7 were a spherical photographic film. Rotation of the crystal would cause reflections which would be recorded on the film in a certain pattern. Now this pattern would be identical with the pattern formed on the smaller "sphere of reflection" if each reciprocal lattice point, as it moves around the axis during the rotation, were to leave a spot where it touches the sphere of reflection. The film pattern could thus be interpreted by imagining that the reciprocal lattice punctured it during rotation. In practice, of course, spherical films would be inconvenient and cylindrical or flat films are used, with the result that the pattern of reflected spots on the film is a distorted version of this pattern on the sphere. It is interesting to note, however, that when the

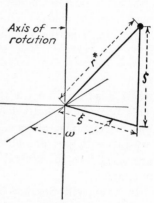

Fig. 9. Cylindrical coordinates for reciprocal lattice points.

reflection sphere is very large compared with the spacings of the reciprocal lattice points, then the portion of the sphere near the origin is almost a plane surface. The pattern on the sphere is then like the pattern on a flat film. This is the situation when electrons of very short wavelength are diffracted; the electron diffraction pattern on a flat film appears to be made by swinging the film through the reciprocal lattice.

To relate spots on a film to points in the reciprocal lattice it is best to use the *cylindrical coordinates* for the spots and the reciprocal lattice points. These coordinates are indicated in Fig. 9 where ξ (xi) is the perpendicular distance from the axis of rotation to a lattice point, ζ (zeta) is the distance parallel to the axis from the origin to the point, and ω (omega) is the angular position with respect to some reference line. Since ω acquires all values during a complete rotation, ω for reflections is undetermined in a rotation photograph, but ξ and ζ can be computed for each lattice point by measurements of the position of the corresponding spot on the film.

The ξ and ζ coordinates can be read directly by superimposing the film on a chart ruled with lines of constant ξ and ζ values. Figure 10 is a chart of this type ruled for cylindrical films of 57.3 mm diameter.[1] The straight lines are parallel to the layer lines of rotating-crystal patterns, and are lines of constant ζ; the curved lines of constant ξ superimpose on the row lines of the pattern. The direct beam spot on the film is placed at the central point of the chart. The coordinates ξ and ζ for spots on the film, when divided by the wavelength, give the corresponding coordinates in the reciprocal lattice.[2] The coordinate ω in the reciprocal lattice is always equal to ω in the crystal.

The Bernal chart (Fig. 10) permits a quick determination of unit cell dimensions for any crystal. The crystal is rotated about any axis a, b, or c that is to be determined, and the ζ values for the various layer lines are read from the chart. The identity distance in the crystal along the axis of rotation I is then obtained from the relation

$$I = \frac{n\lambda}{\zeta_n}$$

where n is the number of the layer line to which the coordinate ζ_n applies. This formula is equivalent to the one given earlier (page 105). The identity distances along a, b, and c are, of course, the unit cell edges. For crystals with axes at right angles to each other the reciprocal lattice axes are parallel to the crystal axes and are of lengths that are reciprocals of a, b, and c.

Indexing with Bernal's Chart. The relations between reciprocal lattice coordinates and indices of reflections are simple if the crystal has axes at right angles to each other (cubic, tetragonal, orthorhombic, orthohexagonal) and is rotated around these. First the a^*, b^* and c^* axes of the reciprocal lattice are determined as outlined in the preceding paragraph. Then using these axes a plot of the reciprocal lattice is made a layer at a time, the layers being those which are normal to the axis of rotation that was used for the film that is being indexed. If a is the rotation axis, for example, these layers will be rectangular networks with cells b^* by c^* in size and will be the horizontal layers of Fig. 6. The indices (coordinates) of all points can then be written down immediately. By comparing the coordinates of these points with the coordinates of the spots on the film, the corresponding spots can be identified and indexed. Attention to

---

[1] J. D. Bernal has published his chart on tracing paper for a 10-cm-diameter camera, and also the equivalent chart for flat films in *Proc. Roy. Soc. (London)*, vol. A113, p. 117, 1926. Charts are sold by The Institute of Physics, London, England.

[2] The reciprocal lattice plotted in this way is the one defined above, with $r^* = 1/d$ and with the reflection circle having a radius $1/\lambda$. Obviously it is more convenient to plot ξ and ζ directly as read and to plot the reflection sphere with a radius equal to the unit of length chosen for the reciprocal lattice plot; this construction is exactly equivalent to the one first described.

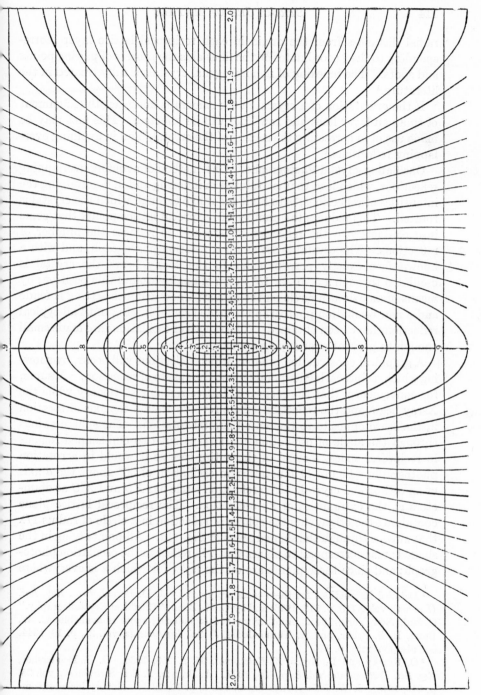

FIG. 10. Bernal's chart for reading reciprocal lattice coordinates from cylindrical films. Scaled to fit cameras of 57.3 mm diameter. Layer lines run lengthwise on the page.

113

radial distances from the origin in each reciprocal lattice layer (corresponding to the ξ coordinates on the film) aids the process of pairing points and spots. The indexing of nonorthogonal crystals is fully treated in the literature.[1]

If the orientation of a crystal in the camera is not exact the alignment of spots on layer lines and row lines will be affected. This fact may be made use of in correcting the setting of the crystal,[2] and in avoiding overlapping reflections.[1]

Oscillating-crystal Photographs. One method of avoiding overlapping reflections, which lead to uncertainties in indexing and in determining the intensities of reflections, is to limit the range through which the crystal is rotated. This reduces the number of reciprocal lattice points that come into contact with the reflection sphere and so reduces the number of reflections. The crystal is set as for a rotation photograph, and with a known face exactly perpendicular to the X-ray beam the crystal is oscillated through a 5, 10, or 15° range of angles around this position; by means of an azimuth circle on the camera a new azimuth setting is made and a new oscillation photograph is made around it, etc., until all typical reflections have been obtained. The ranges of oscillations are made small enough to prevent overlapping spots.

A graphical construction predicts which reflections will occur, by showing which reciprocal lattice points touch the sphere of reflection. Assume, for convenience, that the reciprocal lattice remains stationary while the X-ray beam and the reflection sphere revolve around the axis of rotation in the sense opposite to the actual crystal rotation. The sphere swings through the angle of oscillation and sweeps out two cup-shaped regions in reciprocal space, instead of the entire tore as it would in a rotation photograph. Figure 11 illustrates an oscillation of 30° about the a axis of an orthogonal crystal. The reflection circle has XO and $X'O$ as diameters at the extremities of its oscillation. The reciprocal lattice plane containing the origin cuts the sphere of reflection in a circle of radius $1/\lambda$ that sweeps through the shaded areas of Fig. 11a. All points lying in the shaded areas correspond to planes that will reflect in the oscillation photograph; and since these points are on the layer for which h is everywhere

---

[1] Detailed instructions for these cases are given by J. D. Bernal, *Proc. Roy. Soc. (London)*, vol. A113, p. 117, 1926; and by C. W. Bunn, "Chemical Crystallography," Oxford, New York, 1945. Another method of indexing spots is available: C. W. Bunn, H. S. Peiser, and A. Turner-Jones, *J. Sci. Instruments*, vol. 21, p. 10, 1944. See also footnote, p. 116.

[2] O. Kratky and B. Krebs, *Z. Krist.*, vol. 95, p. 253, 1936. O. P. Hendershot, *Rev. Sci. Instruments*, vol. 8, p. 436, 1937. A. Bairsto, *J. Sci. Instruments*, vol. 25, p. 213, 1948. J. W. Jeffery, *Acta Cryst.*, vol. 2, p. 15, 1949. (Jeffery includes comparisons of his method with the earlier methods and a test of its accuracy, which may reach 0.05°.)

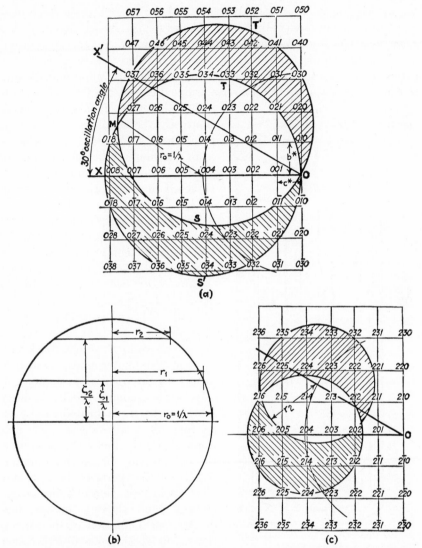

FIG. 11. Reflecting conditions in an orthogonal reciprocal lattice for 30° oscillation of crystal. Points in shaded areas reach reflecting positions. (a) Points in the zero layer; (b) relation between ζ and r; (c) points in the second layer.

zero, all these reflections will fall on the zero layer line on the photograph —the equatorial layer line.

Points on one of the layers above this one will lie on a plane that intersects the sphere of reflection in a circle of smaller radius. A side view of the sphere of reflection is shown in Fig. 11b, where it will be seen that the radius of the circles for these higher sections can be readily scaled from the drawing or computed analytically and varies with each value of ζ. To determine the possible reflecting planes for the second layer line the construction of Fig. 11c is used.   Here it is assumed that the axis of rotation is perpendicular to the plane of the net and that the reciprocal lattice is rectangular so all layers directly superimpose with h00 directly above 000, etc.   The centers of all circles are at distance 1/λ from the points

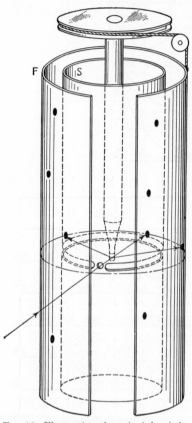

FIG. 12. Illustrating the principle of the Weissenberg X-ray goniometer.

h00.   Reflecting points are again shown by the shading.   In practice, points will reflect that lie 1° or so from the limits indicated, because of crystal imperfection and angular divergence in the primary beam of X-rays.[1]

The Weissenberg Goniometer.   An ingenious camera first designed by Weissenberg[2] completely eliminates overlapping reflections and has other advantages as well, making it highly desirable for the analysis of complex crystals.   The principle of the instrument is illustrated by Fig. 12.   A cylindrical film, F, moves back and forth longitudinally in exact synchronism with the oscillation of the crystal; this is accomplished by a pulley arrangement, as indicated, or by an appropriate set of gears.   A stationary metal shield, S, surrounds the crystal and contains a circumferential slot that permits the recording of a single layer line of spots at one setting.   The shifting of the film during the oscillation of the crystal causes the spots from a single layer line to be spread out over the whole of the film (Fig. 13).   The vertical distance between two spots of Fig. 13 is directly proportional to the angle through which the crystal turns in

[1] Directions for indexing spots in rotating and oscillating crystal patterns and in Weissenberg patterns are given in some detail in N. F. M. Henry, H. Lipson, and W. A. Wooster, "The Interpretation of X-ray Diffraction Photographs," Macmillan, New York, 1951.

[2] K. Weissenberg, *Z. Physik*, vol. 23, p. 229, 1924.   J. Bohm, *Z. Physik*, vol. 39, p. 557, 1926.

going from one reflecting position to another. The indexing of spots on Weissenberg photographs has been worked out in various ways.[1]

In making photographs of the higher layer lines there is an advantage in adjusting the incident beam so that both incident and diffracted beams make equal angles with the axis of rotation, giving what is termed an

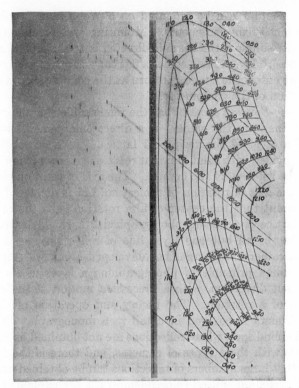

FIG. 13. Weissenberg photograph of a monoclinic crystal rotated about the c axis, with unfiltered copper radiation. Lines along which one index changes are sketched at right.

equi-inclination photograph. A Weissenberg photograph is simply a two-dimensional projection of one of the reciprocal lattice levels. The rows of points of the reciprocal lattice appear in a distorted form on the photograph and can be recognized with experience or with the aid of appropriate charts. (Note the lines of constant k and l indices in Fig. 13.) When the lines are recognized on the film, indexing of spots can be done simply by inspection. In equi-inclination photographs the rows of reciprocal lattice points fall on curves of similar shape on the films for all layers of the reciprocal lattice. Hence a single transparent template can be

[1] For a detailed treatment of moving-film techniques and methods of interpretation see M. J. Buerger, "X-ray Crystallography," Wiley, New York, 1942.

employed to mark the rows on the film.[1]   Weissenberg cameras constructed with precision and designed to make full use of the back-reflection region can reach a precision of about six significant figures, permitting computation of crystallographic angles with a precision of a few seconds of arc—greater accuracy than the few minutes of arc usually obtained in an optical goniometer.[2]

A Geiger counter can be mounted on a Weissenberg goniometer for accurate intensity measurements.   Mounting and turning the counter becomes quite simple if the beam is directed onto the crystal at an angle such that the nth layer line becomes a flat cone, for then each reflection of the layer line enters the counter in turn as the counter swings around the axis of rotation of the goniometer.

The *de Jong-Bouman camera*[3] has the remarkable characteristic that a photograph made in the camera is a direct enlargement, without distortion, of a level of the reciprocal lattice.   To accomplish this, the camera is provided with a flat film that rotates in its own plane in synchronism with the rotation of the crystal.   The axis of rotation of the film is parallel to the axis of rotation of the crystal but is displaced from it by such an amount that the center of film rotation is at the origin of the reciprocal lattice layer being photographed.   A shield between crystal and film absorbs all but one layer line of reflections, as in the other moving-film cameras.   Buerger has developed a camera employing the de Jong-Bouman principle of photographing a layer of the reciprocal lattice without distortion, with a precession motion of the crystal and film instead of a rotation.   The theory and operation of the Buerger precession camera is covered in detail in a monograph.[4]   There is an unavoidable blind spot, where reflections are not obtained, in most photographs made with these types of cameras, and there is the further disadvantage that large numbers of reflections can be obtained only if short-wavelength radiation is used (molybdenum $K\alpha$ is customary).   But the cameras are very convenient for many problems.   With molybdenum radiation, lattice dimensions are obtained to 0.04 per cent without

---

[1] In a further development of Weissenberg photograph technique M. J. Buerger shows that it is possible in many cases to determine the space-lattice type and the space group of a crystal by the simple inspection of a properly chosen set of Weissenberg photographs, without indexing any of the spots.

[2] M. J. Buerger, *Z. Krist.*, vol. A97, p. 433, 1937.

[3] W. F. de Jong and J. Bouman, *Z. Krist.*, vol. 98, p. 456, 1937–1938; *Physica*, vol. 5, pp. 220, 817, 1938. See also discussion in M. J. Buerger, "X-ray Crystallography," Wiley, New York, 1942.

[4] M. J. Buerger, "The Photography of the Reciprocal Lattice," American Society of X-ray and Electron Diffraction, Cambridge, Mass., August, 1944.

employing correction procedures.[1] Interaxial angles can be determined easily and with precision.

The Reciprocal Lattice in Vector Notation. Vector algebra is becoming almost universally used for the discussion of space lattices, reciprocal lattices, and diffraction. It will be introduced here by reviewing some principles that have already been mentioned.

Let the vector to any corner of the unit cells of a crystal be

$$\mathbf{r} = u\mathbf{a} + v\mathbf{b} + w\mathbf{c}$$

where u, v, w, are any integers and $\mathbf{a}$, $\mathbf{b}$, $\mathbf{c}$, are the vectors defining the unit cell edges which are of lengths a, b, c, respectively. In the reciprocal lattice, with cell edges $\mathbf{a}^*$, $\mathbf{b}^*$, $\mathbf{c}^*$, let the vector to any unit cell corner be $\mathbf{r}^* = h\mathbf{a}^* + k\mathbf{b}^* + l\mathbf{c}^*$. The reciprocal axis $\mathbf{a}^*$ is normal to axes $\mathbf{b}$ and $\mathbf{c}$ of the crystal, similarly $\mathbf{b}^*$ is normal to $\mathbf{a}$ and $\mathbf{c}$, and $\mathbf{c}^*$ is normal to $\mathbf{a}$ and $\mathbf{b}$. Now since the scalar product ("dot product") of two vectors is the product of their magnitudes times the cosine of the angle between them, it follows that

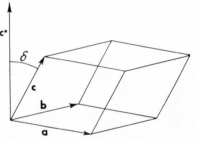

Fig. 14. Axis $\mathbf{c}^*$ of the reciprocal lattice is normal to $\mathbf{a}$ and $\mathbf{b}$ of the crystal.

$$\mathbf{a}^* \cdot \mathbf{b} = \mathbf{a}^* \cdot \mathbf{c} = \mathbf{b}^* \cdot \mathbf{a} = \mathbf{b}^* \cdot \mathbf{c} = \mathbf{c}^* \cdot \mathbf{a} = \mathbf{c}^* \cdot \mathbf{b} = 0 \qquad (1)$$

The length of $\mathbf{c}^*$ is determined by the scalar product $\mathbf{c}^* \cdot \mathbf{c} = 1$, which means that $c^*c \cos \delta = 1$, the angle δ being indicated in Fig. 14. From this figure it will be seen that $c \cos \delta$ is the spacing of the (001) planes, so the length of $\mathbf{c}^*$ is the reciprocal of this length. Similarly for the other axes,

$$\mathbf{a}^* \cdot \mathbf{a} = \mathbf{b}^* \cdot \mathbf{b} = \mathbf{c}^* \cdot \mathbf{c} = 1 \qquad (2)$$

From these equations it is clear that if the crystal axes are at right angles to each other the reciprocal axes will also be at right angles and will be parallel to the crystal axes; in this special case the reciprocal axes will have lengths that are the reciprocals of the lengths of the crystal axes. Relations (1) and (2) and those derived below apply to all crystals regardless of symmetry.

The reciprocal axes will now be related to the *volume of the unit cell* of the crystal. The vector product $\mathbf{a} \times \mathbf{b}$ is a vector, normal to $\mathbf{a}$ and $\mathbf{b}$,

[1] H. T. Evans, S. G. Tilden, and D. P. Adams, *Rev. Sci. Instruments*, vol. 20, p. 155, 1949.

of magnitude $ab \sin \gamma$ where γ is the angle between **a** and **b**. In Fig. 14 the area of the base of the unit cell is $ab \sin \gamma$ and is therefore equal to the magnitude of $\mathbf{a} \times \mathbf{b}$; the altitude of the cell is $c \cos \delta$, so one may write the volume V as

$$V = (\mathbf{a} \times \mathbf{b}) \cdot \mathbf{c} = (\mathbf{b} \times \mathbf{c}) \cdot \mathbf{a} = (\mathbf{c} \times \mathbf{a}) \cdot \mathbf{b} \tag{3}$$

The vectors $\mathbf{a}^*$, $\mathbf{b}^*$, $\mathbf{c}^*$ are in the directions of $\mathbf{a} \times \mathbf{b}$, $\mathbf{b} \times \mathbf{c}$, $\mathbf{c} \times \mathbf{a}$, respectively, and to be consistent with Eqs. (2) they must be of lengths such that

$$\mathbf{a}^* = \frac{(\mathbf{b} \times \mathbf{c})}{V} \qquad \mathbf{b}^* = \frac{(\mathbf{a} \times \mathbf{c})}{V} \qquad \mathbf{c}^* = \frac{(\mathbf{a} \times \mathbf{b})}{V} \tag{4}$$

as can be shown by taking suitable scalar products of both sides of these equations, as, for example, $\mathbf{a}^* \cdot \mathbf{a} = \mathbf{a} \cdot (\mathbf{b} \times \mathbf{c})/V = 1$

The reciprocal of the reciprocal lattice is the crystal lattice. This may be seen by setting up relations (4) with reciprocal axes instead of crystal axes. Thus $(\mathbf{a}^*)^* = (\mathbf{b}^* \times \mathbf{c}^*)/V^*$ and if the right member is multiplied by $\mathbf{a} \cdot \mathbf{a}^*$ which by Eq. (2) is unity then

$$(\mathbf{a}^*)^* = (\mathbf{a} \cdot \mathbf{a}^*)(\mathbf{b}^* \times \mathbf{c}^*)/(\mathbf{a}^* \cdot \mathbf{b}^* \times \mathbf{c}^*)$$
$$= \mathbf{a}(\mathbf{a}^* \cdot \mathbf{b}^* \times \mathbf{c}^*)/(\mathbf{a}^* \cdot \mathbf{b}^* \times \mathbf{c}^*) = \mathbf{a}$$

Lattice spacings may often be computed more conveniently in terms of the reciprocal lattice than in terms of the crystal lattice. Since the spacing d_{hkl} of the crystal plane hkl is equal to the length of the reciprocal lattice vector $\mathbf{r}^*_{hkl} = h\mathbf{a}^* + k\mathbf{b}^* + l\mathbf{c}^*$ it follows that

$$\frac{1}{d^2_{hkl}} = |\mathbf{r}^*_{hkl}|^2 = (h\mathbf{a}^* + k\mathbf{b}^* + l\mathbf{c}^*) \cdot (h\mathbf{a}^* + k\mathbf{b}^* + l\mathbf{c}^*)$$
$$= h^2 a^{*2} + k^2 b^{*2} + l^2 c^{*2} + 2hk a^* b^* \cos \gamma^* + 2kl b^* c^* \cos \alpha^*$$
$$+ 2lh c^* a^* \cos \beta^* \tag{5}$$

where the interaxial angles α^*, β^*, γ^* in the reciprocal lattice are related to the angles α, β, γ of the crystal lattice by equations that can be derived from spherical trigonometry as applied to the two sets of axes:

$$\cos \alpha^* = \frac{\cos \beta \cos \gamma - \cos \alpha}{\sin \beta \sin \gamma}$$

$$\cos \beta^* = \frac{\cos \alpha \cos \gamma - \cos \beta}{\sin \alpha \sin \gamma}$$

$$\cos \gamma^* = \frac{\cos \alpha \cos \beta - \cos \gamma}{\sin \alpha \sin \beta}$$

Planes of a zone have their normals perpendicular to the zone axis; so if the zone axis is in the direction of the crystal vector $\mathbf{r}_{uvw} = u\mathbf{a} + v\mathbf{b} + w\mathbf{c}$ and the normal to a plane is $\mathbf{r}^*_{hkl} = h\mathbf{a}^* + k\mathbf{b}^* + l\mathbf{c}^*$, this plane belongs to the zone $[uvw]$ provided that the condition $\mathbf{r}_{uvw} \cdot \mathbf{r}^*_{hkl} = 0$ is met, and by relations (1) and (2) this reduces to the zone law

$$hu + kv + lw = 0 \tag{6}$$

Diffraction in a crystal will be discussed by considering the waves scattered by two atoms separated by the crystal vector **r,** Fig. 15. If the direction of the incident beam is represented by the unit vector **S₀** and the direction of the diffracted beam by the unit vector **S,** then the path difference will be the difference between the projection of **r** on **S** and the projection of

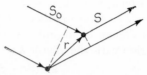

Fig. 15. Scattering by a pair of atoms.

r on **S₀,** or $\mathbf{r} \cdot \mathbf{S} - \mathbf{r} \cdot \mathbf{S}_0 = \mathbf{r} \cdot (\mathbf{S} - \mathbf{S}_0)$. Multiplying this path difference by $2\pi/\lambda$ gives the phase difference

$$\phi = \frac{\mathbf{r} \cdot (\mathbf{S} - \mathbf{S}_0)2\pi}{\lambda} \tag{7}$$

The vector $(\mathbf{S} - \mathbf{S}_0)/\lambda$ is best expressed in terms of coordinates in the reciprocal lattice:

$$\frac{\mathbf{S} - \mathbf{S}_0}{\lambda} = h\mathbf{a}^* + k\mathbf{b}^* + l\mathbf{c}^* \tag{8}$$

and when this is done the phase difference is

$$\phi = 2\pi(u\mathbf{a} + v\mathbf{b} + w\mathbf{c}) \cdot (h\mathbf{a}^* + k\mathbf{b}^* + l\mathbf{c}^*)$$
$$= 2\pi(hu + kv + lw) \tag{9}$$

Now if the scattering matter in a crystal is distributed with the periodicity

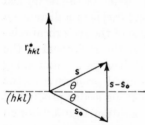

Fig. 16. Illustrating Bragg reflection.

of the space lattice there will be identical scattering power at each lattice point, and it is always possible to choose axes in such a way that these points are at $u\mathbf{a} + v\mathbf{b} + w\mathbf{c}$ where u, v, w are whole numbers. Equation (9) for the diffracted beam will then be satisfied when h, k, l are also whole numbers, and by Eq. (8) this means that the vector $(\mathbf{S} - \mathbf{S}_0)/\lambda$ must touch a point of the reciprocal lattice for diffraction to occur. When the vector touches the point with coordinates hkl the diffracted beam will have indices hkl.

Bragg's law can be shown to be equivalent to the condition stated above. Consider the crystal plane that is perpendicular to $\mathbf{r}^*_{hkl}$ in Fig. 16. This plane is drawn to bisect the angle between **S₀** and **S.** Since **S₀** and **S** are both unit vectors they are of equal length and $\mathbf{S} - \mathbf{S}_0$ must therefore be perpendicular to the bisecting plane. The incident ray and the diffracted ray both lie at an angle θ to this plane, and diffraction is thus similar to reflection in this plane. From the figure it is clear that $\mathbf{S} - \mathbf{S}_0 = 2 \sin \theta$, and by using Eq. (8) together with the relation $r^*_{hkl} = 1/d_{hkl}$ it will be seen that

$$\frac{(\mathbf{S} - \mathbf{S}_0)}{\lambda} = \frac{2 \sin \theta}{\lambda} = \frac{1}{d_{hkl}} \tag{10}$$

which is Bragg's law.

The *Laue equation* for a periodic distribution of scatterers along the a axis can be obtained from Eq. (8) by taking the scalar product of each side with the vector $\mathbf{a}$:

$$\frac{\mathbf{a} \cdot (\mathbf{S} - \mathbf{S}_0)}{\lambda} = \mathbf{a} \cdot (h\mathbf{a}^* + k\mathbf{b}^* + l\mathbf{c}^*) = h \tag{11}$$

The other Laue equations may be obtained by similar operations.

To express the reflecting condition in terms of the *sphere of reflection*, the construction of Fig. 17 is used. A sphere is drawn touching the origin of the reciprocal lattice with the vector $\mathbf{S}_0/\lambda$, which passes through the origin, as a radius. Since $\mathbf{S}_0$ is a unit vector the radius will be of length $1/\lambda$. The vector $\mathbf{S}/\lambda$ for the diffracted beam will then also be a radius, and $(\mathbf{S} - \mathbf{S}_0)/\lambda$ will be a chord extending from the origin to the reciprocal lattice point that has coordinates hkl, the indices of the reflection. When the sphere touches any reciprocal lattice point, reflection will occur.

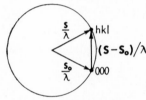

FIG. 17. The reflecting sphere.

The *layer lines* of rotating-crystal photographs correspond to layers of reciprocal lattice points—layers normal to the crystal axis $[uvw]$ about which the crystal is rotated. A point $h\mathbf{a}^* + k\mathbf{b}^* + l\mathbf{c}^*$ of the reciprocal lattice lies on the nth layer line if its projection on $[uvw]$ is at a distance n times the distance to the first layer, d_{uvw}. Because of the reciprocal relation between reciprocal lattice and crystal, d_{uvw} is the reciprocal of the length of the vector $u\mathbf{a} + v\mathbf{b} + w\mathbf{c}$ in the crystal. The unit vector along $[uvw]$ is therefore $d_{uvw}(u\mathbf{a} + v\mathbf{b} + w\mathbf{c})$. The required projection of the vector r^*_{hkl} on the axis $[uvw]$ is obtained by taking the scalar product of r^*_{hkl} with the unit vector just mentioned, so the condition that hkl lies on the nth layer line takes the form

$$(h\mathbf{a}^* + k\mathbf{b}^* + l\mathbf{c}^*) \cdot (u\mathbf{a} + v\mathbf{b} + w\mathbf{c})d_{uvw} = nd_{uvw}$$

which by Eqs. (1) and (2) becomes

$$hu + kv + lw = n \tag{12}$$

Many other crystallographic principles are advantageously derived by using vectors[1] and dyadics.[2]

[1] R. W. James, "The Optical Principles of the Diffraction of X-rays," G. Bell, London, 1948.

[2] W. H. Zachariasen, "Theory of X-ray Diffraction in Crystals," Wiley, New York, 1945.

CHAPTER VII

THE POWDER METHOD

The powder method, devised independently by Debye and Scherrer[1] and by Hull,[2] is by far the most useful method in the field of applied X-rays. Many special cameras and techniques have been developed.[3] A comprehensive treatment of all these is neither possible nor desirable here, but an attempt is made to cover the more important ones that are now in widespread use. The fundamental principles of the method have been presented in Chap. IV and need not be repeated here.

Cylindrical Cameras. A good X-ray powder camera has several basic requirements. The film must be bent accurately to a reproducible diameter and protected from light and from unwanted X-rays. There must be provision for centering the specimen at the axis of the cylindrical film and for rotating the specimen. X-rays must be directed accurately normal to the axis of the cylinder through carefully designed pinholes or slits. Scattering from the air should be minimized by carefully designed entrance and exit tubes that surround the beam throughout most of its path within the camera. Diffraction patterns caused by the beam striking the pinholes or the ports must be prevented from reaching the film. These requirements together with other desirable features[4] are available in commercial instruments. One design is illustrated in Fig. 1. The film is expanded against the inside surface of the lightproof camera by means of a movable finger B that pushes against one end of the film, the other end being pressed against a fixed stop. The specimen is centered on the axis of the camera by a "pusher" A that extends in radially to bear against the specimen mount and is viewed with a small magnifying lens while being adjusted. The entrance tube containing pinholes and the exit tube containing fluoroscopic screen and lead glass partition are removable and extend close to the specimen. All properly mounted cameras have provision for easy alignment in the X-ray beam and for accurate return to the aligned position after they have been taken to the darkroom for loading.

---

[1] P. Debye and P. Scherrer, *Physik. Z.*, vol. 18, p. 291, 1917.

[2] A. Hull, *Phys. Rev.*, vol. 10, p. 661, 1917.

[3] The X-ray instrument suppliers have offered an increasing number of types of cameras in recent years. As these rapidly change no attempt will be made to catalogue them. However, a list of manufacturers is given in Chaps. V and VI.

[4] M. J. Buerger, *J. Applied Phys.*, vol. 16, p. 501, 1945. W. Parrish and E. Cisney, Philips *Tech. Rev.*, vol. 10, p. 157, 1948.

A powder camera that has been very popular, particularly in England, is the "Bradley type" developed in Sir Lawrence Bragg's laboratories.[1] It is used in various sizes, and with various modifications.[2] It provides the necessary features discussed above and has provision for evacuation. As used by Zachariasen the precision of specimen centering and beam collimation in the camera and the low background density made it possible for him to obtain patterns of many compounds of the new and rare radioactive elements when only micrograms were available. Knife-edges

FIG. 1. Powder cameras. (A) plunger for centering specimen on axis of rotating shaft, (B) movable finger for expanding film against cylindrical surface, (C) specimen holder, (D) pinhole for incident beam, (E) exit tube for beam, (F) film. (North American Philips Company, Inc.)

are built into the camera to cast sharp shadows on the film and thus furnish reference marks from which the diffraction angles can be measured; because of this the film need not be continuous around the camera but can be in two separate strips. (In the large 18-cm-diameter cameras a single strip would be of awkward length.)

Beam collimation in any camera is important. The principles that are used in most of the better cameras are sketched in Fig. 2. Whether the openings are pinholes or slits they should be designed so that openings 1

[1] A. J. Bradley, W. L. Bragg, and C. Sykes, J. Iron Steel Inst. (London), vol. 141, p. 63, 1940. A. J. Bradley, H. Lipson, and N. J. Petch, J. Sci. Instruments, vol. 18, p. 216, 1941. See also the discussion of camera technique by H. Lipson and A. J. C. Wilson, J. Sci. Instruments, vol. 18, p. 144, 1941.

[2] A committee of the X-ray Analysis Group of the Institute of Physics has published recommendations for a standard design; J. Sci. Instruments, vol. 22, p. 57, 1945.

and 2 prevent the beam from striking the edges of openings 3 and 4, and care should be taken that the supporting metal for these openings does not shield more than the minimum of the circumference of the film, for both the very low and very high angle portions of the film frequently provide valuable data. Some laboratories use the focal spot as the effective source slit, employing the rays that leave the target face at 2 or 3° instead of the conventional 6°, thereby obtaining sharp diffraction lines without excessively narrow slits.

The usual specimen for Debye cameras is a thin-walled capillary tube 0.3 to 0.5 mm in diameter of lithium borate glass, silica, polystyrene, or cellophane, which is filled with powder that has been passed through a sieve of about 250 mesh. Filling may be done by tapping the end into the powder, by providing a funnel-type arrangement, or by attaching the capillary to a vacuum line and sucking the powder in until it strikes a plug of glass wool. Specimens are also prepared by mixing the powder with a small amount of collodion, dilute shellac, or other adhesive that causes no diffraction lines, and then

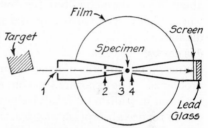

FIG. 2. Collimator design. Beam is collimated by openings 1 and 2 so as to avoid striking the metal at 3 and 4. Diffracted rays from the edges of 2 do not pass 3, and back scatter from fluorescent screen is shielded by 4.

rolling into small cylinders or extruding from small glass or steel capillaries, using a wire to force the mixture out. Powders may also be coated on the outside of fibers of glass, silica, or hair.[1] Wires of polycrystalline metals in the recrystallized condition are like coarse powders and give spotty lines. To obtain smooth lines it is necessary to rotate the specimen, and shifting of the specimen combined with rotation is sometimes desirable.[2] It should be remembered that any metal wire or other wrought shape, either cold worked or annealed, probably contains a preferred orientation of the grains that will alter the intensities of some diffraction lines relative to others and may suppress some reflections entirely. This effect is best avoided by using powders.

[1] Notes on techniques for sample preparation will be found in the following references: W. P. Davey, "A Study of Crystal Structure and Its Applications," p. 117, McGraw-Hill, New York, 1934. A. Taylor, "X-ray Metallography," p. 59, Wiley, New York, 1945. L. K. Frevel, *Ind. Eng. Chem.*, Anal. Ed., vol. 16, p. 209, 1944. K. Lonsdale and H. Smith, *J. Sci. Instruments*, vol. 18, p. 133, 1941. A. A. Burr, *J. Sci. Instruments*, vol. 18, p. 127, 1942. J. B. Nelson and D. P. Riley, *Proc. Phys. Soc. (London)*, vol. 57, p. 477, 1945. G. A. Harcourt, *Am. Mineral.*, vol. 27, p. 63, 1942. J. S. Lukesh, *Rev. Sci. Instruments*, vol. 11, p. 200, 1940.

[2] This may be done automatically: C. S. Barrett and A. G. Guy, *Rev. Sci. Instruments*, vol. 15, p. 13, 1944. M. J. Buerger, *J. Applied Phys.*, vol. 16, p. 501, 1945.

The amount of powder needed for a good powder pattern varies with the excellence of the camera design. A few milligrams usually serves nicely, but with care micrograms and even a few tenths of a microgram may suffice.

If a specimen holder is made to oscillate rather than rotate it can be used with the "wedge technique" in which a pressed block or wedge of powder is mounted so that a sharp edge cuts into the beam from the slits and provides a thin line of diffracting material.

Choice of Camera Dimensions. For rapid exposures and for materials of poorly developed crystallinity a small camera is favored, usually one of about 5 cm diameter, but for complicated patterns or other problems where high dispersion is required it is better to use larger ones. If the diameter is made 57.3 or 114.6 mm then the conversion of film readings to θ is easier. A camera of 19 cm diameter ($\theta = 5$ to $85°$) is useful in alloy studies,[1] and cameras of even 35 cm diameter serve for occasional special problems. The exposure time increases roughly as the cube of the diameter,[2] and in addition it is advisable to fill the largest cameras with hydrogen to reduce absorption and scattering from the air, yet these disadvantages are frequently overcome by the advantage of greater contrast between background and lines and greater dispersion.[3]

High-temperature Cameras. A number of designs have been published for cameras that operate with the specimen at an elevated temperature.[4] Hume-Rothery and Reynolds[5] have employed a camera in which the specimen (sealed in a capillary tube) is mounted on the axis of a wire-wound furnace. An aluminum radiation shield protects the film from the heat. The camera body is water-cooled. By careful furnace design the temperature gradient in the irradiated portion of the specimen is reduced to $1°$ at $1000°C$ and lattice constants can be determined with a reproducibility of 0.0001 A.

[1] A. J. Bradley, W. L. Bragg, and C. Sykes, *J. Iron Steel Inst. (London)*, vol. 141, p. 63, 1940. A. J. Bradley, H. Lipson, and N. J. Petch, *J. Sci. Instruments*, vol. 18, p. 216, 1941.

[2] O. S. Edwards and H. Lipson, *J. Sci. Instruments*, vol. 18, p. 131, 1941.

[3] A. J. Bradley and H. Lipson, *Proc. Roy. Soc. (London)*, vol. A167, p. 421, 1938.

[4] A. Westgren and G. Phragmén, *Z. physik. Chem.*, vol. A102, p. 1, 1922. W. Cohn, *Z. Physik*, vol. 50, p. 123, 1928. O. Ruff and F. Ebert, *Z. anorg. Chem.*, vol. 180, p. 19, 1929. H. Braekken and L. Harang, *Z. Krist.*, vol. 75, p. 583, 1930. N. P. Goss, *Metal Progress*, vol. 28, p. 163, October, 1935. A. Goetz and R. C. Hergenrother, *Phys. Rev.*, vol. 40, p. 643, 1932. R. Berthold and H. Höhm, *Metallwirtschaft*, vol. 11, p. 567, 1932. A. H. Jay, *Z. Krist.*, vol. 86, p. 106, 1933; *Proc. Phys. Soc. (London)*, vol. 45, p. 635, 1933. M. J. Buerger, N. W. Buerger, and F. G. Chesley, *Am. Mineral.*, vol. 28, p. 285, 1943. F. Schossberger, *Z. Krist.*, vol. 98, p. 259, 1938. E. A. Owen, *J. Sci. Instruments*, vol. 20, p. 190, 1943. Paul Gordon, *J. Applied Phys.*, vol. 20, p. 908, 1949. H. J. Goldschmidt, *J. Sci. Instruments*, vol. 27, p. 177, 1950.

[5] W. Hume-Rothery and P. W. Reynolds, *Proc. Roy. Soc. (London)*, vol. A167, p. 25, 1938.

Camera designs rather closely related to this and to the Bradley powder camera have been published and have appeared on the market.[1] For reaching higher temperatures it is possible to use induction heating of a metal cylinder surrounding the specimen, and photographs at temperatures above 2500°K then become possible.[2] One design has appeared that provides for a flat specimen that is rotated in its plane and oscillated through a small angle about an axis in the plane.[3] In this camera the known expansion of silver powder mixed with the specimen is used for calibration. Some have calibrated the temperature of the diffracting surface of their specimens by using the known transition temperatures of polymorphic compounds such as ammonium nitrate, ammonium perchlorate, potassium perchlorate, and quartz.[4] For use with Geiger counter spectrometers a flat specimen is also used in a design that employs a specimen in contact with the resistance-heated furnace element[5].

Low-temperature Cameras. Powder photographs have been made at low temperatures by blowing cold air over a specimen or by attaching a specimen to a copper conductor cooled by liquid air.[6] If the conductor is in the form of a rod or tube on which a heating coil is wound between the liquid air container and the specimen, a variation in the heating current will permit a range of temperatures to be maintained at the specimen. The simplest low-temperature cameras may be made by merely having a fine stream of liquid air or liquid nitrogen flow down the length of the specimen as it is mounted in a powder camera. A dry atmosphere is necessary to prevent moisture condensation, and may be provided simply by having evaporated liquid air fill the camera enclosure. To follow phase changes at low temperatures it is effective to have a powder or polycrystalline specimen cooled to a controllable temperature by one of the principles just mentioned, and mounted in a Geiger counter spectrometer.[7] Since many substances that are liquid at ordinary temperatures are solid at liquid nitrogen temperature (-195°C, 78°K) their diffraction

[1] A. J. C. Wilson, *Proc. Phys. Soc. (London)*, vol. 53, p. 235, 1941. E. A. Owen, *J. Sci. Instruments*, vol. 20, p. 190, 1943. Bulletins of Unicam Instruments (Cambridge) Ltd., Cambridge, England.

[2] J. W. Edwards, R. Speiser, and H. L. Johnston, *Rev. Sci. Instruments*, vol. 20, p. 343, 1949.

[3] E. A. Owen, *J. Sci. Instruments*, vol. 26, p. 114, 1949.

[4] M. J. Buerger, N. W. Buerger, and F. G. Chesley, *Am. Mineral.*, vol. 28, p. 285, 1943.

[5] L. S. Birks and H. Friedman, *Rev. Sci. Instruments*, vol. 18, p. 576, 1947.

[6] M. Wolf, *Z. Physik*, vol. 53, p. 72, 1929. R. F. Mehl and C. S. Barrett, *Trans. AIME*, vol. 89, p. 575, 1930. O. Kratky and P. Losada in F. Halla and H. Mark, "Röntgenographische Untersuchung von Kristallen," p. 149, Barth, Leipzig, 1937. F. Feher and F. Klötzer, *Z. Elektrochem.*, vol. 41, p. 850, 1935. W. H. Barnes and W. F. Hampton, *Rev. Sci. Instruments*, vol. 6, p. 342, 1935. N. W. Taylor, *Rev. Sci. Instruments*, vol. 2, p. 751, 1931.

[7] C. S. Barrett and O. Trautz, *Trans. AIME*, vol. 175, p. 579, 1948.

patterns can readily be obtained and used, for example, for identifying the substances. Low temperatures are also useful occasionally to improve the diffraction pattern of substances that give weak lines at ordinary temperatures.

High-pressure Cameras. Although many polymorphic transformations are known to occur at high pressures there has been relatively little diffraction study of the transformation products. Up to pressures of about 1000 kg per sq cm Frevel has used a thin-walled glass capillary containing the powder sample, sealing it off when filled with a liquid like toluene, then warming the shank of the tube to raise the pressure by expansion of the liquid.[1] Jacobs[2] has used pressures of helium and argon in small cameras up to 5000 kg per sq cm. A camera suited to still higher pressures is based on a small beryllium bomb in which the sample is compressed by a plunger. The rays pass in and out through the beryllium, which superimposes a Laue spot pattern on the powder pattern, but by using large-grained beryllium the powder lines can be seen between the spots.[3] Pressure is applied and maintained simply by compressing a spring. Neoprene rings serve as packing to retain the oil surrounding the powder. The bomb is backed up by a steel cylinder in which ports are machined for incoming and outgoing beams. Pressures somewhat above 15,000 kg per sq cm have been reached and maintained during long exposures without difficulty.

Focusing Cameras. Cameras in which the slits, specimen, and film all lie on the circumference of the same cylinder (Fig. 18, page 84) have been much used since their development by Seemann and Bohlin.[4] Since all the diffracted rays from a large area of the specimen are focused to a sharp line, the exposure times are relatively short; a second advantage is the fact that dispersion of these cameras is twice that of a Debye camera of the same radius. Westgren and Phragmén in their extensive studies of alloy constitution have used focusing cameras in which the range from 16 to 82° is covered by three separate cameras in order to obtain optimum conditions in each range.[5] Figure 3 illustrates the films obtained from these. The range from 17.5 to 77° has also been covered in a single camera of high dispersion. The specimen is held on an oscillating arm, pivoted at the center of the camera.

Focusing cameras of this type are calibrated by taking photographs of

[1] L. K. Frevel, *Rev. Sci. Instruments*, vol. 6, p. 214, 1935.

[2] R. B. Jacobs, *Phys. Rev.*, vol. 54, p. 325, 1938; vol. 56, p. 211, 1939.

[3] A. W. Lawson and N. A. Riley, *Rev. Sci. Instruments*, vol. 20, p. 763, 1949. Preliminary tests indicate that a diamond may be substituted for the beryllium to advantage, extending the pressure range up to about 25,000 atm.

[4] H. Seemann, *Ann. Physik*, vol. 59, p. 455, 1919. H. Bohlin, *Ann. Physik*, vol. 61, p. 421, 1920.

[5] A. F. Westgren, *Trans. AIME*, vol. 93, p. 13, 1931.

standard materials. The position of a diffraction line is measured from the shadow of one of the knife-edges at the ends of the film. The distance from a knife-edge shadow to a line is corrected for shrinkage or expansion of the film by multiplying by the distance between knife-edges on the standard film and dividing by the distance between knife-edges on the film being measured, thus effectively reducing each film to standard length. Single emulsion films should be used because of the oblique

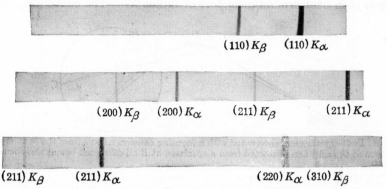

Fig. 3. Powder pattern of α-iron in Phragmén focusing cameras with overlapping ranges. Diffraction angle increases from left to right. Unfiltered iron radiation.

incidence of the diffracted rays. Specimens may be prepared by coating a layer of powder on a strip of paper with a small amount of an adhesive or by placing a layer of powder on paper and covering it with Scotch tape. The specimen is clamped in place so that it accurately fits the cylindrical surface of the camera. Symmetrical back-reflection focusing cameras are discussed in the following section.

The conditions that must be fulfilled in focusing cameras have been discussed by Brentano,[1] who has developed a cylindrical camera that focuses rays from a specimen with a curved surface that oscillates at the center of the camera. With a thick powder layer this arrangement gives relative line intensities that are independent of the absorption coefficient of the powder and are the same as from a thin nonabsorbing powder. An approximation of this arrangement is employed in X-ray spectrometers where a flat plate of powder is centrally located and turned at half the angular rate of the Geiger counter.

Guinier[2] and others[3] have used bent crystals to provide monochromatic

[1] J. C. M Brentano, *J. Applied Phys.*, vol. 17, p. 420, 1946; *Proc. Phys. Soc. (London)*, vol. 37, p. 184, 1925; vol. 49, p. 61, 1937.

[2] A. Guinier, *Compt. rend.*, vol. 204, p. 1115, 1937; *J. Sci. Instruments*, vol. 22, p. 139, 1945; *Ann. phys.*, vol. 12, p. 161, 1939; "Radiocrystallographie," Dunod, Paris, 1945.

[3] J. Laval, *Bull. soc. franç. minérat.*, vol. 62, p. 137, 1939. T. Johansson, *Z. Physik*, vol. 82, p. 507, 1933. C. S. Smith, *Rev. Sci. Instruments*, vol. 12, p. 312, 1941.

beams for focusing cameras (Fig. 4). Bozorth and Haworth report that the intensity of the background between lines can be reduced to one-eighth that of the usual focusing camera and yet exposures are scarcely double the normal ones.[1]

Thin quartz crystals (~ 0.3 mm thick) may be bent elastically between cylindrical metal holders, but the best focus is obtained if the reflecting surface is ground to a cylindrical shape having a radius $2R$ and this surface is then bent around a support of radius R.[2] The converging-beam

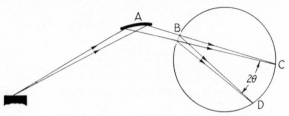

FIG. 4. Bent-crystal monochromator with a focusing camera. Rays from the bent crystal A focus at C, and when diffracted from a specimen at B all diffracted beams also focus on film D.

focusing of Fig. 4 has also been employed without crystal reflection, using Soller slits to direct the beam from a broad-focus tube.[3]

Back-reflection Cameras. Precision determinations of lattice constants are best made at high diffraction angles because of the greater dispersion in this range. Cameras for this purpose using flat films or photographic plates[4] are usually provided with means for rotating the specimen and film to make smoother lines. By placing a shield over the

[1] R. M. Bozorth and F. E. Haworth, *Phys. Rev.*, vol. 53, p. 538, 1938. They used a rock-salt crystal 3.3 by 1.7 by 0.24 cm which was clamped between cylindrical forms while immersed in a concentrated solution of sodium chloride. The crystal was bent to a radius of 20 cm, then dried, and the concave side ground to a radius of 10 cm and etched with water until clear. Synthetic rock salt crystals are preferred for this purpose.

[2] For example, a quartz plate cut to the face (10$\bar{1}$1) may be ground to 600 mm radius and bent around a 300 mm radius cylindrical support; this reflects Cu $K\alpha$ with an angle of incidence of 13°21′ to a focus at 142 mm from the crystal. For Mo $K\alpha$ the corresponding radii are 1200 and 600 mm; for Fe $K\alpha$ the same radii as for Cu are recommended by Guinier. Unsymmetrical cuts that shorten the distance to the focus are also employed. A variable-curvature arrangement is described by W. A. Wooster, G. N. Ramachandran, and A. R. Lang, *J. Sci Instruments*, vol. 26, p. 156, 1949.

[3] L. K. Frevel, *Rev. Sci. Instruments*, vol. 8, p. 475, 1937. V. Vand, *J. Applied Phys.*, vol. 19, p. 852, 1948. The slits may be made by a converging stack of thin razor blades with 0.025-mm aluminum foil made into wedges to serve as spacers.

[4] G. Sachs and J. Weerts, *Z. Physik.*, vol. 60, p. 481, 1930. G. Sachs, *Trans. AIME*, vol. 93, p. 39, 1931. F. Wever and A. Rose, *Mitt. Kaiser-Wilhelm-Inst. Eisenforsch., Düsseldorf*, vol. 17, p. 33, 1935.

film and exposing a segment at a time, it is possible to put several exposures on one film (see Fig. 5). Film-to-specimen distances can be measured by micrometers or determined by calibration spectra. By setting the pinhole at the proper distance from the film it is possible to obtain a

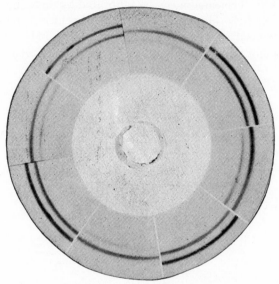

FIG. 5. Back-reflection powder pattern on a flat film. Alternate segments are from solid-solution alloys of different composition and different lattice parameter. $K\alpha_1$ and $K\alpha_2$ lines are fully resolved.

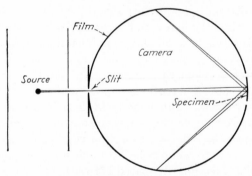

FIG. 6. Symmetrical back-reflection focusing camera.

focusing condition on one diffraction line (the pinhole, specimen, and line on film must lie on the circumference of a circle).[1] However, the focusing condition does not extend over the entire film in a camera of the flat-film type.

Cylindrical back-reflection cameras of the type indicated in Fig. 6 provide

[1] A camera using this principle together with a Geiger counter has been proposed by L. A. Carapella and H. F. Kaiser, *Rev. Sci. Instruments*, vol. 16, p. 214, 1945.

focusing over their entire range and are very effective in precision studies of noncubic metals, as Jette and Foote have shown.[1] A movable arm for shifting the specimen is advantageous but must be so constructed that friction of the moving parts does not raise the temperature of the specimen more than 1°C.   The camera can be calibrated by direct measurement of its diameter, and the films can be corrected by proper extrapolation to 0 = 90°.   This is discussed in a later section (page 144).   Figure 7 illustrates the camera arranged for use with a bent crystal monochromator.

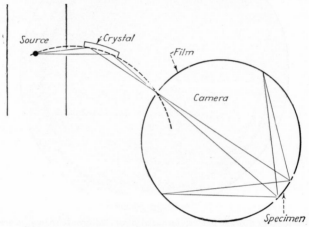

Fig. 7. Crystal monochromator for a focusing camera.

Choice of Radiation.   To produce satisfactory photographs it is necessary to avoid fogging the film with fluorescent radiation from the sample. One way of doing this is to employ molybdenum radiation, which has a fairly short wavelength, and to filter the fluorescent radiation by placing a zirconium filter between the specimen and the film.   This technique gives satisfactory films for most materials,[2] and suitable filter strips are available on the market.   But longer wavelengths are often needed, and it is then important to choose a target that emits a line spectrum of longer wavelength than the K absorption edge of the sample, if this is practicable.   A filter to remove the $K\beta$ radiation is optional (see page 57, Chap. III).   This is ordinarily placed between the tube and the camera, but if it is placed between the sample and the film it will serve also to filter out fluorescent radiation.   Radiations of Cr, Mn, Fe, Co, Ni, Cu, and Zn are commonly used, and some have also used Au $L\alpha_1$ and $L\alpha_2$ after removing the $L\beta$ and $L\gamma$ lines with a Ga filter.[3]   In precision work, radiation is

[1] E. R. Jette and F. Foote, *J. Chem. Phys.*, vol. 3, p. 605, 1935.

[2] J. D. Hanawalt, H. W. Rinn, and L. K. Frevel, *Ind. Eng. Chem., Anal. Ed.*, vol. 10, p. 457, 1938.

[3] O. S. Edwards and H. Lipson, *J. Sci. Instruments*, vol. 18, p. 131, 1941.

chosen to yield diffraction lines at high angles, preferably above $\theta = 70°$, and to give sufficient lines in this neighborhood it is helpful to use alloy targets.[1] A table of wavelengths is given in Appendix VIII.

Powder Spectrometers. Much use has been made in recent years of the Bragg spectrometer[2] modified by replacing the ionization chamber by a Geiger counter. A powder specimen is used in the form of a flat plate about 10 by 20 mm in area, placed at equal distances from the focal spot, which is generally used as the source slit, and the receiving slit at the Geiger tube.[3] The spectrometer arm carrying the Geiger tube is geared to the specimen holder in such a way that the angle between the specimen face and the primary X-ray beam (θ) is always half the angle between the Geiger tube and the primary beam (2θ), thus maintaining optimum focusing of the diffracted rays. For precision work the intensity at each setting may be obtained from the number of counts per unit of time. More convenient operation with sufficient accuracy in diffraction angles and intensities for most problems may be had by driving the spectrometer arm and specimen holder with a synchronous motor and making a continuous record of the counting rate with an automatic strip-chart recorder. Scanning in this way can thus give directly a plot of intensity vs. θ, provided that the X-ray tube current and voltage and the variables of the electronic circuit are held constant at values for which the apparatus has been calibrated for X-ray intensity vs. chart reading.[4]

Spectrometers are much used for qualitative and quantitative chemical analysis,[5] as in problems of inspection and control of industrial materials. They permit much greater precision in the measurement of intensities than can be obtained with films, and are thus of service in crystal-structure analysis, and in studies of microstresses in cold-worked metals, particle size from line widths, and preferred orientation determination, as is discussed in later pages. The ability of the spectrometer to trace the changing intensity of a diffraction line while changes are occurring in the

---

[1] E. R. Jette and F. Foote (*J. Chem. Phys.*, vol. 3, p. 605, 1935) have used 50 atomic per cent alloys of Fe-Mn, Fe-Ni, Fe-Cr, Cu-Ni, Fe-Co, Ni-Cr, Ni-Co, and Cu-Mn.

[2] W. H. Bragg and W. L. Bragg, *Proc. Roy. Soc. (London)*, vol. A88, p. 428, 1913; *Proc. Phys. Soc. (London)*, vol. 33, p. 222, 1921.

[3] H. Friedman, *Electronics*, vol. 18, p. 132, 1945. J. Bleeksma, G. Kloos, and H. J. Digiovanni, *Philips Tech. Rev.*, vol. 10, p. 1, 1948.

[4] In scanning work it is well to realize that the recorded intensity, the position of the peak intensity, and the shape of the lines are dependent upon scanning rate, time constants in the electronic circuits, and sensitivity adjustment of the recorder circuit. Regarding calibration see p. 67 (Chap. III); W. Parrish, *Science*, vol. 10, Oct. 7, 1949. Techniques and errors are also discussed by C. Wainwright, *Brit. J. Applied Phys.*, vol. 2, p. 157, 1951, and A. J. C. Wilson, *J. Sci. Instruments*, vol. 27, p. 321, 1950.

[5] C. L. Christ, R. Bowling Barnes, and E. F. Williams, *Anal. Chem.*, vol 20, p. 789, 1948 (organic materials). J. L. Abbott, *Iron Age*, Feb. 13, 20, and 27, 1947 (metallurgical applications).

sample is a valuable asset in following chemical reactions and in observing phase changes when the temperature of the sample is changed. For this purpose the specimen can be cooled to fixed or variable low temperature[1] or raised to high temperatures in vacuum or in controlled atmospheres.[2] The conventional spectrometer uses copper characteristic radiation with a filter. Differential filtering has also been tried,[3] and for measuring extremely wide lines where the intensity of the line relative to the background is small it is found necessary to employ crystal monochromatized radiation.[4] Reference should be made to the manufacturers' bulletins for details of construction, calibration, and operation of commercial instruments.[5]

Interpretation of Powder Patterns. A powder or polycrystalline specimen has crystalline particles at all orientations. Consequently the diffracted rays from it travel outward in all directions that make an angle of 2θ with the direct beam, where θ is the Bragg angle. Thus each order of reflection from each set of planes forms a cone of semiapex angle 2θ concentric with the primary beam and produces a diffraction line on the film. The θ values are computed for all the reflecting planes from measurements of the line positions. Identification of the lines is a simple matter with cubic crystals but is difficult with crystals of lower symmetry and generally impossible with monoclinic or triclinic crystals. Fortunately, most of the metals and alloys are cubic, tetragonal, or hexagonal. It should be emphasized that great caution is necessary when determining crystal structures solely from powder data, for several incorrect unit cells have been deduced in this way even by experienced crystallographers.

Identification of the lines in a powder pattern is always based on comparing the measured list of θ values with a list predicted for a unit cell of assumed dimensions. Given the parameters a, b, c, α, β, γ of a cell and the wavelength to be used, one can quickly compute all possible reflections by using the spacing equation (page 76, and Appendix III) and inserting all possible values of h, k, and l. With cubic crystals the equation is

$$\sin^2 \theta = K(h^2 + k^2 + l^2) \tag{1}$$

where $K = \lambda^2/4a^2$. It will be noted that reflections 100, 010, and 001 all fall on the same ring; likewise, reflections from all planes of the general

[1] C. S. Barrett and O. Trautz, *Trans. AIME*, vol. 175, p. 579, 1948.

[2] L. S Birks and H. Friedman, *Rev. Sci. Instruments*, vol. 18, p. 576, 1947.

[3] W. P. Davey, F. R. Smith, and S. W. Harding, *Rev. Sci. Instruments*, vol. 15, p. 37, 1944.

[4] B. E. Warren and B. Averbach, *J. Applied Phys.*, vol. 21, p. 595, 1950. Some investigators prefe rproportional counters (see page 67) to Geiger counters combined with filters or monochromators.

[5] North American Phillips Co., Inc., New York, N. Y. General Electric X-ray Corp., Milwaukee, Wis.

form $\{hkl\}$ superimpose. However, this is not true of noncubic crystals, as can be seen, for example, from the equation for the orthorhombic class:

$$\sin^2 \theta = \frac{\lambda^2}{4} \left(\frac{h^2}{a^2} + \frac{k^2}{b^2} + \frac{l^2}{c^2} \right) \tag{2}$$

The quantity $(h^2 + k^2 + l^2)$ in Eq. (1) has small integral values—in fact, by a proper choice of indices this quantity can have any value from 1 through 6, 8 through 14, 16 through 22, etc. To identify the lines of a cubic pattern it is necessary merely to choose a set of these integers so that $(\sin^2 \theta)/(h^2 + k^2 + l^2)$ will have the same value, K, for every line in the pattern. The value of the constant K then permits a computation of a since $K = \lambda^2/4a^2$. It is obvious, of course, that Eq. (2) and other noncubic formulas do not permit the lines to be indexed so easily.

To facilitate computations of the lattice constant or, conversely, to speed the calculation of cubic patterns when a is known, a table of reflecting planes is included in Appendix VII with logarithms of $(h^2 + k^2 + l^2)$.[1]

Only with simple cubic lattices will there be reflections for all possible values of $(h^2 + k^2 + l^2)$; other space-lattices will have *characteristic absences* by means of which it is possible to distinguish body-centered cubic from face-centered cubic. Consider the structure-factor formula

$$|F|^2 = [\Sigma f \cos 2\pi(hu + kv + lw)]^2 + [\Sigma f \sin 2\pi(hu + kv + lw)]^2 \tag{3}$$

discussed in Chap. IV. If this is applied to a unit cell of any *simple space-lattice*, there is a single equivalent point in the cell, at $uvw = 000$; hence, $|F|^2 = f^2$ for any reflection, regardless of indices, and there will be no missing reflections. On the other hand, if it is applied to a *body-centered* cell with equivalent points at uvw equal to 000 and $\frac{1}{2}\frac{1}{2}\frac{1}{2}$, we see that $|F|^2 = 0$ whenever $(h + k + l)$ is odd and so these reflections will be absent, for example, 100, 111, 210, etc. In a *face-centered* lattice one can easily show in the same way that all reflections will be missing for which the indices h, k, l are mixed odd and even, for example, 100, 211, etc. These rules apply to all crystal systems. There are also characteristic absences for the *diamond cubic* structure.[2] The characteristic sequence of lines in cubic crystals is illustrated in Fig. 8, where $h^2 + k^2 + l^2$ is indicated for each line that is observed in simple, body-centered, face-centered, and diamond cubic spectra.

Crystallographers have solved many cubic and noncubic powder pat-

---

[1] For more extensive tables see "Internationale Tabellen zur Bestimmung von Kristallstrukturen," vol. II, Bornträger, Berlin, 1935; L. W. McKeehan, *Am. J. Sci.*, vol. 17, p. 548, 1929.

[2] The structure of diamond, silicon, germanium, and gray tin, with atoms at 000, $\frac{1}{2}\frac{1}{2}0$, $\frac{1}{2}0\frac{1}{2}$, $0\frac{1}{2}\frac{1}{2}$, $\frac{1}{4}\frac{1}{4}\frac{1}{4}$, $\frac{3}{4}\frac{3}{4}\frac{1}{4}$, $\frac{3}{4}\frac{1}{4}\frac{3}{4}$, $\frac{1}{4}\frac{3}{4}\frac{3}{4}$. The reflections that can be obtained for each of these lattices are indicated in the table, Appendix VII.

terns by merely inspecting the relations between $\sin^2 \theta$ or $\log \sin^2 \theta$ values, starting with the lowest indices and working through to the higher. Many workers, however, rely on graphical aids to speed the solution of noncubic patterns.

Methods of Solving Patterns. The logarithmic scales of a *slide rule* provide a rapid means of solving cubic patterns. Various arrangements have been proposed,[1] one of the best being illustrated in Fig. 9,[2] in which

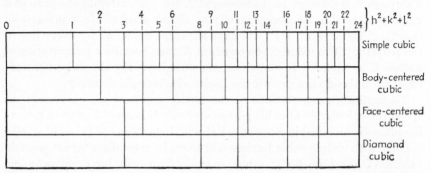

Fig. 8. Powder patterns for different cubic crystals, illustrating characteristic reflections for each type.

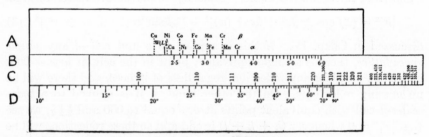

Fig. 9. Slide rule for solving powder patterns of cubic crystals. The wavelength scale (A), lattice parameter scale (B), indices scale (C), and θ scale (D) are set for Co $K\alpha$ radiation and iron specimen with $a_0 = 2.86$. (*Thomas.*)

four logarithmic scales are used, A, B, C, D. Along the log scale A are marked all wavelengths to be used, including $K\beta$ as well as $K\alpha$. Scale B is an ordinary log scale for reading the cube dimension a. Distances along C are proportional to $\log \sqrt{h^2 + k^2 + l^2}$ and are marked with the corresponding hkl indices. Scale D has distances proportional to $\log \sin \theta$ with graduations in θ values. The four scales are laid out so that the equality $(\sin \theta)/\sqrt{h^2 + k^2 + l^2} = \lambda/2a$ is represented by one setting. If a series of θ values is marked along the D scale, their indices will be

[1] E. Schiebold, *Z. Physik.*, vol. 28, p. 355, 1924. G. Kettman, *Z. Physik*, vol. 53, p. 198, 1929; vol. 54, p. 596, 1929. Wheeler P. Davey, "A Study of Crystal Structure and Its Applications," McGraw-Hill, New York, 1934.

[2] D. E. Thomas, *J. Sci. Instruments*, vol. 18, p. 205, 1941.

found when the rule is adjusted to the position for which they simultaneously match the marks on scale C, and at this setting of the slide the a value (scale B) will appear under the wavelength used (scale A). If both $K\alpha$ and $K\beta$ lines appear on the pattern, these require independent settings of the slide.

Powder patterns for lattices with two parameters (tetragonal, hexagonal, and rhombohedral) can be solved with the aid of *charts* devised by

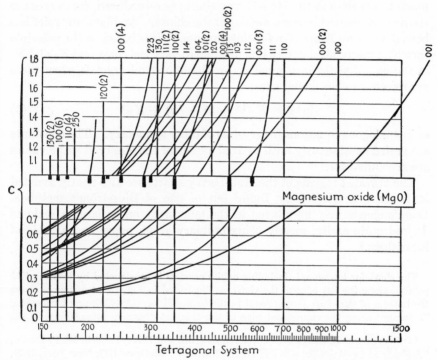

Fig. 10. Illustrating a Hull-Davey chart and its use in indexing the powder pattern of MgO. (*Wyckoff.*)

Hull and Davey, giving the relative spacings for unit cells having all possible axial ratios within their range.[1] The charts are made with lattice-plane spacings plotted along the axis of abscissas according to a logarithmic scale, as indicated in Fig. 10, and different axial ratios $C = c/a$ appear at different vertical levels on the chart. At a given axial ratio the distances from left to right are given by the formula

$$\log d = \log \left(\frac{a}{\sqrt{h^2 + k^2 + \dfrac{a^2}{c^2} l^2}} \right) = \log a - \log \sqrt{h^2 + k^2 + \dfrac{a^2}{c^2} l^2} \quad (4)$$

[1] A. W. Hull and W. P. Davey, *Phys. Rev.*, vol. 17, p. 549, 1921. W. P. Davey, *Gen. Elec. Rev.*, vol. 25, p. 564, 1922.

A strip of paper is marked with the spacings calculated from a diffraction pattern and is moved over the chart to various horizontal positions until the marks coincide with curves on the chart (see Fig. 10). Doing so amounts to trying various c/a and a values until the predicted pattern agrees with the observed one. Indices for each of the lines are then read from the curves. Figure 11 is the chart for simple tetragonal lattices.[1]

It is desirable to have a graphical method in which the scale can be much larger than in the Hull-Davey charts as reproduced, for curves are too densely packed in some regions of the charts. An ingenious ruler has been devised by Bjurström for this purpose.[2] It is based on the principle that by a mechanical device it is possible to vary the constants K_1 and K_2 in the equation for hexagonal or for rhombohedral crystals when these are referred to hexagonal axes:

$$\sin^2 \theta = K_1(h^2 + k^2 + hk) + K_2 l^2 \tag{5}$$

or in analogous equations for crystals of other symmetry. The constants are varied continuously until by trial and error the observed $\sin^2 \theta$ values are accounted for.

The crowded regions of the Hull-Davey charts are also neatly avoided in a chart developed by Bunn[3] out of one of Bjurström's methods. Bunn's charts may be plotted in the laboratory on as large a scale as desired quite easily, merely using ordinary graph paper and a table of logarithms.[4]

The chart for tetragonal (including cubic) crystals is constructed by locating "hk points" along the left edge of the chart, as illustrated in Fig. 12, at distances above the bottom of the chart proportional to the values of log $(h^2 + k^2)$, and by locating "l points" along the right-hand edge of the chart at distances proportional to the

[1] Others appear in the preceding references (Hull and Davey) and in W. P. Davey, "A Study of Crystal Structure and Its Applications," McGraw-Hill, New York, 1934, and Fairbanks, "Laboratory Investigation of Ores," McGraw-Hill, New York, 1928.

[2] T. Bjurström, *Z. Physik*, vol. 69, p. 346, 1931.

[3] C. W. Bunn, "Chemical Crystallography," Oxford, New York, 1945. The method is based on the spacing equation which, for tetragonal crystals, can be arranged in the form $1/d^2 = (h^2 + k^2 - l^2)/a^2 + l^2(1/a^2 + 1/c^2)$ which is of the form $y = K_1 x + K_2$ for a constant value of h, k, l, where $x = 1/a^2$, provided $(1/a^2 + 1/c^2)$ is made a constant; plotting y against x then yields a straight line. Bunn uses the logarithmic form of this relation in order to make a chart applicable to unit cells of all sizes. The ordinates are log $(1/d^2)$ and distances along the axis of abscissas are related to the c/a ratio—the distance from right to left, expressed as a fraction of the total width (Fig. 12) is $1/(1 + a^2/c^2)$.

[4] A set of five Bunn charts, 2 by 4 ft each, has been marketed by The Institute of Physics, 47 Belgrade Square, London S.W.1, England. These cover tetragonal crystals with $5.0 > c/a > 1$ and with $0.224 < c/a < 1$, hexagonal crystals with $10 > c/a > 0.9$ and with $0.1 < c/a < 0.9$, and layer lines of single-crystal rotation photographs of crystal having rectangular cell bases.

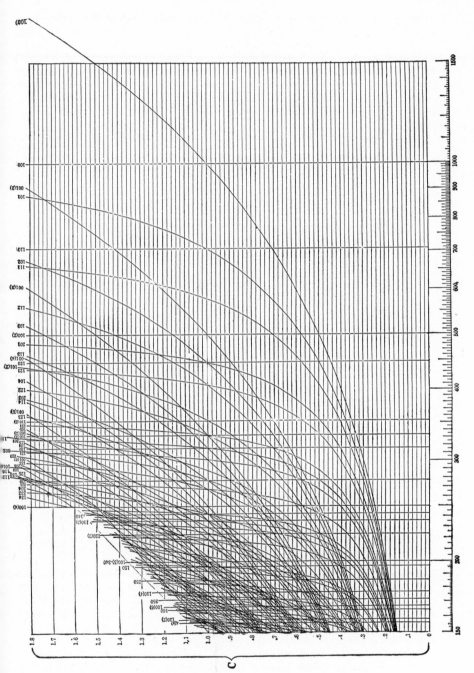

FIG. 11. Hull-Davey chart for simple tetragonal lattice.

values of log l^2. Each of the hk points is then joined to each of the l points by a line which represents the hkl spacing. Construction of the lines may be illustrated by the 213 line, which joins point 21 (at position log 5) with 3 (at position log 9). The numerical interval from 5 to 0 is divided, say, into 10 equal parts (5.4, 5.8, etc.) and the logarithms of each of these values is looked up: log 5.4, log 5.8, log 6.2, etc.

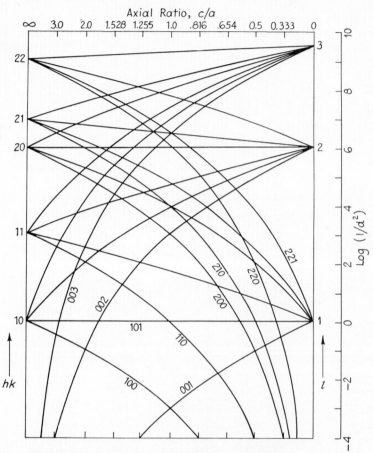

Fig. 12. Bunn's chart for indexing tetragonal crystals. Plotted with equal intervals along the base; a better form has the intervals proportional to the logarithms of these.

These logarithms give the distance of the 213 line above the base of the chart at $\frac{1}{10}$ intervals along the base from left to right. To use the chart a strip is marked with log $(1/d^2)$ values (*i.e.*, 2 log d), using the same scale as was used for the vertical scale of the chart. This is moved about over the plot, always keeping the strip parallel to the vertical sides of the chart, until a match between the strip marks and the lines is obtained, a procedure like that used for Hull-Davey charts.

To construct the Bunn chart for hexagonal and rhombohedral crystals the vertical distances are plotted to correspond to the values of log $(h^2 + hk + k^2)$ along the left edge and to correspond to log l^2 along the right edge. The points along the left edge and along the right edge are again joined by lines plotted as before. For example, the curve for the 200 reflection joins point $hk = 20$ (at distance log 4 above the base on the left side) with point $l = 0$ (at position log $0 = 0$) on the right-hand edge. The interval between the numbers 4 and 0 is divided into 10 parts and the logarithms of these are used for the equally spaced ordinates; thus the ordinate at $\frac{1}{10}$ the chart width is log 3.6, at $\frac{2}{10}$ is log 3.2, etc.

The scale of abscissas on these charts is related to the c/a ratio, but except to mark out the mid-point of the tetragonal chart, for which $c/a = 1$ (the cubic position) there is no advantage in marking off or using this scale for c/a determination. The axial ratio should be determined, instead, from the spacings of selected reflections, a being determined from any $hk0$ reflection and c from any $00l$ (favoring the high-angle reflections which permit greater accuracy), or better, both a and c being determined at once by the use of normal equations and least-squares averaging to be discussed later.

Bunn points out that extremely large or extremely small axial ratios occur in crowded regions of the charts described above, and recommends that the axis of abscissas be expanded logarithmically. This may be done by plotting the ordinates that have been discussed above at positions log $\frac{1}{10}$, log $\frac{2}{10}$, etc., instead of evenly spaced along the base line. The regions of the chart at c/a near ∞ and 0 then lie at infinity.

The purpose of all graphical methods is to aid in tentatively identifying the diffraction lines. They should not be trusted for the final assignment of indices or for the accurate determination of the lattice constants, which should be done by putting the tentative indices in the spacing formulas and computing $\sin\theta$ or $\sin^2\theta$ values for direct comparison with measured values.

A systematized *numerical method* of indexing is discussed by Hesse[1] usable with precision data ($\sin^2\theta$ errors of 0.0001 to 0.0005). Details will not be given here, but it is well to mention a test for tetragonal and hexagonal crystals. Both have quadratic forms of the type $\sin^2\theta = AM + Cl^2$, where M, which depends upon h and k, has values 0, 1, 2, 4, 5, 8, 9, etc., in tetragonal crystals and 0, 1, 3, 4, 7, 9 in hexagonal crystals. Assuming that A/C is not a ratio of small integers, it is possible to find pairs of planes of the $hk0$ type by applying the requirement that $c_1 \sin^2\theta_1 = c_2 \sin^2\theta_2$ for these, where c_1 and c_2 are small integers with no common factor and are not squares of integers. For these pairs of planes only certain ratios c_2/c_1 can occur in the tetragonal (T) or hexagonal (H) systems. The simpler ratios, with c_1 and c_2 less than 10, derived from the M values listed above are as follows:

c_2/c_1 for T: 2, 4, 5, 8, 9, $\frac{2}{5}$, $\frac{2}{9}$, $\frac{4}{5}$, $\frac{4}{9}$, $\frac{5}{8}$, $\frac{5}{9}$, $\frac{8}{9}$

c_2/c_1 for H: 3, 4, 7, 9, $\frac{3}{4}$, $\frac{3}{7}$, $\frac{4}{7}$, $\frac{4}{9}$, $\frac{7}{9}$

(c_2/c_1 occurring in neither T nor H: 6, $\frac{2}{3}$, $\frac{2}{7}$, $\frac{3}{5}$, $\frac{3}{8}$, $\frac{5}{6}$, $\frac{5}{7}$, $\frac{6}{7}$, $\frac{7}{8}$)

These ratios provide a convenient test for the T and H systems and a start toward indexing the lines. (These planes are the ones that have vertical lines on Hull-Davey charts.)

[1] R. Hesse, *Acta Cryst.*, vol. 1, p. 200, 1948.

Orthorhombic crystals may also be indexed by noting certain relations between $\sin^2 \theta$ values that are listed by Hesse, by making use of differences between $\sin^2 \theta$ values when plotted graphically in a "difference diagram"[1] or by graphical aids analogous to Hull-Davey Charts.[2]

A pattern of a substance is quickly solved if one recognizes from the pattern that the substance is isomorphous with a substance that has previously been fully investigated. Frevel has employed this principle both for indexing and for identifying substances from the powder patterns.[3] Frevel has also made use of the anisotropic thermal expansion of noncubic crystals as an aid to identification of the crystal system and to indexing.[4] The shifting of lines with changing specimen temperature corresponds to a percentage change in spacing that differs from line to line in a way that indicates the symmetry and the principal axes. In a similar way, patterns of two or more isomorphous substances can be indexed more easily if one notes the relative magnitudes of the shifts of corresponding lines from substance to substance.[5]

Precision Determinations of Lattice Constants. Precise lattice-constant determinations are important for the determination of solubility limits in constitution diagrams. Other applications in research include determinations of the coefficients of thermal expansion of metals and alloys, studies of precipitation from solid solution, and determination of composition of samples and of diffusion rates in solids.

Much work in the past has been done with forward-reflection Debye cameras, but they are inherently less precise than back-reflection cameras, which operate in the sensitive range of θ values near $\theta = 90°$. Precision work with Debye cameras is hampered by many factors: (1) film shrinkage, (2) errors in measuring the camera radius, (3) displacement of the specimen from the center of the camera by improper adjustment, (4) displacement of the effective center of the specimen from the center of the camera by absorption of the rays in the sample, (5) X-ray beam divergence, and (6) finite height of slits. Careful design of cameras and careful technique reduce many types of error, and correction formulas have been employed to eliminate some, but the greatest improvements

---

[1] H. Lipson, *Acta Cryst.*, vol. 2, p. 43, 1949. Methods applicable to long-spacing organic compounds are given by V. Vand, *Acta Cryst.*, vol. 1, pp. 109, 290, 1948.

[2] C. W. Jacob and B. E. Warren, *J. Am. Chem. Soc.*, vol. 59, p. 2586, 1937. Discussed on p. 168 below.

[3] L. K. Frevel, *J. Applied Phys.*, vol. 13, p. 109, 1942. L. K. Frevel, *Ind. Eng. Chem., Anal. Ed.*, vol. 14, p. 687, 1942 (data for cubic isomorphs). L. K. Frevel, H. W. Rinn, and H. C. Anderson, *Ind. Eng. Chem., Anal. Ed.*, vol. 18, p. 83, 1946 (data for tetragonal isomorphs).

[4] L. K. Frevel, *J. Applied Phys.*, vol. 8, p. 553, 1937.

[5] L. K. Frevel, *J. Applied Phys.*, vol. 13, p. 109, 1942.

have come from the more recent methods for eliminating systematic errors by extrapolation.

Errors and Corrections in Debye Cameras. When a film is put through the developing, fixing, and washing baths, it undergoes expansion or contraction of uncertain amounts. Further alteration occurs in storage and while it is being measured. This *film shrinkage* alters the apparent circumference of the camera. A remedy for it is to print a scale on the film at the time the photograph is made. Subsequent measurement of this scale then reveals the amount of shrinkage that has taken place. Unless the film has been mishandled or has dried unevenly, it can be assumed that shrinkage is uniform throughout the length of the strip; hence, the same percentage correction can be applied to all measured distances on the film.

One method of correcting for film shrinkage, originated by Straumanis, is to wrap the film around the camera in such a way that the ends come together on one side, midway between the entrance and exit holes. The position $\theta = 0$ is then determined as midway between right- and left-hand arcs of small-angle Debye rings, and the position $\theta = 90°$ is similarly determined from the large-angle rings; other θ values are then obtained by interpolation.

Alternately, the film may be cut long enough to overlap; the inner end is then in position to cast a sharp shadow on the overlapping end at a distance along the film that equals the effective circumference of the camera. If the film subsequently shrinks, this distance also shrinks in proportion. Since a diffraction ring for $\theta = 90°$ would cause two spots on the film separated by a full circumference it follows that

$$\frac{\theta°}{90°} = \frac{S}{S_0} \tag{6}$$

where S is the distance from one arc of a diffraction line to its mate and S_0 is the effective circumference.

Another common method of marking a standard distance on the film is to build two knife-edges into the camera so that they will form sharp limits to the exposed (darkened) portion of the film. The camera then requires calibration experiments to determine the camera dimensions. The preceding formula is then replaced by

$$\frac{\theta°}{\theta°_1} = \frac{S}{S_1} \tag{7}$$

where θ_1 is the diffraction angle for a line exactly at the knife-edges and S_1 is the circumferential distance between them.[1]

---

[1] This may be done by measuring the camera directly (which is recommended by A. J. C. Wilson and H. Lipson, *Proc. Phys. Soc. (London)*, vol. 53, p. 245, 1941) or,

The principle of calibration can be applied to individual films if the powders of the unknown sample and the standard substance are mixed and the superimposed spectra are obtained. The angles of reflection from the standard powder, which are known accurately, are plotted against the measurements of the corresponding lines to give a calibration curve for the film. Then the corrected angles for other lines are read from the curve.[1] Some cameras contain a septum that divides the interior into two independent compartments, one for the standard specimen and one for the unknown. To attain precision with this type of instrument the operator must be careful to center the specimens in the axis of the camera and to equalize the absorption of rays in the two specimens by diluting with an amorphous material like flour.

Attempts have been made to correct for the *radius of the specimen* by using correction formulas, though the results are less reliable than those obtained by calibration methods.[2] The simplest formula, which assumes that the incident rays are parallel and are completely absorbed in the specimen so that reflected rays come only from the surface layers of the specimen, is

$$S_c = S' - \delta \qquad (8)$$

where S' is the film measurement between outer edges of the two arcs of a Debye ring, δ is the diameter of the cylindrical specimen, and S_c is the corrected value of the ring measurement from which θ is obtained ($\theta = S_c/4R$ radians if R is the camera radius).

Graphical Extrapolation Methods for Debye Films. To compute the error in lattice spacing, Δd, that results from an error of $\Delta\theta$ in the measurement of θ we may put Bragg's law in the form

$$d \sin \theta = \frac{n\lambda}{2} \qquad (9)$$

which by differentiation yields

$$d \cos \theta \, \Delta\theta + \sin \theta \, \Delta d = 0 \qquad (10)$$

alternatively, by taking a photograph of a substance of known lattice spacings [see A. J. Bradley and A. H. Jay, *Proc. Phys. Soc. (London)*, vol. 44, p. 563, 1932].

Quartz (the clear variety, not smoky) is recommended for a calibrating substance. The quartz spectrum has been listed by A. J. Bradley and A. H. Jay, *Proc. Phys. Soc. (London)*, vol. 45, p. 507, 1933, but their spacing values have been criticized and amended by H. Lipson and A. J. C. Wilson, *J. Sci. Instruments*, vol. 18, p. 144, 1941. Much attention must be given to the question of the purity of any calibration substance, for dissolved impurities alter the spacing.

[1] Interpolation formulas have also been used for this procedure (see F. Wever and O. Lohrmann, *Mitt. Kaiser-Wilhelm-Inst. Eisenforsch., Düsseldorf*, vol. 14, p. 137, 1932).

[2] F. Wever and O. Lohrmann, *Mitt. Kaiser-Wilhelm-Inst. Eisenforsch., Düsseldorf*, vol. 14, p. 137, 1932.

from which

$$\frac{\Delta d}{d} = - \cot \theta \, \Delta\theta \qquad (11)$$

Thus the precentage error in spacing measurement caused by a given error in angle measurement approaches zero as $\cot \theta$ approaches zero, hence as θ approaches 90°. Kettmann[1] used this fact to eliminate errors by simply plotting the apparent lattice constant determined from each line against the value of θ for that line; a smooth curve drawn through the plotted points and extrapolated to $\theta = 90°$ gave the corrected value of the lattice constant.

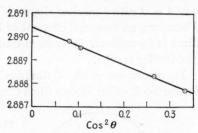

Bradley and Jay[2] have improved upon Kettmann's method by handling the data in such a way that the extrapolated curve is approximately a straight line. From the geometry of a forward-reflection Debye camera they show that two important systematic errors can be effectively treated. Fractional errors in lattice spacings, $\Delta d/d$, that arise from incorrect centering (*eccentricity*) of the specimen in the camera depend upon θ in the following way:

FIG. 13. Extrapolation of lattice parameters to $\theta = 90°$ by plotting against $\cos^2 \theta$. Specimen was 85.5 per cent Fe, 14.5 per cent Al. (*Bradley and Jay.*)

$$\frac{\Delta d}{d} = C_1 \cos^2 \theta \qquad (12)$$

where C_1 is a constant for all lines of a given film. Similarly, the fractional spacing errors arising from the *absorption* of rays in the sample are given by the approximate equation

$$\frac{\Delta d}{d} = C_2 \frac{1}{\theta} \cos^2 \theta \qquad (13)$$

where C_2 is another constant for all lines of one photograph. Both errors approach zero at $\theta = 90°$, as does the sum of the two, and both vary approximately in proportion to the factor $\cos^2 \theta$. Therefore by plotting computed values of a against $\cos^2 \theta$, as in Fig. 13, a curve through the points approximates a straight line at high values of θ. This line extrapolates to the corrected a at $\cos^2 \theta = 0$. The linear extrapolation becomes the more precise the nearer the points are to $\theta = 90°$ and the smaller the systematic errors.

[1] G. Kettmann, *Z. Physik.*, vol. 53, p. 198, 1929.
[2] A. J. Bradley and A. H. Jay, *Proc. Phys. Soc. (London)*, vol. 44, p. 563, 1932.

Shrinkage and *radius* errors do not lead to a straight line on a plot of this kind,[1] for they produce spacing errors of magnitude

$$\frac{\Delta d}{d} = \frac{\Delta R}{R} \, \theta \cot \theta \qquad (14)$$

where ΔR is the error in equivalent radius, R, caused by shrinkage or by incorrect measurement of the camera radius. If shrinkage errors of any importance are present, the curve on a Bradley and Jay plot approaches $\cos^2 \theta = 0$ with a marked slope which makes extrapolation very uncertain. Therefore, an essential element of Bradley and Jay's technique for Debye films is to *calibrate the camera and correct for shrinkage in the film before plotting the results.*

Extrapolation with Cylindrical Back-reflection Cameras. In the forward-reflection Debye films discussed in the preceding paragraphs the

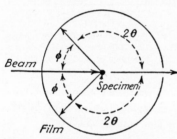

FIG. 14. Angles in a back-reflection Debye camera.

most precise values of the lattice constants are obtained from the lines on the extreme ends of the films where shrinkage corrections are the greatest. It is much better to reverse the film to the back-reflection position so that shrinkage errors approach zero as θ approaches 90°, or to use the Straumanis method, which also provides a continuous film at the $\theta = 90°$ position. Any camera employing this arrangement may be called a back reflection camera.

The correction of systematic errors by extrapolation is simple and effective in the back-reflection cameras,[2] which admit the beam from the X-ray tube through a hole at the center of the film. As sketched in Fig. 14, the angle 2ϕ rather than 2θ or 4θ is measured, and θ is obtained from the relation $\phi = \pi - 2\theta$.

The errors in ϕ caused by film shrinkage and radius are proportional to ϕ, and the error due to displacement of the sample from the center of the camera is proportional to $\sin (\phi/2) \cos (\phi/2) = \frac{1}{2} \sin \phi$ which for small values of ϕ is approximately proportional to ϕ, as Bradley and Jay showed. The error introduced by absorption in the sample is also proportional to ϕ for small values of ϕ with highly absorbing samples (the usual condition, since long-wavelength radiation is commonly used in precision

[1] M. J. Buerger, "X-ray Crystallography," Wiley, New York, 1942.

[2] W. Stenzel and J. Weerts, *Z. Krist.*, vol. 84, p. 20, 1933. J. Weigel, *Helv. Phys. Acta*, vol. 7, pp. 46, 51, 1934. M. U. Cohen, *Z. Krist.*, vol. 94, p. 288, 1936. M. J. Buerger, "X-ray Crystallography," Wiley, New York, 1942. B. E. Warren, *J. Applied Phys.*, vol. 16, p. 614, 1945.

work), as Warren has shown.[1]   The position of maximum intensity in the diffraction line is measured for extrapolations of this sort.   Therefore all systematic errors add together to produce a combined error, $\Delta\phi$, that is proportional to ϕ to a very good approximation, *i.e.*, $\Delta\phi = -2\Delta\theta = D\phi$, and Eq. (11) can be written

$$\frac{\Delta d}{d} = D \frac{\phi}{2} \tan \frac{\phi}{2} \tag{15}$$

For small values of ϕ this is closely approximated by the relation

$$\frac{\Delta d}{d} = D \sin^2 \frac{\phi}{2} = D \cos^2 \theta \tag{16}$$

so that if a series of values of a lattice constant, calculated from individual diffraction lines, is plotted against $\cos^2 \theta$ and extrapolated to $\theta = 90°$ by using a straight-line extrapolation in the range of θ near $90°$, the extrapolated value is free from systematic errors.   Alternately, values of $\sin^2 \theta$ can be plotted and linearly extrapolated to $\theta = 90°$ since $\sin^2 \theta$ is linearly related to $\cos^2 \theta$.   The same systematic error in $\Delta d/d$ also occurs in *back-reflection symmetrical focusing cameras* and may be eliminated in the same way.   These simple extrapolations are best used in the range from $\theta = 60$ to $90°$ and if there are too few lines in this region when a given X-ray target is used it may be necessary to employ an alloy target.[2]

Cohen's Method.   Cohen has shown[3] that the extrapolation to eliminate systematic errors can be performed with increased accuracy by an analytical method, which is applicable to noncubic as well as cubic crystals.

Bragg's law, by squaring and taking logarithms, can be put in the form

$$\log \sin^2 \theta = 2 \log \frac{(n\lambda)}{2} - 2 \log d$$

[1] B. E. Warren, *J. Applied Phys.*, vol. 16, p. 614, 1945.

[2] J. B. Nelson and D. P. Riley [*Proc. Phys. Soc. (London)*, vol. 57, p. 160, 1945] have shown that there is an extrapolation function that is linear over a greater range than the one mentioned above.   For a camera with negligible eccentricity error, the apparent lattice constants are plotted against $\frac{1}{2}(\operatorname{cosec} \theta + \theta^{-1}) \cos^2 \theta$ and extrapolated to zero value of this function.   With a specimen of optimum absorption (radius $= 1/\mu$ where μ is the linear absorption coefficient) the extrapolation is linear from $\theta = 30$ to $90°$.   A table of values of this function is given in the paper.   However, the low θ lines should be given so little weight that there seems little point in using them.

[3] M. U. Cohen, *Rev. Sci. Instruments*, vol. 6, p. 68, 1935; vol. 7, p. 155, 1936; *Z. Krist.*, vol. 94, pp. 288, 306, 1936.   See also discussions by E. R. Jette and F. Foote, *J. Chem Phys.*, vol. 3, p. 605, 1935; M. J. Buerger, "X-ray Crystallography," p. 426, Wiley, New York, 1942; and B. E. Warren, *J. Applied Phys.*, vol. 16, p. 614, 1945.

and differentiating gives

$$\frac{\Delta \sin^2 \theta}{\sin^2 \theta} = -2 \frac{\Delta d}{d}$$

Substituting Eqs. (15) and (16) in this expression leads to values of $\sin^2 \theta$ that are incorrect by an amount

$$\Delta \sin^2 \theta = -D \phi \tan \frac{\phi}{2} \sin^2 \theta = -\frac{D}{2} \phi \sin \phi \qquad (17)$$

or, in terms of θ approximately by

$$\Delta \sin^2 \theta \cong -2D \sin^2 \theta \cos^2 \theta = -D \sin^2 2\theta \qquad (18)$$

where D is different from film to film but is constant throughout any one film, provided that back-reflection cameras are used (in which the beam enters rather than leaves the camera through the center of the film).   The spacing formula may therefore be corrected for the effect of systematic errors in these cameras by adding the corrective term, Eq. (17), giving

$$\frac{\lambda^2}{4d^2} = \cos^2 \frac{\phi}{2} - \frac{D}{2} \phi \sin \phi \qquad (19)$$

or, alternatively, from Eq. (18)

$$\frac{\lambda^2}{4d^2} = \sin^2 \theta - D \sin^2 2\theta \qquad (20)$$

An equation of this type is written for each line of the pattern, expressing d in terms of the known indices and the unknown lattice constants.   The entire series of equations is then used in setting up least-squares normal equations to solve for the most probable values of the lattice constants and the film constant D.

For cubic crystals, Cohen rewrites Eq. (20) in the form

$$K(h^2 + k^2 + l^2) + D \sin^2 2\theta = \sin^2 \theta \qquad (21)$$

where $K = \lambda^2/4a^2$, and uses the normal equations

$$K \Sigma \alpha_i^2 + D' \Sigma \alpha_i \delta_i = \Sigma \alpha_i \sin^2 \theta_i$$
$$K \Sigma \alpha_i \delta_i + D' \Sigma \delta_i^2 = \Sigma \delta_i \sin^2 \theta_i \qquad (22)$$

where $\alpha_i = h^2 + k^2 + l^2$, $D' = D/10$, and $\delta_i = 10 \sin^2 2\theta_i$.   The factor 10 is used merely so that the coefficients of the normal equations will be of the same magnitude.   The summations extend over all the equations for the individual lines that lie in the appropriate range of θ.   Solution of the two simultaneous normal equations gives the corrected value of K and thus the lattice constant a.   This method of calculation is readily extended to other systems with additional parameters; for hexagonal crystals, Eq. (21) is replaced by

$$\alpha K_1 + \gamma K_2 + \delta D = \sin^2 \theta \qquad (23)$$

where $\alpha = h^2 + hk + k^2$, $\gamma = l^2$, $\delta = 10 \sin^2 2\theta$, $K_1 = \lambda^2/3a^2$, $K_2 = \lambda^2/4c^2$, and now three normal equations must be solved simultaneously for the three unknowns. Orthorhombic crystals are handled in a similar way.

Jette and Foote[1] have discussed the evaluation of standard errors and fiduciary limits of results from a single film and from a set of films when computed by Cohen's method. Results obtained on cubic and hexagonal crystals with a 10-cm symmetrical focusing camera gave five significant figures; fiduciary limits for 95 per cent probability were ± 2 to 7 parts per 100,000.

Hess's Modification. Hess has shown[2] that Cohen's method assigns equal weight to the lattice constants obtained from each of the diffraction lines. But equal weights should, instead, be given the individual measurements of line positions on the film, provided that the lines are sharp enough to permit precision work.[3] If this is done, the lattice constants computed for the lines near $\phi = 0$ will be given much greater weight than the others, which is proper. This principle amounts to weighting the individual observation equations [such as Eq. (20) for cubic crystals] by the weighting factor $\operatorname{cosec}^2 \phi$. Choosing Eq. (19) rather than the less accurate and less convenient Eq. (20), we may write, for cubic crystals,

$$A_0 \alpha' + D\delta' = \gamma' \qquad (24)$$

where $A_0 = 1/a_0^2$, a_0 = corrected lattice constant, $\alpha' = (\lambda^2/2)(h^2 + k^2 + l^2)$, $\delta' = \phi \sin \phi$, and $\gamma' = 2 \cos^2 (\phi/2)$—calculated more easily in its equivalent form $\gamma' = 1 + \cos \phi$.

Hess employs the Deming generalization of the least-squares technique[4] to derive weighted normal equations that have the form

$$\left. \begin{array}{l} \Delta A\, \Sigma \alpha_i'^2 w_i \operatorname{cosec}^2 \phi_i - K \Sigma \alpha_i' \delta_i' w_i \operatorname{cosec}^2 \phi_i = \Sigma \alpha_i' F_i w_i \operatorname{cosec}^2 \phi_i \\ \Delta A\, \Sigma \alpha_i' \delta_i' w_i \operatorname{cosec}^2 \phi_i - K \Sigma \delta_i'^2 w_i \operatorname{cosec}^2 \phi_i = \Sigma \delta_i' F_i w_i \operatorname{cosec}^2 \phi_i \end{array} \right\} \qquad (25)$$

where $\Delta A = A_a - A_0$, $A_a = 1/a_a^2$, a_a is an assumed approximate value of the lattice constant, $F = \alpha' A_a - \gamma'$ is the deviation of the measured value of $2 \cos^2 (\phi/2)$ from that calculated using the approximate lattice contant, and w_i is the statistical weight of the measurements of the diameter

[1] E. R. Jette and F. Foote, *J. Chem. Phys.*, vol. 3, p. 605, 1935.

[2] J. B. Hess, *Acta Cryst.*, vol. 4, p. 209, 1951.

[3] H. Ekstein and S. Siegel, *Acta Cryst.*, vol. 2, p. 99, 1949.

[4] W. E. Deming, "Statistical Adjustment of Data," Wiley, New York, 1943. Deming's generalized least-squares treatment of data covers the handling of any number of variables that are subject to error, any number of adjustable parameters, and both linear and nonlinear observation equations.

of the ith set of Debye arcs.   The statistical weight w_i can be determined by a statistical study of many readings of each line; but since all lines are found to be readable with the same precision unless they are abnormally weak, w_i may be taken as unity for all the better lines and only assigned lower values for weak lines.   The assumed value, a_a, should be a good approximation to the lattice constant a_0, such as may be obtained from measurements of the highest angle diffraction lines, ignoring the presence of systematic errors.   By using this initial approximate parameter, a_a, the computation is reduced to the determination of a small correction to this, and the number of significant figures required in the coefficients of the normal equations is greatly reduced.

No Refraction Correction for Small or Powdered Crystals.   The index of refraction of X-rays in crystals differs from unity by a few parts per

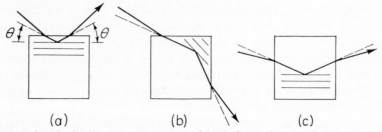

Fig. 15.   Index of refraction may cause measured θ to be larger than true θ as in a, or smaller, as in c; intermediate cases occur, as in b.   A variety of conditions occur in powder particles.

million, which means that a beam of X-rays is bent slightly when it passes obliquely through a surface in entering or leaving a solid.   In passing into the solid from the air the ray is bent away from the normal to the surface, for the phase velocity of the waves in the crystal is higher than in air; in passing out it is bent toward the normal.   Now when a crystal is mounted in an X-ray spectrometer and the diffraction angle θ is measured with precision in seconds of arc, it is necessary to apply a correction to the measured value in order to obtain the true θ at which the beam strikes the reflecting plane within the crystal; this is done in all precision single-crystal and double-crystal spectrometer studies.[1]   Unfortunately there has been widespread confusion with regard to the need for a similar correction in powder photographs and rotating-crystal photographs using small, nonabsorbing crystals.[2]   It is quickly seen by referring to Fig. 15 that the crystal spectrometer, which measures rays that enter and leave the same surface as in the sketch on the left, gives a θ reading that is too large.   On the other hand, a θ value obtained from transmission through

[1] A. H. Compton and S. K. Allison, "X-rays in Theory and Experiment," Van Nostrand, New York, 1935.

[2] The author is indebted to W. H. Zachariasen for pointing this out.

a thin crystal as in the sketch on the right is too small. The rays reflected by a small, nonabsorbing crystal in an X-ray goniometer are of both types together with intermediate types; the rays through some faces are deviated one way and those through other faces are bent the opposite way. The net result is that there is a negligible net deviation of the beam that is composed of a superposition of these individual rays; therefore no refraction correction should be applied. In powder samples also the beam enters and leaves many surfaces of each particle; so with powders also no refraction correction should be applied. (Fortunately the correction that has been applied by many crystallographers is small, amounting to between 1 part in 10,000 and 1 part in 50,000.)

Values of Wavelengths. For many years, up until about 1947, the scale of wavelengths used in precision X-ray work was based on Siegbahn's values,[1] which was based on the assumption that the spacing of d_{100} in calcite is 3.02945 A at 18°C and the assumption that Avogadro's number N is 6.0594×10^{23}. This scale of wavelengths is now known to be based on a unit, the kx unit, that differs slightly from angstroms (10^{-8} cm). By international agreement in 1946, the Siegbahn wavelengths are to be converted to angstroms by multiplying by 1.00202.[2] The factor is probably correct to 0.003 per cent. A table of wavelengths is given in Appendix VIII.

Since the values of all lattice spacings are related to the wavelengths by Bragg's law, all spacings and lattice constants reported during the years when the kx unit was used should be converted to angstroms by multiplying by the same factor, i.e., $d_A = 1.00202 d_{kx}$.

In calculating the X-ray density D_x of a crystal using the angstrom scale of wavelengths the current values of the physical constants should be used. In terms of the values of the constants that were considered the best values at the time the 1.00202 factor was decided upon, the density formula is

$$D_x = \frac{1.66020 \, \Sigma A}{V}$$

where ΣA is the sum of the atomic weights of the atoms in the unit cell and V is the volume of the unit cell in angstrom units cubed; the factor 1.66020 is 10^{-24} times the reciprocal of the current value of Avogadro's number.[3]

---

[1] M. Siegbahn, "Spectroscopie der Röntgenstrahlen," 2d ed., Springer, Berlin, 1931.

[2] W. L. Bragg, *J. Sci. Instruments*, vol. 24, p. 27, 1947; reprinted in *Acta Cryst.*, vol. 1, p. 46, 1948.

[3] The chemical scale of atomic weights as calculated by J. W. M. DuMond and E. R. Cohen (*Rev. Modern Phys.*, vol. 20, p. 82, 1948) puts the value of N at $(6.0235 \pm 0.0004) \times 10^{23}$ in satisfactory agreement with the above equation. Discussion of the calculation of D_x is given by M. E. Straumanis (*Acta Cryst.*, vol. 2,

Qualitative Analysis by X-ray Diffraction. The possibility of chemical analysis by the powder method was clearly stated by Hull[1] in 1919 when he pointed out that every crystalline substance gives a diffraction pattern; that the same substance always gives the same pattern; that in a mixture each substance produces its pattern independently of the other, just as if each of the components had been exposed separately for the same length of time; and that quantitative analysis could be made by suitable measurements of the relative intensities of the lines from the various components. Hanawalt and his coworkers at the Dow Company added another useful fact to this list—*viz.*, that the thousands of patterns representing the thousands of different chemical substances can be classified so as to be readily usable for the identification of an unknown substance or even a mixture of unknowns.[2] The classification system they adopted as the result of carrying out several thousand analyses in a period of many years is highly effective. The reader is referred to the article by Hanawalt, Rinn, and Frevel[3] for details of the technique.

The problem was to devise a classification system somewhat analogous to that employed for filing fingerprints, so that any pattern similar to an unknown could be quickly located in the file and compared with the unknown; this was successfully accomplished by using the *interplanar spacings*, *d*, of the lines together with their relative *intensities*. The spectra are classified according to the spacing of the three strongest lines. A set of diffraction data was prepared by an ASTM subcommittee, in which is recorded the spacing and intensity data for over a thousand substances.[4] Three cards are included for each substance, one giving the strongest line first, one giving the second strongest line first, and one the third strongest. All cards are arranged in a file in the order of the spacing of the first line listed. On the cards are printed spacings and relative intensities, I/I_1, for all lines of the spectrum, referred to the intensity of the strongest line. An example taken from the original article,[3] in which 1000 patterns were published, is given in Table VI. In addition to the relative intensities I/I_1, the approximate absolute intensities are given for

---

p. 82, 1949), who concludes that Ag, Cu, Fe, Pb, Te, LiF, $Pb(NO_3)_2$, and calcite have D_x agreeing with the measured density D_M within experimental error. Earlier work on the subject is summarized in A. H. Compton and S. K. Allison, "X-rays and Electrons in Theory and Experiment," Van Nostrand, New York, 1935.

[1] A. W. Hull, *J. Am. Chem. Soc.*, vol. 41, p. 1168, 1919.

[2] J. D. Hanawalt and H. W. Rinn, *Ind. Eng. Chem., Anal. Ed.*, vol. 8, p. 244, 1936. J. D. Hanawalt, H. W. Rinn, and L. K. Frevel, *Ind. Eng. Chem., Anal. Ed.*, vol. 10, p. 457, 1938.

[3] J. D. Hanawalt, H. W. Rinn, and L. K. Frevel, *Ind. Eng. Chem., Anal. Ed.*, vol. 10, p. 457, 1938.

[4] Obtainable from the American Society for Testing Materials, Philadelphia, Pa.

a few lines in order to provide a basis for judging relative proportions of components in a mixture of substances.

TABLE VI. POWDER DIFFRACTION SPECTRUM FOR FeO (SERIAL NUMBER 425 OF HANAWALT, RINN, AND FREVEL)

d	I Absolute intensity	I/I_1 Intensity relative to strongest line
2.47	(20)	0.50
2.14	(40)	1.00
1.51	(25)	0.63
1.293	....	0.15
1.238	....	0.08
1.072	....	0.03
0.984	....	0.03
0.959	....	0.05
0.876	....	0.03

The steps in conducting an analysis are as follows:

1. Calculate d values for all lines of the unknown spectrum, and estimate their relative intensities.

2. Search the section of the card file containing all substances with the strongest line having d values near that of the unknown.

3. Locate the entries in this section that have the second strongest line near the second strongest of the unknown (usually a range of d values 0.01 A on each side of the measured value should be searched).

4. Check the third strongest and all the weaker lines against the spectra thus located.   The best check is always to compare the films of the known and unknown substances.

When the unknown is a single phase this procedure will find it if listed, but when the unknown is a mixture there will be lines left over that are not explained by the printed spectrum.   These leftovers must be treated similarly, as the pattern of one or more additional substances.   Another difficulty arises if the constituent giving the strongest line of the unknown pattern is not listed or if the strongest line should happen to be so by virtue of the superposition of weaker lines.   Then one must proceed by using the second strongest line to locate the material in the file, etc. Superimposed lines can often be detected by anomalous intensities in the unknown compared with the standard spectra.   The procedure when properly conducted should not fail to locate any and all components of a mixture that are listed in the file, provided that the components are present in sufficient quantity, purity, and perfection to yield readable patterns.

The apparatus with which the original patterns were prepared consisted of an early-model multiple-diffraction unit employing molybdenum radiation; $K\beta$ filters of zirconium dioxide were used in front of the film and Fluorazure intensifying screens were placed immediately behind the double-emulsion film.   Intensities were judged by comparison with narrow blackened strips that were given exposures in the ratios 1, 2, 4, 8, 10, 15, 20, 30, 50, 75, 125, 175, 250, 325.

The X-ray Diffraction Data Index has been continuously expanded and revised since the publication of the first set of cards.   Joint committees have brought about cooperation among British, Canadian, and American X-ray workers leading to publication of a first and a second supplement, and a revised, rearranged printing of the data on larger cards with additional crystallographic data.   Approximately 4000 substances, including inorganic and organic substances and minerals, are now covered in the index.   The more frequent users of the index have become interested in the use of punched cards for this work so that mechanical sorting methods can be employed for locating individual substances or classes of substances.[1]

Applications and Limitations of the Diffraction Data Index.   An appreciation of the limitations of chemical analysis by the use of the index is important.   It is found that some substances will produce a pattern in a mixture if they represent only 1 per cent or so of the material being examined; but many will not show at less than 10 per cent, and some will not show plainly even at 50 per cent.   Elements present in solid solution may not be detected by the method as described—in fact the change of lattice constants by solid-solution formation may be sufficient to hamper the identification of the substance.   Trouble is occasionally encountered when different substances have the same or nearly the same crystal structures and when the unit cell dimensions of these structures are nearly identical.   Frevel has listed some examples,[2] and many will be found in tabulations of crystal structures.   Ambiguities that result from isomorphism or structural similarity are usually resolvable by supplemental tests (chemical analysis, spectroscopic analysis, or some physical criterion such as solubility in water or melting point).   Structural irregularities and defects may cause an unknown to produce a pattern somewhat different from that of the standard pattern for the substance, particularly if the unknown or the standard substance was formed under nonequilibrium

[1] F. W. Matthews, A Punched Card Code for X-ray Diffraction Powder Data, *Anal. Chem.*, vol. 21, p. 1172, 1949.   The revised printing of the index on the new format will provide a margin on each card that can be punched by the user if he desires to use a punched-card code system, but punch coding is a task involving too much labor to be justified by the occasional user and appears too expensive to be done during the printing of the cards.

[2] L. K. Frevel, *Ind. Eng. Chem.*, vol. 16, p. 209, 1944.

conditions. In this category are layer structures in which there is some degree of randomness in the stacking of the layers, and defect structures in which the unit cell contains a fractional stoichiometric weight such as $Fe_{1-x}R$, where R may be O, S, Se, or Te, and where there are changes in the lattice constants with x. Alloy systems having structures that appear only in transition when one phase is transforming to another can cause difficulties. Perhaps more common are the troubles that arise from incorrect degree of hydration, and from chemical reactions between standard or unknown substances and water, oxygen, or carbon dioxide.[1] Mistakes and experimental inaccuracies in the index, and important lines that have been missed because of the low-angle limit of the particular camera used for the standard pattern are the subject of continued research by committees and will be less troublesome in later printings than in the original printing of the index. About 5 per cent of the solid inorganic substances give only an amorphous pattern with no distinct lines. Liquids can be analyzed only if they are photographed in the solid state at low temperatures. The use of a different radiation than was used for the standard pattern causes some alteration in relative intensities, chiefly with lines differing considerably in diffraction angle, but seldom prevents the successful identification of a substance.

The unique advantages of the diffraction method of analysis are that it identifies conclusively amounts of material even as small as a fraction of a milligram, or with sufficient care even a microgram; it differentiates different phases of the same composition and different states of chemical combination; it supplies a permanent record of the original data; and it does not destroy the sample.

The list of successful industrial uses of analysis by powder diffraction has become almost endless. Striking examples are its use in solving boiler-water treatment problems,[2] refractories,[3] industrial dusts,[4] and minerals.[5] The method has furnished decisive testimony in many patent disputes and court trials. It is used extensively in trouble shooting, control of raw materials and processing, and product development.

[1] L. K. Frevel, *Ind. Eng. Chem.*, vol. 16, p. 209, 1944.

[2] C. E. Imhoff and L. A. Burkardt, *Ind. Eng. Chem.*, vol. 35, p. 873, 1943; *ASTM, Standards*, vol. 43, p. 1276, 1943. L. M. Clark and C. W. Bunn, *J. Soc. Chem. Ind.*, vol. 59, p. 155, 1940; vol. 57, p. 399, 1938. R. C. Corey, B. J. Cross, and W. T. Reid, *Trans. ASME*, vol. 67, p. 279, 1945.

[3] A. H. Jay and J. H. Chesters, *Trans. Brit. Ceram. Soc.*, vol. 37, p. 209, 1938. A. H. Jay, *Trans. Brit. Ceram. Soc.*, vol. 38, p. 455, 1939.

[4] G. L. Clark and D. H. Reynolds, *Ind. Eng. Chem., Anal. Ed.*, vol. 8, p. 36, 1936. J. W. Ballard, H. I. Oshry, and H. H. Schrenk, *J. Optical Soc. Am.*, vol. 33, p. 667, 1943. H. P. Klug, L. Alexander, and E. Kummer, *J. Ind. Hyg. Toxicol.*, vol. 30, p. 166, 1948; *Anal. Chem.*, vol. 30, p. 607, 1948. G. Nagelschmidt and E. J. King, *Biochem. J.*, vol. 35, p. 152, 1941.

[5] For numerous examples see *Am. Mineral.*

Quantitative Analysis. The usual method of estimating the amount of various phases in a mixture is to calibrate the intensities of certain lines in the combined diffraction pattern by using a series of samples having known analyses. Visual comparison of films with standard films permits an accuracy to be reached that may become as high as ±5 per cent of the amount present. Higher accuracies are attained with densitometers, and still higher with X-ray spectrometers, provided the particle size is sufficiently small to give good diffraction lines.[1] Preferred orientation of the particles must be avoided in quantitative work, since this alters relative intensities. Massive polycrystalline metal samples, which are rarely free from preferred orientations, are generally unsuitable for quantitative determination.

Retained austenite in steels has been measured by methods based on the peak intensities of lines and calibration standards.[2] Greater precision, however, has been reached by measuring the integrated intensity of lines (the area under a plot of intensity vs. θ), since these, unlike peak intensities, are relatively free from errors due to variable line broadening.[3] By using a monochromator to lessen the background darkening, and computed corrections for the various crystallographic and geometrical factors that govern the integrated intensity,[4] Averbach and Cohen[3] have measured retained austenite in quantities as low as 0.5 per cent. The method employed by them did not depend on metallographic determinations of retained austenite in standard samples, but was found to yield percentages of retained austenite that agreed with metallographic percentages.[5] A similar procedure can be used with spectrometers. If the specimen is suitably mounted in the X-ray beam there is no absorption correction[6] to be made; the possibility that extinction is present, however, must be considered. This may be lessened by operating with low-intensity reflections.

Particle-size Determination. The determination of the size of colloidal particles using X-ray diffraction needs but a brief mention, for the great majority of problems in this field can be attacked more successfully by the electron microscope. Elaborate techniques have been worked out for the X-ray method,[7] but these are unnecessary when experiments are

[1] H. P. Klug, L. Alexander, and E. Kummer, *Anal. Chem.*, vol. 20, p. 607, 1948.

[2] K. Tamaru and S. Sakito, *Sci. Repts., Tôhoku Imp. Univ.*, vol. 20, p. 1, 1931. F. S. Gardner, M. Cohen, and D. P. Antia, *Trans. AIME*, vol. 154, p. 306, 1943.

[3] B. L. Averbach and M. Cohen, *Trans. AIME*, vol. 176, p. 401, 1938.

[4] These are discussed in Appendix I.

[5] The percentages agreed to within 1 per cent of the total sample when metallographic etching was done with 1 per cent zephiran chloride in 4 per cent nital. The X-ray specimens were oscillated and the films were microphotometered.

[6] Z. W. Wilchinsky, *J. Applied Phys.*, vol. 15, p. 806, 1944.

[7] For summaries, see George L. Clark, "Applied X-rays," 3d ed., McGraw-Hill, New York, 1940. "Symposium on Radiography and X-ray Diffraction," American

confined to particles of about 200 A diameter or less and when no attempt is made to determine the distribution of sizes or the shape of particles. This discussion will therefore be limited to the simplest procedure, the method of mixtures.[1]

Because of the lack of resolving power of very small crystallites each diffraction line is broadened. A plot of intensity vs. angle for such a line will have approximately the shape of an error curve when conditions are favorable for the simplest technique. The breadth of this curve, in radians, is measured from one side of the curve to the other at the level midway between base and peak. Let this measured breadth be B_m. To correct this width for the many factors arising from the finite width and height of the camera slits, the wavelength distribution in the X-ray beam, the divergence of the beam through the slits, and the penetration of the rays below the surface of the sample, a calibration substance is mixed with the sample. A substance is chosen in which there is no widening of lines from particle size, the substance having particles in the range of 10^{-4} to 10^{-5} cm. A line from this substance is chosen that lies near the previously measured line; let its breadth be B_s. Under the above conditions the broadening due to particle size alone will then be

$$B_{ps}^2 = B_m^2 - B_s^2$$

and the corrected quantity B_{ps} may be put in the Scherrer formula

$$L_{hkl} = \frac{0.89\lambda}{B_{ps} \cos \theta}$$

where L_{hkl} is the thickness of the particles in angstroms in the direction normal to the reflecting plane (hkl), λ is the wavelength in angstroms, and θ is the Bragg reflecting angle.[2]

It is necessary, of course, that the standard substance (for example, copper powder) produce no lines overlapping those of the sample which are to be measured, that the slits be narrow enough for B_s to be small compared with B_m, and that the intensity curve be the shape of an error curve (a partly resolved $K\alpha$ doublet cannot be used without further correction).

Society for Testing Materials, Philadelphia, 1936. J. T. Randall, "The Diffraction of X-rays and Electrons by Amorphous Solids, Liquids and Gases," Wiley, New York, 1934. R. Brill, *Kolloid-Z.*, vol. 69, p. 301, 1934; vol. 55, p. 164, 1931. C. C. Murdock, *Phys. Rev.*, vol. 31, p. 304, 1928; vol. 35, p. 8, 1930.

[1] B. E. Warren, *J. Applied Phys.*, vol. 12, p. 375, 1941.

[2] Scherrer's original formula contained the constant 0.94 instead of 0.89. For a simple derivation of the constant 0.89 see W. L. Bragg, "The Crystalline State," G. Bell, London, 1933. The exact value of the constant is of little importance in most applications.

Line broadening begins to be detectable when particle size is reduced below about 1000 A. A back-reflection camera with narrow slits of the order of 0.001 in. in width is necessary with this range of sizes, while particles 200 A or less in diameter may be studied in a Debye camera, preferably with radiation from copper or a similar element. In studies of MgO by Birks and Friedman[1] average particle sizes in the range 40 to 1000 A calculated from X-ray data taken on a Geiger-counter spectrometer agreed to about ±10 per cent with sizes measured on an electron microscope.

Other approximate methods for evaluating line widths have been used. Jones[2] fitted the intensity curves for widened lines and the unwidened lines from calibration samples by expressions of the form $e^{-k^2x^2}$, $1/(1 + k^2x^2)$, or $\sin^2 (kx)/k^2x^2$, and made corrections accordingly. Each $K\alpha$ line is a doublet; this can be allowed for by making use of the fact that near one extreme edge of the combined line the intensity is entirely due to the nearer component of the doublet and the fact that nearer the center of the combined line there is a contribution from the farther component, which is broadened the same as the nearer component, is at a known distance from the nearer one, and has a known intensity with respect to it.[3] Curve-fitting methods of Jones[2] and others[4] lead to values of the corrected "integral breadth" of lines, defined as the area of the line above the background divided by its height above the background.

It is possible to correct line widths by methods of greater accuracy than these, methods that do not depend upon curve fitting with some assumed shape for the lines, which usually is not highly satisfactory. In the method of Stokes,[5] the intensity vs. θ curves for broadened and for standard lines are expressed by Fourier series; the corrected line is then derived from a Fourier series in which the coefficients of each of the terms is readily derived from the coefficients of the previous two series. Paterson has achieved a similar result by a method based on successive approximations.[6]

[1] L. S. Birks and H. Friedman, *J. Applied Phys.*, vol. 17, p. 687, 1946.

[2] F. W. Jones, *Proc. Roy. Soc. (London)*, vol. A166, p. 16, 1938.

[3] J. W. M. DuMond and P. Kirkpatrick, *Phys. Rev.*, vol. 37, p. 136, 1931. W. A. Rachinger, *J. Sci. Instruments*, vol. 25, p. 254, 1948.

[4] C. G. Shull, *Phys. Rev.*, vol. 70, p. 769, 1946. W. A. Wood and W. A. Rachinger, *J. Inst. Metals*, vol. 75, p. 571, 1949. A Taylor, *Phil. Mag.*, vol. 31, p. 339, 1941. P. Scherrer, "Kolloidchemie," 3d ed., p. 387, Zsigmondy, 1920. W. A. Wood, *Proc. Roy. Soc. (London)*, vol. A172, p. 231, 1939. B. E. Warren, *J. Chem. Phys.*, vol. 2, p. 551, 1934. A. L. Patterson, *Phys. Rev.*, vol. 56, p. 972, 1939.

[5] A. R. Stokes, *Proc. Phys. Soc. (London)*, vol. 61, p. 382, 1948.

[6] M. S. Paterson, Dissertation, University of Cambridge, 1949. Relaxation methods were used, as devised by R. V. Southwell, "Relaxation Methods in Engineering Science," Oxford, New York, 1940; "Relaxation Methods in Theoretical Physics," Oxford, New York, 1946.

Particle Size from Small-angle Scattering. Line widths can yield particle sizes only if the particles are crystalline, and only if internal strains and imperfections contribute a negligible amount to the broadening, or are somehow corrected for in the calculations. Another method, however, is independent of the internal structure of the particles—they may be polycrystalline or may even be amorphous—and depends only upon the difference between the electron density of the particles and the surrounding medium. This method employs the intensity distribution in the background scattering at small angles, and is the X-ray analogue of the diffuse halo around the moon caused by diffraction from fog particles. In its elements it is simple, but it has been elaborated on at length to increase the precision of the method, and in an attempt to develop techniques that would yield not merely a mean effective size, but also some idea of size distribution and shape distribution (which is difficult and uncertain).[1] It is effective in the range 20 to 500 A, and has been used to study the size of molecules having molecular weights of 10,000 to 100,000. It has been used to study clustering of atoms in solid solutions and early-stage precipitates in age-hardening alloys, and here it is possible to make use of the fact that the clusters or particles are oriented in certain planes of the parent crystal; the diffraction halo from these may be anisotropic and can be analyzed to give an idea of their shape. Various forms of cellulose, carbon blacks, rubber, colloids, and catalysts have been studied with the method.

If one assumes that particles are uniform in size and shape, randomly oriented and separated so that the total diffracted beam is merely the sum of the beams from individual particles (negligible particle-to-particle scattering or coherence in the beam from groups of particles), then the intensity I at an angle ϵ from a primary beam consisting of parallel, mono-

---

[1] A. Guinier ("Radiocristallographie," p. 220, Dunod, Paris, 1945; *J. chim. phys.*, vol. 40, p. 133, 1943) gives a review of the principles. Discussions of the method and its applications are given in the following: J. A. Gray and W. H. Zinn, *Can. J. Research*, vol. 2, p. 291, 1930; S. B. Hendricks, *Z. Krist.*, vol. 83, p. 503, 1932; B. E. Warren, *J. Chem. Phys.*, vol. 2, p. 551, 1934; A. Guinier, *Compt. rend.*, vol. 206, p. 1641, 1938; O. Kratky, *Naturwissenschaften*, vol. 26, p. 94, 1938; R. Hosemann, *Z. Physik*, vol. 113, p. 751, 1939; A. Guinier, *J. phys.*, vol. 3, p. 124, 1942 (heterogenieties in solid solutions); B. E. Warren, *J. Applied Phys.*, vol. 13, p. 364, 1942 (carbon black): H. Brusset, J. Devaux, and A. Guinier, *Compt. rend.*, vol. 216, p. 152, 1943; A. Guinier, *Proc. Phys. Soc. (London)*, vol. 57, p. 310, 1945, and *Ann. phys.*, vol. 12, p. 161, 1939; R. Hosemann, *Z. Physik*, vol. 114, p. 133, 1939, and *Z. Elektrochem.*, vol. 46, p. 535, 1940; P. B. Elkin, C. G. Shull, and L. C. Roess, *Ind. Eng. Chem., Anal. Ed.*, vol. 18, p. 172, 1946; O. Kratky and G. Porod, *J. Colloid Sci.*, vol. 4, p. 35, 1949; C. G. Shull and L. C. Roess, *J. Applied Phys.*, vol. 18, pp. 295, 308, 1947; K. L. Yudowitch, *J. Applied Phys.*, vol. 20, p. 174, 1949; Rosalind E. Franklin, *Acta Cryst.*, vol. 3, p. 158, 1950; B. Imelik and Y. Carteret, *Compt. rend.*, vol. 231, p. 280, 1950.

chromatized X-rays of intensity I_0 and wavelength λ will be

$$I = I_0 A e^{-4\pi^2 R^2 \epsilon^2 / \lambda^2} \tag{26}$$

when A is a constant for the specimen used, and R is a measure of the size of the particle. Specifically, R is the radius of gyration of the particle, i.e., R^2 is the mean of the squares of the distances of each of the atoms in the particle from its center of gravity; for a sphere, $R = 0.77r$ where r is the radius of the sphere. From this equation it will be seen that measured values $\log_e I$ for a given specimen, when plotted against ϵ^2, should give a straight line, from the slope of which one could calculate R.

If there is a range of sizes, each size makes its individual contributic of the type given by Eq. (26), and the sum is no longer a simple exponential; therefore $\log_e I$ is no longer a linear function of ϵ^2. The intensity at small angles is increased, tending toward a slope near $\epsilon = 0$ that corresponds to that for the largest particles in the sample. If a mean value of R is computed from the curve it will be a mean that weights the particles in proportion to the number of electrons in each, so the mean will be larger than the average particle.

If the particles become more densely packed, Eq. (26) no longer holds. But as the density continues to increase, as in sintering, the voids become small and separated. These, then, become the source of small-angle scattering. They scatter as they would if the holes were filled and the space between the holes were empty (or of lower electron density) and Eq. (26) again holds.

CHAPTER VIII

THE DETERMINATION OF CRYSTAL STRUCTURE

Metals and alloys tend to assume the simpler crystal structures, which can be solved by relatively simple X-ray investigations. It is sometimes possible to guess the structure and to confirm the guess by a few photographs; the position of the alloying elements in the periodic table is usually the background for such a guess, as will be discussed in Chap. XI. On the other hand, many organic and inorganic compounds have crystal structures so complex that they have resisted years of research without being deciphered. Intermediate between these two extremes are the many structures that can be solved by the methods discussed in the preceding chapters. The steps that are generally followed in such a crystal-structure determination are briefly outlined in this chapter.

There is no completely standardized procedure for determining a structure, for each crystal presents new difficulties that may have to be overcome by devising new methods of attack. To do effective work in this field of research requires a critical attitude toward experimental data and inferences drawn from them and a generous expenditure of patience, understanding, and ingenuity.

In solving crystal structures of great complexity it is possible to obtain great benefits from the mathematical device of using Fourier series to analyze the diffraction data. As this is a special development that is infrequently used with alloys, it has been treated in Appendix II rather than in the present chapter.

The usual steps in determining the structure of a crystal are as follows:

1. Determination of symmetry class (macroscopic symmetry).
2. Determination of size of unit cell.
3. Determination of space-lattice.
4. Calculation of number of atoms or molecules in the unit cell.
5. Determination of space group.
6. Tabulation of all possible atomic arrangements and choice of correct one; determination of parameters of this arrangement that fix the exact positions of the atoms within the cell.

With crystals of great complexity, it is sometimes impossible to complete all these steps, although the first five can generally be completed if suitable specimens are available.

Determination of Symmetry Class. Macroscopic symmetry is evident in the arrangement of the growth faces of a crystal. The angles between

161

well-formed growth or cleavage faces are measured on an optical goniometer.   It is convenient to plot the data stereographically so as to recognize
more readily the presence of symmetry axes and planes.   Measurements
of these faces must be interpreted with care, however, for certain faces
may be suppressed or the sample may be twinned, with the result that the
specimen may appear to have higher symmetry than it actually possesses.
The danger of this is lowered by critical examination of several crystals.
A study of etch pits on the faces reveals the presence or absence of some
symmetry elements that would otherwise be in doubt.

Important information on symmetry is obtained from the optical constants of a crystal when it is transparent.   Other physical properties
(pyroelectricity, piezoelectricity, etc.) are also useful.   Standard books
on crystallography and petrography cover the various aspects of this
field.   The important compilation of crystal forms and crystal properties
presented by Groth in his "Chemische Krystallographie" has been the
starting point for countless structure determinations.   Laue photographs
are widely employed to determine symmetry, and Weissenberg photographs can also be used, though X-ray methods are usually unable to distinguish between the presence and absence of a center of symmetry.

Determination of the Unit Cell.   The rotating-crystal method is preferred when choosing the correct unit cell from the various cells that can
be imagined, for there is then less likelihood of adopting a cell in which
some edge is a multiple of the true unit cell.   Rotation photographs
around each cell edge in turn give the edge lengths directly from layer-
line spacings.   Laue photographs may also be used and serve as a check
on the determination.   For precise measurement of axial lengths the
powder method is usually preferred, although it is possible to achieve
precision in a rotating-crystal photograph with back-reflection technique.

To prevent confusion it has been necessary to adopt conventional rules
regarding the choice of axes for the unit cell and the labeling of these axes.
It is the custom among crystallographers to choose the shortest three
axes that will give a unit cell having the symmetry of the crystal.   If
orthogonal axes are desired in spite of the symmetry (*e.g.*, orthohexagonal
axes), the shortest three orthogonal axes are chosen.   A test for the
proper unit cell is that each cell edge must be shorter than the face
diagonals of all faces touching it.   Base-centered or face-centered tetragonal cells are discarded in favor of smaller cells that are simple or body-
centered tetragonal; hexagonal and rhombohedral cells are always chosen
so as to be simple, and monoclinic cells either simple or base-centered.
Triclinic crystals are referred to axes giving smallest simple cells.[1]

---

[1] For the triclinic system there are 24 possible ways of attaching the labels *a, b,*
and *c* to the axes—there would be 48 ways if crystallographers did not universally
adhere to right-handed coordinate axes.   There has been no universal convention;

Determination of Space-lattice and Space Group. If a unit cell is not simple but is centered on one or more faces or is body-centered, then certain reflections will be absent. From the structure-factor equation, it can be seen that the following criteria hold:

I—body-centered lattices: reflections absent if $h + k + l$ is odd.
F—face-centered lattices: reflections absent if h, k, l are mixed odd and even.
Base-centered lattices:
    A—face-centered: reflections absent if $k + l$ is odd.
    B—face-centered: reflections absent if $h + l$ is odd.
    C—face-centered: reflections absent if $h + k$ is odd.
P—simple primitive space-lattices: no systematic absences.

These characteristics result from the fact that in the directions corresponding to missing reflections the waves scattered by body- or face-centered atoms are exactly out of phase with those scattered by the atoms at the cell corners. That is, the spacings of certain planes are halved, and odd-order reflections from such planes are consequently destroyed.

Microscopic symmetry elements likewise reduce certain spacings and destroy corresponding reflections. A glide plane halves the spacings in the direction of glide. A twofold screw axis halves the spacings along the screw axis, while a threefold screw axis reduces spacings along itself to thirds, etc. Table VII summarizes the reflection characteristics of lattices and symmetry elements. The reflections that are present are listed, rather than those that are absent.

A systematic application of these principles to each of the 230 space groups has now been completed, and characteristic extinctions have been tabulated for each.[1] To determine the space group or the several possible space groups to which a crystal belongs, the crystallographer first assigns indices to his observed reflections, lists them, notes the characteristic absences, and then searches the tables for space groups having similar absences. In so doing he must bear in mind that his choice of a, b, and c edges may be interchanged with respect to those listed in the tables and must take precautions to avoid being misled by this. (For example, he may list the absences in terms of every possible permutation of a, b, and c

---

some writers have chosen the long dimension of an acicular crystal as the c axis; some have followed a rule that $c < a < b$. The latter is recommended by J. D. H. Donnay (*Am. Mineral.*, vol. 28, p. 313, 1943), with angles α and β obtuse. M. J. Buerger recommends $a < b < c$ with all angles either acute or obtuse as demanded by the structure, a practice that leads to a reciprocal lattice cell that has all angles acute when the crystal angles are obtuse and vice versa.

[1] "International Tabellen zur Bestimmung von Kristallstrukturen," Bornträger, Berlin, 1935, or current edition of this. W .T. Astbury and K. Yardley, *Phil. Trans. Roy. Soc. (London)*, vol. A224, p. 221, 1924. C. Hermann, *Z. Krist.*, vol. 68, p. 257, 1928. J. D. H. Donnay and D. Harker, *Naturaliste can.*, vol. 67, p. 33, 1940.

TABLE VII. REFLECTION CHARACTERISTICS OF LATTICES AND SYMMETRY ELEMENTS

Class of reflection	Condition for reflection (n = an integer)	Lattice or symmetry element	Symbol
hkl	$h + k + l = 2n$	Body-centered lattice	I
	$h + k = 2n$	C—face-centered lattice	C
	$h + l = 2n$	B—face-centered lattice	B
	$k + l = 2n$	A—face-centered lattice	A
	h, k, l all even or all odd	Face-centered lattice	F
	$-h + k + l = 3n$	Rhombohedral lattice indexed according to hexagonal axes	R
	$h + k + l = 3n$	Hexagonal lattice indexed according to rhombohedral axes	H
	All values h, k, l	Simple primitive lattice	P
$0kl$	$k = 2n$	(100) glide plane with glide of $b/2$	b
	$l = 2n$	(100) glide plane with glide of $c/2$	c
	$k + l = 2n$	(100) glide plane with glide of $b/2 + c/2$	n
	$k + l = 4n$	(100) glide plane with glide of $b/4 + c/4$	d
$h0l$	$h = 2n$	(010) glide plane with glide of $a/2$	a
	$l = 2n$	(010) glide plane with glide of $c/2$	c
	$h + l = 2n$	(010) glide plane with glide of $a/2 + c/2$	n
	$h + l = 4n$	(010) glide plane with glide of $a/4 + c/4$	d
$hk0$	$h = 2n$	(001) glide plane with glide of $a/2$	a
	$k = 2n$	(001) glide plane with glide of $b/2$	b
	$h + k = 2n$	(001) glide plane with glide of $a/2 + b/2$	n
	$h + k = 4n$	(001) glide plane with glide of $a/4 + b/4$	d
hhl	$l = 2n$	($1\bar{1}0$) glide plane with glide of $c/2$	c
	$h = 2n$	($1\bar{1}0$) glide plane with glide of $a/2 + b/2$	n
	$h + l = 2n$	($1\bar{1}0$) glide plane with glide of $a/4 + b/4 + c/4$	n
	$2h + l = 4n$	($1\bar{1}0$) glide plane with glide of $a/2 + b/4 + c/4$	d
$h00$	$h = 2n$	[100] screw axis of types 2_1, 4_2	
	$h = 4n$	[100] screw axis of types 4_1, 4_3	
$0k0$	$k = 2n$	[010] screw axis of types 2_1, 4_2	
	$k = 4n$	[010] screw axis of types 4_1, 4_3	
$00l$	$l = 2n$	[001] screw axis of types 2_1, 4_2, 6_3	
	$l = 3n$	[001] screw axis of types 3_1, 3_2, 6_2, 6_4	
	$l = 4n$	[001] screw axis of types 4_1, 4_3	
	$l = 6n$	[001] screw axis of types 6_1, 6_5	
$hh0$	$h = 2n$	[110] screw axis of type 2_1	

axes.) A large number of indexed reflections should be available in order to show the characteristic absences well.

Properly done, this procedure yields a list of every possible space group to which the crystal could belong. Prism-face reflections (one index zero) are studied carefully to distinguish between systematic absences and "accidental" extinctions arising from the particular position of certain atoms in the cell, and an attempt is made to single out the space group that explains all systematic absences. If it is known to which of the 32 classes a crystal belongs, it is generally possible to establish the space group unequivocally, but when the symmetry class is in doubt this may not be possible. Reflection planes and rotation axes do not cause extinctions, and therefore the presence or absence of them cannot be determined from lists of reflections. Another source of ambiguity should be mentioned: the shielding of some characteristic extinctions by a more general class of extinctions. When there is a characteristic set of extinctions in some general class of reflections, this includes corresponding extinctions in a less general class. For example, a body-centered lattice produces extinctions in hkl reflections whenever $h + k + l$ is odd, but it also extinguishes $h0l$ reflections when $h + l$ is odd and $h00$ reflections when h is odd. If the body-centered crystal in this example contained a screw axis 2_1, this could not be detected, for it also would extinguish $h00$ reflections when h is odd.

Certain sets of special atomic positions occur in many different space groups. Such a set is called a *lattice complex*. For example, the body-centered cubic set of points (coordinates 000, $\frac{1}{2}\frac{1}{2}\frac{1}{2}$) is a special position of the space group O_h^9—$Im3/m$, but it is found also in space group O_h^1—$Pm3/m$. Heavy atoms may be located at such a set of points and give strong reflections, while light atoms, scattering weakly, may be at places corresponding to only one of these space groups. Lists of lattice complexes are used by some crystallographers to aid in recognizing the various possibilities.

Another convenience in space-group tables is a list of *point symmetries*, which gives the symmetry of the group of atoms that exists around a given point position in the crystal. A study of such a list shows possible positions for a group of atoms, such as a silicate group, and eliminates incompatible positions. Other tables together with all well-established formulas and charts that have proved useful in crystallographic work will be found in the current edition of "International Tables for Crystal Structure Determination."

Number of Atoms or Molecules per Unit Cell. The number of molecules in the unit cell is determined from the measured density of the substance, ρ, the known mass of each molecule, M, and the volume of the cell, V. The obvious relation is $\rho = nM/V$, where n is the number of molecules in the cell and M is the molecular weight multiplied by the mass of an atom of unit molecular weight (1.66×10^{-24} g). In a chemical compound with definite molecular formula, n is integral and is determined as the integer that most nearly satisfies the relation $n = \rho V/M$. Not all substances, however, have the ideal structure implied by this statement. If a substance has a "defect structure" there may be a nonintegral number of atoms of one kind or of several kinds per unit cell. In the case of alloys the concept of "molecules" is of no value and the density formula should be put in terms of the number of atoms of each kind per unit cell (see Chap. XI).

Determination of Atomic Positions. If the space group or possible groups have been identified and the number of atoms of each kind in the cell is known, the space-group tables give at once the possible arrangements of the atoms. If it is found, for example, that there are four atoms of a certain kind in the unit cell, it can be assumed that they will lie on a set of equivalent positions containing four atom positions. (In defect structures, particularly alloys, there are exceptions to this rule which are discussed in Chaps. XI and XII.) There are usually several arrangements to be considered, and each is likely to involve one or more variable parameters. The choice of atom arrangement and the fixing of parameters depend upon relative intensities of different reflections and are accomplished by finding the atom positions that give the best match between calculated and observed intensities throughout a long list of reflections. Relative intensities are computed by the structure-factor equation (preferably modified by the other intensity factors of Appendix I). Simplified formulas for the structure factor will be found in space-group tables.

Crystals with one or two parameters can be solved rather directly (graphical aids are useful in this work),[1] and more parameters can be handled if they happen to be separable into independent pairs. In complicated structures it is impossible to guess or to deduce by straightforward methods what values of the many parameters are likely because there is a multiple infinity of atom positions to be considered. For these crystals the methods of Fourier series are of great value in fixing parameters and indicating atomic arrangements. These are discussed in Appendix II. In complex crystals it often happens that atoms of a certain kind, owing to their restricted number, must occupy special positions in the cell, as specified by the space group. These are frequently heavy atoms which make a large contribution to the structure factor, and the analysis can begin with these, using preliminary computations which are followed by successive approximations until all atoms are located. An example is West's analysis of potassium dihydrogen phosphate.[2] Very complex

---

[1] W. L. Bragg, *Nature*, vol. 138, p. 362, 1936. W. L. Bragg and H. Lipson, *Z. Krist.*, vol. 95, p. 323, 1936. J. M. Robertson, *Nature*, vol. 138, p. 683, 1936.

[2] J. West, *Z. Krist.*, vol. 74, p. 306, 1930.

crystals have been solved, when they are one of an isomorphous series of compounds, by substituting a different element for one of the elements of the compound. This frequently can be done without altering atomic positions in the unit cell, thus changing the intensities of certain reflections and thereby revealing the positions of the substituted atoms.

A knowledge of atomic and ionic sizes and of the habitual groupings of atoms—coordination and the factors governing it—can aid the crystallographer by forming a basis for judging whether a given atomic arrangement is possible.[1]

Sizes of Atoms and Ions. The distances between atom centers in crystals can be interpreted as the sum of the radii of the two neighboring atoms, as if they were tightly packed spheres. After lengthy study of crystallographic data it was found that a consistent set of radii can be assumed so a given element always has approximately the same radius when in the same valence state and in similar surroundings. Sizes depend on whether an atom is closely bonded to 1, 2, 3, 4, 6, 8, or 12 neighbors; as the coordination (number of nearest neighbors) increases, the radius of an atom or ion increases. Goldschmidt's values for variation of size with coordination are as follows:

Coordination Number	Radius
12	1.00
8	0.97
6	0.96
4	0.88

Sizes also depend upon the nature of the binding forces in a crystal—ionic, covalent, metallic, or van der Waals. When electrons are added to a neutral atom its size increases; when they are subtracted it decreases, and these effects are not small, as will be seen, for example, from the following radii of ions with various positive and negative charges:

O^{--}	1.32	S^{2-}	1.74	Fe	1.24	Cu	1.28
O	0.60	S	1.04	Fe^{2+}	0.83	Cu^+	0.96
		S^{6+}	0.34	Fe^{3+}	0.67		

Variations are also introduced by the valence state of neighboring ions and by their sizes (radius ratio effect). When these factors are taken into account, the sizes become extremely useful aids in crystal-structure determination. For tables of radii and discussions of how they apply in crystal-structure determination, the crystallographer should refer to

---

[1] Determining the positions of atoms in the unit cell is covered in greater detail in current books on X-ray crystallography; for the beginner an excellent treatment will be found in C. W. Bunn's "Chemical Crystallography," Oxford, New York, 1945.

original papers on empirical and theoretical radii[1] or to recent summaries.[2] Values for radii of atoms in metallic crystals are plotted on page 252, Chap. XI.

Example of Structure Determination. Jacob and Warren's determination[3] of the structure of uranium will serve to illustrate many of the steps in a determination of crystal structure. Powder-diffraction data alone were sufficient to solve the structure, even though it is orthorhombic.

Thirty-nine lines were measured on a powder pattern[4] and were graded in intensity as strong, medium, weak, or very weak. Simple tests showed that the structure was not cubic, hexagonal, or tetragonal. It proved possible to solve it on the basis of an orthorhombic cell. The orthorhombic reciprocal lattice points are related to the spacings by the equation

$$\frac{1}{d^2} = h^2 a^{*2} + k^2 b^{*2} + l^2 c^{*2}$$

Any network of points in this lattice that contains the a^*, b^*, or c^* axes will be an orthogonal net and the lattice can be considered as constructed of a series of these nets. A Hull-type chart was made for the two-dimensional nets by using the logarithm of this expression with $k = 0$. The experimental d values were plotted on a strip and by moving the strip over the chart in the usual way several positions were found at which the d values fitted the lines of the chart. Each of these indicated two possible axes of the reciprocal lattice, at least one of which was either a^*, b^*, or c^* and consideration of these tentative solutions led to assuming a unit cell with $a = 2.852$, $b = 5.865$, $c = 4.945$, which was found to predict all observed spacings satisfactorily.

After assigning indices to each reflection it was noticed that the general reflections hkl occur only for $h + k$ even (111, 131, etc.); and among the prism reflections, $h0l$ occurs only for h and l even, $0kl$ only for k even, and $hk0$ only for $h + k$ even. Reference to tables showed that these characteristics are found in the orthorhombic space groups only in D_{2h}^{17}—$Cmcm$. The number of atoms in the cell was computed and found to be 4. If

[1] V. M. Goldschmidt, *Trans. Faraday Soc.*, vol. 25, p. 253, 1929. L. Pauling, *J. Am. Chem. Soc.*, vol. 49, p. 765, 1927; vol. 50, p. 1036, 1928; vol. 53, p. 1367, 1931; *Proc. Roy. Soc. (London)*, vol. A114, p. 181, 1927. W. H. Zachariasen, *Z. Krist.*, vol. 80, p. 137, 1931. L. Pauling and M. L. Huggins, *Z. Krist.*, vol. 87, pp. 205, 222, 1934. L. Pauling, *J. Am. Chem. Soc.*, vol. 69, p. 542, 1947.

[2] C. W. Stillwell, "Crystal Chemistry," McGraw-Hill, New York, 1938. Current edition of "International Tables of Crystal Structure Determination." R. C. Evans, "An Introduction to Crystal Chemistry," Cambridge, London, 1948.

[3] C. W. Jacob and B. E. Warren, *J. Am. Chem. Soc.*, vol. 59, p. 2588, 1937.

[4] Copper radiation was filtered through nickel to remove $K\beta$, and 0.002 in. aluminum covered the film to remove fluorescent M radiation from the sample. Copper filings were mixed with the uranium filings in some exposures for calibration.

these were placed at the special positions $4a$ or $4b$ they would halve the c spacings and cause hkl to occur only if l were even; so it was concluded that the atoms were in the third set of special positions, $4c$, with coordinates $0y\frac{1}{4}$, $0\bar{y}\frac{3}{4}$; $\frac{1}{2},y+\frac{1}{2},\frac{1}{4}$; $\frac{1}{2},\frac{1}{2}-y,\frac{3}{4}$ and the value of y was then determined. The structure factor for the space group with atoms in $4c$ reduces to $F = 4f \sin 2\pi ky$ when l is odd and to $F = 4f \cos 2\pi ky$ when l is even.

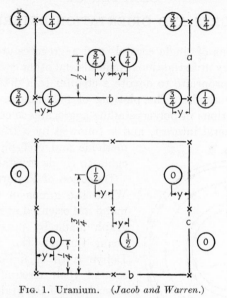

Fig. 1. Uranium. (*Jacob and Warren.*)

From the fact that 020 and 022 are very weak it follows that $\cos 2\pi 2y$ is nearly zero and y is approximately $\frac{1}{8}$.

By trial it was found that assuming $y = 0.105 \pm 0.005$ gave satisfactory agreement with observed intensities when the relative intensities of pairs of neighboring lines were considered (in order to minimize errors from the strong absorption in the sample). A plot of the structure is shown in plan and elevation in Fig. 1, with the height of atoms above the plane of the drawing indicated by the fractions of the cell edges marked at the atom positions. Plots and models aid in locating important interatomic distances and in understanding the structure; in this case a study of drawings disclosed that the structure can be considered as distorted close-packed hexagonal in which 4 of the 12 nearest neighbors are moved in to appreciably closer distances.

CHAPTER IX

POLE FIGURES AND ORIENTATION DETERMINATION

The orientations of single crystals and aggregates are of such importance in laboratory investigations of metals and other crystalline materials that it seems appropriate to devote a chapter to a detailed explanation of orientation methods. The plotting of pole figures which show the preferred orientations in polycrystalline aggregates is covered first, since it is of most general interest, and is followed by a treatment of X-ray methods and etch-pit methods applicable to single crystals.

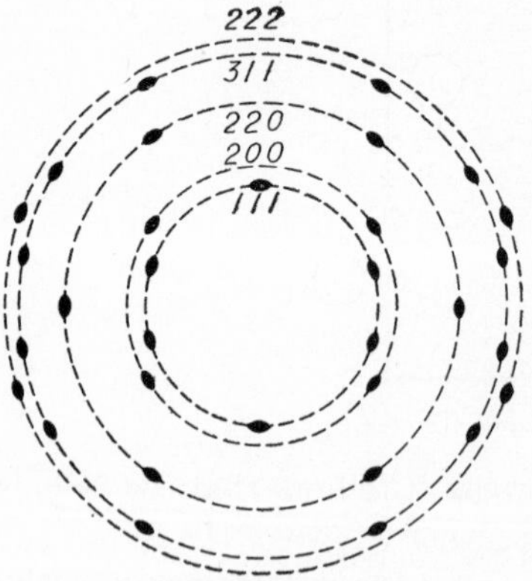

Detection of Preferred Orientations. When the grains of a polycrystalline metal are oriented at random, a photograph made by passing a "pinhole" beam through the metal will show Debye rings of uniform intensity all around their circumference. On the other hand, if the grains cluster around certain orientations so the metal has a *texture* or *preferred orientation*, then more grains will be in position to reflect to certain segments of the diffraction rings than to others, and the rings will have maxima.

Fig. 1. Pattern of cold-drawn aluminum wire. Radiation of a single wavelength incident perpendicular to the wire axis, which is vertical.

Figure 1 illustrates the pattern that is obtained with monochromatic X-rays from a cold-drawn wire of aluminum, which is a face-centered cubic metal that becomes oriented with the [111] direction in each grain parallel to the axis of the wire. The dashed circles represent Debye rings that would be present if the metal had a random orientation, with all orientations present. The limited number of orientations that are present in the wire permit only a few spots in the Debye rings to appear strongly, as indicated in the figure. A common axis in all grains or crystalline fragments is parallel to the wire, but all other axes have a random distribution around the wire; *i.e.*, all azimuthal orientations around the axis are equally probable. An X-ray photograph of the wire is in effect a rotating-crystal photograph in which the axis of rotation

170

of the crystal corresponds to the axis of the wire.[1]   The textures of wires are appropriately called *fiber textures*, for they resemble the structure of fibrous materials.   The axis of symmetry of the texture (the longitudinal axis of a wire) is the *fiber axis*.   In a rolled sheet, on the other hand, there is no longer an equal probability of all orientations around the direction of elongation (the direction of rolling), and a more detailed analysis is necessary.   The stereographic projection is almost universally used for this purpose.

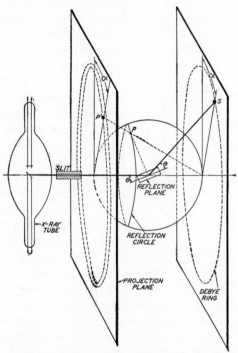

Fig. 2. Relation between crystal plane, diffracted beam, and stereographic projection. Pole *P*, diffracted spot *S*, and projection *P'* all lie in a plane, which also contains the incident beam.

Stereographic Projection of Data.   There is a simple and direct relation between spots on a preferred orientation pattern and their stereographic projection.   This is illustrated in Fig. 2.   A crystal plane is here shown in position to reflect a beam of X-rays to form a spot *S* on the film. The plane normal intersects the reference sphere, which is inscribed about it, at the point *P*, which projects stereographically to the point *P'* in the projection plane.   The incident beam, the reflected beam, and the pole

---

[1] The intense spots on the Debye rings are actually on layer lines.   If the axis of the wire has indices $[uvw]$ in each oriented grain, then the nth layer line will contain the spots hkl for which $hu + kv + lw = n$.

of the reflecting plane all lie in the same plane tipped at an angle α from the vertical. Thus, when the film and projection plane are placed normal to the beam as shown, it will be seen that the angle α on the projection will be exactly equal to α on the film.

Since the angle of incidence, θ, of the beam on an (hkl) plane is determined by the Bragg law $n\lambda = 2d \sin \theta$ whenever reflection occurs, it follows that the poles of all such (hkl) planes capable of reflecting must lie at a constant angle $90 - \theta$ from the incident beam and must intersect the

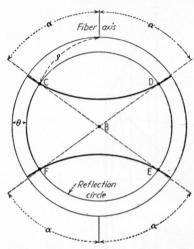

reference sphere only along the circle known as the "reflection circle," a circle on the projection $90 - \theta$ from the centrally located beam. Both the azimuthal and radial positions on the pole figures are thus determined.

Fiber Textures. Let us consider an ideal fiber texture in which all grains have a certain crystallographic direction, say [111], parallel to the fiber axis. The stereographic projection of the (100) planes would then form the pole figure of Fig. 3, in which (100) poles of various grains lie at various spots along the latitude lines shown as heavy lines at an angle $\rho = 54°44'$ from the fiber axis, since this is the angle between [111] and [100] poles. Now if a beam entered

Fig. 3. Ideal pole figure for (100) planes in a wire of a cubic metal having a [111] fiber texture. Poles at C, D, E, F can reflect when X-ray beam is at B.

the reference sphere at B, perpendicular to the fiber axis, and reflected from the planes at the Bragg angle θ, reflections would occur at the intersections C, D, E, and F. All reflections would fall upon the film at equal angles, α, from the projection of the fiber axis.

It was remarked earlier that the angle α is identical on projection and film, but Fig. 3 shows that this is not exactly equal to the angle ρ between the pole of the reflecting plane and the fiber axis. From the spherical trigonometry of the figure when the beam is normal to the fiber axis, it follows that

$$\cos \rho = \cos \alpha \cos \theta$$

which approaches the relation $\alpha = \rho$ as θ approaches 0. If the fiber axis is inclined so it makes an angle β with the incident beam, the corresponding equation is

$$\cos \rho = \cos \beta \sin \theta + \sin \beta \cos \theta \cos \alpha$$

Thus a series of ρ values can be computed for the observed spots on a film, and from these the indices of the fiber axis may be deduced with the aid of tables of angles between crystallographic directions.[1] Some textures are composed of two fiber textures superimposed; for example, iron after compression has some grains with [111] parallel to the fiber axis and others with [100], forming a *duplex fiber texture* [111] + [100].

A graphical determination of fiber axis from a series of ρ values is shown in Fig. 4. On a stereographic projection the point is found (F.A.) that is the proper angle ρ from the pole of each reflecting plane; such a point is then the projection of the fiber axis and can be identified by reference to a standard projection. In Fig. 4 the fiber axis coincides with [112]. Note that the arcs in the figures are loci of points at equal *angles* from reflecting poles, not equal *distances*. If there is a considerable range of orientation

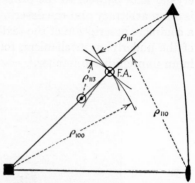

Fɪɢ. 4. Method of determining fiber axis (F.A.) on a standard stereographic projection of a cubic crystal. Angle ρ for each reflection is laid off from a corresponding pole of projection.

in the specimen, both maximum and minimum ρ values may be plotted and an *area* determined on the standard projection rather than a *point*.

If a plane (hkl) is perpendicular to the fiber axis in each grain, it is advantageous to tilt the wire with respect to the X-ray beam so as to reflect from this plane. A tilt of θ_{hkl} will obviously do this, since the reflection circle will then touch the fiber axis. For the case of aluminum wire, the fiber axis is [111] and for molybdenum rays $\theta_{111} = 10.1°$. The tilted condition is represented in the (111) pole figure of Fig. 5. The reflection in the vertical plane is very strong, since all grains of the texture contribute to it, while only a small fraction of the grains contribute to the other reflections. Thus, for example, a weak texture in iron after compression can readily be shown by this kind of tilting of the specimen,[2] although it has been overlooked in some less sensitive tests.

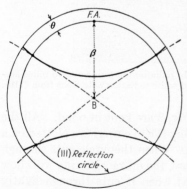

Fɪɢ. 5. Stereographic projection showing fiber axis tilted to cause strong reflection from planes normal to F.A. Beam is at B.

[1] Curves have been published that make possible a graphical computation of the data from rotating-crystal patterns and fiber patterns. When many orientations of crystals of a given substance are to be determined the work can be accelerated by using these. J. Thewlis, *Z. Krist.*, vol. 85, p. 74, 1933. R. M. Bozorth, *Phys. Rev.*, vol. 23, p. 764, 1924.

[2] C. S. Barrett, *Trans. AIME*, vol. 135, p. 296, 1939.

Plotting of Pole Figures. Preferred orientations produced by deformation other than simple uniaxial elongation or compression are complex. While they are often described in terms of *ideal orientations* with certain crystal axes parallel to the principal axes of strain, the choice of indices is often arbitrary and the description is incomplete. *Pole figures* provide a complete description of the texture and provide a safer basis for studies of the underlying mechanism, for they represent the observational data in an unprejudiced manner.[1]

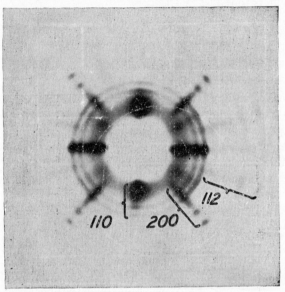

Fig. 6. Diffraction pattern of cold-rolled steel. Mo radiation perpendicular to rolled surface, rolling direction vertical. Shows $K\alpha$, $K\beta$, and white radiation reflections from (110), (200), and (112) planes.

To plot a pole figure, the relations of Fig. 2 are kept in mind. All the intensity maxima on a single diffraction ring (Debye ring) are plotted on a single reflection circle on the pole figure. When the circle cuts through heavily populated regions on the pole figure, the diffraction ring will show intense blackening at the same azimuth; when it cuts through lightly populated regions, the corresponding arc of the diffraction ring will be weak. To determine the true extent of the areas on the pole figure it is necessary to plot a series of reflection circles that form a network covering the projection. This is accomplished by taking a series of diffraction patterns with the specimen tilted increasing amounts in steps of 5 or 10°. The number of exposures in such a series may vary from 5 to 20, depending upon the detail required in the pole figure. An oscillating-film

[1] F. Wever, *Mitt. Kaiser-Wilhelm-Inst. Eisenforsch. Düsseldorf*, vol. 5, p. 69, 1924; *Z. Physik*, vol. 28, p. 69, 1924; *Trans. AIME*, vol. 93, p. 51, 1931.

arrangement can be used in texture cameras so that one exposure gives the information ordinarily obtained from many individual exposures of the stationary type (see later section on cameras, page 177).

The plotting of the data will be illustrated, using rolled steel as an example. If the radiation from molybdenum is used, the photographs will resemble Fig. 6, with concentric Debye rings (incomplete) from $K\alpha$ and $K\beta$ characteristic radiation and an inner band from white radiation. The diffraction from the ferrite {110} planes will occur at $\theta \cong 10°$, and the reflection circle will lie $90 - \theta = 80°$ from the center of the pole figure. If the first photogram is made with the beam normal to the surface of the specimen, the surface will appear on the projection as the basic circle and the reflection circle will lie concentric with it.

Let us suppose that the specimen is then rotated about a vertical axis and a new photogram taken with the specimen turned, say 30°, the near side rotating to the left as we look away from the X-ray tube. We first plot the data as before, with the projection plane again normal to the beam and the reflection circle again concentric. This is illustrated in Fig. 7, where the reflection circle is shown as a dashed circle and an intensity maximum is indicated between the limits A and B. But with this setting of the specimen its surface will lie at a tilt of 30° from the projection plane (the right side tilted up from the projection plane), and all data from this setting must be rotated 30° back to the right in order to plot a pole figure in which the plane of the

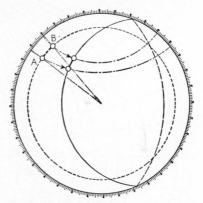

FIG. 7. Plotting a pole figure. (.............), reflection circle with beam normal to projection plane. (——) and (——), reflection circle with plane of specimen as projection plane.

specimen is the projection plane. The rotation is done with the Wulff net, each point on the reflection circle being moved to the right along its latitude line a distance of 30° of longitude. This is shown in Fig. 7, where the reflection circle with the intensity maximum on it is plotted after rotation as a full line. Part of the rotated reflection circle on the right-hand side passes to the negative hemisphere and is shown as a broken line. The process is repeated with different settings of the specimen and corresponding rotations of the data until the areas on the pole figure are sufficiently well defined.

Much of the labor of plotting may be eliminated if a chart is made up in which the series of reflection circles are shown in the position they would have after rotation back to the normal setting, *i.e.*, their position with respect to the surface of the specimen as the projection plane. A different chart is required, of course, for every different value of θ that is used, thus for different wavelengths, different specimen materials, and different reflecting planes. Wever[1] has published charts for copper $K\alpha$ radiation reflecting from {001} and from {111} planes of aluminum and for iron $K\alpha$ radiation reflecting from {110} of iron. Figure 8 presents a chart for molybdenum $K\alpha$ radiation reflecting from {110} planes of iron ($\theta = 10°$) with reflection circles plotted for

[1] F. Wever and W. E. Schmid, *Mitt. Kaiser-Wilhelm-Inst. Eisenforsch., Düsseldorf,* vol. 11, p. 109, 1929. F. Wever, *Trans. AIME,* vol. 93, p. 51, 1931.

every 5° rotation interval from 0 to 90°.   The azimuthal positions on all the circles are given by their intersections with the latitude lines that are drawn on the chart and labeled with values of the angle α (the numbers around the circumference).   When the reflection circles lie on the back hemisphere, they are shown as dashed lines, but the same lines of constant α apply as on the near hemisphere.   This same chart will serve for plotting the {200} reflections from iron if one reads the intensity maxima on

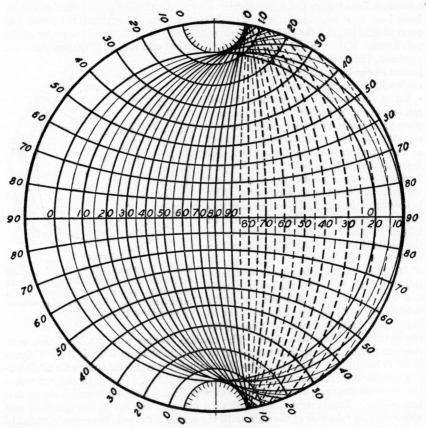

FIG. 8. Pole-figure chart for Mo $K\alpha$ radiation reflecting from (110) planes of iron ($\theta = 10°$).

the broad ring caused by general (white) radiation.   In this instance, the most intense portion of the {200} reflection of the general radiation from a tube operating at 30 or 40 kv is in the neighborhood of $\theta = 10°$.   The maximum intensity of general radiation from {110} planes is around $\theta = 7°$ and is particularly suitable for pole-figure work, for it is free from overlapping {200} reflections and shows clearly the slight differences of intensity that are sometimes important.

Areas near the top and bottom of the pole figure are not crossed by any reflection circles on the chart.   To fill in these areas the specimen may be turned 90° on its own plane and then rotated a small amount about the vertical axis, as before.   (This requires turning the pole figure plot 90° with respect to the reflection-circle chart.)   The number of exposures may be reduced by making use of the symmetry of the orientations in the structure; in rolled sheet, for example, a symmetry plane may be anticipated normal to the rolling direction and another normal to the transverse direction in the sheet, but it is always advisable to test for these symmetry planes before assuming them.

A pole figure for a mild-steel sheet rolled to a reduction of thickness of 85 per cent and etched so that the surface layers are removed is shown in Fig. 9.[1] The rolling plane is parallel to the projection plane, with the rolling direction at the top. This figure illustrates why it is that preferred orientations appear more prominently in photograms made with the beam along or near to the transverse axis of a rolled-steel sheet than with the beam normal to the rolling plane. The (110) reflection

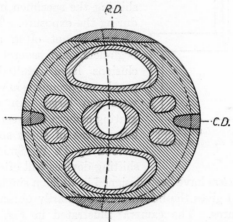

FIG. 9. Pole figure for <110> poles of mild steel reduced 85 per cent in thickness by cold rolling. Two reflection circles shown (dashed). (*Gensamer and Mehl.*)

circle for a beam of white radiation normal to the rolling plane is shown as a dotted circle near the periphery and nowhere passes into regions of greatly differing intensity. On the other hand, the reflection circle for a beam along the transverse direction appears as a dotted line extending from top to bottom near the center of the projection and passes through regions of both maximum and minimum intensity, which would yield more pronounced maxima and minima on the (110) diffraction rings.

Specimens and Cameras for Texture Studies. When a sheet specimen is used for pole-figure studies, there is an absorption correction that depends markedly on the angle of setting in the camera.[2] Bakarian[3] has improved the technique by cutting a stem out of the sheet metal with a jeweler's saw, then grinding the stem to a cylindrical shape, as in Fig. 10. Rotation of this specimen around its axis does not change the absorption.

[1] M. Gensamer and R. F. Mehl, *Trans. AIME*, vol. 120, p. 277, 1936.

[2] This has been computed by J. F. H. Custers (*Physica*, vol. 14, p. 461, 1948) and is most easily applied when a sample is first tilted $90 - \theta$ from its position normal to the beam, then rotated in a series of steps about its surface normal; equations for variable tilt angle are given by R. Smoluchowski and R. W. Turner (*Rev. Sci. Instruments*, vol. 20, p. 173, 1949).

[3] P. W. Bakarian, *Trans. AIME*, vol. 147, p. 266, 1942.

With adequate calibration of the films for exposure, it is then possible to make a fairly reliable estimate of the relative number of grains in each orientation region of the pole figure.

Large-grained specimens must be exposed in cameras that bring more than the usual number of grains into reflecting position in the beam. This can be done by oscillating the specimen through a slight range of angles on an oscillating-crystal camera or by shifting the specimen in its own plane during the exposure. The importance of this is not often appreciated by beginners, and several incorrect conclusions have resulted from photographs of specimens in which the grains were too large. An elaborate integrating camera to sweep the beam over large areas of sheet specimens is described by D. W. Smith,[1] but simple shifting devices will often serve.

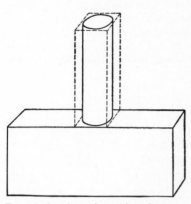

FIG. 10. Specimen for preferred orientation photograph of sheet material. (*Bakarian.*)

Texture goniometers have been designed in which a single exposure with an oscillating film gives the information ordinarily obtained from many individual exposures. The camera[2] illustrated in Fig. 11 provides a film *F*, which shifts longitudinally in synchronism with the oscillation of the specimen *P*. The incident beam is parallel to the axis of the cylinder and strikes the specimen which is oscillating about the vertical axis *D*. A single Debye ring is allowed to reach the film through the slit *S* in a shield *A* surrounding the specimen.

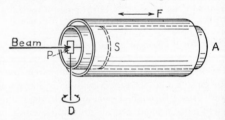

FIG. 11. Principle of texture goniometer with cylindrical film shifted longitudinally in synchronism with oscillation of specimen.

It will be seen that a chart can easily be prepared to convert positions on the film to positions on a pole figure.[3] Back-reflection cameras have been used in a few texture studies but are not well suited because

[1] D. W. Smith, "Symposium of Radiography and X-ray Diffraction," American Society for Testing Materials, Philadelphia, 1937. Blueprints of this camera have been made available by the Research Laboratories of the Aluminum Company of America. An integrating camera has been manufactured by O. van der Heyde, Newton Highlands, Mass.

[2] O. Kratky, *Z. Krist.*, vol. 72, p. 529, 1930.

[3] Other designs will be found in W. E. Dawson, *Physica*, vol. 7, p. 302, 1927; *Phil. Mag.*, vol. 5, 7th ser., p 756, 1928; C. S. Barrett, *Trans. AIME*, vol. 93, p. 75, 1931.

of the small amount of information that can be obtained from an individual film.

Use of X-ray Spectrometers for Texture Studies. The intensities of the various areas of a pole figure can best be measured with an X-ray spectrometer. The visual estimation of film darkening and of absorption that is characteristic of most pole-figure work of the past can be replaced by quantitative measurement, and pole figures can now be drawn with precision contours when desired.

Norton[1] has employed a series of cylindrical specimens (Fig. 10) for the purpose, cutting each at a different angle in the rolled sheet or other object being studied, mounting each in turn on the axis of a Geiger-counter spectrometer, and turning the specimen slowly through 360° while the Geiger counter is set to receive a reflection of low indices. Automatic chart recording is used when the specimen is rotated in synchronism with the chart. On a pole figure of a rolled sheet in which the plane of the sheet is the plane of projection, each specimen provides data for points along a diameter of the pole figure. A disadvantage of the method is that a new specimen is required for each new diameter that is to be plotted. No correction for absorption is required.

A method of using a flat transmission sample, a parallel beam, and a mathematically computed absorption correction has been described.[2] The most convenient method proposed to date appears to be that of Schulz,[3] since a flat specimen is used and no corrections for absorption or for changes in geometry during rotation of the specimen are necessary from the center of the pole figure (normal to the surface of the sample) out to about 70°.

In Schulz's method, a reflection specimen is mounted in a goniometer head of the type sketched in Fig. 12 on plate C. The post P of the goniometer head is mounted on the axis of the X-ray spectrometer. This post supports a ring R_1 in which rests a smaller ring R_2 that can be turned through angles ϕ indicated by graduations on the ring. A second post, H, supports the specimen, which is cut to circular shape. The post is adjustable so that the specimen surface coincides with the ring axis FF'. The collimating system is composed of slits S_1 and S_2 which permit negligible divergence in the vertical direction.[4] The horizontal lengths of the slits S_1 and S_3 are limited by wedges W_1 and W_2. Slit S_2 permits radiation to strike only a narrow strip along the diameter of a circular specimen at the position of the ring axis FF'. Wedge W_2 permits the entire width of a Debye ring to enter the counter, and S_3 sharply limits the length of the arc that enters. Readings are taken with varying angles ϕ to give data along one diameter of the pole figure. The setting of the specimen on the circle C is

[1] J. T. Norton, *J. Applied Phys.*, vol. 19, p. 1176, 1948.

[2] B F. Decker, E. T. Asp, and D. Harker, *J. Applied Phys.*, vol 19, p. 388, 1948.

[3] L. G. Schulz, *J. Applied Phys.*, vol. 20, p. 1030, 1949.

[4] For use with the original model Norelco spectrometer S_1 and S_2 are about 0.020 in. and S_3 is between 0.020 and 0.050 in.

then changed by rotating the specimen in its own plane, to obtain data for another diameter.

Certain limitations of the Schulz method should be kept in mind. The arrangement is intended for specimens thick enough to provide effectively complete absorption of the beam. Since the area irradiated is small—of the order of 0.020 by 0.3 in.—there is danger that orientations in the irradiated area are not a representative sam-

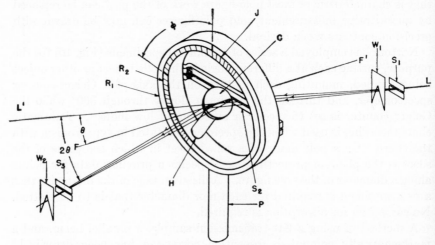

FIG. 12. Slits and goniometer head for Schulz's reflection method of texture determination in an X-ray spectrometer. Beam through S_1, W_1, and S_2 reflects from specimen at C and into Geiger counter through S_2 and W_2.

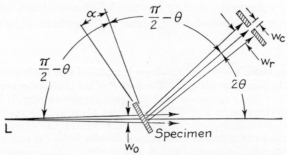

FIG. 13. Geometry of Schulz's transmission method for texture studies. Counter slit width w_c is small compared with w_r; diverging rays from line source L pass through slit of width w_o at the specimen.

pling of the average orientations over the surface (unless an integrating mechanism is provided); in addition, any reflection method such as this is limited to the surface layers reached by the beam.

Since the above technique applies without correction only out to 70 or 80°, Schulz employs a transmission method for the outer rim of the pole figure,[1] in which by using a thin specimen and appropriate slits it is possible to avoid corrections throughout a considerable range near the rim. Diverging rays leave a point source or a slit not more than 0.005 in. wide and 0.050 in. high at L, Fig. 13, diverging to a width w_o at the

[1] L. G. Schulz, *J. Applied Phys.*, vol. 20, p. 1033, 1949.

specimen and to a width w_r at the counter.   There is a band at the outside of the pole figure about 25° wide where no absorption correction is required if the counter slit width w_c is made small compared with the reflected beam width, if the specimen is thin compared with w_0 (say 0.005 in. or less compared with w_0 of the order of 0.050 in.) and if μT, the product of the linear absorption coefficient and the specimen thickness, lies in the neighborhood of 0.3 to 0.4.   The spectrometer is adjusted to the maximum intensity position in the center of the reflected beam.   The specimen is then turned to different angles α from the position in which it bisects the angle between incident and reflected beams; α is the angle between the pole of the reflecting plane and the basic circle of the pole figure.

Whatever arrangement is used, there is an advantage in comparing diffracted intensities with those from a standard sample that has been prepared with a random orientation, for then it is possible to describe the density in any area of a pole figure as some multiple (or fraction) of the density of a random sample.   If the randomly oriented standard properly matches the unknown sample as to absorption and geometry, this multiple is merely the ratio of the observed intensities for the two samples.

Orientation of the Axis of Single-crystal Rods.   The orientation of the axis of a cylindrical specimen may be determined by taking a photograph with the crystal rotating about its axis, which yields a rotating-crystal pattern.   Since the axis of rotation is usually a crystallographic direction of high or irrational indices, the usual methods for solving rotating-crystal patterns are unsatisfactory.   But the graphical analysis discussed in the earlier section on fiber textures (Fig. 4) will apply, for the rotation axis is a "synthetic" fiber axis.   The orientation of the axis only is determined, of course, but this is all that is required for some research such as mechanical tests.

Complete Orientation of Single Crystals.   An oscillating-crystal method developed by Davey[1] and described in detail by Wilson[2] (often referred to as the Davey-Wilson method) has proved valuable for determining orientations of single crystals and individual grains in metallographic specimens.   It makes possible the solution of complex orientation problems such as one encounters when investigating the many orientations that may exist in an oriented overgrowth or among precipitated crystals within a grain.   It has also been used to study the distortion of grains during freezing, deformation, and recrystallization.

Two concentric cylindrical films are used, the rays passing through the inner one to the outer one and making a record on both.   The inner film is mounted on the carriage that holds the specimen and oscillates back and forth with the specimen, while the outer film remains stationary.   Each spot is identified by its θ value, which is read from the stationary film with a chart on which θ values are marked, as in Fig. 14.   (Characteristic radiation is used so that identification by θ values is possible.)

[1] W. P. Davey, *Phys. Rev.*, vol. 23, p. 764, 1924.

[2] T. A. Wilson, *Gen. Elec. Rev.*, vol. 31, p. 612, 1928.

The same chart may be graduated to read the angle α (see Fig. 2) giving the azimuthal position of the reflected and incident beams.

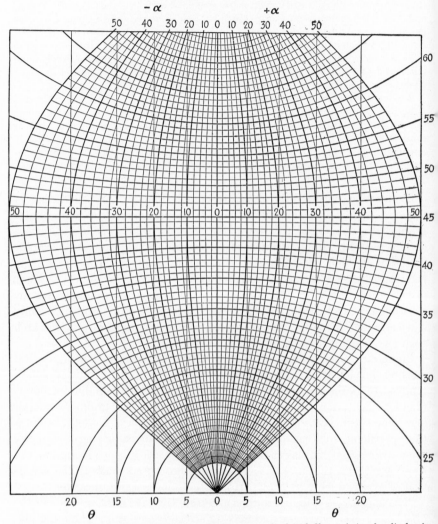

FIG. 14. Chart for reading α and θ from stationary cylindrical film. Axis of cylinder is horizontal. Chart must be enlarged until distance from $\theta = 0$ to $\theta = 45°$ is one-fourth of film circumference.

The spot may be plotted immediately on a stereographic projection, as in Fig. 15, at a point $\theta°$ in from the basic circle and $\alpha°$ from the vertical. The point C on this projection represents the reflecting plane as it was when reflection occurred, and it is then necessary to correct for the amount of rotation of the specimen that permitted the reflection to occur. Suppose a crystal is adjusted on the oscillating carriage so that the X-ray beam just grazes the surface at the end of the oscillation, as in Fig. 16a, and in so doing makes a spot at *a* on the oscillating film and at *b* on the stationary film. Then, when a reflection occurs, the specimen will have rotated from this position and

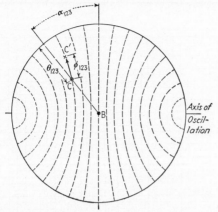

Fig. 15. Plotting a (123) reflection from known θ and α values.   Position after rotating ϕ is shown by cross.

the reflection ray will cause spots a' and b' on the two films, respectively.   The amount of this rotation, ϕ, will be given by the difference of the angles ϕ_1, measured on the stationary film, and ϕ_2 on the moving film (Fig. 16*b*):

$$\phi = \phi_1 - \phi_2$$

The ϕ values can be read with charts of the type illustrated in Fig. 17 enlarged to the proper size for each film.   The point on the stereographic projection is then rotated

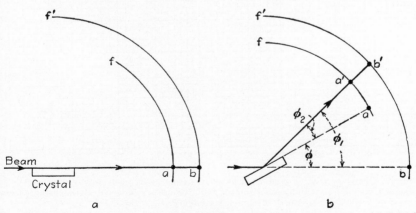

Fig. 16. Arrangement of films in Davey-Wilson orientation goniometer.   (*a*) Initial setting, (*b*) after rotating into reflecting position.

$\phi°$, point *C* going to C' in Fig. 15 along the latitude line of a Wulff net.   This procedure is followed for a number of reflections, each being identified by its θ value, plotted, and rotated the amount ϕ determined for it, giving a final plot resembling Fig. 18. The position of any other poles can then be found by rotating a standard projection of the crystal into coincidence with the plotted poles.

In this method it is necessary to pair off the spots on the two films correctly. Often

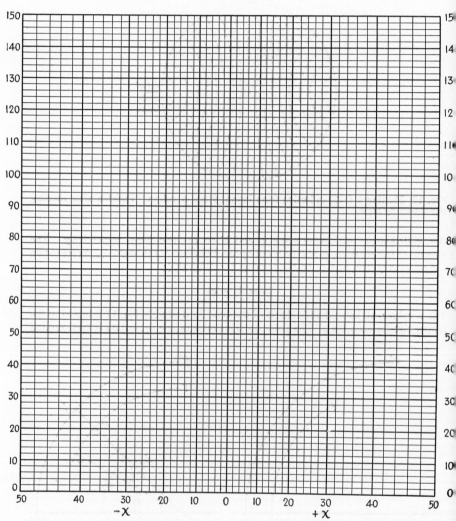

FIG. 17. Chart for reading ϕ and χ coordinates from cylindrical films of Davey-Wilson camera. Axis of film cylinder is horizontal. Chart must be enlarged until the distance from $\phi = 0$ to $\phi = 90°$ is one-fourth of film circumference.

this can be accomplished by noting the shape of the spots, but it may be necessary to rely upon measurements. For this purpose it is convenient to use the vertical lines of the chart in Fig. 17. These measure a coordinate, χ, that is the same for both spots of a pair—i.e., if a spot on the moving film lies on a certain χ line of the moving film chart, then the related spot on the stationary film must lie on the same χ line on the stationary-film chart.

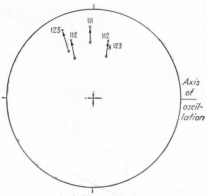

FIG. 18. Projection showing final positions of reflections after rotation of each point the amount ϕ determined for it.

Back-reflection Laue Method for Determining Crystal Orientation.

One of the most convenient and accurate methods of determining the orientation of a single crystal or an individual grain in an aggregate is the

FIG. 19. Camera for back-reflection Laue photographs.   Crystal is adjustable with horizontal and vertical graduated circles A and B; its distance from film in cassette F is adjusted by C.   Portion of gas X-ray tube shown.   (*Greninger.*)

back-reflection Laue method.[1]   It is a method that is useful not only for laboratory research but also in the production of commercial crystals, such as quartz crystals cut for piezoelectric control of radio circuits.   An

[1] L. Chrobak, *Z. Krist.*, vol. 82, p. 342, 1932.   W. Boas and E. Schmid, *Metall-wirtschaft*, vol. 10, p. 917, 1931.   A. B. Greninger, *Trans. AIME.* vol. 117, p. 61, 1935; *Z. Krist.*, vol. 91, p. 424, 1935.

exceedingly simple camera will yield accuracies of the order of $\frac{1}{2}°$, and cameras for more precise work are not elaborate, as will be seen from the one illustrated in Fig. 19. The interpretation of a photograph may be carried out in a few minutes by making use of the chart developed by Greninger[1] together with a stereographic net and a standard projection of the crystal. When the incident beam in a back-reflection Laue camera is made to straddle a boundary between two grains, two components of a twin, or two imperfect regions of a crystal so that the two are jointly

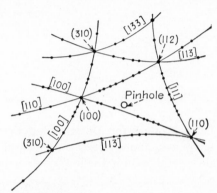

FIG. 20. Back-reflection Laue pattern of α-iron with principal zones and spots identified.

recorded on the film, it is possible to determine their relative orientations to within a few minutes of arc.[2]

Tungsten target X-ray tubes are best suited for the work, but any tube giving appreciable general radiation with or without characteristic radiation will serve.[3] A back-reflection pattern of a body-centered cubic crystal (α-iron) is shown in Fig. 20. The circle at the center indicates the hole that is punched to enable the film to slip over the pinhole system. It will be seen that the Laue spots lie on hyperbolas. The spots on each of these rows are reflections from various planes of a given zone, i.e., planes parallel to a line that is the zone axis. The geometrical conditions are sketched in Fig. 21. A cone of reflected rays is formed for each zone of planes in the crystal, such as the one shown in the drawing, and each

[1] A. B. Greninger, *Trans. AIME*, vol. 117, p. 61, 1935; *Z. Krist.*, vol. 91, p. 424, 1935.

[2] A. B. Greninger, *Trans. AIME*, vol. 117, p. 75, 1935; vol. 122, p. 74, 1936.

[3] In typical experiments a tungsten tube with a 2-mm focal spot operating at 8 ma, 40 kv requires exposures of 15 to 60 min with a pinhole 0.8 mm diameter, 6 cm long, and crystal-to-film distance of 3 cm, with standard X-ray film and Fluorazure intensifying screens. A 5- by 7-in. film is convenient at this distance. For metals such as Cu, Zn, Fe, etc., there is considerable fogging from fluorescent radiation, but this may be reduced by a filter, for example, by 0.01-in. aluminum sheet placed in front of the film.

cone intersects the flat film to form a row of spots (C, D, E) along a hyperbola.   If the zone axis AB is inclined to the film, the hyperbola will lie at a distance from the center of the film, a distance that is related to the angle of inclination, ϕ;[1] if AB is parallel to the film ($\phi = 0$), the hyperbola will degenerate into a line passing through the center of the film.   If the axis of the cone is projected perpendicularly upon the film, forming the line $A'B$, it is obvious that the hyperbola will be symmetrical with respect to this line.

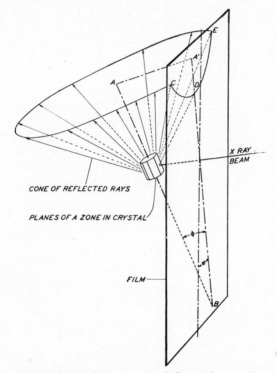

FIG. 21. Back-reflection Laue pattern of planes of a zone in a crystal.

In determining the orientation of a crystal from a pattern of this type it is necessary to assign the proper indices to some of the zones causing these hyperbolas or to some of the individual spots.   The technique for doing this is much simplified if attention is directed merely to the hyperbolas which are the most densely packed with spots and to those spots which lie at the intersections of three or more prominent hyperbolas, for then only low indices are involved.

On every film of a cubic crystal will be found prominent rows of spots

[1] The closest approach of the hyperbola to the center of the film is given by the relation $S = R \tan 2\phi$, where R is the distance from the specimen to the film, and S is the minimum distance of the hyperbola from the center.

from the zones [100], [110], and [111] and less prominent ones from the zone [113].   Many other zones also appear but are not easily recognized. The spots at the intersections of these principal hyperbolas are reflections from the planes common to the principal zones in the crystal; in the body-

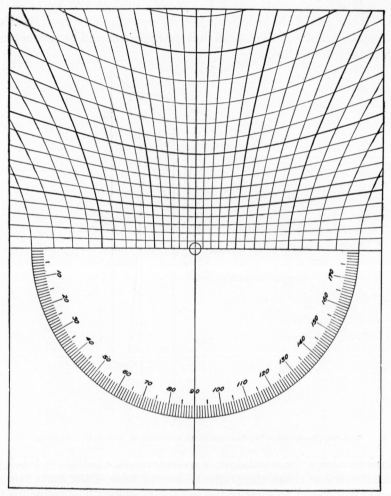

Fig. 22. Chart for back-reflection photographs.   Printed for 3-cm distance from specimen to film; graduated in 2° intervals.

centered cubic patterns they are (100), (110), (112), and others of higher indices, which are less prominent.   In the face-centered cubic patterns, (111) appears in addition to these.   These important spots with low indices are always of high intensity and are somewhat isolated from their neighbors on the hyperbola (see Fig. 20).

Figure 22 is Greninger's chart for reading angular relations on back-reflection films and is reproduced in the proper size for a 3 cm separation of specimen and film. Any row of spots on the film can be made to coincide with a hyperbola extending across the chart horizontally by suitably turning the film about its center when it is placed centrally on the chart. The angle of inclination, ϕ, of the zone axis to the film is given directly from the chart; hyperbolas have been drawn for each 2° of ϕ, with heavy lines each 10°. The amount of rotation of the film that is required to get a row to coincide with a horizontal hyperbola on the chart is a direct

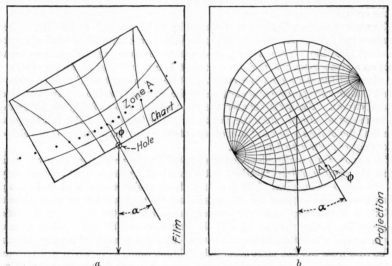

a   *b*

FIG. 23. (*a*) Back-reflection Laue film superimposed on chart. (*b*) Stereographic projection paper superimposed on net; the zone of spots is plotted at *A*.

measure of the azimuthal angle α (see Fig. 21), for it is the angle between the line $A'B$ and the vertical reference line.

It is most convenient to solve the films by plotting a sterographic projection; this can be done rapidly by a method which will be described with reference to Fig. 23. The plane of the projection is made perpendicular to the primary X-ray beam (parallel to the plane of the film), and the film is read from the side opposite to that on which the reflected rays were incident, so as to give a projection of the crystal that corresponds to viewing it from the position of the X-ray tube. An arrow is marked on the film parallel to some fiducial mark on the specimen, and the film is superimposed on the chart, as in Fig. 23*a*, with its central hole at the center of the chart. A piece of tracing paper is then placed on a stereographic net and pivoted at the center of it with a pin. An arrow is drawn on the paper radially outward from the central pin. The zones recorded on the film are then plotted on the paper, as indicated in Fig. 23*b*, by turning the paper and film together so that both arrows are parallel and point to the same angle α and by plotting the angle ϕ upward from the basic circle of the projection. The point A thus plotted is the projection of the zone responsible for the entire row of spots on the film.

Tentative indices are assigned by determining the angles between prominent zones and comparing the angles with a table (see the table on page 36). This tentative assignment of one or more possible sets of indices is merely for the purpose of saving time in the final operation, which is that of finding a position of a standard projection of zone axes and an amount of rotation of the standard such that its points will coincide with all the plotted ones and thus will disclose their indices. When a match has been found between each zone and a corresponding zone from a rotated standard projection, it is possible, of course, to rotate any other zone or any pole of the standard by the same amount and thus to show its position in the crystal. The final plot expresses the crystal orientation graphically; in addition, it can also be described in terms of the angles between the crystallographic axes and convenient marks or surfaces on the crystal.[1]

The above technique is but one of several by which one may deduce the indices of the zones and spots. No use has been made in this procedure of the vertical curves of the chart (Fig. 22). These have been drawn to measure angular relations between spots on a given hyperbola and are spaced at 2° intervals just as are the others; i.e., two planes of the same zone in a crystal that lie at an angle of 2° to each other will reflect to form two spots separated by one of the intervals marked out by two adjacent vertical curves. The angle between the two principal spots of Fig. 20, for example, can be measured directly from the chart and will be found to be 45°; this suggests at once that the indices of one of the spots are (100) and of the other are (110), although it does not tell which spot is which.

If the spots thus partly identified are plotted on the projection, they will greatly reduce the number of trial rotations of the standard projection that are necessary to find the complete solution. The pole of a plane causing a spot is plotted by a procedure analogous to that of Fig. 23, except that the spot is made to lie on the *central vertical line* of the chart, and the corresponding pole is plotted $\phi°$ *up from the center* of the projection, rather than $\phi°$ up from the circumference (since the pole is normal to its zone axis). Poles thus plotted are useful for a rapid solution of the film, but zones can be read from the film more accurately. Much time can be saved if, after prominent zones are plotted, the important great circles shown in the standard projection of Fig. 9, p. 35, are looked for.

The Transmission Laue Method. It has been mentioned in Chap. V that a transmission Laue pattern has a symmetry around the center similar to the symmetry of the axis or plane in the crystal along which the X-ray beam is directed. If a cubic crystal is mounted on a goniometer head and turned until the Laue pattern has fourfold symmetry, it becomes at once obvious that the incident beam is parallel to a cube axis, [100]; similarly, threefold symmetry indicates that the beam is parallel to a cube diagonal, [111]. With crystals of high reflecting power and with intense radiation it is possible to see these patterns on a fluorescent screen

---

[1] An alternative scheme is to use the vector relations between reciprocal lattice vectors to determine the orientation of desired crystal directions from coordinates of spots on the film that have been indexed. Suppose for a cubic crystal the vectors from 000 to 011 and 100 reciprocal lattice points are known from reading the film; then the addition of these two vectors gives the vector from 000 to 111. The computations may be made by using components of the vectors along arbitrary X and Y axes parallel to the plane of the film. B. F. Decker, *J. Applied Phys.*, vol. 15, p. 610, 1944.

and to adjust the crystal quickly to a symmetrical position, though it is necessary to work in a darkened room with the eyes fully accommodated to the dark, and with the hands protected from direct and scattered radiation.

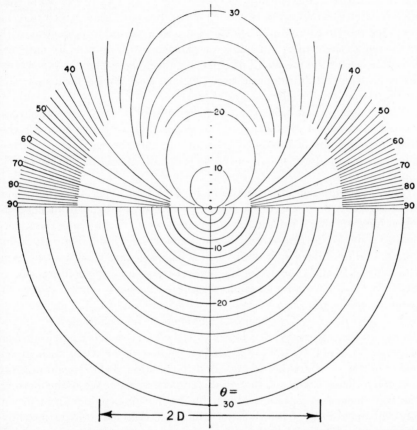

FIG. 24. Chart for transmission Laue photographs with specimen-film distance D (3 cm). Upper half gives curves along which lie spots of a single zone when zone axis is at indicated angle from the beam. Lower half gives θ for individual spots. (*Dunn.*)

To find the orientation of an unsymmetrically oriented crystal one can transfer each of the spots on a transmission photograph to a stereographic projection. The prominent zones then appear as points along great circles of the projection and can be identified either by the symmetry of their arrangement or by the angles between them. Figure 24 is a chart that aids this plotting.[1] When enlarged to the size that corresponds to the correct crystal-film distance, D, the ellipses and hyperbolas in the upper half of the chart represent zones of Laue spots. If the chart is centered

[1] C. G. Dunn and W. W. Martin, *Trans. AIME*, vol. 185, p. 417, 1949.

on the direct beam spot of a Laue pattern and pivoted about the center, any zone of spots can be made to superimpose on one of the curves (or on a curve interpolated between these); the angle between the zone axis and the beam is then read directly from the chart by means of the numbered curves and the 2° interpolated curves. The lower half of the chart consists of circles numbered with values of the Bragg angle θ, which may be used for plotting individual spots. On a stereographic projection with the beam at the center, a zone axis is plotted by going radially outward from the center the measured angular distance, and a plane is plotted by going $\theta°$ inward from the basic circle, in each case along a radius parallel to the radius on the film.

When many orientations are to be determined it may lessen the work if a set of standard photographs is prepared with which to compare the Laue photographs of unknown orientation,[1] but the work of preparing hundreds of standards usually exceeds the work of solving the necessary films directly.

The Determination of Orientations by Etch Pits. Various orientation methods have been employed for the reflection of light from crystallographic etch pits. Bridgman's method[2] consists in attaching the specimen to a sphere (a transparent sphere is convenient[3]), holding it at arm's length, and marking a spot on it when it has been turned so that the etch pits reflect light into the eye of the observer from a lamp standing behind him. It has an accuracy of about 2° and is extremely rapid. A greater accuracy can be obtained by causing the reflected light to fall on a screen, as has been done by Czochralski,[4] Chalmers,[5] and Schubnikov.[6] Tammann and his coworkers[7] developed a method for estimating the number of grains in a polycrystalline aggregate having orientations in a given region of the stereographic triangle and thus obtained statistical information about deformation and recrystallization textures. While the method has had some use,[8] it is not applicable to the majority of problems in physical metallurgy. Smith and Mehl[9] determined orientations by plotting the directions of the sides of individual etch pits on a stereo-

[1] M. Majima and S. Togino, *Sci. Papers Inst. Phys. Chem. Research (Tokyo)*, vol. 7, pp. 75, 259, 1927. C. G Dunn and W. W. Martin, *Trans. AIME*, vol. 185, p. 417, 1949.

[2] P. W. Bridgman, *Proc. Am. Acad. Arts Sci.*, vol. 60, p. 305, 1925.

[3] J. B. Baker, B. B. Betty, and H. F. Moore, *Trans. AIME*, vol. 128, p. 118, 1938.

[4] Czochralski, *Z. anorg. u. allgem. Chem.*, vol. 144, p. 131, 1925.

[5] B. Chalmers, *Proc. Phys. Soc. (London)*, vol. 47, p. 733, 1935.

[6] A. Schubnikov, *Z. Krist.*, vol. 78, p. 111, 1931.

[7] G. Tammann, *J. Inst. Metals*, vol. 44, p. 29, 1930. G. Tammann, and H. H. Meyer, *Z. Metallkunde*, vol. 18, p. 339, 1926.

[8] K. J. Sixtus, *Physics*, vol. 6, p. 105, 1935.

[9] D. W. Smith and R. F. Mehl, *Metals & Alloys*, vol. 4, pp. 31, 32, 36, 1933.

graphic projection. The accuracy is limited to about 3°, and the method requires careful polishing and high magnification.

The most useful methods involve the measurement of the angles between the etch-pit faces using a goniometer. Weerts[1] has given a lengthy discussion of a technique using a three-circle goniometer and polarized light. A less elaborate method, which gives an accuracy that is sufficient for the great majority of investigations, consists simply in measuring the orientations of the etch-pit faces on a two-circle optical goniometer.[2] It has an accuracy of $\frac{1}{2}$ or 1°. The method operates satisfactorily with grains as small as 0.1 mm diameter and has been used with cold-worked and annealed grains and single crystals.[3] An inexpensive goniometer for this work may be constructed from an old surveyor's transit[3] or more conveniently, from an old astro compass.[4]

ETCHING TECHNIQUE. An ideal etchant would be one that develops etch pits or facets with plane faces accurately parallel to crystallographic planes of low index. The etched metal specimen would then appear intensely bright when the normals to these planes bisected the angle between telescope and collimator and perfectly black in all other positions. Actually, however, the etch-pit faces are always more or less rounded, causing the intensity of the reflected light gradually to build up to and drop off from a maximum as the reflecting plane approaches and recedes from the reflecting position. For the same metal and etchant the position and sharpness of the maxima vary with the etching time and the temperature of the etchant. When the maxima are sharp enough to be reproducible within $\frac{1}{2}$°, their positions usually coincide with the crystallographic poles, but sometimes they tend to fall a degree or two away from true crystallographic poles. For example, maximum reflections from cubic etch pits are often 88 or 89°, rather than 90°, apart. Since only two poles are necessary to determine the orientation and three can usually be measured, the observed poles can be corrected by moving them a minimum amount to make them mutually perpendicular. Occasionally, a few large noncrystallographic pits are developed; these may be readily recognized as such, since they have no definite maximum. In Table VIII directions are given for etching various metals for orientation work. The etching times are for etchants at room temperature and for strain-free metals of the purity indicated; for cold-worked metals the etching time usually must be reduced.

METHOD OF PLOTTING. The readings on the two circles of the goniometer corresponding to a reflection maximum (a cube pole in this discussion) can be plotted directly as a point on a stereographic projection. The data are plotted on tracing

[1] J. Weerts, *Z. tech. Physik*, vol. 9, p. 126, 1928.

[2] L. W. McKeehan, *Nature*, vol. 119, p. 705, 1927. L. W. McKeehan and H. J. Hodge, *Z. Krist.*, vol. 92, p. 476, 1935. H. H. Potter and W. Sucksmith, *Nature*, vol. 119, p. 924, 1927. C. S. Barrett and L. H. Levenson, *Trans. AIME*, vol. 137, p. 112, 1940.

[3] C. S. Barrett, *Trans. AIME*, vol. 135, p. 296, 1939. C. S. Barrett and L. H. Levenson, *Trans. AIME*, vol. 137, p. 76, 1940.

[4] The vertical circle is detached from the horizontal circle and mounted far enough back from the center of the instrument to provide room for a specimen holder and specimen; the surface of the specimen is brought to the position at the intersection of the axes of the two circles. (G. T. Gow, private communication.)

TABLE VIII. DIRECTIONS FOR ETCHING

Metal	Purity, per cent	Etchant*	Etching time, min	Planes developed	Remarks
Aluminum	99.95	9 parts HCl 3 parts HNO₃ 2 parts HF 5 parts H₂O	2	{100}	Use large quantity of etchant with respect to surface of specimen, and avoid heating of etchant
Alpha-iron	H₂ purified decarburized mild steel	1 part HNO₃ 4 parts H₂O	4	{100}	Avoid heating, as above, wipe during etching
Copper	Oxygen-free high-conductivity copper	1 part HCl 1 part HO₂; mixture saturated with FeCl₃·6H₂O	10	{100} and {110}	The {100} reflections are stronger than the {110}
Brass	Cartridge brass (70-30)	1 part etch for Cu 1 part H₂O	20	{100} and {111}	Agitate etchant at 2-min intervals; {110} also reported
Lead	99.9	3 parts H₂O₂ 2 parts glacial acetic acid 2 parts H₂O	10	{100}	
Tin	99.991	1 part etch for Cu 1 part H₂O	10	{100} and {110}	Wipe off at 2-min intervals
Tungsten		100 parts saturated K₃Fe(CN)₆ 5 parts saturated KOH 95 parts H₂O	15	{110}	Agitate etchant at 2-min intervals. Composition of etch is critical
Zinc	99.99	7 parts saturated CuCl₂·2H₂O 3 parts HCl 90 parts H₂O	3	{10$\bar{1}$l}, l having many values	Wipe off deposited copper at 30-sec intervals. Maximum reflections lie in three planes intersecting at pole of basal plane. Hexagonal axes lie 90° from the intersection and midway between these planes

* For other etchants that have been used by various investigators see references in C. S. Barrett and L. H. Levenson, *Trans. AIME*, vol. 137, p. 76, 1940, and in J. S. Bowles and W. Boas, *J. Inst. Metals*, vol. 74, p. 501, 1948. A. Taylor recommends for silicon ferrite 100 g ferrous sulfate, 10 cc conc. sulfuric acid in 1000 cc water, for {100} pits. Pitting of metals by oxidation has been studied by A. T. Gwathmey and A. F. Benton, *J. Chem. Phys.*, vol. 8, p. 431, 1940 (copper); B. Chalmers, R. King, and R. Shuttleworth, *Proc. Roy. Soc. (London)*, vol. A193, p. 465, 1948. P. A. Beck etches high-purity aluminum with 80 cc HCl, 25 cc HNO₃, 20 cc H₂O, 5 cc HF; other have used 150 g CuCl₂ in 1000 cc water followed by a rinse in concentrated HNO₃. .

paper fastened over a stereographic net by a pin at the center of the net, the paper being left free to turn about the pin.

Transferring data from the goniometer to the projection is direct and simple, for readings on the horizontal circle of the goniometer correspond to radial distances from the center of the projection and readings on the vertical circle correspond to azimuthal positions around the center if one makes the plane of projection parallel to the surface of the specimen.

Taylor has worked out an instrument that plots the data from an optical goniometer automatically.[1] A plotting table is rotated in synchronism with one circle of a two-circle goniometer, and a pointer is moved by a mechanical device so that radial distances on the plot are stereographic radial distances determined by rotations of the second circle. By counting the number of brightly reflecting grains in various settings, a pole figure for the cube etch pits of a sample of transformer steel may be plotted in less than $\frac{1}{2}$ hr.

APPLICATION TO DEFORMED METALS. An optical goniometer has especial value in the study of lattice orientations in deformed grains and single crystals, in which fields X-ray work is difficult. In general, with either single crystals or grains of a polycrystalline aggregate, the orientation after deformation varies considerably and in an irregular manner over each grain. In determining the range of orientation, a grain is divided into a number of areas, and the orientation of each area is measured separately and transferred to a standard projection.[2] The grouping of points on the final projection gives a pole figure of the preferred orientations present. This technique has been used to prepare pole figures of polycrystalline specimens, in both cold-worked and recrystallized states,[3] the individual grains of which were a few millimeters in diameter; but it does not, of course, detect the fragments of microscopic or submicroscopic size that can be registered by X-rays.

[1] A. Taylor, *J. Sci. Instruments*, vol. 25, p. 301, 1948.

[2] C. S. Barrett and L. H. Levenson, *Trans. AIME*, vol. 137, p. 112, 1940.

[3] C. S. Barrett, *Trans. AIME*, vol. 137, p. 128, 1940.

CHAPTER X

DETERMINATION OF CONSTITUTION DIAGRAMS WITH X-RAYS

The variety of properties encountered in different alloys or that may be induced in one alloy by different heat-treatments makes it essential to have a guide to each alloy system in the form of a constitution diagram showing the various phases that exist in the system and the ranges of temperature and composition within which they are stable or metastable. At the present time, only a small fraction of the great number of possible binary alloy systems and almost no systems with three or more component metals have been investigated with the care necessary to provide accurate phase diagrams; most of the existing diagrams must be considered merely as approximations. Many of the errors and inconsistencies in these have resulted from the use of impure materials; some from a lack of appreciation of the faults of the methods used in their determination; others from a failure to apply the most suitable methods; some from failure to regard the phase rule; and some, of course, from incomplete experimental work. X-ray diffraction has been of great value in the determination of the constitution of alloys.

Binary Diagrams. Disappearing-phase Method. The accepted manner of presenting data on the constitution of alloys is to plot a diagram on which single-phase and polyphase regions are plotted against composition as abscissa and temperature as ordinate, as in Fig. 1. It will be remembered that, when such diagrams represent equilibrium in the alloys, they must be drawn in accord with the relations embodied in Gibbs's phase rule.[1]

It follows that, in an equilibrium diagram for binary alloys at atmos-

---

[1] This states that, if the equilibrium between the phases is influenced only by temperature and pressure and not by gravitational, electrical, or magnetic forces or by surface conditions, then $P + F = C + 2$, where P is the number of stable phases present, F is the number of degrees of freedom, and C is the number of components. A phase may be defined as any physically distinct part of a system that is separated from the other parts of the system by definite bounding surfaces. The number of degrees of freedom of a system is the number of independently variable factors (such as temperature and pressure of the system and composition of any phase) that must be specified completely to define the conditions in the system. The number of components of a system is the smallest number of independently variable substances by means of which the composition of any phase present can be expressed. In most alloy systems this is the number of elemental metals present in the alloy.

pheric pressure, there will be regions of single- and two-phase equilibria alternating with each other across the diagram at any constant temperature. If X-ray diffraction patterns are made of a series of alloys in such a system, the films will show single patterns with single-phase alloys and

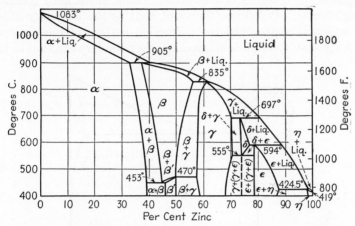

FIG. 1. Constitution diagram for copper-zinc alloys. Compositions in weight per cent. (*National Metals Handbook.*)

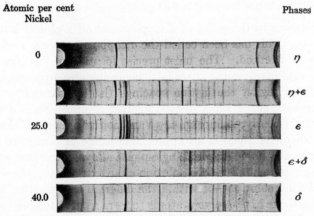

FIG. 2. Powder-diffraction patterns of alternating one-phase and two-phase regions in aluminum-rich aluminum-nickel alloys. [*A. J. Bradley and A. Taylor, Proc. Roy. Soc. (London), vol. A159, p. 56, 1937.*]

two superimposed patterns with two-phase alloys. Figure 2 is a reproduction of typical powder diffraction patterns for one- and two-phase specimens. This principle alone could be used to establish the solid portion of the diagram in a rough fashion, but much labor is saved by using the "lever principle" in the two-phase regions. Reference to Fig. 3 shows that an alloy of composition P in equilibrium at a certain temperature in the two-phase region $\alpha + \beta$ contains the α and β phases in the proportions given by the relative lengths of the lines Px and Py; i.e., amount of α: amount of $\beta = Py:Px$; or, equivalently, Py/xy of the total alloy is α and Px/xy is β. The intensity of the diffraction pattern of a phase is proportional to the quantity of that phase present in the alloy (barring disturbing effects). It follows, therefore, that as the boundary of a two-phase region is approached the diffraction pattern of the disappearing phase will steadily diminish in intensity; the boundary can thus be located

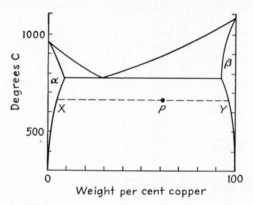

Fig. 3. The lever principle illustrated in the two-phase region of the copper-silver diagram.

by extrapolation to the point of disappearance on a plot of intensity vs. composition. This has been called the *disappearing-phase method*.

Parametric Method. The most precise location of the phase boundaries by X-rays involves the use of lattice-spacing measurements. Within a single-phase region the lattice spacings (lattice parameters) usually follow a smooth curve when plotted against composition and not infrequently vary linearly, as in Fig. 4. Variation with composition is to be expected whenever there is an appreciable range of composition within which there exist homogeneous single-phase alloys, regardless of whether the single-phase region is a solid solution at an extremity of the diagram—a terminal solid solution—or within the diagram and whether the solute atom replaces one of the solvent atoms to form a substitutional solid solution, or fits interstitially between the solvent atoms to form an interstitial solid solution, or replaces more than one solvent atom to form a defect lattice. Within a two-phase region of a binary diagram, on the other hand, the lattice spacings of each phase are invariant with composition at constant temperature. The spacings of each phase are those corresponding to alloys with compositions at the ends of the tie line[1] drawn on the binary diagram through the point representing the two-phase alloy. For

---

[1] A tie line is a line joining the two points that give the composition of the two coexisting phases in equilibrium.

example, in Fig. 3 the alloy P will yield the superimposed diffraction spectra of the α phase of composition x and the β phase of composition y, which are at the ends of the tie line through P. The lattice parameter of the α phase in this alloy will match some point on the lattice-parameter curve for the α field, a curve that is determined by quenching from the temperature at which solubility is a maximum; the composition corresponding to the point of equal lattice parameter will be the composition of the α phase on the boundary of the α field at the temperature chosen. To locate the entire curve giving the limit of solubility for the α phase, it

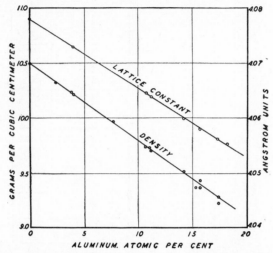

FIG. 4. Lattice constants and densities of silver-aluminum alloys. (*Foote and Jette.*)

is merely necessary to homogenize alloys in the two-phase region at a series of temperatures, to determine the corresponding lattice parameters after quenching from these temperatures, and to compare these parameters with the parameter curve for the solid solution. For example, in an investigation of the Ag-Al system the data in Fig. 4 were first assembled, then the parameters were determined for alloys in the adjoining two-phase field after quenching from the homogenizing temperature. Comparison of the quenched parameters with Fig. 4 gave the solubility limits shown in Fig. 5.[1]

Accuracy of the Methods. It is well to review the difficulties that may be encountered with this parametric method. The accuracy with which the solubility limits can be determined is directly proportional to the slope of the lattice-parameter curve in the single-phase region; the method is unworkable when there is no variation in lattice dimensions with composition as, for example, in aluminum-rich Ag-Al alloys. Unless suitable

[1] F. Foote and E. R. Jette, *Trans. AIME*, vol. 143, p. 151, 1941.

precautions are taken, this parametric curve may be in error as a result of (1) improper removal of segregation in the sample; (2) oxidation; (3) sublimation; (4) contamination by diffusion from adjoining solids or by reaction with vapors; (5) internal strains resulting from quenching, filing, or grinding the samples; and (6) alteration of surface composition by the selective action of an etchant.   The data from the two-phase region are

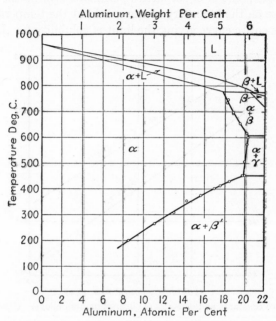

FIG. 5. Constitution diagram of silver-rich silver-aluminum alloys determined with the aid of Fig. 4.   (*Foote and Jette.*)

subject to the same errors, especially those arising from the lack of equilibrium in the specimen.   When the degree of supersaturation in a two-phase alloy is slight and the rate of diffusion is slow, it sometimes requires prohibitive annealing times to reach equilibrium; it is then advantageous to speed up the equilibration by cold-working the alloy before the annealing treatment.   In other cases, reaction rates are so fast that it is difficult or impossible to retain the high-temperature state by quenching.

The devices used to minimize these difficulties are varied and must be altered to fit particular cases.   A technique that gives excellent results when it can be employed is as follows: The alloy is first homogenized, then powdered by filing (or crushing) and sealed into small capsules of glass or silica.   The capsules are annealed at the required temperatures for a sufficient number of hours to produce equilibrium and are then plunged into water and smashed immediately, so that the hot particles of powder are individually brought into contact with the quenching medium and are cooled instantly. The powder is then collected, dried, and mounted for use in the X-ray camera. Internal strains from quenching are avoided by the small size of the individual particles, and decomposition of the high-temperature state is minimized by the drastic quench.

To minimize the loss of a volatile constituent, filings may be packed into a capillary tube so as to leave the minimum of dead space. The tube should be sealed off with a small flame to avoid heating the filings.[1] The homogeneity of the ingot from which the filings are made may be tested by comparing the lattice constants of samples taken from different parts of the ingot. Homogenization is always more rapid when the ingot is alternately deformed and annealed. The filings themselves reach equilibrium with regard to the phases present and the compositions of these phases much faster than does a large-grained solid specimen.[1]

Chemical analyses of filings require particular care.[2] Computing the percentage of one element by difference may be wholly unreliable, for dust, moisture, etc., may amount to as much as 1.0 per cent when filing is done under ordinary conditions. Filing and screening under argon is recommended. Screening is desirable to eliminate the larger particles that yield spotty films and unsymmetrical lines in a spectrometer; but it must be realized that screening may alter the composition of the sample. This will happen if the filings from one phase tend to be smaller than those from another. With the disappearing-phase method this would introduce serious error.

It is instructive to read Hume-Rothery and Raynor's critical discussion of techniques of phase-diagram determination and Owen and Morris's rebuttal of their article. The pitfalls and safeguards are fully discussed and illustrated.

Naturally, the accuracy attained with the parametric method is dependent upon the accuracy of the X-ray technique. The design of slits to give diffraction lines of suitable sharpness without excessively long exposures is a matter of some importance; the details of camera design are also of considerable importance when the method of disappearing phases is employed. Good technique not infrequently permits the detection of a phase that amounts to only about 0.5 per cent of the sample. X-ray spectrometers are effective in the measurement of intensities for the method of disappearing phases but should be used with care to avoid preferred orientations in the sample, or too large grains or particles; spinning samples are desirable.

Ternary Diagrams. The commercial importance of ternary and more complex alloys has focused an increasing amount of attention on them in

[1] E. A. Owen and D. P. Morris, *J. Inst. Metals*, vol. 76, p. 145, 1949.

[2] W. Hume-Rothery and G. V. Raynor, *J. Sci. Instruments*, vol. 18, p. 74, 1941.

recent years.   X-ray methods have proved very effective both in rough
survey work and in more precise determinations of diagrams.   Owing to
the fact that the individual regions within a ternary equilibrium diagram
may represent single-phase, two-phase, or three-phase equilibria, the

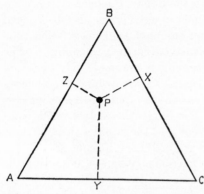

principles governing ternary diagrams and their determination
necessarily differ somewhat from
those employed with binary alloys.

To plot the phases in a three-
component system, it is best to
use an equilateral-triangle plot.
The three pure metals are represented by the corners of the diagram, as indicated by the letters
A, B, C in Fig. 6.   All the binary
alloys of these metals will be represented by points along the bound-

FIG. 6. Triangular plot for ternary systems.

aries of the triangle, and alloys con-
taining all three components will lie within the triangle.   The location of
a point within the triangle gives its composition; thus the alloy P in Fig.
6 contains amounts of metals A, B, and C in proportion to the perpendicular distances PX, PY, and PZ
respectively.[1]   The same principle
holds, of course, for points along the
boundaries where the alloys contain
only two metals.   Atomic percentages are of more significance than
weight percentages in determining
the extent of phase fields and are
usually preferred in research work.

Figure 7 illustrates a possible dis-
position of phase fields in a ternary
diagram and gives the equilibrium
relations for one temperature.   It is
an isothermal section through a
three-dimensional plot having the

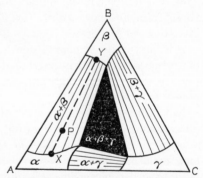

FIG. 7. Isothermal section of a hypothetical ternary diagram showing one-, two-,
and three-phase fields as open, ruled, and
black areas respectively.

composition triangle as a base and temperature as the ordinate.   A succession of such plots for different temperature levels would be necessary
for a full specification of the ternary constitution, but usually only a
few are of sufficient practical importance to be mapped out in detail.

    [1] This method of plotting is possible because the sum of the perpendicular dis-
tances from any interior point to the three sides is always the same, a length which is
taken as 100 per cent.

The geometry of an isothermal diagram is important, for the X-ray method depends upon it. Three-phase fields are always triangular. They always have boundaries in common with two-phase fields and corners that touch one-phase fields at cusps on the one-phase boundaries.[1]

The tie lines within the two-phase fields, which give the compositions of the two coexisting phases, are straight lines that never cross each other and that change in direction gradually from one side of the area to the other. The relative proportion of two phases in equilibrium is given by the lever relation just as with binary alloys. Referring to Fig. 7, the lever principle applied to alloy P gives

$$\frac{\text{Amount of } \alpha}{\text{Amount of } \beta} = \frac{\text{length of } Py}{\text{length of } Px}$$

or, equivalently, Py/xy of the total alloy is α.

In any three-phase region the compositions of the coexisting phases are given by the three corners of the three-phase triangle and are independent of the over-all composition of the alloy. The relative proportion of the phases present in a three-phase region may be found by the construction shown in Fig. 8, where an alloy P lies within a three-phase region containing α, β, and γ phases. The amounts of the individual phases are given by drawing a line through P and one corner of the three-phase triangle and setting up equations of the type

$$\frac{\text{Amount of } \beta}{\text{Amount of } (\alpha + \gamma)} = \frac{\text{length of } Px}{\text{length of } Pv}$$

and

$$\frac{\text{Amount of } \alpha}{\text{Amount of } \gamma} = \frac{\text{length of } xw}{\text{length of } xu}$$

Disappearing-phase Method in Ternary Diagrams. Boundaries of two-phase regions and corners of three-phase regions can be located by applying the above relations to the relative intensities of the spectra of the individual phases. This procedure is analogous to the disappearing-phase method discussed in connection with binary diagrams. It has been employed with marked success by Bradley and his associates[2] in various ternary systems of iron, nickel, aluminum, and copper, although it has

---

[1] Certain rules govern the angle relationships that are permitted at these corners. Extrapolation of the single-phase boundaries at a corner should result either in two lines extending into the three-phase triangle or in two lines extending into the two-phase regions, but not in one line extending into each.

[2] A. J. Bradley, H. J. Goldschmidt, H. Lipson, and A. Taylor, *Nature*, vol. 140, p. 543, 1937. A. J. Bradley and H. Lipson, *Proc. Roy. Soc. (London)*, vol. A167, p. 421, 1938. A. J. Bradley, W. L. Bragg, and C. Sykes, *J. Iron Steel Inst. (London)*, vol. 141, p. 63, 1940.

not been held in high regard by many investigators, perhaps for the reason that full use is not often made of intensity data and the lever relations mentioned above, and perhaps because imperfectly crystallized transition phases may exist that lead to diffuse spectra of the minor constituent. Bradley and Lipson succeeded in detecting a phase when it was only $\frac{1}{600}$ of the total alloy and regularly used films showing a phase that constituted only $\frac{1}{100}$ of the specimen, usually employing for this purpose a cylindrical

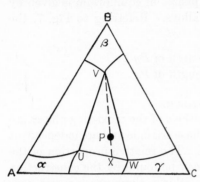

FIG. 8. The lever principle in three-phase ternary fields.

camera of 19 cm radius, nicely adjusted, with suitably chosen radiation that had been passed through a filter.

Parametric Method in Ternary Diagrams. While the method of disappearing phases is useful for survey work, there seems no doubt that lattice-parameter measurements are required for precision determinations of ternary diagrams, just as with binaries. The principles involved have been summarized by Bradley and his coworkers[1] and in greater detail by Andersen and Jette.[2]

The investigator first determines the variation of the lattice spacings within the single-phase regions of the three binary constitution diagrams, then over the single-phase regions of the ternary diagram. He then prepares diffraction patterns for alloys in the three-phase regions and uses the principle that each phase in any three-phase alloy will have the same lattice spacings as the alloy at the corresponding corner of the three-phase triangle. For example, the alloy P in Fig. 8 will contain an α phase with the same parameter as alloy u. Thus comparison with the spacings of the one-phase regions touched by the triangle corners will immediately locate the position of the corners and thereby the whole triangular region. By locating the three-phase triangles in this way, the investigator has also located some of the boundaries of the contiguous two-phase regions. The remaining boundaries of each two-phase area are located by measurements on a series of alloys within the area. Each alloy will give the superimposed spectra of the two alloys at the ends of the tie line through the point representing the alloy. Turning again to Fig. 7, for example, the alloy P will yield the spectra of alloys x and y. The lattice spacings of x and y, of course, will coincide with the spacings for certain compositions in the single-phase regions and will thereby determine the compositions

[1] A. J. Bradley, H. J. Goldschmidt, H. Lipson, and A. Taylor, *Nature*, vol. 140, p. 543, 1937.

[2] A. G. H. Andersen and E. R. Jette, *Trans. ASM*, vol. 24, pp. 375, 519, 1936.

of the ends of the tie line. With a series of alloys in the two-phase region, a series of points will be determined on the curved boundaries of the region. The fixing of all boundaries of three-phase and two-phase regions completes the diagram, for the one-phase regions are then fully outlined.

Laborsaving Principles. Let us now consider how the labor can be minimized in this procedure. By judicious choice of alloys the number

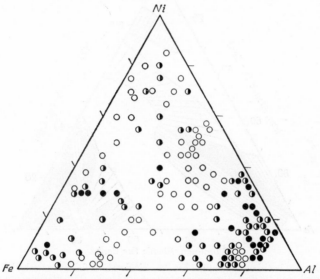

FIG. 9. Plot of alloy compositions used in an X-ray investigation of the iron-nickel-aluminum system. Open, half-filled, and filled circles represent alloys found to contain one, two, and three phases, respectively. [*A. J. Bradley and A. Taylor, Proc. Roy. Soc. (London), vol. A166, p. 353, 1938.*]

that must be studied to work out a ternary system can be greatly reduced. Bradley and Taylor,[1] for example, used 130 alloys spaced as much as possible near the boundaries of one-phase regions and obtained results comparable in accuracy with those that would have been obtained with 741 alloys equally spaced at 2.5 atomic per cent intervals. Their choice of alloys for an X-ray investigation of the system Fe-Ni-Al is shown in Fig. 9, with open, half-filled, and filled circles indicating alloys that were found to contain one, two, and three phases, respectively. The ternary diagram derived from these data is reproduced in Fig. 10.

As a rule, the phases along the three binaries extend considerable distances into the interior of the triangle, and there are relatively few single-

---

[1] A. J. Bradley and A. Taylor, *Proc. Roy. Soc. (London)*, vol. A166, p. 353, 1938.

phase regions that are entirely divorced from the boundaries.[1]   There also appears to be a tendency in some ternary diagrams for the phase boundaries and the tie lines to run roughly parallel to the lines of equal ratios of valence electrons to atoms—an extension of the Hume-Rothery rule in binary alloys.   When similar structures occur at similar electron-to-atom

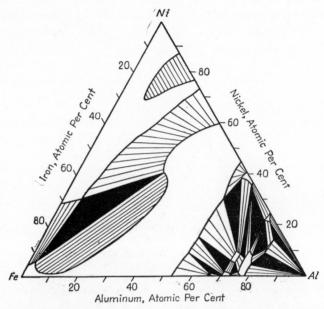

FIG. 10.   Diagram based on the data of Fig. 9.   Single-phase fields are unshaded, two-phase fields are ruled with tie lines, three-phase regions are black.   Superlattices are present but are not indicated.

ratios on two of the binaries, it is not unlikely that a single-phase region will extend entirely across the ternary triangle from one to the other, as is the case, for example, in the Fe-Ni-Al system where a phase exists that has a cubic structure with aluminum atoms at cube corners and iron or nickel atoms at cube centers and extends from the composition NiAl across to the composition FeAl (see Fig. 10).   These rough generalizations enable the investigator to guess somewhat more readily the possible

[1] A point of view that is useful in this work is based on the relative free energies of ternary phases. (G. V. Raynor, *Phil. Mag.*, vol. 39, p. 218, 1948.)   If, on a triangular base representing ternary compositions, one constructs a three-dimensional model of free energy for this isothermal section and then brings a plane into contact with any three points of the model, these three tangent points will be at the compositions of the corners of a three-phase triangle.   Suppose now that one of the phases has exceptionally great stability (indicated, perhaps, by a large heat of formation).   The tangent plane may pivot about its contact with this phase on the model so that all or nearly all ternary triangles have this phase at one corner.

configuration of the phase fields and thereby minimize the number of alloys to be made. It has been remarked that the mapping of a ternary is often less laborious—after the component binaries are known—than mapping out a single complicated binary system.

Interpolation is important if one is to reduce the labor of the lattice-parameter method of fixing the phase boundaries. Andersen and Jette[1] have developed a convenient way of interpolating in ternary diagrams based on plotting the lattice parameters for any phase as ordinate on the composition triangle as a base. In such a three-dimensional plot, the

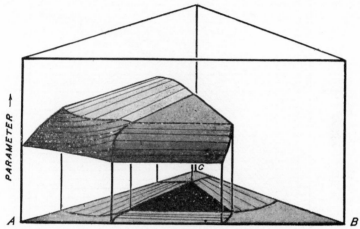

Fig. 11. Sketch of α-phase parametric surface for the hypothetical diagram of Fig. 7.

parameters will form a surface—the "parametric surface." This surface will have the following properties illustrated by the drawing in Fig. 11, which is supposed to represent the α-phase parametric surface for Fig. 7. In three-phase regions it will be a horizontal plane of constant parameter. In two-phase areas it will be, in general, a curved surface; horizontal sections through this will be straight lines identical with tie lines. In one-phase regions, the parametric surface is generally curved and need not contain any sections that are straight lines. The surface for a single-phase region must intersect the surface for the adjoining two-phase region along the boundary line between these regions (generally a curved line) and must touch the three-phase parametric plane at the corner of the three-phase triangle.

With these facts in mind, it is not difficult to interpret the parameter measurements in terms of phase boundaries or to devise schemes for interpolation. Andersen and Jette recommend instead of a solid model of the surface, which is a cumbersome device to use, a series of vertical sections

[1] A. G. H. Andersen and E. R. Jette, *Trans. ASM*, vol. 24, pp. 375, 519, 1936.

of the surface projected orthogonally upon a plane. Figure 12 illustrates this procedure for the phase in the iron corner of the Fe-Cr-Si system, where a family of similarly shaped parameter curves have been drawn through the experimental points labeled Fe, 6, 9 . . . 63. It will be seen that the method of drawing these parameter curves amounts to graphical interpolation both in the plane of constant iron content and in the direction perpendicular to this plane. A horizontal section through this plot

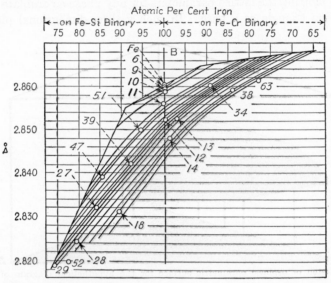

Fig. 12. Parameters along sections of constant iron content in iron-chromium-silicon alloys, projected on a plane of constant iron content. (*A. G. H. Andersen and E. R. Jette, Trans. Am. Soc. Metals, vol.* 24, *pp.* 375, 519, 1936.)

gives the compositions along a contour of the parametric surface, which can then be plotted as a contour map on the composition triangle, as in Fig. 13. The solid lines in this figure indicate the single-phase region and the dotted lines the adjacent two-phase regions whose contours must connect at the phase boundary with those in the single-phase region. When these two surfaces intersect at an appreciable angle the boundary can be fixed with accuracy, but when the contours pass from one to the other without a distinct change in direction the investigator must resort to the method of disappearing phases to place the boundary. When it is found that the tie lines of a two-phase field converge to a point, it must be concluded that a compound of substantially invariant composition occurs at that point, and from the degree of convergence the extent of the homogeneity range of this phase can be estimated. A suitable choice of vertical sections through the parametric surfaces near a phase boundary aids in making the exact position of the boundary evident.

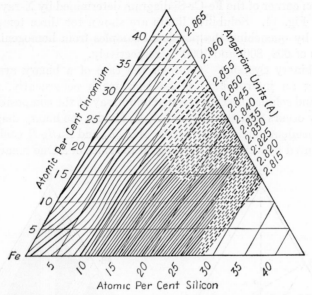

FIG. 13. Parametric surface indicated by contours of equal parameter derived from Fig. 12

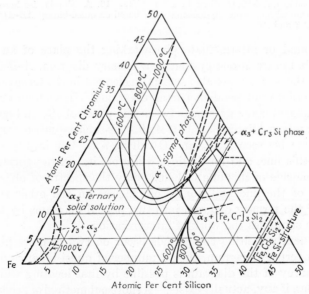

FIG. 14. The iron-rich corner of the iron-chromium-silicon system determined by X-rays; isothermal sections at 600, 800, and 1000°C.

The iron corner of the Fe-Cr-Si diagram determined by X-rays is reproduced in Fig. 14. Solubility limits are shown for three temperatures, obtained by quenching the powdered samples from homogenizing temperatures of 600, 800, and 1000°C, respectively.

Quasi-binary Systems. Consider the case of a binary system A-B containing an intermediate phase that melts congruently, *i.e.*, with liquidus and solidus meeting at a maximum, say at the composition A_mB_n. It usually occurs that the phase at A_mB_n divides the binary diagram into two independent partial systems, *viz.*, A-A_mB_n and A_mB_n-B, each of which is represented by a diagram obeying all the rules of a true binary system,

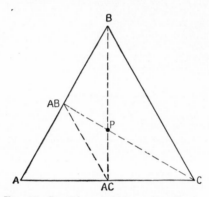

Fig. 15. Possible quasi-binary lines in a ternary diagram with congruently melting compounds AB and AC.

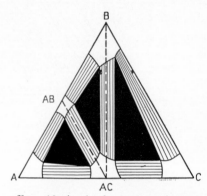

Fig. 16. A simple isothermal section based on quasi-binary AB-AC and AC-B.

the compound or intermediate phase taking the place of an element. Now if this binary is one system in a ternary diagram, A-B-C, it may occur that the A_mB_n phase also acts as an element in the ternary, dividing the diagram into independent partial diagrams. In such an event there will be a quasi-binary system between the phase A_mB_n and some other element or intermediate phase. If A_mB_n-C is such a quasi-binary system, then the line between A_mB_n and C will be a tie line in any two-phase region on this line, and no tie lines will cross it. X-ray spectra of any alloy on one side of this line will show only the spectra of phases on the same side of the line and none from phases on the other side. The division of the ternary diagram into two partial diagrams by the quasi-binary line simplifies the work of interpretation.

If congruently melting compounds occur on two or more binary diagrams of a ternary diagram, then a number of quasi binaries may exist. A rapid survey of the diagram is possible by first locating which of the possible ones, if any, actually exists. A short-cut method of accomplishing this was worked out by Guertler (*Klärkreuzverfahren*) and is illustrated in the isothermal section sketched in Fig. 15. The method is based on the rule that *quasi-binary lines cannot cross each other.* Thus the quasi binaries in Fig. 15 may be any of those shown as dashed lines except that *AB-C* and *AC-B* cannot both exist. Therefore, examination of an alloy *P* at the intersection of two possible quasi binaries will reveal which of these two systems, if any, actually occurs. For example, if the alloy *P* shows by microscopic or X-ray examination only the phases *AC* and *B*, then it is inferred that *AC-B* is a quasi binary. Then if another alloy is examined on the line *AC-AB* and shows only phases *AC* and *AB*, it can be inferred that the isothermal section has three partial diagrams and may appear as in Fig. 16, or it may contain other fields in addition to these. Naturally, merely the examination of one isothermal section cannot establish whether or not a quasi binary exists between two components at all temperatures or only over a limited range of temperatures.[1] A complete exploration of a diagram, either binary or more complex, requires the use of the older methods, particularly in the range of temperatures near the liquidus and solidus.

Complexities. It might be well to remind the reader that alloys often are not so simple as they might be. If they have not been brought to equilibrium, they may not obey the phase rule. They may contain transition structures that disappear on further annealing, as, for example, martensite, the familiar transition structure forming from the eutectoid inversion in the Fe-C system; or the θ' phase that forms during the first stages of precipitation from the aluminum-rich matrix in Al-Cu alloys and later decomposes to the stable precipitate. These transition states may be fully developed three-dimensional crystallites, or they may be segregated layers or imperfectly formed structures capable of developing only two-dimensional grating diffraction, as in the case of binary Al-Ag alloys[2] and the ternary alloys of Fe, Cu, and Ni.[3] Alloys that have not been brought to equilibrium may contain phases that are supercooled from a region of stability at higher temperatures. The presence of coring in crystals that solidified from the melt may cause weak and diffuse X-ray diffraction lines that are seen with difficulty. The observer may find the

---

[1] If ternary compounds exist within a ternary diagram, these may also act as components of various quasi-binary systems, connecting them with other compounds or with the corners of the ternary. The distributions that are possible are discussed in R. Vogel, Der Heterogenen Gleichgewichte, vol. II, "Handbuch der Metallphysik," Akademische Verlagsgesellschaft m.b.H., Leipzig, 1937, and in J. S. Marsh, "Principles of Phase Diagrams," McGraw-Hill, New York, 1935. An analogous short-cut method is useful in quaternary diagrams. A discussion of the general case is given by P. A. Beck, *J. Applied Phys.*, vol. 16, p. 808, 1945.

[2] C. S. Barrett, A. H. Geisler, and R. F. Mehl, *Trans. AIME*, vol. 143, p. 134, 1941.

[3] A. J. Bradley, W. L. Bragg, and C. Sykes, *J. Iron Steel Inst. (London)*, vol. 141, p. 63, 1940.

atoms in his alloy distributed on the atomic sites of a phase in any degree of order from complete randomness to complete order; *i.e.*, he may find a superlattice of one of the types discussed in Chap. XII.

Successful determination of phase diagrams rests not only on the matters of technique that have been mentioned here, but also on an understanding of the principles underlying the diagrams. It is useful, for example, to know the relation of the diagrams to the free-energy curves of the phases,[1] and to be familiar with the principles governing equilibria between phases, very few of which have been touched upon here.

[1] A treatment of this subject will be found in A. H. Cottrell, "Theoretical Physical Metallurgy," Longmans, New York, and E. Arnold & Co., London, 1948.

CHAPTER XI

THE STRUCTURE OF METALS AND ALLOYS

Numerous summaries of crystal structures have been published, the most extensive being the various volumes of "Strukturbericht" and "Structure Reports,"[1] which contain abstracts of all X-ray crystal-structure determinations. More condensed listings of structures are available in recent books.[2] Phase diagrams for metallic systems are covered in the extensive book by Hansen[3] and elsewhere.[4] The treatment in this chapter and the two following chapters does not attempt a complete listing of structures, but is directed toward a correlation of the structures and an understanding of the principles underlying the structures of the metallic phases.

Crystals may be classified as to types of binding forces as follows:

1. *Metallic* crystals consist of positive ions immersed in a "gas" of negative electrons. The attraction of the positive ions for the negative electrons holds the structure together and balances the repulsive forces of the ions for one another and of the electrons for other electrons. The electrons move freely through the lattice and provide good electrical and thermal conductivity.

2. *Ionic* crystals are bound together by the electrostatic attraction between positive and negative ions. They are combinations of strongly electronegative and electropositive elements. In NaCl, for example, the

---

[1] Published serially in *Z. Krist.* and also as separate volumes by Akademische Verlagsgesellschaft m.b.H., Leipzig, from 1931 on, and continued as "Structure Reports" by the International Union of Crystallography.

[2] R. W. Wyckoff, "The Structure of Crystals," 2d ed., 1931, and "Supplement to the Second Edition," Reinhold, New York, 1935; "Crystal Structures," Interscience Publishers, New York, 1948.

[3] M. Hansen, "Der Aufbau der Zweistofflegieren," Springer, Berlin, 1936.

[4] "Metals Handbook," American Society for Metals, Cleveland, Ohio, 1948. G. Sachs and K. R. Van Horn, "Practical Metallurgy," American Society for Metals, Cleveland, Ohio, 1940. E. Janecke, "Kurzgefasstes Handbuch aller Legierungen," Otto Spamer, Leipzig, 1937. "Alloys of Iron Research," Monograph Series, McGraw-Hill, New York. "Strukturbericht" and "Structure Reports," ref. 1, above. H. J. Goldschmidt, "The Structure of Carbides in Alloy Steels," *J. Iron Steel Inst. (London)*, vol. 160, p. 345, 1948. D. P. Smith, "Hydrogen in Metals," University of Chicago Press, Chicago, 1948. C. J. Smithells, "Metals Handbook," Butterworth, London, and Interscience Publishers, New York, 1949. H. Nowotny, "FIAT Review of German Science, 1939–46," Inorganic Chemistry, Part IV, pp. 67–96.

electron affinity of chlorine atoms causes a transfer of electrons from the electropositive sodium atoms to yield Na^+ and Cl^- ions.

3. *Covalent* crystals ("homopolar," or "valency," crystals) are held together by the sharing of electrons between neighboring atoms. Diamond is a typical example, in which each carbon atom shares its four valence electrons with the four nearest neighbors and thus completes an outer shell of eight electrons in each atom. The crystals are characterized by poor conductivity and great hardness.

4. *Molecular* crystals are composed of inactive atoms or neutral molecules bound by weak van der Waals forces. They have low melting points. Typical examples are the rare gases.

TABLE IX. SOME PROPERTIES ASSOCIATED WITH CRYSTALS OF THE FOUR BOND TYPES

Property	Metallic	Ionic	Covalent	Molecular
Hardness	Variable, malleable	Hard	Hard	Soft
Melting point	Variable	Fairly high	Variable	Low
Coefficient expansion	Variable	Low	Low	High
Electrical conductivity	High; by electrons	Fair; by ions	Insulator	Insulator
Coefficient of resistivity	Plus*	Minus	Minus	
Bonds	Not directed in space	Nondirected	Directed, limited in number	Nondirected
Coordination number	High, often a maximum	High	Low	High

* Plus means increasing resistance with increasing temperature.

Many crystals are intermediate between these "ideal" types. For example, some alloy phases have metallic conductivity and other properties associated with metallic binding yet at the same time resemble covalent crystals. It is possible to have some interatomic bonds in a crystal be of one type, say ionic, and others be of another, say covalent. Or each bond may be somewhat intermediate in type between some of those listed above.[1] The correlation of physical properties with bond type is indicated in a rather crude fashion by Table IX.

STRUCTURES OF THE ELEMENTS

The crystal structures of the elements are listed in Appendix IX. We are concerned here with the more common types and their relation to the periodic table.

---

[1] For a more detailed survey of the bond types and their characteristics see R. C. Evans, "An Introduction to Crystal Chemistry," Cambridge, London, 1948.

The structures of most metals are face-centered cubic (f.c.c.), close-packed hexagonal (c.p.h.), or body-centered cubic (b.c.c.) (Fig. 1). These are structures in which each atom is surrounded by 12 or 8 near neighbors in one of the simple ways of packing spheres. Elements in the same group of the periodic table tend to have the same structures—for example, the alkali metals Li, Na, K, Rb, Cs are all b.c.c.; Be, Mg, Zn, Cd are c.p.h.; Cu, Ag, Au are f.c.c., as are most of the eighth-group elements in at least one of their modifications.

The electropositive elements, those toward the left of the periodic table (Fig. 2), tend to have these structures. In this class are the alkali metals with one valence electron, the alkaline-earth elements with two valence

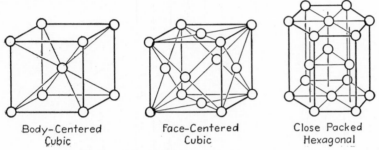

Body-Centered   Face-Centered   Close Packed
Cubic   Cubic   Hexagonal

Fig. 1. The principal structures of the metals.

electrons (Be, Mg, Ca, Sr, Ba), and most of the transition elements in which the process of forming a new shell of electrons awaits the filling of interior shells. The latter are boxed in the figure and include 21 Sc to 28 Ni in the first long period, 39 Y to 46 Pd in the second, and 57 La through the rare earths to 78 Pt in the third.

Close-packed hexagonal and face-centered cubic crystals are much more closely related than would appear from Fig. 1. Both are structures that represent spheres in closest packing. In the c.p.h. crystal structure the close-packed (0001) layers are stacked above each other in the sequence *ABAB . . .* ; *i.e.*, atoms of the third layer are directly above those of the first. In the f.c.c. structure the [111] planes have the same c.p.h. array of atoms and are stacked in the sequence *ABCABC . . .* so that the fourth layer is directly above the first.[1] The atoms in each layer fit in the hollows of the layer beneath. Tightly packed rows of atoms run in six directions through c.p.h. and f.c.c. structures and in four directions through the less densely packed b.c.c. lattice.

The 8 − *N* Rule. The *B* subgroup elements, in which the outer shells are again in the process of being filled, are in general less closely packed.

---

[1] The regular c.p.h. sequence may have frequent errors in it, as has been noted in cobalt and in lithium after some treatments; this will be discussed later.

The binding becomes more a covalent binding between certain neighboring atoms instead of a binding among positive ions and electrons. The homopolar character increases toward the end of the periods until it is a true covalent bond in the diatomic molecules F_2, Cl_2, Br_2, and I_2.

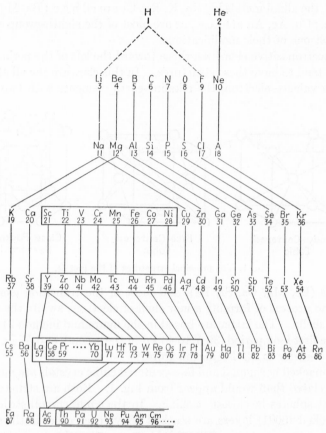

Fig. 2. The periodic table.

Most of the structures in the B subgroups follow Bradley and Hume-Rothery's interesting "8 − N rule," which states that each atom has 8 minus N close neighbors, where N is the number of the group to which the element belongs.

Consider first the structure of diamond, Fig. 3. The atoms are arranged on two interpenetrating f.c.c. lattices. Projected upon the basal plane the atom positions are as indicated in Fig. 3a, where the fractions give the coordinate normal to the plane of projection. A perspective view of the structure, Fig. 3b, shows more clearly that each atom has four

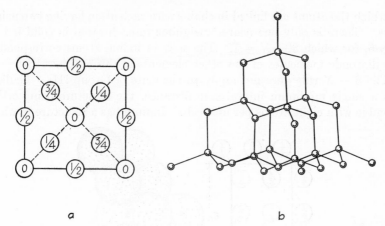

a *b*

FIG. 3. The structure of diamond. (*a*) Projection on the basal plane. Fractions in circles indicate heights above the basal plane. (*b*) Perspective drawing, showing that each atom has four nearest neighbors.

near neighbors.[1] Gray tin, Si, and Ge of Group IV_B also have this diamond cubic structure with coordination number 4.

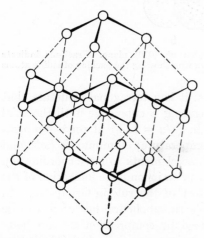

In Group V_B, As, Sb, and Bi have rhombohedral structures with each atom surrounded by three (Fig. 4). These closely bonded atoms form puckered layers (horizontal in Fig.

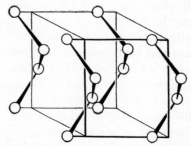

FIG. 4. The structure of antimony. Each atom has three nearest neighbors, as indicated by the connecting lines.

FIG. 5. The structure of tellurium. Atoms are arranged in spiral chains in which each atom has two nearest neighbors.

4); within the layers the bonding is covalent, and between the layers it is partially metallic. Group VI_B has Se and Te with the structure of Fig. 5,

---

[1] Neither of these common ways of drawing crystal structures shows the effective size of the atoms in relation to their distance apart, for they are usually spheres in contact with the nearest neighbors. Only the positions of the atom centers are indicated.

in which the atoms are linked in chains with each atom having two neighbors. There is only one nearest neighbor to each atom in solid iodine, Fig. 6, for which $8 - N = 1$. The pairs of iodine atoms correspond to the diatomic molecules of the other elements of this group.

The $8 - N$ rule does not apply to elements of Group III_B. Gallium has a single minimum interatomic distance, the structure being orthorhombic with eight atoms per unit cell. Indium has a structure in which

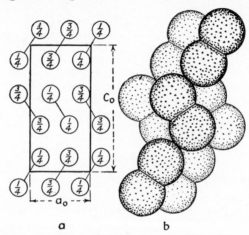

a   b

Fig. 6. The structure of iodine. (*a*) Projection on (010) plane. Fractions indicate distances below the plane of the paper. (*b*) Drawing showing the packing of iodine atoms in the structure. (*Wyckoff.*)

all atoms have four nearest neighbors: it is a tetragonal structure that may be derived from the f.c.c. by elongating a cube edge until the axial ratio is $c/a = 1.08$. Thallium is c.p.h. ($c/a = 1.59$) at room temperature and b.c.c. above its transition temperature; aluminum is f.c.c. and boron is uncertain. The failure of these elements to have coordination number 5 is attributed by Hume-Rothery to incomplete ionization of the atoms.[1] There seems to be some effect of the rule in Group II_B. In this group, Hg crystallizes in a simple rhombohedral lattice; it can be visualized as a f.c.c. structure deformed by compression along a body diagonal; the interatomic distances within a rhombohedral (111) plane are greater than the distances to the six nearest neighbors in the two adjacent (111) planes. Also in this group are c.p.h. Zn and Cd, but the unit cells of these metals are not the normal shape expected of close-packed spheres ($c/a = 1.633$) but are stretched along the c axis to axial ratios of approximately 1.9. Consequently, each atom has six nearest neighbors in the (0001) plane in which it lies, while the atoms in the planes next above and below this are more distant.

[1] W. Hume-Rothery, "The Structure of Metals and Alloys," Institute of Metals, London, 1936 (and revisions).

Polymorphism. Many of the elements can be made to take different structures when temperature or pressure is varied, or when unusual thermal or mechanical treatments are resorted to. Details are discussed in a later chapter on transformations, and examples will be found in Appendix IX; the more important ones will be mentioned here. The low-temperature b.c.c. form of iron (α-Fe) changes to f.c.c. on heating to 910°C (γ-Fe) and reverts to b.c.c. again at about 1400°C (δ-Fe). Manganese exists in four forms, the α, β, γ, and δ. Tin has a metallic form at ordinary temperatures (white, or β) but a nonmetallic gray (α) form having the diamond type of structure is stable below about 18°C. This low-temperature form is the "tin pest" to which some tinned articles are subject when exposed to cold weather.

Several metals that are c.p.h. at low temperatures transform to b.c.c. at higher temperatures; these include zirconium, titanium, thallium, and lithium. Metals that are f.c.c. at low temperatures sometimes transform to c.p.h. at higher temperatures; e.g., calcium, lanthanum, and scandium. Cobalt, on the other hand, is stable in the c.p.h. form (commonly with frequent errors in the stacking of atom layers) at *low* temperatures and is f.c.c. at *high* temperatures.

Among the nonmetallic elements striking polymorphism is found in phosphorous (white, black, and red forms) and carbon. The diamond structure of carbon (Fig. 3) is very different from the layer structure of graphite. The familiar form of graphite has a hexagonal structure with atoms at (or very close to) the positions 000, $00\frac{1}{2}$, $\frac{1}{3}\frac{2}{3}0$, $\frac{2}{3}\frac{1}{3}\frac{1}{2}$, the basal planes consisting of a hexagonal network in which each atom is linked with three neighbors (not four as in diamond). Interatomic bonds within the basal planes are strong, but those between the layers are very weak so that they glide easily over each other and give graphite the quality of being a good lubricant. The second form of graphite has a unit cell three layers high instead of the two-layer cell of the normal form, an *ABCABC* . . . sequence instead of *ABAB* . . . , and is therefore rhombohedral. Atoms in this form are at 000, $\frac{1}{3}\frac{2}{3}0$, $00\frac{1}{3}$, $\frac{2}{3}\frac{1}{3}\frac{1}{3}$, $\frac{1}{3}\frac{2}{3}\frac{2}{3}$, $\frac{2}{3}\frac{1}{3}\frac{2}{3}$. Most samples seem to have a mixture of the two forms with the hexagonal form predominating in the ratio of 4 or 5 to 1 over the rhombohedral form.[1]

Polymorphic transformations are usually brought about by temperature changes, but several have been induced by high hydrostatic pressures, or by high pressures combined with drastic cold work, as Bridgman's

---

[1] H. G. Lipson and A. R. Stokes, *Proc. Roy. Soc. (London)*, vol. A181, p. 101, 1942. H. Jagodzinski, *Acta Cryst.*, vol. 2, p. 298, 1949. There are faults in the stacking sequence of the hexagonal layers. Jagodzinski inclines to the belief that the sequence *ABAB* . . . is normal at high temperatures and that this is metastable with respect to the *ABCABC* . . . sequence (rhombohedral) at low temperatures.

extensive research has shown.   The transformations with increasing pressure are always to more dense modifications, which is an expression of Le Châtelier's principle.   An unusual transformation in which both high- and low-pressure forms are f.c.c. has been discovered in cerium.[1]   The high-pressure form has 16.55 per cent smaller volume than a sample has at atmospheric pressure.

Metallic selenium (gray, hexagonal) has a structure in which the selenium atoms are arranged in spiral chains and are covalently bonded together within the chains.   This is the stable form at all temperatures below the melting point.   Selenium is common in the vitreous form and can also be prepared in two red, monoclinic forms which decompose irreversibly to the stable form on heating.   The α (monoclinic) form, according to Burbank's detailed study[2] using Fourier synthesis, is based on molecules composed of puckered rings containing eight atoms.   There are a few bonds between the atoms of one ring and those of a neighboring ring in α-selenium that are abnormally short compared with the distance to be expected for bonding of the van der Waals type.   But when α decomposes to metallic selenium the number of these short bonds increases to 32 per eight atoms, which suggests that they are the reason for the greater stability of the metallic form.   It has also been proposed that the abnormal shortness of these bonds (3.49 instead of about 4.0 A) is due to their having a partially metallic nature.[3]

SOLID SOLUTIONS

Types of Solid Solution.   The lattice of nickel can accommodate atoms of copper without losing its f.c.c. structure.   Substitution of copper atoms for nickel atoms on the f.c.c. lattice points is an example of the formation of a *substitutional solid solution*.   In the Cu-Ni system the two elements can be substituted in all proportions and are said to form a continuous series of solid solutions.   All alloys of the system consist of a f.c.c. lattice with copper and nickel atoms distributed at random on the lattice points.

An important factor governing solution behavior is the relative size of the atoms.   Detailed discussions of atomic radii are available (see page 167) and are of great value in crystal-structure determination, but for the

[1] A. W. Lawson and Ting-Yuan Tang, *Phys. Rev.*, vol. 76, p. 301, 1949.   The transformation is thought to be due to the $4f$ electron being literally squeezed into a $5d$ state.   Cerium is the first element in the periodic table to have a $4f$ electron, and the energy difference between $4f$ and $5d$ levels is small.   The transformation also occurs on cooling at ordinary pressures (A. F. Schuck and J. H. Sturdivant, *J. Chem. Phys.*, vol. 18, p. 145, 1950).

[2] R. D. Burbank, *Tech. Rept.* XXXVII, Laboratory for Insulation Research, MIT, 1950 (to be published).   Space group $P2_1/n$.

[3] A. R. von Hippel, *J. Chem. Phys.*, vol. 16, p. 372, 1948.   F. De Boer, *J. Chem. Phys.*, vol. 16, p. 1173, 1948.

discussion here the distances between nearest atoms in the elements will serve (see table in Appendix IX). An idea of the periodic variation with atomic number can be had from the plot on page 252.

A continuous series of solid solutions is found only between elements of the same crystal structure and only when the sizes of the atoms differ by less than about 15 per cent. Usually the lattice of an element is expanded by dissolving atoms larger than those of the solvent and contracted by

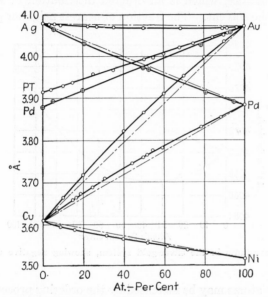

Fig. 7. Lattice constants in systems exhibiting a continuous series of solid solutions. Dot-dash lines indicate Vegard's law.

dissolving atoms smaller than those of the solvent, as indicated by dot-dash lines in Fig. 7. The law of linearity, Vegard's law, was discovered with solid solutions of salts, which are ionic crystals. As applied to metallic solid solutions, there are almost invariably deviations from the law—sometimes quite striking ones, as shown in Fig. 8—and the deviations may be either positive or negative, *i.e.*, parameters greater or less than the Vegard's law value.[1]

Ideally, solute and solvent atoms are distributed at random on the atom sites but this completely disordered distribution is probably rarely attained. If *like* atoms have a preferential attraction for each other that

[1] This is discussed further on pp. 228 and 229. It may be argued that the cube of the lattice parameter rather than the parameter itself should vary linearly with atomic per cent (R. F. Mehl, *Trans. AIME*, vol. 111, p. 91, 1934); also that the average length of all bonds to nearest neighbors is the quantity that should vary linearly (W. Betteridge, *J. Inst. Metals*, vol. 75, p. 559, 1949).

predominates over the attraction between unlike atoms there is likely to be precipitation of a second phase when an alloy is annealed at low temperatures. The influence of this attraction is likely to persist throughout a considerable range of temperature above the precipitation range, producing local, unstable clusters of like atoms that are continually dispersed by thermal agitation. On the other hand, if the attraction of *unlike* atoms is the predominating one, annealing at a low temperature may induce a *superlattice*, which is an ordered distribution of atoms on the atom sites of the solvent. The fraction of nearest neighbor pairs that are

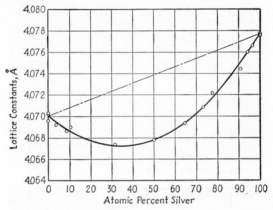

Fig. 8. Lattice constants in the silver-gold system, showing negative deviations from Vegard's law.

pairs of unlike atoms may be increased by the ordering process. Another factor may also be involved in superlattice formation: the local strains caused by the irregular distribution of atoms of different size, strains which are lessened by ordering. This tendency of atoms in some alloys to occupy certain atom positions rather than others predominates at low temperatures over the shuffling action of thermal agitation. As the temperature is raised, however, the thermal vibrations increase until the ordered array which existed throughout large blocks of a crystal is broken up; above this critical temperature the ordering tendency produces only local ordering in regions less than perhaps 10 unit cells in diameter, and at the highest temperatures complete randomness may prevail. Superlattice formation is discussed more fully in the following chapter.

Interstitial solid solutions are formed when atoms with small radii are accommodated in the interstices of the lattice of a solvent. The solid solution of carbon in γ-Fe (austenite) is an example of this type; the iron atoms are on f.c.c. lattice points, and the carbon atoms occupy interstitial positions. The largest "holes" in the lattice are at the mid-points of the unit cell edges, $00\frac{1}{2}$, etc., and at $\frac{1}{2}\frac{1}{2}\frac{1}{2}$. These positions are crystallographically equivalent, and one is indicated in Fig. 9a. Each of these interstices is surrounded symmetrically by six solvent atoms. Smaller interstices exist at positions like $\frac{1}{4}\frac{1}{4}\frac{1}{4}$, which are surrounded by a tetrahedral arrangement of four solvent atoms. In γ-Fe the larger interstices have room for a spherical atom of 0.52 A radius, and the smaller for one of only 0.28 A,[1] so the larger interstices accommodate a carbon atom (0.8 A radius) or a nitrogen atom (0.7 A radius) only with a resultant expansion of the lattice, and the smaller holes are probably inaccessible to the dissolved atoms. Body-centered cubic metals have the largest interstices at

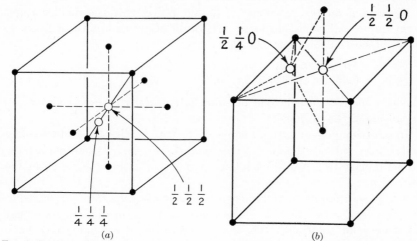

Fig. 9. Interstitial positions in f.c.c. and b.c.c. structures. (a) The largest interstices in f.c.c. are at $\frac{1}{2}\frac{1}{2}\frac{1}{2}$ and equivalent positions; (b) in b.c.c. the largest are at $\frac{1}{2}\frac{1}{4}0$ and equivalent positions.

$\frac{1}{2}\frac{1}{4}0$ and at equivalent positions (Fig. 9b). A spherical atom here would touch four spherical atoms of the solvent. In α-Fe there would be room here for an interstitial atom of 0.36 A radius. Smaller holes are found at the mid-points of the edges (00$\frac{1}{2}$, etc.) and at the equivalent positions $\frac{1}{2}\frac{1}{2}0$, etc., one of which is indicated in the figure; in α-Fe there is room for a sphere of only 0.19 A radius here if the iron atoms are considered as spheres in contact with each other. It therefore appears that interstitial solution in α-Fe should be more difficult than in γ-Fe (as is the case) and that severe distortion should result from interstitial solution.

There is much evidence to indicate that the carbon atoms in α-Fe are located in the (00$\frac{1}{2}$) positions rather than in the largest interstices. The distortion of the structure produced by an individual carbon atom is anisotropic since it is nearer two of the iron atoms than the other four near

[1] Further discussion will be found in C. H Johansson, *Arch. Eisenhüttenw.*, vol. 11, p. 241, 1937; and L. W. Strock. *Z. Krist.*. vol. 93, p. 285, 1936.

neighbors; the effect is to distort the lattice from cubic to tetragonal symmetry.[1] This accounts for the tetragonality of martensite, the body-centered tetragonal structure that is formed when austenite is quenched and transforms rapidly, without opportunity for the carbon atoms to form a carbide. Another consequence of the anisotropic distortion from interstitially dissolved elements is that an applied force can alter the distribution of the solute atoms among the holes, causing them to prefer holes that are enlarged by the applied stress rather than those that are contracted. The shifting of atoms has not been detected by X-rays but causes marked internal friction effects.[2]

Because of the restricted size of the interstices only the smaller atoms form interstitial solid solutions. The radii of atoms known or likely to form interstitial solutions are all less than 1.0 A:

H	B	C	N	O
0.46	0.97	0.77	0.71	0.60

When a solvent accepts one of these interstitially, there is always an expansion of the unit cell.

In multicomponent systems some atoms may be dissolved interstitially and others substitutionally, as in manganese steel, where manganese atoms replace iron atoms on lattice points and carbon atoms enter the interstices.

A solid solution at an extremity of a binary-alloy diagram is referred to as a *terminal solid solution*. There are also intermediate phases that are true solid solutions. These *intermediate solid solutions* may have either narrow or wide ranges of homogeneity and may or may not include a composition having a simple chemical formula. One is justified in classifying intermediate phases as *intermetallic compounds* only if they have a narrow range of homogeneity and simple stoichiometrical proportions and if atoms of identical kinds occupy identical points on the lattice. In general, the term "compound" is inappropriate. The homogeneity range may not actually include a composition having a simple chemical formula—the phase "CuAl," for example, exists in a homogeneity range that does not include the composition CuAl. In systems such as Ag-Cd the ϵ phase corresponds to the composition $AgCd_3$, but the structure is c.p.h., and it is impossible to place the Ag atoms on one set of equivalent points and the Cd atoms solely on another set; in fact, the two kinds of

---

[1] It has been suggested that this distortion can occur easily, thus making the hole easily expandable, able more easily to accommodate the interstitial atom than can the hole at $\frac{1}{2}\frac{1}{4}0$ with its equidistant neighbors.

[2] J. L. Snoek, *Physica*, vol. 8, p. 711, 1941. L. J. Dijkstra, *Philips Research Repts.*, vol. 2, p. 357, 1947. T. S. Kê, *Phys. Rev.*, vol. 74, pp. 7, 16, 1948. C. Zener, "Elasticity and Anelasticity of Metals," University of Chicago Press, Chicago, 1948. T. S. Kê, *Trans. AIME*, vol. 176, p. 448, 1948.

atoms are distributed at random on the atom positions, just as in a solid solution. Intermediate phases may be of any type between the ideal solid solution on the one hand and the ideal chemical compound on the other. An alloy may be a true solid solution at high temperatures and yet resemble a compound at low temperatures if it becomes an ordered superlattice as is discussed later. The tendency to form an ordered superlattice may be so weak that ordering cannot be detected, or so strong that the alloy melts before thermal agitation is able to produce detectable disorder.

Determination of the Type of Solid Solution. The types of solid solutions are distinguished from each other by density comparisons. The density of an alloy computed from an X-ray measurement of the unit-cell size will agree with the observed density if the correct type of solution is assumed. For a substitutional solid solution the calculated density ρ_c is given by the relation

$$\rho_c = \frac{n\bar{A}}{VN}$$

where n is the number of atoms contained in the unit cell of volume V, N is Avogadro's number, and $\bar{A}$ is the mean atomic weight of the atoms.[1]

For an interstitial solid solution there is a contribution to the density by the interstitial atoms in addition to the contribution from the lattice-point atoms given by the above formula. There is usually a fraction of an interstitial atom, on the average, in each cell. If we call this n^* and let n be the number of lattice-point atoms per cell, then we may determine n^* from the relation $n^*:n =$ atomic per cent interstitial atoms: atomic per cent lattice-point atoms. If the interstitial atoms have a mean atomic weight $\bar{A}^*$, their contribution to the density amounts to $n^*\bar{A}^*/VN$. This is added to the contribution $n\bar{A}/VN$ of the lattice-point atoms having the mean atomic weight $\bar{A}$.

Generalizations Concerning Solubility. Several factors are now known that control the ranges of solubility in alloy systems: the type of crystal

---

[1] The mean atomic weight is computed from the atomic percentages p_1, p_2, etc., of the elements comprising the alloy and the atomic weights A_1, A_2, etc., with the formula

$$\bar{A} = \frac{p_1 A_1}{100} + \frac{p_2 A_2}{100} + \cdots$$

The atomic percentages are obtained from weight percentages w_1, w_2, etc., by the relation

$$p_1 = \frac{w_1/A_1}{w_1/A_1 + w_2/A_2 + \cdots} \cdot 100$$

Cyril S. Smith has published logarithm tables for interconversion of atomic and weight percentages of binary alloys: "Metals Handbook," p. 196, American Society for Metals, Cleveland, Ohio, 1948.

structure of the alloying elements, the relative sizes of the atoms (the "size factor"), the electronegativity of one element with respect to the other, and the concentration of valence electrons in the alloys. These factors are understood largely through the work of Hume-Rothery at Oxford University.[1]

Complete solid solubility of two elements in all proportions is never encountered unless the elements have the same crystal structure and similar atomic radii. Silver and gold, which form a continuous series of solid solutions, are both f.c.c. and the atoms differ only 0.2 per cent in size. Molybdenum, which is b.c.c. in structure, is completely soluble in tungsten, which is also b.c.c. with similar atomic radius. However, molybdenum has only limited solubility in silver, which differs only 6 per cent in atomic radius but is f.c.c.

When atomic radii differ less than about 15 per cent, the *size factor* is favorable to solid-solution formation. The size factor must be favorable if a complete series of solid solutions is to occur; an unfavorable size factor (radii differing more than 15 per cent) restricts solubility. In fact, the greater the difference in size, the more limited the solubility, other things being equal. If the sizes differ by 8 per cent or more but are still in the favorable range, there is usually a continuous series of solutions but a minimum in the liquidus curve; this represents a tendency toward the formation of a eutectic.[2]

Another factor controlling solubility is the *chemical-affinity effect*.[3] The more electronegative the solute element and the more electropositive the solvent, or vice versa, the greater is the tendency to restrict solid-solution ranges and to form intermetallic compounds. The electronegativity of elements in the periodic table increases from left to right in any period and from the bottom to the top in any group. Thus elements of Group VI$_B$ (S, Se, Te) form stable sulfides, selenides, and tellurides with the electropositive metals, and solid solutions of these elements in normal metals are usually very limited. Group V$_B$ (P, As, Sb, Bi) with somewhat less pronounced electronegative character usually dissolve up to a few atomic per cent in the electropositive metals, and as the metals approach each other in the electrochemical series the solid solutions tend to become more extensive.

[1] W. Hume-Rothery, "The Structure of Metals and Alloys," Institute of Metals, London, 1936, and revisions.

[2] For detailed discussions of the effect of size and polarizability on solubility, see papers by W. Hume-Rothery and G. V. Raynor, *Phil. Mag.*, vol. 26, pp. 129, 143, 152, 1938.

[3] Hume-Rothery calls this the "electronegative valency effect" since it depends on the separation of the elements in the electromotive series. It seems more appropriate to give it a name that emphasizes the role of affinity between the unlike atoms and that avoids confusion with the relative valency effect.

The *relative valency effect* also governs solubility. It may be described by saying that a metal of lower valency tends to dissolve a metal of higher valency more readily than vice versa. Silicon, which crystallizes according to the 8 − N rule, has a structure that depends on each atom's having four neighbors. Each atom shares an electron with each of the four neighbors so that an octet of electrons is built up. If an atom of copper is substituted for a silicon atom there will be insufficient electrons to form the covalent bonds, and it is therefore understandable that solubility is

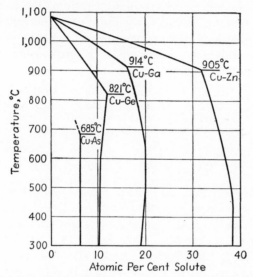

FIG. 10. Solidus and solid solubility curves for some copper-alloy systems.

very restricted—silicon dissolves less than 2.0 atomic per cent copper. On the other hand, copper dissolves 14 atomic per cent of the higher valence silicon. Magnesium (valence 2) dissolves less than 0.2 atomic per cent gold (valence 1), but gold dissolves magnesium to the extent of 20 or 30 atomic per cent. In other words, removal of valence electrons from truly metallic phases is more serious than the addition of a limited number of electrons above the fundamental electron-atom ratio for the structure.

A solvent possesses a definite capacity to absorb the valence electrons of a solute when the size factor is favorable. Copper, univalent, can dissolve another univalent element in unlimited amounts (with a favorable size factor) and forms a continuous series of solutions with nickel, for example. But copper dissolves decreasing amounts as the valency of the solute increases, as illustrated in Fig. 10. Each atom of zinc contributes one additional electron to the solution, each atom of gallium contributes two, germanium three, and arsenic four. The maximum solubilities in

copper (and silver) are approximately 40 atomic per cent for one additional electron, 20 per cent for two, 12 per cent for three, and 7 per cent
for four in reasonable agreement with the percentages 40, 20, 13, 10 that
would be expected if the number of valence electrons that can be accommodated per atom is the same in each alloy. The maximum solubility
corresponds to a ratio of valence electrons to atoms of 1.4 to 1—an
electron concentration of 1.4.

Attention has been devoted recently to discrepancies between observed
solubilities and the valence electron-atom ratio of 1.4, in the belief that
those should be understandable as the result of factors other than electron
concentration. Striking discrepancies occur, as Owen points out,[1] particularly with metals dissolved in gold. Electron-atom ratios at maximum solubility are as follows:

Au-Cd	Au-Al	Au-Zn	Au-In	Au-Hg	Au-Sb
1.33	1.31	1.30	1.255	1.20	1.045

If one contrasts these values with the following ones,

Ag-Cd	Ag-In	Ag-Al	Ag-Zn	Ag-Sn	Ag-Sb
1.428	1.404	1.403	1.40	1.335	1.29

it is immediately clear that solubilities in gold are much smaller than corresponding ones in silver, yet all the systems listed have favorable size
factors, and the radii of Ag and Au atoms are almost identical (1.44).
But the ionic radii differ: Au^+, 1.37; Ag^+, 1.13. Since the lattice constants are similar but the silver ions are smaller than the gold ions, there
is more space between the ions in silver than in gold for the valence electrons. Owen proposed that this makes it easier to introduce foreign
atoms into silver than into gold.[2] Copper resembles silver rather than
gold in its radii, for these are 1.28 and 0.96 for atom and ion, respectively,
and its electron-atom ratios at maximum solubility are as follows:

Cu-Al	Cu-Zn	Cu-Ge	Cu-As
1.40	1.38	1.34	1.27

Raynor,[3] on the other hand, suggested that these various relations are due
to the deformation of the solvent ions by the atoms of the solute. Solvent
ions of gold should be deformed ("polarized") more than the smaller ions
of copper or silver; the deformation may be considered as bringing some
electrons in the gold ions so much under the influence of the dissolved

[1] E. A. Owen and E. W. Roberts, *Phil. Mag.*, vol. 27, p. 294, 1939. E. A. Owen and
V. W. Rowlands, *J. Inst. Metals*, vol. 66, p. 361, 1940. E. A. Owen and E. A. O'D.
Roberts, *J. Inst. Metals*, vol. 71, p. 213, 1945.

[2] E. A. Owen, *J. Inst. Metals*, vol. 73, p. 471, 1947.

[3] G. V. Raynor, *Phil. Mag.*, vol. 26, p. 152, 1938; *J. Inst. Metals*, vol. 71, p. 553,
1945; "Progress in Metal Physics," vol. I, Interscience Publishers, New York, 1949.

atom as to be effectively free electrons. This tendency would be equivalent to raising the number of electrons contributed per atom dissolved, and lowering the electron-atom ratio as normally computed. The effect should increase as the size of the solute ion shrinks and its charge increases, which accounts for the decreasing apparent electron-atom ratio in the series Au-Cd to Au-Sb.

Hume-Rothery has also pointed out that the liquidus temperatures and likewise the solidus temperatures of various copper alloys are almost identical at identical electron concentrations, and the same is true of silver alloys.

It is a general rule (to which there are exceptions) that in a binary system the solubility in the high-melting metal is greater than in the low-melting metal.

Apparent Atomic Size in Alloys. The number of substitutional solid solutions that obey Vegard's law are few. The law is obeyed moderately well in the systems Au-Pt, Au-Pd, Mo-W, Pt-Ir, Pt-Rh, Pb-Tl, and possibly Sb-Bi, but negative deviations (smaller lattice constants) are found in Cu-Ni, Au-Ag, Ag-Pd, Ag-Pt, Co-Ni, and Cr-Fe, and positive deviations are found in Cu-Au, Cu-Pd, Fe-Cr (Fe-rich), Cu-Ag (both Cu-rich and Ag-rich), and many others. Atoms of very similar size and electronic structure tend to form systems in which Vegard's law is followed, while negative deviations tend to occur in those systems in which intermetallic compounds are formed.[1] As a rule, alloy systems in which the liquidus curve bows upward have negative deviations, while the opposite is true for systems with a sagging liquidus.[2]

Since factors other than size govern lattice constants of solid solutions it is natural to expect electron concentration to play a role, and, in fact, the lattice expansion of silver for dilute solutions of Cd, In, Sn, or Sb correlates rather well with electron concentration.[3] The expansion produced by one atom of solute is proportional to the valence of the solute. There is unquestionably a tendency to follow this rule in many alloys, but strict proportionality to valency does not exist.[4]

Axon and Hume-Rothery propose that four factors must be considered if lattice parameters in solutions are to be understood:[5] (1) the relative

[1] A. Westgren and A. Almin, *Z. physik. Chem.*, vol. B5, p. 14, 1929. E. R. Jette, *Trans. AIME*, vol. 111, p. 75, 1934.

[2] F. Halla, "Kristallchemie und Kristallphysik metallischer Werkstoffe," Barth, Leipzig, 1939.

[3] W. Hume-Rothery, G. F. Lewin, and P. W. Reynolds, *Proc. Roy. Soc. (London)*, vol. A157, p. 167, 1936.

[4] E. A. Owen and E. W. Roberts, *Phil. Mag.*, vol. 27, p. 294, 1939. E. A. Owen and E. A. O'D. Roberts, *J. Inst. Metals*, vol. 73, p. 471, 1947. G. V. Raynor in "Progress in Metal Physics," vol. I, Interscience Publishers, New York, 1949.

[5] H. J. Axon and W. Hume-Rothery, *Proc. Roy. Soc. (London)*, vol. A193, p. 1, 1948.

volume per valency electron in crystals of the solvent and solute; (2) the relative radii of the ions of solvent and solute; (3) effects due to the overlap of Brillouin zones (discussed in Chap. XIII); and (4) the difference between solvent and solute in the electrochemical series. The interplay of these factors is seen in their effect on the "apparent atomic diameter." If the lattice parameter vs. atomic per cent curve for dilute solutions in Cu, Ag, or Au is extrapolated to 100 per cent solute, the extrapolated value refers to a hypothetical f.c.c. parameter, and the corresponding distance between nearest neighbors is the apparent atomic diameter of the solute when dissolved in the given solvent.

The apparent atomic diameter of a particular solute may vary considerably: for Ge it is 2.97 A when dissolved in Al but only 2.78 when dissolved in Cu. The principal controlling factor is the volume per valence electron, V_e, in the crystals of the solute and solvent. In general any element with large V_e dissolved in one of small V_e tends to have a small apparent diameter, and the converse also holds (a solute of small V_e dissolved in a solvent of large V_e tends to yield a large apparent diameter). Metals with large V_e, such as univalent lithium, tend to have high compressibility; aluminum, on the other hand, is trivalent and has low compressibility. When lithium is dissolved in aluminum it is to be expected that, at least in dilute solutions, the stronger binding forces between aluminum atoms control interatomic distances so much as to compress the lithium atom more than is normal for it in the weakly bound lithium crystal. Thus for Li in Al the apparent diameter for lithium should be small; actually it is nearly as small as aluminum itself.

Some exceptions to the above V_e principle can be accounted for by the second factor: if the solute ion is considerably larger than the solvent ion so the electron clouds are forced to interpenetrate, the apparent diameter of the solute is increased. The effect of Brillouin-zone overlap in producing expansion of the crystal in the direction in which it occurs, hence a larger apparent diameter, will be discussed in connection with the electron theory of metals in a later chapter. The electrochemical factor, the last of those listed above, acts to make the apparent diameter smaller when solute and solvent are widely separated in the electrochemical series. (This is another statement of the generalization mentioned earlier regarding systems in which intermetallic compounds are formed; it represents a tendency toward ionic binding.)

INTERMEDIATE PHASES

It is rare to find alloy systems in which intermediate phases obey the normal valencies of the elements. This is a consequence of the fact that most of the phases have *metallic* binding, which means that valence electrons are free to move about in the lattice, as contrasted with inorganic or organic compounds in which the electrons are tightly bound into stable groups of atoms. Attempts at first were made to define an intermetallic compound and to distinguish it from an intermediate solid solution, but the attempts were a source of confusion rather than of clarification. It was later realized that some phases had chemical formulas that followed valence rules and yet had the metallic conductivity and reflectivity characteristic of metallic binding, consequently that the compounds possessed an intermediate type of binding between covalent and metallic,

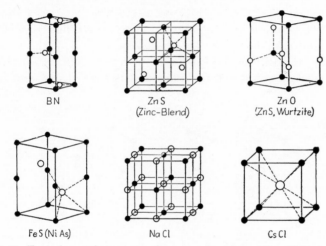

BN ZnS (Zinc-Blend) ZnO (ZnS, Wurtzite)

FeS (NiAs) NaCl CsCl

Fig. 11. Typical crystal structures of compounds of type AX. (*Goldschmidt.*)

resulting from a partial breakdown of covalent bonds. Intermediate types of binding can exist, in fact, between all the ideal types of binding: ionic, homopolar, molecular, and metallic.

Structures of Compounds with Normal Valency. From the early work of Goldschmidt[1] and others it was found that the simple structures illustrated in Figs. 11 and 12 are common to a great number of compounds, including many intermetallic phases that obey normal valency laws.

The structure of *rock salt* ($NaCl$) may be considered as two interpenetrating f.c.c. lattices of the two types of atoms, with the corner of one located at the point $\frac{1}{2}00$ of the other. The *fluorite* structure (CaF_2) is also cubic, with Ca atoms at cube corners and face centers and with F atoms at all quarter-way positions along the cube diagonals ($\frac{1}{4}\frac{1}{4}\frac{1}{4}$, $\frac{1}{4}\frac{3}{3}\frac{3}{4}$,

[1] V. M. Goldschmidt, *Trans. Faraday Soc.*, vol. 25, p. 253, 1929.

etc.). These typically ionic structures are found frequently among alloys of metals with elements of Groups IV_B, V_B, and VI_B:

NaCl Structure		CaF₂ Structure		
MgSe	SrTe	Mg₂Si	Cu₂S	CuCdSb
CaSe	SnTe	Mg₂Ge	Cu₂Se	CuMgSb
SrSe	BaTe	Mg₂Sn	Be₂C	CuBiMg
BaSe	MnTe	Mg₂Pb	Sn₂Pt	AgAsMg
MnSe	SnTe	Cu₂Se	Al₂Ca	LiMgN
PbSe	PbTe	Li₂S		LiZnN
	CaTe	Na₂S		Li₃AlN
				Li₃GaN₂

The NaCl structure is also found with many oxides, fluorides, chlorides, hydrides, and carbides, as well as many compounds of the rare earths with As, Sb, and Bi; the CaF₂ structure with many oxides, fluorides, and some intermetallic phases of the noble metals with Al, Ga, and In (page 240).

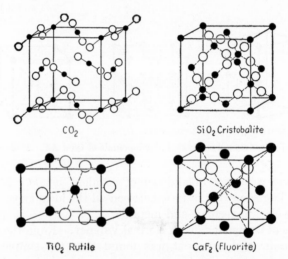

CO₂ SiO₂ Cristobalite

TiO₂ Rutile CaF₂ (Fluorite)

Fɪɢ. 12. Typical crystal structures of compounds of type AX_2. (*Goldschmidt.*)

The *diamond* structure is formed by elements having a ratio of 4 electrons to 1 atom (C, Si, Ge, Sn). Among alloys we also find closely related structures when the electron-atom ratio is 4. The *zinc blende structure* (ZnS) may be regarded as two interpenetrating face-centered lattices of the elements, with the corner of one located at the position $\frac{1}{4}\frac{1}{4}\frac{1}{4}$ of the other, as in the diamond structure. Figures 11 and 12 show the close similarity between ZnS and CaF₂ structures. The *wurtzite structure* (ZnS, ZnO) has one kind of atom on c.p.h. positions and the other at intermediate points, where each atom is surrounded symmetrically by four atoms of the other kind.[1]   The hexagonal layers are stacked in one sequence in wurtzite, and in another in zinc blende, and stacking faults are frequent.[2]

Normal valency rules hold for these so-called *adamantine compounds*, for their binding is covalent.   They are formed between an element that is a certain number of places to the left of the column containing C, Si, Ge, Sn and an element an equal number of places to the right in the periodic table:

Zinc Blende Structure			Wurtzite Structure
BeS	BeSe	BeTe	MgTe
AlP	AlAs	AlSb	CdSe
GaP	GaAs	GaSb	α-AgI
α-CdS	CdSe	CdTe	β-ZnS
α-ZnS	ZnSe	ZnTe	β-CdS
HgS	HgSe	HgTe	
β-AgI	CuI	CuBr	
InP	InSb	GeSb	

The *nickel arsenide structure* ($NiAs$) is frequently formed by the transition metals Cr, Mn, Fe, Co, Ni, Cu, Pd, and Pt alloyed with the metalloids S, Se, Te, As, Sb, and Bi.   The structure is composed of alternating layers of metal and metalloid atoms, each layer being a c.p.h. (0001) plane. The alloys have metallic conductivity and there can be more than 50 atomic per cent of the metal present; so for these reasons they are more metallic than ionic.   The following examples are known:

Nickel Arsenide Structure			
CrS	VSe	AuSn	PdSb
CoS	CoTe	CuSn	PtSb
FeS	FeTe	PtSn	MnAs
NiS	NiTe	NiSn	NiAs
VS	CrTe	CoSb	NiBi
CoSe	MnTe	FeSb	MnBi
FeSe	PdTe	NiSb	
NiSe	PtTe	CrSb	
CrSe	FeSn	MnSb	

Phases with this structure often have wide homogeneity ranges, and the range does not always include the *AB* composition.   The NiAs type of structure is found, for example, in the following phases:

Co_2Ge	Fe_2Ge	Cu_2In	Mn_2Sn
Ni_2Ge	$NiTe_2$	Ni_2In	

These characteristics indicate that there is much metallic character associated with many of the phases; in fact they may be regarded in some

---

[1] Coordinates are zinc: 000 and $\frac{1}{3}\frac{2}{3}\frac{1}{2}$, and oxygen: $00u$ and $\frac{1}{3}\frac{2}{3}u+\frac{1}{2}$, where u is approximately $\frac{3}{8}$ and c/a is roughly 1.63.

[2] H. Jagodzinski, *Acta Cryst.*, vol. 2, p. 298, 1949.

instances as typical metallic phases obeying electron-concentration rules that will be discussed later. The metallic character increases as the metalloid element becomes less electronegative.

Zintl's rule[1] states that in saltlike ionic compounds only those elements are able to become negative ions that precede the noble gases by 1 to 4 places. Exceptions to the rule were found by Hellner and Laves[2] in alloys of In and Ga with Ni, Pd, Pt, Cu, Ag, and Au: many phases containing indium and gallium (5 places before the noble gases) show definite tendencies for the indium and gallium to become negative ions in typically saltlike compounds (CsCl or the closely related Ni_2Al_3 type of compound), judging by abnormally short distances between unlike atoms in these phases. Thus the rule should apparently include elements 1 to 5 places before a noble gas rather than 1 to 4.

Hume-Rothery[3] has shown that two generalizations are possible regarding normal valency compounds: (1) There is a general tendency for all metals to form normal valency compounds with elements of Groups IV_B, V_B, and VI_B. (2) This tendency and the stability of the compound are greater the more electropositive the metal and the more electronegative the B subgroup element.

Electronegativity increases in any one period in passing toward higher atomic numbers and in any one group in passing upward (toward lower atomic numbers). Thus, for example, Mg_2Si, Mg_2Sn, and Mg_2Pb are listed in what one would expect to be the order of decreasing stability, for in the electrochemical series Si is more electronegative than Sn, and the latter is more electronegative than Pb. The melting points of these normal valency compounds serve as a rough indication of stability and they bear out this principle, for they are, respectively, 1102, 780, and 553°C.

Electron Compounds and Hume-Rothery's Rule. It has long been noted that equilibrium diagrams for alloys of Cu, Ag, and Au with metals of the B subgroups show remarkable similarities. When the structures of the intermediate phases were determined by X-rays, largely by Westgren and Phragmén in Sweden, the similarities became even more impressive, for phases of the same structure occurred in many systems.

The system Cu-Zn is typical of these structurally analogous systems. As indicated on the diagram (page 197), there is a sequence of phases, with approximate compositions as follows:

α solid solution, Cu-rich (f.c.c.).

β phase, CuZn, disordered (b.c.c.) or ordered (CsCl type, β').

[1] E. Zintl, J. Goubeau, and W. Dullenkopf, Z. physik. Chem., vol. A154, p. 1, 1931. E. Zintl and H. Kaiser, Z. anorg. u. allgem. Chem., vol. 211, p. 113, 1933.

[2] E. Hellner and F. Laves, Z. Naturforsch., vol. 2a, p. 177, 1947.

[3] W. Hume-Rothery, "The Structure of Metals and Alloys," Institute of Metals, London, 1936.

γ phase, Cu_5Zn_8 (cubic, 52 atoms per cell).

ϵ phase, $CuZn_3$ (close-packed hexagonal).

η solid solution, Zn-rich (c.p.h.).

Similar sequences of structurally analogous phases are found in many alloy systems, but a given phase does not occur at the same composition in all systems. The $CuZn_3$ phase, for example, is analogous in structure to the Cu_3Sn and Ag_5Al_3 phases.

Hume-Rothery[1] pointed out that some fundamental principles become apparent in these analogous systems if the number of valence electrons per atom is computed for each alloy. The β phases are found to exist at or near the compositions in each system that have a ratio of 3 valence electrons to 2 atoms. This structure is found in AgCd, for example, where one electron is contributed by each atom of Ag and two by each atom of Cd, making three electrons for the two atoms. The same structure occurs in Cu_3Al, where the three valence electrons from the Al and the one from each Cu atom make up six electrons to four atoms. In Cu_5Sn the same phase occurs with nine electrons to six atoms (four from Sn, one from each Cu). Hume-Rothery found that other electron-atom ratios tended to be characteristic of the γ and ϵ phases in many structurally analogous systems, and proposed the following list of electron concentrations:

Phase	β	γ	ϵ
Electron-atom ratio	3:2	21:13	7:4

The valences were assumed to be the number of electrons in excess of the last completed shell, as follows:

Valence	Element
1	Cu, Ag, Au (Group I)
2	Be, Mg, Zn, Cd, Hg (Group II)
3	Ga, Al, In (Group III)
4	Si, Ge, Sn, Pb (Group IV)
5	P, As, Sb, Bi (Group V)
0	Fe, Co, Ni, Ru, Rh, Pd, Pt, Ir, Os (Group VIII)*

* There is basis for assuming different valences for the transition elements Cr, Mn, Fe, Co, Ni, as is discussed in later sections.

It is found that in some systems at the electron-atom ratio of 3:2 a phase appears that is isomorphous with the complicated structure of beta-manganese. This is a cubic crystal with 20 atoms per unit cell.[2] Recent work suggests that the structure of the 3:2 electron compounds depends upon the valency of the alloying element, for in the series Cu-Zn,

[1] W. Hume-Rothery, *J. Inst. Metals*, vol. 35, pp. 295, 307, 1926.

[2] G. D. Preston, *Phil. Mag.*, vol. 5, p. 1207, 1928.

Cu-Ga, Cu-Ge, in which the valency of the alloying element increases progressively, the 3:2 compound in the first is b.c.c., in the second is b.c.c. at high temperatures and c.p.h. at lower temperatures, and in the third is c.p.h. only.[1]

The structures of the γ phases are not all identical but are strikingly similar, and all have large unit cells. The unit cell of gamma-brass (Cu_5Zn_8) contains 52 atoms and may be considered as made up of 27 unit cells of beta brass (which would amount to 54 atoms) with two atoms removed and the rest shifted somewhat in position. The phase Cu_5Zn_8 has a b.c.c. space-lattice; Cu_9Al_4 has a simple cubic space-lattice with 49 to 52 atoms in the unit cell; $Cu_{31}Sn_8$ (or $Cu_{41}Sn_{11}$) has a cubic space-lattice with 416 atoms per unit cell.[2] The ternary alloys of Cu-Zn-Al have a γ structure when the electron to atom ratio is 21:13.

Table X lists the approximate formulas of a number of electron compounds.[3]

Here again, as with the electron-concentration factor that limits maximum solubility, there are many deviations from the "ideal" electron-atom ratios 3:2, 21:13, and 7:4. This may be seen from the plot of homogeneity ranges in Fig. 13.

Some generalizations are possible about the deviations;[4] for example, increasing temperature widens the homogeneity range for β phases. The tendency for these phases in Au, Ag, and Cu alloys to become ordered superlattices follows the sequence Au > Ag > Cu, which is evidence that increasing electrochemical difference favors ordering of the phases. Variations in electron-atom ratio are found in the γ phases, as in the others.[5]

---

[1] I am indebted to W. Hume-Rothery for a discussion of this and other points, to be covered in a forthcoming edition of "Atomic Theory for Students of Metallurgy," *Inst. Metals (London)*, 1946.

[2] A. Westgren and G. Phragmén, *Z. anorg. u. allgem. Chem.*, vol. 175, p. 80, 1928.

[3] W. Hume-Rothery, "The Structure of Metals and Alloys," Institute of Metals, London, 1936. H. Witte, *Metallwirtschaft*, vol. 16, p. 237, 1937.

[4] W. Hume-Rothery, P. W. Reynolds, and G. V. Raynor, *J. Inst. Metals*, vol. 66, p. 191, 1940.

[5] A. L. Norbury (*J. Inst. Metals*, vol. 65, p. 355, 1939) suggested that γ phases might be viewed as constructed out of 27 b.c.c. unit cells by replacing two atoms by two electrons, giving an electron-atom ratio of 83:52. By a similar scheme he modifies 7:4 to arrive at ratios of 14:8, 13:9, and 15:7 for ϵ phases and modifies 5:2 to arrive at 39:17, 37:19, 35:21, and 42:14 for NiAs structures, these being in reasonable agreement with observed ratios. That these ratios are significant is very doubtful; an interpretation (W. Hume-Rothery, J. O. Betterton, and J. Reynolds, in press) of the abnormally high value in the Cu-Al system is that it is due to a strong electrochemical factor contributing to the binding and tending to account for an unusually high melting point. When atoms in a gamma phase differ markedly in size, the phase is displaced to lower electron concentrations, as in Cu-Hg, Cu-Cd, and Cu-In.

In general it appears that size factor, temperature, solute valency, and electrochemical difference (chemical affinity effect) must all be considered as playing a part along with electron concentration in determining homogeneity ranges and compositions. A surprising example of the importance of the electron-concentration factor in governing the structure

TABLE X. STRUCTURALLY ANALOGOUS PHASES

Electron-atom ratio 3:2		Electron-atom ratio 21:13	Electron-atom ratio 7:4
β Structure (b.c.c.)	β-Manganese structure (cubic, complex)	γ-Brass structure (cubic, complex)	ε-Brass structure (c.p.h.)
AgCd	Ag_3Al	Ag_5Cd_8	$AgCd_3$
AgMg	Au_3Al	Ag_5Hg_8	Ag_3Sn
AgZn	Cu_5Si	Ag_5Zn_8	Ag_5Al_3
AuCd	$CoZn_3$	Au_5Cd_8	Ag_5In_3
AuMg		Au_5Zn_8	$AgZn_3$
AuZn		Cu_5Cd_8	$AuCd_3$
CuBe		Cu_5Hg_8	$AuZn_3$
CuZn		Cu_5Zn_8	Au_3Sn
Cu_3Al		Cu_9Al_4	Au_3Hg
Cu_3Ga		Cu_9Ga_4	Au_5Al_3
Cu_5Sn		Cu_9In_4	$CuCd_3$
CoAl		$Cu_{31}Si_8$	$CuZn_3$
FeAl		$Cu_{31}Sn_8$	Cu_3Ge
NiAl		Co_5Zn_{21}	Cu_3Si
		Fe_5Zn_{21}	Cu_3Sn
		Ni_5Zn_{21}	$FeZn_7$
		Pd_5Zn_{21}	
		Rh_5Zn_{21}	
		Pt_5Zn_{21}	
		Ni_5Cd_{21}	
		$Na_{31}Pb_8$	
		$Cu_7Zn_4Al_2$	

of a β phase is given by the phase NiAl (page 245) in which as the composition is altered from 50 atomic per cent Ni to lower Ni concentrations the structure prefers the drastic step of omitting atoms from its structure, leaving vacant lattice sites, to increasing the number of electrons per unit cell above three.[1] (The number of electrons per cell is a more fundamental quantity than the electron-atom ratio, but except in cases such as this these two parameters are equivalent.)[2] For the β, γ, and ε electron com-

[1] This example can be objected to on the basis that another theory, having nothing to do with electron concentration, has been proposed for this phase; *viz.*, a theory based on the packing of the different sized atoms.

[2] An example that is perhaps better to cite is a gamma phase in the Cu-Ga system

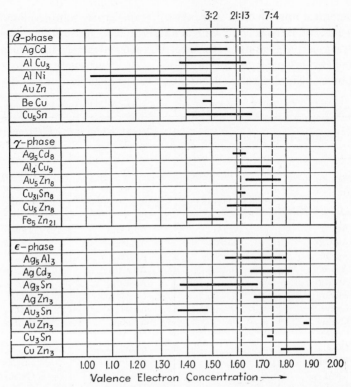

FIG. 13. Valence electron concentrations for several typical β, γ, and ε phases, compared with Hume-Rothery's ratios.

pounds not only must the electron concentration lie between 1 and 2, but the ratio of atomic radii must also be less than 1:2.

The mean *volume per atom* in intermediate phases is nearly always less than in the pure metals. This is especially true for the β phases containing aluminum (FeAl, CoAl, NiAl, Cu₃Al), in which the contraction may amount to as much as 15 per cent[1] and is probably associated chiefly

---

(J. O. Betterton and W. Hume-Rothery, *J. Inst. Metals*, in press). The 52 atoms per unit cell of this cubic phase remain almost unchanged as Cu is added from 29 up to 34.5 atomic per cent, but the number steadily drops as the percentage of Cu increases above this. Yet the number of electrons per unit cell remains constant at 86.5 throughout. The b.c.c. phase in the Cu-Al-Ni system is a similar example, in which the alloy prefers to have vacancies rather than to have the electrons per unit cell increase beyond a critical number that is presumed to be the number that fill the zone up to a level where more rapid energy increase accompanies further additions. (See H. Lipson and A. Taylor, *Proc. Roy. Soc.*, vol. A173, p. 232, 1939.)

[1] A. Westgren, *Z. angew. Chem.*, vol. 45, p. 33, 1932. A. Westgren and A. Almin, *Z. physik. Chem.*, vol. B5, p. 14, 1929. E. Zintl and G. Brauer, *Z. physik. Chem.*, vol. B20, p. 245, 1933.

with the aluminum atom. Pronounced contraction also occurs in the γ-phase alloys (Cu_9Al_4, Ni_5Cd_{21}, Ag_3Li_{10}, and $Na_{31}Pb_8$).[1] Bernal[2] has pointed out that contraction increases as the structure departs more and more from the metallic, and Zintl[3] concluded that the Hume-Rothery electron-concentration rules should not necessarily apply when the contractions are large.

The Nickel Arsenide Structure. Alloy phases with the NiAs-type structure can be considered as electron compounds with an electron-atom ratio of 2.5. This corresponds to 10 electrons per unit cell (since the unit cell contains two molecules), a figure that applies to both normal, ideal structures and those in which atom sites are vacant. In computing the electron concentration, however, Raynor[4] assumes that the valence-electron contribution per atom of the transition metals is not always zero, but depends upon the nature of the alloying partner and its relative amount: Ni contributes no electrons in NiSb, perhaps one in NiSn, and it appears to absorb one in NiS.

Phases with composition differing from *AB* may be of the *defect* type (with atom sites of the NiAs-type structure vacant) or *interstitial* type (excess metal atoms entering interstices). Thus starting with NiTe, individual Ni atoms can be removed until the composition is $Ni_{0.5}Te$ without destroying the stability of the phase; and excess Co atoms can be added to CoSb with the excess going into the interstices.

Laves and Wallbaum[5] have found a continuous series of NiAs-type structures with varying c/a ratio as follows:

Structure	NiS	NiSe	NiAs	Ni_3Sb_2	Ni_3Sn_2	Ni_2Ge	Ni_2In
c/a	1.633	1.46	1.39	1.31	1.27	1.28	1.23

and with intermediate axial ratios being obtainable from solid solutions between adjacent compounds in the list. At the left of this list is the NiAs structure with $c/a = 1.633$ as required for the hexagonal close packing of spheres. Here the sulfur cations pack tightly together and the nickel fills octahedral interstices between them. (All octahedral interstices are filled in NiAs, but extra Ni atoms can be accommodated in tetrahedral interstices.) The binding is chiefly ionic in character. The axial ratio decreases steadily along the series to the value $\sqrt{3}/\sqrt{2} = 1.225$

[1] Charles W. Stillwell, "Crystal Chemistry," McGraw-Hill, New York, 1938.

[2] J. D. Bernal, *Trans. Faraday Soc.*, vol. 25, p. 367, 1929.

[3] A. Westgren, *Z. angew. Chem.*, vol. 45, p. 33, 1932. A. Westgren and A. Almin, *Z. physik. Chem.* vol. B5, p. 14, 1929. E. Zintl and G. Brauer, *Z. physik. Chem.*, vol. B20, p. 245, 1933.

[4] G. V. Raynor in "Progress in Metal Physics," vol. I, Interscience Publishers, New York, 1949.

[5] F. Laves and H. J. Wallbaum, *Z. angew. Mineral.*, vol. 4, p. 17, 1942.

that would correspond to a pseudo-cubic structure. Both octahedral and tetrahedral interstices are filled in Ni_2In. The metallic character increases from left to right; Ni_2In, at the extreme right, has a diffraction pattern and a structure remarkably near that of γ-brass and other Hume-Rothery γ phases of metallic nature. (The formula Ni_9In_4 has the Hume-Rothery electron-atom ratio for γ phases if Ni is counted as univalent.)

There is thus a progressive alteration of structure through this series, which correlates with position of the metalloid in the periodic table, and with the metallicity. And the series may be extended still further, for at the left may be put NiO which has the NaCl structure (as truly an ionic structure as can be imagined) and at the right may be placed a true representative of the metallic Hume-Rothery γ phases, Cu_9Ga_4.[1]

The Fluorspar Structure. The CaF_2 structure, frequently found in alloy systems, and easily understood as a normal valency compound, may also be treated as an electron compound. The examples listed on page 232 meet an electron-atom specification of 8:3. In addition the following can be assumed to have electron-atom ratios of 8:3 if Au, Pt, and Ni atoms are assumed to contribute two electrons each:

$$AuAl_2 \quad AuGa_2 \quad AuIn_2 \quad PtAl_2 \quad PtGa_2 \quad PtIn_2 \quad NiIn_2$$

The Zinc Blende and Wurtzite Structures. In zinc blende and wurtzite each atom is surrounded by four nearest neighbors at the corners of a tetrahedron, just as in diamond. This suggests covalent binding. On the other hand, it may also be described as an electron compound with (invariably) the electron-atom ratio of 4.

The Laves Phases. Many intermediate phases have one of three related structures of the type of $MgCu_2$, $MgZn_2$, and $MgNi_2$, as will be seen from the following list:

MgCu₂ type (cubic)		MgZn₂ type (hexagonal)		MgNi₂ type (hexagonal)
$AgBe_2$	$TaCo_2$	$CaMg_2$	$ZrRe_2$	$CrBe_2$
$TiBe_2$	$CeNi_2$	$TiMn_2$	ZrV_2	$MnBe_2$
$NaAu_2$	$CeCo_2$	$ZrMn_2$	$CaLi_2$	VBe_2
$TiCo_2$	$LaMg_2$	$NbMn_2$	$ZrOs_2$	$ReBe_2$
$CaAl_2$	$CeMg_2$	$TaMn_2$	$ZrCr_2$	$MoBe_2$
$LaAl_2$	ZrW_2	$TiFe_2$	KNa_2	FeB_2
$CeAl_2$	$PbAu_2$	$NbFe_2$	$SrMg_2$	WBe_2
$ZrFe_2$	$BiAu_2$	$TaFe_2$	$BaMg_2$	$TiCo_2$
$ZrCo_2$	KBi_2			$ZrFe_2$
$NbCo_2$				$NbCo_2$ with approximately 7.4 per cent excess of B metal
				$TaCo_2$

[1] That the γ phase belongs in this series may be questioned, according to G. Masing, "Lehrbuch der Allgemeinen Metallkunde," p. 160, Springer, Berlin, 1950.

The relation between these structures can be understood without going into the details.[1] They are all constructed from double layers with hexagonal symmetry. Consider the Mg atoms first; the first pair of layers consists of Mg atoms at the points of a simple hexagonal lattice. The second double layer is like the first but is shifted laterally (just like the second layer in close-packed hexagonal structures). In $MgZn_2$ the third double layer is directly above the first so that the sequence of double layers is $ABAB \ldots$; in $MgCu_2$ the sequence is $ABCABC \ldots$, for the fourth double layer, not the third, is over the first; in $MgNi_2$ the sequence is $ABACABAC. \ldots$ The atoms of the other metals are grouped around the Mg atoms in tetrahedral schemes that differ somewhat in the three types.

In these Laves phases size relationships are perhaps more important than electron concentration, but both factors are necessary to explain the facts regarding homogeneity ranges of these phases in binary, ternary, and quaternary alloys.[2] These AB_2 compounds have atom-radius ratios, R_A/R_B, between 1.2 and 1.3. Of the three structures, $MgCu_2$ is found at the lowest electron-atom ratio (1.3 to about 1.8), $MgZn_2$ at the highest (about 2:0), and $MgNi_2$ at intermediate ratios (if Ni is counted as zero valent).

Pauling's Theory of Resonant Covalent Bonds. Pauling[3] has developed a theory of binding in metals and metallic phases based on the conscept that the metallic bond is essentially covalent in nature. He proposethat each atom in a metal shares valence electrons with the neighboring atoms, forming covalent bonds, these bonds resonating among the available interatomic positions. The theory correlates magnetic and other properties and has been used by Pauling as a basis for a system of atomic radii for metallic phases, an elaboration of the principle that in covalent crystals the atom-to-atom distance depends upon whether a single, double, or triple bond is involved. In the metal phases a portion of the valence electrons remain in the atomic orbitals of individual atoms and do not contribute to the bonding. In early versions of the theory the remainder of the valence electrons resonate between all the neighboring atoms in a synchronous manner. In the 1949 version it is proposed that the shifting of one electron in an atom from one bond to another is independent of the shifting of others, and the orbitals that accomodate the electrons are divided into the classes nonbonding, bonding, and metallic.[4]

[1] F. Laves and H. Witte, *Metallwirtschaft*, vol. 14, p. 645, 1935.

[2] F. Laves and H. Witte, *Metallwirtschaft*, vol. 15, p. 840, 1936.

[3] L. Pauling, *Phys. Rev.*, vol. 54, p. 899, 1938; "The Nature of the Chemical Bond," 2d ed., Cornell University Press, Ithaca, New York, 1940; *Physica*, vol. 15, p. 23, 1949; *J. Am. Chem. Soc.*, vol. 69, p. 542 1947. F. J. Ewing and L. Pauling, *Rev. Modern Phys.*, vol. 20, p. 112, 1948.

[4] L. Pauling, *Proc. Roy. Soc. (London)*, vol. A196, p. 343, 1949. The proposed

Details of the effective valences and of the manner in which Pauling relates his assumed electron distributions to observed radii cannot be given here. A critical discussion of Pauling's interpretation will be found in a review by Hume-Rothery[1] in which is pointed out the empirical nature of the correlations, the numerous *ad hoc* assumptions involved that make generalization and prediction difficult, and, on the other hand, the points in which the interpretation is in agreement with prior suggestions or provides a useful alternative to them. For the zone theory of metallic phases and for predictions of the direction of boundaries in ternary alloy systems it happens that in many instances both Pauling's valences and Hume-Rothery's[2] give similar electron-atom ratio relationships.[3]

Transition Elements as Electron Absorbers. Raynor[4] has shown that when the transition metals Cr, Mn, Fe, Co, and Ni form binary or multicomponent systems with aluminum there are intermediate phases formed having compositions and homogeneity ranges that are understandable as electron compounds provided that the transition metals act as *absorbers* of valence electrons. In this class of phases are, for example, Co_2Al_5, Co_2Al_9, $NiAl_3$, $FeNiAl_9$, $(CuMn)Al_4$, $Ni_4Mn_{11}Al_{60}$, $FeCu_2Al_7$, Cu_3NiAl_6, Mn_3SiAl_9, and $Co_2Cu_5Al_{13}$.

In ternary and quaternary alloys of aluminum with transition elements, prominent features of the isothermal phase diagrams are the phase boundary lines running in the direction for which electron concentration is constant. For example, in the phase Cr_2Al_{11} the Cr may be replaced by Mn in almost any proportion, with the electron concentration remaining constant throughout. In computing the electron concentration Al and Si were assumed to contribute 3 and 4 electrons per atom to the structures, and Cr, Mn, Fe, Co, and Ni were assumed to accept 4.66, 3.66, 2.66, 1.71

---

valences are as follows (in the 1949 version): Fe is assigned a valence of 5.78, which is viewed as an average of 6 and 5 in the ratio of 78:22; the electrons are distributed among the orbitals so as to yield unpaired electron spins that would account for the observed ferromagnetic saturation moment of 2.22. Grey Sn has valence 4, white Sn is assigned 2.5 (a 3:1 mixture of valences 4 and 2). Other valences are: 6 for Co, Ni, Ru, Rh, Pd, Os, Ir, Pt, Mo, Tc, W, Re; 6 or 3 for Cr; 6 or 4 for Mn; 5 for V, Cb, Ta; 4 for Ti, Zr, Hf; 3 for Sc, Y, Lu; 5.5 for Cu, Ag, Au; 4 for Zn, Cd, Ge; 3.5 for Ga, Hg; 2.5 for In; and 2 for Tl.

[1] W. Hume-Rothery, "Annual Reports of the Chemical Society," vol. 46, p. 42, 1949.

[2] W. Hume-Rothery, "The Structure of Metals and Alloys," Institute of Metals, London, 1936; *Phil. Mag.*, vol. 39, p. 89, 1948.

[3] A. I. Snow, *J. Chem. Phys.*, vol. 18, p. 233, 1950. The Hume-Rothery valences deduced from ternary alloy diagrams were Cu, 1; Zn, 2; Al, 3; Mn, 2; Fe, 1; Ni, 0.4 to 0.6.

[4] G. V. Raynor in "Progress in Metal Physics," vol. I, Interscience Publishers, 1949; *J. Inst. Metals*, vol. 70, p. 531, 1944. J. N. Pratt and G. V. Raynor, *Proc. Roy. Soc. (London)*, vol. A205, p. 103, 1951.

and 0.61 electrons per atom, respectively. For further discussion see page 206.

Solubility in Ternary Alloys. As has been mentioned earlier, electron-concentration effects are prominent in many ternary-alloy diagrams. Additional factors aid in constructing and interpreting ternary diagrams.

Hume-Rothery[1] points out that, when there is a compound of definite composition, B_xC_y, in a ternary system ABC, the solubility of B and C in A can be approximated by the equilibrium relation of solution chemistry, $[B]^x[C]^y = K$, where $[B]$ is the atom fraction of B, $[C]$ is the atom fraction of C, and K is a constant. In other words, this formula gives the compositions of points on the $\alpha/(\alpha + B_xC_y)$ solid solubility line of the isothermal diagram. The same relation holds for the liquidus line.[2] Size effects are often seen to modify the electron-concentration rules. Unfavorable size factors tend to restrict solubility to a value less than electron concentration would predict; but if the atoms of one element tend to neutralize the distortion from the atoms of another (atoms of one kind being too small and the other too large to match the solvent) the solubilities in the ternary diagram may be *greater* than would be expected from the solubilities of the binary diagrams.

Interstitial Compounds. The transition metals alloy with H, B, C, and N to produce compounds that are metallic, have high melting points, and are extremely hard. Dispersed in steel they harden it, or cemented together they form high-speed long-life cutting tools.

Gunnar Hägg has been largely responsible for systematizing these structures, appropriately called interstitial compounds.[3] He has shown that they may be classified according to the relative sizes of the transition metal and metalloid atoms, i.e., the radius ratio R_X/R_M, where R_X is the radius of the small nonmetallic atom H, B, C, or N and R_M is the atomic radius of the transition metal. When R_X/R_M is less than 0.59, the structures are simple; when the ratio is more than 0.59, they are complex.

1. When the radius ratio is under 0.59, the metal atoms are nearly always on a lattice that is f.c.c., c.p.h., or in a few instances b.c.c.; occasionally, they are on a lattice that is a slightly distorted form of one of these. The small metalloid atoms are located interstitially, as in interstitial terminal solid solutions. Nitrides, carbides, and hydrides with the formula MX are generally cubic with the metal atoms at f.c.c. positions and with the metalloids at interstitial positions in a structure

---

[1] W. Hume-Rothery, *Phil. Mag.*, vol. 22, p. 1013, 1936.

[2] Different temperatures correspond to different values of K, and these values are related to each other by the relation $(d \log K)/dT = -Q/RT^2$.

[3] G. Hägg, *Z. physik. Chem.*, vol. B12, p. 33, 1931; vol. B11, p. 433, 1930. A. Westgren, *J. Franklin Inst.*, vol. 212, p. 577, 1931.

of the NaCl type or the zinc blende type (positions indicated by open circles in Fig. 11). Examples are the nitrides ZrN, ScN, TiN, VN, CrN; the carbides ZrC, TiC, TaC, VC; and the hydrides ZrH and TiH. An exception is TaH, which is based on a b.c.c. lattice.

The compounds M_2X generally have the metal atoms arranged in hexagonal close-packing (Fe_2N, Cr_2N, Mn_2N; W_2C, Mo_2C, Ta_2C; Zr_2H, Ta_2H, Ti_2H), but sometimes they are cubic (Pd_2H, W_2N, Mo_2N).

In the system Ti-H the compound TiH has the zinc blende structure, and TiH_2 has the fluorite (CaF_2) structure; the difference between these is merely that half the interstices are filled in the former, and all are filled in the latter (see Fig. 12). Neutron diffraction can disclose the positions of the hydrogen atoms in hydrides, so that a complete structure determination may be accomplished. This has been done, for example, with ThH_2, ThD_2, and ZrD_2, each of which has been found to be body-centered tetragonal with atoms arranged in a distorted fluorite (CaF_2) structure.[1]

2. Large radius ratios ($R_X/R_M > 0.59$) nearly always go with complex crystal structures. In this class are the carbides of Cr, Mn, Fe, Co, and Ni ($R_X/R_M = 0.60 - 0.61$) and the borides of Fe and N.

In dicarbides the C_2 groups may enter as parallel units into the largest interstices of the metal lattice instead of entering as individual atoms.[2] This results in tetragonal rather than cubic cells for the isomorphous phases CaC_2, SrC_2, BaC_2, LaC_2, CeC_2, PrC_2, and NdC_2, and the structures are a slightly deformed type of NaCl structure. The compounds of carbon, nitrogen, and hydrogen with the transition metals are more metallic in character than the similar compounds with nontransition metals. The carbides of calcium, strontium, and barium, for example, are transparent crystals.

Rundle, in his discussion of the metallic interstitial compounds of composition MX, where X is carbon, nitrogen, or oxygen, points out that nearly all of these have the NaCl structure, no matter what the structure or radius of the metal M.[3] Monocarbides, mononitrides, and monoxides are formed only with the A-subgroup metals of Groups III, IV, V, and VI. The very high melting points, the brittleness, the conductivity, and the interatomic distances in these compounds led Rundle to propose that the bonds between metal and nonmetal atoms are strong, directional (octahedral), and covalent, and are formed by electrons resonating between the different positions in the manner proposed by Pauling (see page 241), stealing valence electrons from the weaker metal-metal bonds.

[1] R. E. Rundle, C. G. Shull, and E. O. Wollan, *Acta Cryst.*, vol. 5, p. 22, 1952.

[2] M. von Stackelberg, *Z. physik. Chem.*, vol. B9, p. 437, 1930.

[3] R. E. Rundle, *Acta Cryst.*, vol. 1, p. 180, 1948. Exceptions occur or possibly occur with sixth group metals: Cr, Mo. W.

Defect Structures. A solid solution (or compound) in which not all the lattice points are occupied by atoms is a defect structure. Many of these are now known, a familiar one being the β phase in the system Ni-Al.[1] At the composition NiAl the structure consists of Al atoms at cube corners and the smaller Ni atoms at cube centers in a CsCl-type structure. When the Ni content is increased, the smaller Ni atoms substitute for the larger Al atoms in the usual way, but when Al atoms are added, only a few enter the small cube-center positions; beyond about 60 atomic per cent Al some of the cube centers are left vacant. At the composition Ni_2Al_3 every third Ni atom is missing from this structure.

It has been proposed that the structure is prevented from collapsing by the contacts between Al atoms along cube edges, but consideration of ternary alloys that are also based on this phase leads to the conclusion that an understanding of the structure is best obtained by considering it as an electron compound.[2] The NiAl phase prefers to have Ni atoms missing rather than to have the electron-atom ratio exceed the value that is characteristic of the ideal structure.

Another example of a defect structure is the phase "FeO," in which there are vacant points on the lattice of iron atoms.[3] In FeS (which has the NiAs-type structure, page 231) a rigid lattice is formed by S atoms while one-ninth of the equivalent positions occupied by Fe remain empty—the lattice of Fe atoms being incomplete.[4]

Many oxides are defect structures: the larger oxygen ions approach close packing, but there are oxygen positions vacant. Some structures of this class with the formula R_2X_3 may be visualized as distorted CaF_2 structures in which a trivalent metal takes the Ca positions and oxygen ions enter three-fourths of the F positions. This "Tl_2O_3 type" has been found with Be_3N_2, Be_3P_2, αCa_3N_2, Cd_3N_2, bixbyite (Fe, Mn)$_2O_3$, In_2O_3, Mg_3N_2, Mg_3P_2, Mn_2O_3, Zn_3N_2, and many oxides of the rare earths with this formula. (The radius ratio, metal ion/oxygen ion, is about 0.60 to 0.87 for these.)[5]

The "interstitial structures" in which small metalloid H, B, C, or N atoms fit into a few of the interstices in a rigid lattice of metal atoms

[1] A. J. Bradley and A. Taylor, *Proc. Roy. Soc. (London)*, vol. A159, p. 56, 1937· Another example: A. J. Bradley and G. C. Seager, *J. Inst. Metals*, vol. 64, p. 81, 1939·

[2] H. Lipson and A. Taylor, *Proc. Roy. Soc. (London)*, vol. A173, p. 232, 1939. G. V· Raynor in "Progress in Metal Physics," vol. I, p. 18, Interscience Publishers, New York, 1949.

[3] E. R. Jette and F. Foote, *J. Chem. Phys.*, vol. 1, p. 29, 1933.

[4] F. Laves, *Z. Krist.*, vol. 73, pp. 263, 307, 1930. G. Hägg and J. Sucksdorff, *Z. physik. Chem.*, vol. B22, p. 444, 1933.

[5] R. W. G. Wyckoff, "Crystal Structures," Interscience Publishers, New York, 1948.

present several examples of defect structures;[1] the metalloids can be present in varying amounts and consequently cannot always fill all equivalent positions. A striking example of a defect lattice is αAgI in which the large I^- ions build a rigid structure in which smaller Ag^+ ions take up any of the 42 interstices per unit cell, where the coordination number is 6, 4, or 3, and move freely about these positions—practically a "liquid" state for the Ag^+.[2] The structures of αAg$_2$S and αAg$_2$Se are also of the defect type.[3]

The Carbides in Alloy Steels. Extensive reviews of the carbides that are of importance in alloy steels have been published by Austin[4] and by Goldschmidt.[5] Metals differ greatly in their tendency to form carbides. There is no tendency in the rare and the noble metals Ag, Pd, Rh, Ru, Au, Pt, Ir, and Os; carbon forms graphite rather than a carbide when alloyed with these. The weak carbide formers have only metastable carbides that decompose spontaneously or after annealing: Cu, Ni, Co, and Fe. The strong carbide formers are Cr, V, Ti, Mo, Cb, Zr, W, Ta, and Hf, and it is these that provide the materials so widely used in cutting tools, wire-drawing dies, and machine and instrument parts of great hardness and wear resistance, particularly the carbides of Ti, Cb, W, and Ta and mixtures of these. As indicated by the melting point and hardness, the list above for the strong carbide formers is arranged roughly in the order of increasing affinity for carbon: Cr$_{23}$C$_6$ melts at 1550°C, W$_2$C at 2857°C, TaC and HfC at 3880°C (approximate temperatures). The order also correlates with position in the periodic table, and there is a correlation of structure with the periodic table, as will be seen from Fig. 14. The periodic relationship is accounted for in the main by the variation of atomic radii as a function of atomic number in accord with Hägg's rule, since the close-packed cubic and hexagonal carbides have radius ratios below 0.59 and the complex carbides of Cr, Mn, and Fe have ratios above 0.59.

There is much intersolubility between carbides of the different metals, especially between metals of a class, if classes are as indicated by the shaded areas in Fig. 14. For example, there is complete solubility in the systems TaC-CbC and TiC-TaC. There are also varying degrees of solubility between metals in different classes, e.g., TaC-ZrC, TiC-WC— the solubility being relatively small or negligible if the metal atoms differ more than a few per cent in radii. There is no entrance of iron, for

[1] G. Hägg, *Z. physik. Chem.*, vol. B12, p. 33, 1930.

[2] L. W. Strock, *Z. physik. Chem.*, vol. B25, p. 441, 1934; vol. B31, p. 132, 1936.

[3] P. Rahlfs, *Z. physik. Chem.*, vol. B31, p. 157, 1936.

[4] J. B Austin, *Trans. ASM*, vol. 38, p. 28, 1947 (35 references).

[5] H. J. Goldschmidt, *J. Iron Steel Inst.* (*London*), vol. 160, p. 345, 1948 (93 references).

xample, into the cubic carbides as either a solid solution or a ternary ompound, which may be attributed to the difference in radii of iron 1.26 A in γ-Fe) and the metals that form cubic carbides (1.35 to 1.60 A). There is solubility between carbides and some hydrides, borides, nitrides, nd oxides, *e.g.*, the complete solubilities in the systems TaC-TaN and TiC-TiN.

The $Cr_{23}C_6$ structure, which is cubic, accepts iron in replacement for hromium up to about 30 per cent, but the $(Cr, Fe)_{23}C_6$ phase becomes

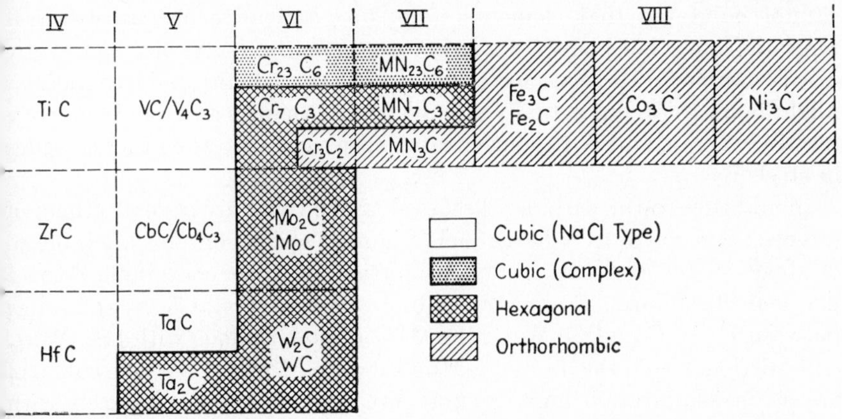

FIG. 14. Relationship between structures of carbides and the position of the metal in the periodic table. Solid solutions are probable between the carbides VC and V_4C_3, CbC and Cb_4C_3, and perhaps also Mo_2C and MoC, and W_2C and WC. (*After H. J. Goldschmidt.*)

unstable above this unless tungsten (or molybdenum) is present.[1] This peculiarity of $(Cr, Fe, W, Mo)_{23}C_6$ is attributed to the fact that the iron atoms are smaller than the chromium atoms so that an intolerable change in the dimensions of the structure occurs unless the larger tungsten or molybdenum atoms are added to counteract it. With sufficient tungsten the iron can entirely replace the chromium, yielding $Fe_{21}W_2C$.

Cementite, Fe_3C, is an orthorhombic, unstable carbide that is quite variable in composition.[2] The iron can be replaced by manganese in any proportion, $(Fe, Mn)_3C$, and also by chromium $(Fe, Cr)_3C$, up to about 15 per cent chromium, and by vanadium, molybdenum, tungsten, nickel, and cobalt to some extent. (None of these atoms is more than 15 per cent larger than iron and there is a distinct tendency for the atoms to dissolve the less, the more they differ from iron in size.) There is some

[1] A. Westgren, *Jernkontorets Ann.*, vol. 117, p. 501, 1933; *Nature*, vol. 132, p. 480, 1933. A. Westgren and G. Phragmén, *Trans. Am. Soc. Steel Treating*, vol. 13, p. 539, 1928; *Jernkontorets Ann.*, vol. 117, p. 1, 1933. The structure is cubic, space group $Fm3m$, 92 metal atoms and 24 C atoms per unit cell, $a_0 = 10.53$–10.66 A.

[2] Space group $Pbnm$, 12 Fe and 4 C atoms per cell; see Chap. XXII.

evidence that the carbon content is variable[1] and that nitrogen can replace carbon. Replacement of carbon by nitrogen has definitely been found in a phase that is homogeneous throughout the range $Fe_2(N, C)$ to $Fe_3(N, C)$ and that is isostructural with Fe_3N, having iron atoms in hexagonal close-packing.[2] Cementite is rendered more stable with respect to graphite when alloyed with manganese, chromium, and other strong carbide formers that can substitute for iron; on the other hand, alloying a steel with a carbide former still weaker than iron tends to promote graphitization, as is found when nickel or silicon is added. It cannot be stated that elements stabilizing cementite necessarily must migrate from other phases in a steel into cementite (since size factors are also favorable for these atoms to enter ferrite or austenite and free energies might favor this), but actually it is found that there is a marked tendency for Mn, Cr, Mo, and W to concentrate in the cementite and other carbides in steels.

In addition to the carbides discussed above there are several others of interest: $(Cr, Fe, W)_7C_3$, hexagonal (trigonal) which contains a minimum of about 35 per cent chromium and appears in steels containing 3 to 15 per cent chromium;[3] $(Fe, W)_6C$, cubic[4] which covers at least the range between Fe_3W_3C and Fe_4W_2C; $(Fe, Mo)_6C$ isomorphous with $(Fe, W)_6C$ and existing within the limits Fe_3Mo_3C and Fe_4Mo_2C; $(CoW)_6C$, cubic, of uncertain composition limits;[5] cubic V_4C_3, which appears in steels with vanadium content in excess of about 0.5 per cent;[6] and $(Cr, Fe)_2C$ found

[1] See, for example, N. J. Petch, *J. Iron Steel Inst. (London)*, vol. 149, p. 142, 1944. H. A. Schwartz, K. R. Van Horn, and C. H. Junge, *Trans. Am. Soc. Steel Treating*, vol. 21, p. 463, 1933. H. J. Goldschmidt suggests that perhaps cementite, $(Cr, Fe, W)_{23}C_6$, together with Fe_4W_2C, and tungsten metal form a pseudo-binary system with some intersolubility and with possibility of some additional stable structures of intermediate composition.

[2] This phase, "epsilon," was made by the action of carbon monoxide on iron nitrites. K. H. Jack, *Nature*, vol. 158, p. 60, 1946; *Proc. Roy. Soc. (London)*, vol. A195, pp. 34, 40, 56, 1948. It appears to be a hexagonal Fe_2C phase discussed by L. J. E. Hofer, E. M. Coh, and W. C. Peebles (*J. Am. Chem. Soc.*, vol. 71, pp. 189–195, 1949), which decomposes into a phase reported by G. Hägg, *Z. Krist.*, vol. 89, pp. 92–94, 1934. Epsilon may be the phase that precipitates from martensite on tempering steels below 200°C, reported by R. D. Heidenreich, L. Sturkey, and H. L. Woods, *J. Applied Phys.*, vol. 17, p. 127, 1946; and by M. Arbusow and G. Kurdjumow, *J. Phys. U.S.S.R.*, vol. 5, p. 101, 1941, though there is also the possibility that iron percarbide $Fe_{20}C_9$ precipitates, according to Jack. The percarbide is either orthorhombic or hexagonal; it decomposes into cementite and carbon on heating.

[3] The unit cell has 56 metal atoms and 24 C atoms; Cr_7C_3 has $a_0 = 14.01$, $c = 4.532$ A.

[4] Space group $Fd3m$, $a_0 = 11.06$ A, 96 metal, 16 C atoms per cell.

[5] $Fm3m$, $a_0 = 10.9 = 11.05$; possibly two phases. See E. J. Sandford and E. M. Trent, Special Report 38, p. 84, Iron and Steel Institute, 1947.

[6] Face-centered cubic NaCl type, $a_0 = 4.14$ to 4.31 A; probably a defect lattice with carbon atoms missing and with composition range extending from VC to V_4C_3.

n chromium steels, a defect structure, cubic.[1] The structures of WC and W₂C differ in the same way as the two structures of graphite: in ordinary α graphite the close-packed layers are stacked so as to superimpose every alternate layer, and in β graphite every third layer; in WC the layers are in the stacking sequence W-C-W-C . . . and in W₂C they are in the sequence W-W'-C-W-W'-C . . . where W' represents a tungsten layer turned 30° with respect to the tungsten layer W. It is possible that stacking errors occur as in graphite.

The composition of carbides in steels depends on the thermal history of the steel—equilibrium is often not reached—as well as the alloying elements present; and whether cementite or some other carbide forms in a steel, or a mixture of several carbides forms is also dependent upon composition and heat-treatment; these relationships, the distribution of alloying elements among the different phases in steels in transient and equilibrium states, and the resulting influence on transformation rates, microstructures, and properties, require much further research in spite of the considerable amount they have already received.

Sigma Phases. An intermediate phase of great importance to users of alloy steels is the σ phase that occurs over a considerable range of composition around FeCr (see Fig. 15, page 250). This phase precipitates from the ferrite phase during annealing below 825°C, with marked effects on the mechanical properties (the phase is very brittle). Recent research indicates that many systems have phases isostructural with this: among alloys of the transition elements Mn, Fe, Co, Ni, the σ phase is found in alloys of vanadium with any of these, chromium with any (except possibly Ni), and Mo with Fe.[2]

Phases Containing Alkali and Alkaline-earth Elements. Zintl and his collaborators[3] have surveyed a large number of systems of the alkali and alkaline-earth elements for examples of β phases at 50 atomic per cent composition. Because the CsCl structure of the β phases is stable only when the radius ratio is greater than 0.73, the investigations were confined to examples in this range. A cesium chloride structure occurs in

---

[1] Face-centered cubic, $a_0 = 3.618$ A, stable only above 1000°C; H. J. Goldschmidt, *Nature*, vol. 162, p. 855, 1948. It is obviously very similar to austenite.

[2] The structure of the phase is tetragonal, with 30 atoms per unit cell, $a = 8.799$ A. $c = 4.546$ A, space group probably C_{4v}^4—$P4mn$ resembling β-uranium. D. P. Shoemaker and B. G. Bergman, *J. Am. Chem. Soc.*, vol. 72, p. 5793, 1950. G. J. Dickens, A. M. B. Douglas, and W. H. Taylor, *J. Iron Steel Inst. (London)*, vol. 167, p. 27, 1951. Much thought is being devoted to the question of whether or not the phase is an electron compound, but the answer is not clear as this is being written. See A. H. Sully, *J. Inst. Metals*, vol. 19, p. 173, 1951; A. M. B. Douglas, *Brit. J. Applied Phys.*, vol. 2, abstract on p. 310, 1951; S. Rideout, W. D. Manly, E. L. Kamen, B. S. Lement, and P. A. Beck, *Trans. AIME, J. Metals*, vol. 3, p. 872, 1951.

[3] E. Zintl and B. Brauer, *Z. physik. Chem.*, vol. B20, p. 245, 1933.

many systems: LiAg, LiTl, LiHg, LiZn, LiCd, LiGa, LiIn; MgTl, CaTl
SrTl; NaIn, NaBi.   In others a structure occurs (NaTl type) that con
sists of two interpenetrating diamond lattices each containing atoms of ;
single element, one lattice being displaced half of a body diagonal witl

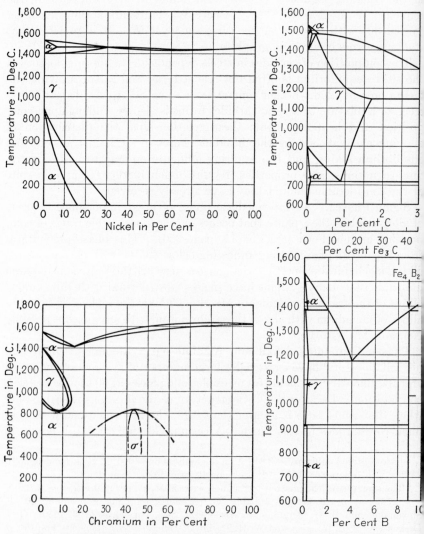

FIG. 15. Classification of binary iron alloys as to extent of the gamma field.

respect to the other; atomic radii are nearly equal in this structure.
Examples are known as follows: LiZn, LiCd, LiGa, LiIn; NaSn, NaTl.

From a study of atomic radii in these compounds it was found that
there is nearly always a contraction which seems to be the result of polar-

ization of the large alkali atoms by neighboring small atoms. Thus the greater the contraction, the more the interatomic bonds differ from the truly metallic. There are many exceptions to Hume-Rothery's rule in these compounds, particularly in phases where contraction is large, presumably because of their nonmetallic character.

Another set of analogous phases has the formula AX_3. The A atoms are at the corners of a cubic lattice, the X at face centers. Examples are $NaPb_3$, $CaPb_3$, $SrPb_3$, $CePb_3$, $CaTl_3$, $CaSn_3$, $CeSn_3$, $LaSn_3$, $LaPb_3$,

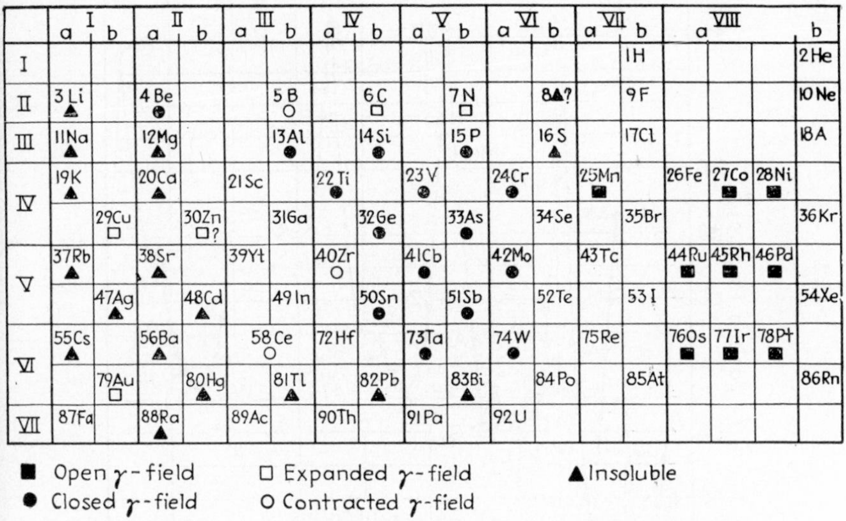

	a I b		a II b		a III b		a IV b		a V b		a VI b		a VII b		a VIII			b
I														1H				2He
II	3Li ▲		4Be ⊕			5B ○		6C □		7N □		8▲?		9F				10Ne
III	11Na ▲		12Mg ▲			13Al ●		14Si ●		15P ●		16S ▲		17Cl				18A
IV	19K ▲		20Ca ▲		21Sc		22Ti ●		23V ◉		24Cr ●		25Mn ■		26Fe	27Co ■	28Ni ■	
		29Cu □		30Zn □?		31Ga		32Ge ◉		33As ●		34Se		35Br				36Kr
V	37Rb ▲		38Sr ▲		39Yt		40Zr ○		41Cb ●		42Mo ◉		43Tc		44Ru ■	45Rh ■	46Pd ■	
		47Ag ▲		48Cd ▲		49In		50Sn ●		51Sb ●		52Te		53I				54Xe
VI	55Cs ▲		56Ba ▲		58Ce ○		72Hf		73Ta ●		74W ●		75Re		76Os ■	77Ir ■	78Pt ■	
		79Au □		80Hg ▲		81Tl ▲		82Pb ▲		83Bi ▲		84Po		85At				86Rn
VII	87Fa ▲		88Ra ▲		89Ac		90Th		91Pa		92U							

■ Open γ-field   □ Expanded γ-field   ▲ Insoluble
● Closed γ-field   O Contracted γ-field

FIG. 16. Periodic table showing behavior of elements in binary iron alloys.

$PrSn_3$, and $PrPb_3$. This structure requires the ratio R_A/R_X in the range 1.0 to 2.4, as shown by Goldschmidt, and actually all the known phases do lie in this range.

Iron Alloy Diagrams. Wever[1] has pointed out some generalizations concerning effects of alloying elements on the range of stability of the γ phase when alloyed with iron. Iron alloys may be grouped into classes exemplified by Fig. 15. In some the alloying element stabilizes the γ phase, increasing its temperature range of stability, as in Fe-Ni and Fe-C, which have "open" and "expanded" γ fields, respectively. In others the stability of the γ phase is decreased, as in Fe-Cr, which has a "γ loop" or "closed" γ field, and Fe-B, which has a "contracted" γ field. When these types are compared with the positions of the alloying elements in the periodic table (Fig. 16) the regularities are striking. Reference to the

[1] F. Wever, "Ergebnisse der technische Röntgenkunde," vol. II, p. 240, Akademische Verlagsgesellschaft m.b.H., Leipzig, 1931; Proc. World Eng. Congr., Tokyo, vol. 34, p. 239, 1931.

atomic radii of the alloying elements (Fig. 17) shows that the radii correlate with the types of systems: the larger atoms are insoluble and the smaller atoms (Group VIII metals) extend the range of the γ phase. But it is apparent that other factors are also involved.

Smoluchowski[1] proposes that an explanation of the periodic relationship is to be found in the structure of the electron energy bands. The electron

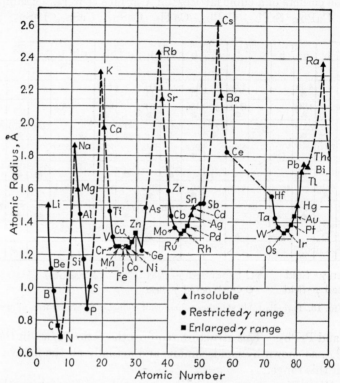

FIG. 17. Relation of atomic radius to behavior of elements in binary iron alloys. (*Wever*.)

theory of metals is discussed later, but the essence of the theory as regards the iron alloys is that the outermost electrons of an atom strongly influence the specific heat and the energy of the phases, hence their relative stability. Since the atoms to the left of iron have fewer outer electrons than iron, they decrease the stability of the γ phase compared with the α. The opposite occurs for elements to the right of iron. Exceptions to this rule (Mn, C, N, Cu, Zn) are accounted for by Smoluchowski on the basis of the energy necessary to transfer electrons up to the energy levels where

[1] R. Smoluchowski, *Phys. Rev.*, vol. 61, p. 390, 1942 (abstract); *Metals Progress*, vol. 41, p. 363, 1942 (letter).

they act as free electrons. Viewing the role of alloying elements as an electron-concentration problem is helpful in understanding the additive effects of some alloying elements in ternary and polycomponent alloys.

Another basis for systematization[1] is that body-centered cubic elements stabilize the body-centered phase, while face-centered elements tend to stabilize the face-centered cubic phase. In agreement with this principle are face-centered cubic Cu, Au, Co, Ni, Rh, Pd, Ir, Pt; Al is an exception, and Ag and Pb are insoluble. Body-centered cubic V, Ta, Cr, Mo, W confirm the principle and the alkali metals are insoluble.

Zener treats the problem from a thermodynamic standpoint, showing that the form of the boundaries in the phase diagrams can be computed from the thermodynamic data. Since ideal solution behavior appears to be followed over a considerable concentration range, he finds it possible to set up a master curve that defines the position of the boundary; this curve is shifted to the right by Ti, Sn, P, V, W, Mo, Si, and Al, raising the α-γ and lowering the γ-δ transformation temperatures; it is shifted to the left, with opposite effects, by Cu, Zn, Mn, Ni, and N; the amount of the shift associated with each element is proportional to its concentration and is independent of the concentrations of the other elements present, so that multicomponent diagrams may be predicted.[2] Additional discussion of the problem has been published by Hume-Rothery and Christian.[3]

Imperfections in Crystals. Countless experiments have shown that crystals contain many flaws and irregularities, a detailed knowledge of which is much to be desired because of their effect on the physical properties. For extensive bibliographies the reader is referred to the various reviews and symposia.[4]

A study of their X-ray-reflecting power led Darwin to conclude that actual crystals diffract as if they are composed of small blocks 10^{-4} to 10^{-6} cm on an edge, each block being a perfect crystal but neighboring blocks being tilted out of registry.[5] The widths of reflected X-ray beams

[1] F. Wever, "Ergebnisse der technische Röntgenkunde," vol. II, p. 240, Akademische Verlagsgesellschaft m.b.H., Leipzig, 1931.

[2] C. Zener, *Trans. AIME*, vol. 167, p. 513, 1946.

[3] W. Hume-Rothery and J. W. Christian, *Phil. Mag.*, vol. 36, p. 835, 1945.

[4] "International Conference on Physics, vol. II, The Solid State of Matter," Physical Society, London, 1935. *Z. Krist.*, vol. 89, 1934, Sonderheft: "Ideal- und Realkristall." W. Hume-Rothery, "The Structure of Metals and Alloys," Institute of Metals, London, 1936. C. A. Zapffe and C. E. Sims, *Trans. AIME.*, vol. 145, p. 225, 1941. Internal Strains in Solids, *Proc. Phys. Soc. (London)*, vol. 52, p. 1, 1940. National Research Council Symposium on Imperfections in Crystals, 1950 (in press). H. E. Buckley, "Crystal Growth," Chapman & Hall, London, 1951.

[5] C. G. Darwin, *Phil Mag.*, vol. 27, pp. 315, 675, 1914; vol. 43, p. 800, 1922. Reviewed in R. W. James, "The Optical Principles of the Diffraction of X-rays," G. Bell, London, 1948.

from single crystals give concrete evidence for imperfection.[1] An ideal crystal produces a diffracted line 3 to 6 sec of arc in width; selected samples of diamond, calcite, quartz, and rochelle salt give reflections of this type.

Most crystals, however, give diffracted lines several hundred seconds in width. Metals appear to be particularly imperfect, as indicated by the following measurements of widths by Bozorth and Haworth[2] (measured at half maximum intensity): W, 360 sec; Fe, 840 sec; Ni, 1500 sec; Al, 1500 sec. The degree of imperfection is governed largely by conditions existing during growth, and it varies widely in different samples of a given crystal. The block size in annealed aluminum seems unlikely to be less than 10^{-4} cm.*

Griffith[3] found that freshly prepared glass fibers, free from cracks, had tensile strengths of a million pounds per square inch, greatly exceeding the normal value. Experiments on rock salt and mica[4] also confirmed the weakening effect of surface cracks. Extending this view, Smekal[4] postulated that solid metals are weakened by internal cracks and flaws, some arising during growth and others during subsequent handling. There is a fundamental difference between the effect of cracks in brittle glass and in ductile metals, however, as Zener points out in his reexamination of the theory.[5]

Buerger[6] and Davey[7] have emphasized the effect of dendritic and branching growth from a nucleus in developing imperfections. As errors in alignment tend to be cumulative during the growth of a dendritic arm or branch, the resulting structure may resemble a columnar grain structure and has been called a *lineage structure* by Buerger. The nature of

[1] "International Conference on Physics, vol. II, The Solid State of Matter," Physical Society, London, 1935. *Z. Krist.*, vol. 89, 1934, Sonderheft: "Ideal- und Realkristall." A. H. Compton and S. K. Allison, "X-rays in Theory and Experiment," Van Nostrand, New York, 1935. R. M. Bozorth and F. E. Haworth, *Phys. Rev.*, vol. 45, p. 821, 1934.

[2] R. M. Bozorth and F. E. Haworth, *Phys. Rev.*, vol. 45, p. 821, 1934.

* Recent research by P. B. Hirsch and P. Gay, using the technique of microbeams about 30 μ in diameter (see P. B. Hirsch and J. N. Kellar, *Proc. Phys. Soc. (London)*, vol. B64, p. 369, 1951), suggests that annealed aluminum has about 10^8 dislocation lines per square centimeter; and since the mosaic block size cannot be less than the average distance between dislocations, it appears that the block size is not less than $1/\rho^{\frac{1}{2}} = 10^{-4}$ cm, where ρ is the dislocation density, 10^8 per square centimeter. [A. H. Cottrell, private communication (to be published).]

[3] A. A. Griffith, *Trans. Roy. Soc. (London)*, vol. A221, p. 180, 1921.

[4] "International Conference on Physics, vol. II, The Solid State of Matter," Physical Society, London, 1935.

[5] C. Zener, "Fracture of Metals Symposium," American Society for Metals, Cleveland, 1948.

[6] M. J. Buerger, *Z. Krist.*, vol. 89, pp. 195, 242, 1934.

[7] W. P. Davey, *Trans. Am. Soc. Steel Treating*, vol. 21, p. 965, 1933.

lineage imperfection is illustrated in Fig. 18, in which the growth from a central nucleus and the flaws at the lineage boundaries are exaggerated. Lineage is often visible to the naked eye. The freezing of drops of liquid that are entirely enclosed by dendrite arms is certainly a fruitful source of imperfection, as are also segregation and coring in the freezing of an alloy. Not infrequently the imperfection is so great that Laue spots are badly distorted, and the solid is better described as a polycrystalline aggregate with a preferred orientation than as a single crystal. In the freezing of single crystals of tin an interesting honeycomblike substructure is often seen, which consists of columnar regions differing $\frac{1}{4}$ to 5° in orientation about a common axis.[1]

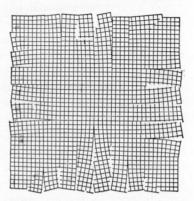

FIG. 18. Sketch illustrating lineage structure. (*Buerger.*)

X-ray reflection micrographs reveal the imperfections strikingly.[2] A grain of cast high-purity aluminum, for example, gave the imperfection pattern shown in Fig. 19. The method is sensitive to changes in orienta-

FIG. 19. X-ray reflection micrograph of a grain in a casting of aluminum (99.9 per cent purity, electropolished). Registered on fine grained photographic plate, enlarged ×50.

tion from point to point in the sample and to changes in reflecting power due to variation in extinction or other causes. Guinier and Tennevin's

---

[1] E. Teghtsoonian and B. Chalmers, *Can. J. Phys.*, vol. 29, p. 370, 1951. R. B. Pond and S. W. Kessler, *J. Metals*, vol. 3, p. 1156, 1951. Imperfections from the dendritic freezing of Pb are discussed by F. Weinberg and B. Chalmers, *Can. J. Phys.*, vol. 29, p. 382, 1951.

[2] C. S. Barrett, *Trans. AIME*, vol. 161, p. 15, 1945. A description of the method is given on p. 96.

Laue spots also provide a means of studying imperfection.[1] In one of their methods the scatter of the reflecting-plane normals can be determined to an accuracy of about 10 sec of arc, and in another the reflecting power is surveyed from point to point in the crystal, much as in reflection micrographs, but minor disorientations are invisible. Both methods have shown the imperfection of crystals of quartz and of aluminum—especially when aluminum has been deformed slightly and annealed to cause certain imperfections (dislocations) to migrate together into surfaces that become subgrain boundaries, subdividing the grains by the process known as "polygonization," which is discussed further in Chap. XVI.

Many who have discussed crystalline imperfection have attempted to show that crystals are composed of a mosaic of quite uniformly sized blocks 10^{-4} or 10^{-5} cm on an edge. Goetz pointed out[2] that etch pits on the cleavage surfaces of bismuth appear to have certain regularities in size and spacing. However, Buerger[3] is confident that these regularities are illusory. A similar observation on regularities in Widmanstätten figures[4] likewise has been strongly objected to.[5] The semiregularity in the spacing of slip lines, while much discussed in this connection, may be a reflection of microscopic segregation during growth or a result of local stresses around the slipped surfaces and is inconclusive evidence for a regular mosaic. Other discussions of possible regular, stable imperfections in crystals[6] have not led to general acceptance of these, although less regular imperfections are unquestionably present. (See discussion of dislocations, Chap. XVI.)

The electron microscope offers an opportunity to investigate details of structure in the micron and submicron range of sizes and should contribute much to our knowledge of imperfections. There is a wealth of detail revealed on the etched surface of metals when replicas of the surfaces are examined;[7] for example, deeply etched copper yields a micrograph, Fig. 20, in which rodlike regions are visible, the rods being about 0.1 to 0.5 μ (1000 to 5000 A) in diameter and about ten times this in length.[8] It is

[1] A. Guinier and J. Tennevin, *Compt. rend.*, vol. 226, p. 1530, 1948; *Acta Cryst.*, vol. 2, p. 133, 1949.

[2] A. Goetz, *Proc. Natl. Acad. Sci.*, vol. 16, p. 99, 1930.

[3] M. J. Buerger, *Z. Krist.*, vol. 89, pp. 195, 242, 1934.

[4] W. P. Davey, *Trans. Am. Soc. Steel Treating*, vol. 21, p. 965, 1933.

[5] R. F. Mehl, *Trans. Am. Soc. Steel Treating*, vol. 21, p. 998, 1933.

[6] A. B. Focke, *Phys. Rev.*, vol. 45, p. 219, 1934; vol. 46, p. 623, 1934. M. Straumanis, *Z. physik. Chem.*, vol. B13, p. 316, 1931. For bibliography, see M. J. Buerger, *Z. Krist.*, vol. 89, pp. 195, 242, 1934; "International Conference on Physics, vol. II, The Solid State of Matter," Physical Society, London, 1935; C. A. Zapffe and C. E. Sims, *Trans. AIME*, vol. 145, p. 225, 1941.

[7] A summary is given by C. S. Barrett in "Electronic Methods of Inspection of Metals," American Society for Metals, 1947.

[8] C. S. Barrett, *Trans. AIME*, vol. 156, p. 62, 1944.

difficult to judge whether the mosaic pattern produced by etching is a true indication of the imperfection in the metal, however, for the etched appearance is not wholly independent of the etchant used. It may or may not be significant that the dimensions of several mosaic patterns of this type were found to correlate with hardness, the harder alloys having the smaller blocks.[1]

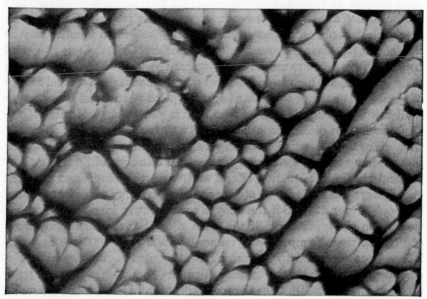

Fig. 20. Portion of a grain of annealed high purity copper, etched with ferric chloride reagent, ×20,000 (1 mm = 500 A; 20 mm = 1μ). A transmission electron-microscope photograph of a replica of the surface prepared by the method of R. D. Heidenreich and V. G. Peck, *J. App. Phys.*, vol. 14, p. 23, 1934.

The possibility that crystals have vacant atom sites has been long realized. As mentioned earlier, there is a class of crystals in which this is definitely proved, *viz.*, the defect structures, which are not uncommon among intermetallic phases. It is also known to be the case in alkali halide crystals.[2] In these crystals electrons may become trapped in vacant halogen-ion positions, forming "*F* centers," and when this occurs the crystals become colored. When the number of *F* centers becomes as great as 2×10^{18} per cc, as it does with the aid of X-ray irradiation of a crystal, there is a decrease of density of the crystal of 1 part in 10^4, which is barely large enough to be measured. In the case of metals, attempts have been made to detect the presence of vacancies by comparison of

[1] R. D. Heidenreich, L. Sturkey, and H. L. Woods, *J. Applied Phys.*, vol. 17, p. 127, 1946. When alloys are age-hardenable the scale of the etching pattern is probably governed by the dispersion of fine particles of precipitate.

[2] For a summary of the field see F. Seitz, *Rev. Modern Phys.*, vol. 18, p. 384, 1946.

densities calculated from precision X-ray measurements with the best available measured densities. A survey[1] of such measurements indicates that the number of vacant sites does not exceed the possible error of the determination in a number of pure metals and in the α solid solutions of Zn in Ag. The difficulty in detecting vacancies is in a large part due to their low concentration at low temperatures. Inasmuch as the equilibrium number of vacancies increases rapidly with increasing temperature (the disorder due to the presence of vacancies means an increase in entropy), it would seem that a greater-than-equilibrium number may be retained at low temperatures by rapid quenching. The effects produced by such "frozen-in" vacancies have recently been studied[2] by means of a technique which is based upon the fact that a reorientation of local groups of atoms (e.g., pairs of solute atoms) takes place when stress is applied to a substitutional alloy. This reorientation is responsible for strain-relaxation effects (see discussion of anelasticity, Chap. XVI and the measured time of strain relaxation is closely related to the mean time between jumps of an atom in the alloy. The α solid solutions of Zn in Ag show particularly large relaxation effects and were, therefore, used in these experiments. An alloy of 30 atomic per cent Zn shows a mean jump time of about 10^7 sec at 50°C if the alloy is cooled slowly from high temperatures. On the other hand, if the same alloy is quenched rapidly from 400°C, the mean jump time is reduced to less than 1000 sec at 50°C. The change produced by quenching is attributed to the presence of a concentration of vacancies greater than the equilibrium number by a factor of more than 10^4, since the probability that a given atom can make a jump is proportional to the concentration of vacant sites available. This nonequilibrium number of vacancies is not completely frozen in at 50°C but gradually decreases over a period of a few hours. Preliminary results[3] show that the mean distance a vacancy must move before effectively disappearing is of the order of 10^3 to 10^4 atomic distances. This implies that a vacancy is lost before it reaches a crystal surface or grain boundary; it probably disappears when it comes to the nearest dislocation (see Chap. XVI). This result is in agreement with an earlier suggestion[4] that vacancies may come to equilibrium with the aid of edge-type dislocations which move at right angles to their slip plane by adding or creating a vacancy. It should be noted that, even in the case of the quenched alloys described above, the mole fraction of "frozen-in" vacancies is only

[1] M. E. Straumanis, *Acta Cryst.*, vol. 2, p. 82, 1949.

[2] A. S. Nowick, *Phys. Rev.*, vol. 82, p. 551, 1951, is a preliminary report of these experiments. Further details are to be published.

[3] A. S. Nowick, private communication.

[4] F. R. N. Nabarro, "Report of a Conference on Strength of Solids," p. 80, Physical Society, London, 1947.

about 10^{-6}. The relatively short distance through which a vacancy must move to reach a dislocation makes it difficult to retain much higher concentrations of vacancies by rapid cooling.

Stacking Disorders. A number of crystals have been found to have errors in the way the atomic layers are stacked above each other. Faults in the stacking of layers are found in several crystals that have strong bonds between atoms of each layer and relatively weak bonds between layers. Imperfect stacking is particularly marked in graphite and carbon black. The structure consists of individual hexagonal layers that are parallel and equidistant, but in some samples there is complete randomness in the way layers are translated and rotated in their own plane with respect to neighboring layers.[1]

Frequent stacking faults are observed in micas[2] because there is more than one position in which a layer of atoms parallel to the cleavage plane can fit on the underlying layer. In this case the layers are displaced parallel to each other without rotation, settling into one of two possible positions on the underlying layer. (Examples in which there are more than two positions in which a layer can rest with approximately equal energy are also possible.) Wurtzite (ZnS) and other minerals offer examples in which stacking faults are common,[3] and also UO_2F_2† and lithium that has transformed at low temperatures.[4]

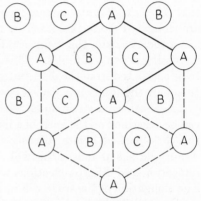

Fig. 21. Sequence of close-packed layers *A*, *B*, and *C* shown projected on a close-packed plane.

Cobalt transforms from face-centered cubic to close-packed hexagonal on cooling, and the hexagonal form contains many faults in stacking.[5] The nature of the stacking errors can be described very simply with reference to Fig. 21, which is a projection of the structure on the hexagonal basal plane. The close-packed hexagonal structure is built up of identical close-packed layers such as the *A* layer; next above an *A* layer is a *B* layer,

[1] B. E. Warren, *Phys. Rev.*, vol. 59, p. 693, 1941.

[2] S. B. Hendricks, *Phys. Rev.*, vol. 57, p. 448, 1940.

[3] H. Jagodzinski and F. Laves, *Schweiz. mineralog. petrog. Mitt.*, vol. 28, p. 456, 1948; H. Jagodzinski, *Acta Cryst.*, vol. 2, p. 298, 1949.

† W. Zachariasen, *Acta Cryst.*, vol. 1, p. 277, 1948.

[4] C. S. Barrett, "Transformations in Pure Metals," National Research Council Symposium on Phase Transformations in Solids, Cornell, 1948.

[5] O. S. Edwards and H. Lipson, *J. Inst. Metals*, vol. 69, p. 177, 1943; *Proc. Roy. Soc. (London)*, vol. A180, p. 268, 1942.

and above that is an A layer again so that atoms in alternate layers are directly above each other in the sequence $ABAB$ . . . . The face-centered cubic structure consists of close-packed layers of the same sort, but arranged in the sequence $ABCABC$ . . . so that every *third* layer superimposes. In either structure a fault is produced if a layer that should be resting in one position rests in another: a layer that should be, say, at B is at C. This can occur without altering the coordination number, and in some crystals only third nearest neighbors are different in the two cases. The result of having frequent errors is to widen certain of the diffraction lines in powder photographs, and to elongate certain spots in rotation photographs into streaks. In the reciprocal lattice of a faulted close-packed hexagonal crystal all points having indices such that $(H - K)/3$ is any integer including zero remain sharp, but the others are elongated along the direction normal to the plane of the faults; *i.e.*, along the c^* axis of the reciprocal lattice. The elongation increases with increasing density of faults. This permits the degree of stacking disorder to be computed from the distribution of intensity in the reciprocal lattice.[1] In cobalt the faults are spaced on the average 10 to 14 layers apart.

A face-centered cubic metal with faults in the stacking of (111) layers can be described on the basis of a hexagonal unit cell three layers high with the close-packed layers forming the basal plane of the new unit cell. Again the sharp reflections will be those for which $(H - K)/3$ is an integer, n, and diffuse reflections will be found when $(H - K) = 3n \pm 1$. The elongation of the spots will be along the normal to the faulted planes, as always. The solid solution of silicon in copper becomes a faulted face-centered cubic structure if an alloy containing 4 or 5 per cent of silicon is cold worked when supersaturated.[2] In the Cu-Si system the α solid solution of silicon in copper must have very nearly the same energy as other types of packing, for the phase in the system that is next highest in silicon (above 552°C) is close-packed hexagonal with practically identical interatomic distances, and with an axial ratio almost exactly 1.633. At lower temperatures also, the next phase in the system is closely related to the close-packed layers of the α phase. It is understandable, then, that when the layers slip over each other during plastic flow there is a marked tendency for them to settle into a wrong position for the face-centered cubic structure, since the right and wrong positions differ but little in energy. The faulting tendency decreases with decreasing silicon content, and also becomes negligible at higher temperatures, where the α phase is not supersaturated. The maximum density of faults in alloys containing

[1] A. J. C. Wilson, *Proc. Roy. Soc. (London)*, vol. A180, p. 277, 1942; "X-ray Optics," Methuen, London, 1949. W. H. Zachariasen, *Phys. Rev.*, vol. 71, p. 715, 1947; *Acta Cryst.*, vol. 1, p. 277, 1948.

[2] C. S. Barrett, *Trans. AIME*, vol. 188, p. 123, 1950.

only the α phase appears to be such that faults occur on the average at spacings of 5 to 10 atom layers.

In the analysis of stacking disorders it is necessary to consider other possible causes of elongated spots. For example, if a phase is present in the form of very thin plates, the reciprocal lattice points will also be elongated, but in this case all points will share the effect, whereas with faults some will remain sharp. Another distinguishing characteristic of the streaks arising from thin plates is that they are symmetrical on two sides of each reciprocal lattice point, whereas this is not the case, in general, with streaks arising from faulting.[1] Another cause of elongated reciprocal lattice points, both symmetrical and unsymmetrical, is coherent segregation in alloys (*cf.* Chap. XXII).

LIQUIDS AND NONCRYSTALLINE SOLIDS

The structure of the liquid state is intermediate between the structures of the solid and gaseous states. In a crystalline solid there is an arrangement of atoms that repeats itself identically at regular intervals in three dimensions. In gases, on the other hand, the arrangement of atoms is completely chaotic. X-ray diffraction has shown that the arrangement of atoms in a liquid is neither so random as in gases nor so regular as in crystals; there is a definite preference for certain interatomic distances, and this statistical distribution causes characteristic diffraction effects. There are no atoms closer than a certain minimum distance from any other atom, but at this minimum distance there are, on the average, several atoms. In the language of the crystallographer, there is coordination in the liquid. The structure has been described as somewhat analogous to the arrangement of ball bearings in a box continuously shaken. At any instant, a number of balls will be in contact with any given ball, or nearly in contact with it, and this ever-changing group will prevent others from forming a group at slightly greater distances. There is, however, no regularly repeating structure, close-packed or otherwise, as there is in crystals.

Earlier Methods of Analysis. The diffraction pattern from a liquid consists of a few diffuse bands—seldom more than two—and at first sight appears to offer a discouragingly small amount of information from which to deduce the "structure" of the liquid. The first attempts to analyze

---

[1] The author is indebted to M. S. Paterson for discussions of this point and of the fact that faulting due to growth, which leads to stacking sequences that differ from those due to deformation, should produce intensity distributions on the streaks that are different from those resulting from deformation. The microstructures of growth-faulted and deformation-faulted metals are quite different [see C. S. Barrett, National Research Council Symposium on Imperfections in Nearly Perfect Crystals, 1950 (in press); also Fig. 2, Chap. XX.

patterns of this sort consisted simply in applying *Bragg's law* to the diffraction angles of the maximum intensity in the bands. It was later recognized that since there is no regularly repeating lattice in the liquid the ordinary Bragg's law cannot apply directly, and a corrected form must be used: $\lambda = 2(0.815r) \sin \theta$, where r is the distance between the centers of two atoms adjacent to each other in the liquid and θ is half the angle of deviation of the beam.[1]

The Radial-distribution Method. In recent years it has become recognized that if the analysis of liquid structure is to be put on a rigorous basis the experimenter must use *all* the information in the diffraction pattern, not merely the position of the one or two peaks. Fortunately, there is now available a method for doing this. The method was suggested by Zernike and Prins[2] and was first successfully used in a study of liquid mercury by Debye and Menke.[3] In this method a monochromatic beam of X-rays is diffracted from a small capillary tube or from a stream of the liquid, and the intensity diffracted at different angles is measured by an ionization chamber or by a microphotometer record of a photographic film. The measured intensities are corrected for absorption in the sample, for polarization in the beam, and for the presence of incoherent radiation and are placed on an absolute-intensity scale so that the intensity is known relative to the intensity of scattering of a single electron. The curve is then analyzed by a Fourier method, yielding a curve that gives the average number of atoms between r and $r + dr$ from any atom in the liquid.[4] A detailed review covering technique and results has been published by Gingrich.[5]

---

[1] This is Ehrenfest's formula. A discussion of it will be found in A. H. Compton and S. K. Allison, "X-rays in Theory and Experiment," p. 172, Van Nostrand, New York, 1935. In comparing the work of different laboratories it is necessary and sometimes difficult to determine whether they used the ordinary Bragg's law or the Ehrenfest formula.

[2] F. Zernike and J. A. Prins, *Z. Physik*, vol. 41, p. 184, 1927.

[3] P. Debye and H. Menke, *Physik. Z.*, vol. 31, p. 797, 1930.

[4] The beam should be monochromatized by reflection from a crystal. If the monochromator is set at the Bragg angle θ_c and the beam is diffracted by the liquid through an angle of deviation $2\theta_1$, the polarization factor is $\frac{1}{2}(1 + \cos^2 \theta_c \cos^2 \theta_1)$, which for molybdenum radiation reflected from rock salt reduces to very nearly the same polarization factor ordinarily used in crystal-structure analysis. Curves are available giving the values for all the elements and giving also the amount of incoherent scattering that will be obtained at various angles. The corrected intensity curve is made to fit the sum of the coherent (f^2) and incoherent curves at high θ values by multiplying the corrected intensities by a suitable factor, and when this is accomplished the corrected intensities have been reduced to absolute units; *i.e.*, the intensities are then known in terms of the scattering from a single electron, since the atoms can be assumed to scatter independently at large angles.

[5] N. S. Gingrich, *Rev. Modern Phys.*, vol. 15, p. 90, 1943.

The formulas for analyzing liquids with a single kind of atom are derived from the *Debye equation*[1]

$$I = Nf^2 \sum_n \frac{\sin sr_n}{sr_n}$$

where I is the intensity of the coherent scattered radiation, $s = 4\pi(\sin\theta)/\lambda$, θ is half the angle of scattering, λ is the wavelength, f is the structure factor, r_n is the separation between the nth pair of atoms in the liquid, and N is the effective number of atoms in the sample. The sum is taken over all pairings of atoms (*i.e.*, for a group of three atoms there would be three pairings of atoms to compute). The formula supposes that on the average the surroundings of all atoms are identical and are oriented at random in space. By introducing a radial distribution function such that $4\pi r^2\rho(r)$ is the number of atoms between r and $r + dr$ from any atom, the equation leads by the use of the Fourier integral theorem to the *Zernike-Prins formula* for a monatomic liquid:

$$4\pi^2\rho(r) = 4\pi r^2\rho_0 + \frac{2r}{\pi} \int_0^\infty s\left(\frac{I}{Nf^2} - 1\right) \sin rs \, ds$$

where $s = 4\pi(\sin\theta)/\lambda$, ρ_0 is the average density of the liquid in atoms per unit volume, and I/N is the coherent scattered intensity in electron units.

The quantity $s[(I/Nf^2) - 1]$ is taken from the corrected intensity curve obtained experimentally, and the integration involved in the equation is carried out graphically or by the use of a harmonic analyzer for a number of different values of r.

Structure of Liquid Elements. An example of the type of radial-distribution curve derived by the thorough analysis of diffracted intensities is shown in Fig. 22, which was obtained for liquid *sodium* at 103°C by Tarasov and Warren[2] and confirmed by Trimble and Gingrich.[3] The density at any distance, r, from an atom is plotted as ordinate against r as abscissa in curve (a), which may be compared with curve (b), the curve for the radial distribution if the density were constant, and with the distribution of atoms in crystalline sodium, plotted as vertical lines in the lower portion of the diagram. The distance from $r = 0$ to the position of the first peak in curve (a) represents the most probable distance to nearest neighbors. The area under the curve between any value r and $r + dr$ gives the average atomic population between the distances r and $r + dr$ from any atom in the liquid. The deviations from the uniform-density curve (b) show that there is a definite tendency for close-packing

[1] P. Debye, *Ann. Physik*, vol. 46, p. 809, 1915.

[2] L. Tarasov and B. Warren, *J. Chem. Phys.*, vol. 4, p. 236, 1936.

[3] F. H. Trimble and N. S Gingrich, *Phys. Rev.*, vol. 53, p. 278, 1938.

arrangements in the liquid, with a concentration at 3.73 A comparable with the distance 3.72 A for nearest atoms in the solid (at room temperature). A similar curve for sodium at 400°C has less pronounced peaks and indicates that the close-packed arrangements become less marked as the temperature is increased. The structure thus approaches somewhat nearer the randomness characteristic of a gas, as a result of the more violent thermal motions.

Most elements have radial distribution curves in which the innermost peak (and sometimes a second peak) are at approximately the interatomic distances of the closest atoms in the crystal, so that the liquid state is

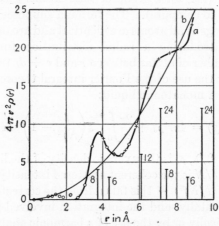

FIG. 22. Structure of liquid sodium. (a) Radial distribution of atoms, $4\pi r^2\rho(r)$. (b) Curve for radial distribution $4\pi r^2\rho_{av}$ if density were constant. (c) Distribution of neighbors in crystalline sodium. The numbers of atoms at the various distances are indicated by the numbers.

moderately well visualized as a blurred derivative of the crystalline state, with frequently interchanging neighbors for each atom. For example, there are about 9.8 atoms of lithium in the innermost peak of the density distribution compared with 8 in the crystalline state, 10.2 to 10.9 in argon at 84°K and 0.8 atm pressure, compared with 12 in solid argon. The better data have been summarized by Gingrich[1] and by Glocker[2] and are presented in Table XI with the number of atoms in the innermost density peaks rounded off to the nearest integers, the "coordination number" for the liquid.

From the table it will be seen that there is good evidence for the existence of certain molecules in the liquid state, viz., N_2, O_2, Cl_2, and P_4. There is a suggestion also of O_3 in liquid oxygen. The structure of liquid tin is much more analogous to crystalline white tin than to that of crystal-

[1] N. S. Gingrich, Rev. Modern Phys., vol. 15, p. 90, 1943.

[2] R. Glocker, Ergeb. exak. Naturw., vol. 22, p. 187, 1949.

TABLE XI. STRUCTURE OF LIQUID PHASES OF THE ELEMENTS

Element	Temperature	Coordination number and nearest atom distance, A		Reference
		In liquid	In crystal	
Aluminum	700°C	10–11 at 2.96	12 at 2.86	1
Argon	84°K	10–11 at 3.79	12 at 3.84	2
Bismuth	340°C	7–8 at 3.32	3 at 3.11	3
Cadmium	350°C	8 at 3.06	6 at 2.98, 6 at 3.31	1
Chlorine	25°C	1 at 2.01	2 at 1.88	1
Gallium	20°C	11 at 2.77	1 at 2.44	3
Germanium	1000°C	8 at 2.70	4 at 2.45	3
Gold	1100°C	11 at 2.86	12 at 2.88	3
Indium	165°C	$8\frac{1}{2}$ at 3.30	4 at 3.25, 8 at 3.38	1
	165°C	8 at 3.17, 4 at 3.88		4
Lead	375°C	8 at 3.40, 4 at 4.37	12 at 3.50	4
Lithium	200°C	10 at 3.24	8 at 3.04	1
Mercury	20°C	8 at 3.0	6 at 3.01, 6 at 3.47, 6 at 4.59	3
Nitrogen	89°K	1 at 1.3		5
Oxygen	89°K	1 at 1.3		5
Phosphorus:				
Liquid yellow	48°C	3 at 2.25		6
Amorphous red and black	20–50°C	3 at 2.28	2 at 2.17, 1 at 2.20	7, 6
Potassium	70°C	8 at 4.64	8 at 4.63	6
Sodium	100°C	8 at 3.83	8 at 3.72	8, 9
Sulfur	20°C	2 at 2.08	4 at 2.12	10
	225°C	1.7 at 2.07		10
Thallium	375°C	8 at 3.30, 4 at 4.22	12 at 3.41	4
Tin	280°C	11 at 3.20	4 at 3.02, 2 at 3.15	3
Zinc	460°C	11 at 2.94	6 at 2.66, 6 at 2.95	1

REFERENCES

[1] C. Gamertsfelder, *J. Chem. Phys.*, vol. 9, p. 450, 1941; *Phys. Rev.*, vol 55, p. 1116, 1939; vol. 57, p. 1055, 1940; vol. 59, p. 926, 1941.

[2] A. Eisenstein and N. G. Gingrich, *Phys. Rev.*, vol. 58, p. 307, 1940; vol. 62, p. 261, 1942; *Rev. Sci. Instruments*, vol. 12, p. 581, 1941.

[3] H. Hendus, *Z. Naturforsch.*, vol. 2a, p. 505, 1947.

[4] R. Glocker and H. Hendus, *Ann. phys.*, vol. 43, p. 513, 1943.

[5] P. C. Sharrah and N. S. Gingrich, *J. Chem. Phys.*, vol. 10, p. 504, 1942.

[6] C. D. Thomas and N. S. Gingrich, *J. Chem. Phys.*, vol. 6, pp. 411, 659, 1938.

[7] R. Hultgren, N. S. Gingrich, and B. E. Warren, *J. Chem. Phys.*, vol. 3, p. 351, 1935.

[8] L. P. Tarasov and B. E. Warren, *J. Chem. Phys.*, vol. 4, p. 236, 1936.

[9] F. H. Trimble and N. S. Gingrich, *Phys. Rev.*, vol. 53, p. 278, 1938.

[10] N. S. Gingrich, *J. Chem. Phys.*, vol. 8, p. 29, 1940.

line gray tin. The coordination number 1.7 in liquid sulfur suggests that an S_8 molecule in the form of an open chain may exist in the liquid, and a value 2 for plastic sulfur at room temperature suggests a closed ring or a long chain. Curves for argon at different temperatures and pressures clearly show the progressive smearing out of the pattern as the temperature increases, and an increase in the scattering at small diffraction angles which is interpreted as evidence of density fluctuations on a scale of 10 A or greater.[1] Additional results, concerned chiefly with the position of intensity peaks, have been published for He I, He II, Ga, Se, Rb, Cs, Hg, Tl, Pb, and Bi.

Liquid Alloys. Liquid hydrocarbons when completely miscible give patterns different from the patterns of either constituent. The principal peak is at a position intermediate between the peaks for the constituents; thus the situation is analogous to that in solid solutions. On the other hand, immiscible hydrocarbons give patterns in which the two individual patterns are superimposed.[2] Similar principles might be expected to govern miscible and immiscible alloys.

Or perhaps it will be found that there is evidence of compound formation in liquid alloys, as concluded by Sauerwald and Teske[3] for liquid alloys of the composition Na_2K, Hg_5Tl_2, and KHg_2. There has been too little work with monochromatic rays and radial density plots to reach a conclusion on this point at present and the early studies with older techniques are inadequate to show clearly the presence or absence of small nuclei or complexes, as Warren[4] points out. A few studies by Hendus[5] on Au-Sn alloys with monochromatic rays are available and give some basis for considering molten AuSn to be in part like a compound (AuSn has the NiAs-type structure) and in part random in atomic distribution, the latter increasing with increasing temperature. Thermodynamic-activity data obtained from emf measurements in a reversible Sn/Sn-Au galvanic cell by Kleppa[6] suggests the presence of some short-range order in liquid Sn-Au alloys, *i.e.*, a strong interaction between the components, since the heats of mixing, the activities, and the entropies of mixing deviate strongly from ideal solution behavior. The Au-Sn bonds must be stronger than Au-Au and Sn-Sn bonds, tending to retain a more than random number of Au-Sn bonds in the melt (as there is in solid AuSn).

[1] A. Eisenstein and N. S. Gingrich, *Phys. Rev.*, vol. 62, p. 261, 1942.

[2] A summary of this work will be found in J. T. Randall, "The Diffraction of X-rays by Amorphous Solids, Liquids, and Gases," Wiley, New York, 1934, and G. W. Stewart, *Phys. Rev.*, vol. 35, p. 726, 1930.

[3] F. Sauerwald and W. Teske, *Z. anorg. Chem.*, vol. 210, p. 247, 1933.

[4] B. E. Warren, *J. Applied Phys.*, vol. 8, p. 645, 1937.

[5] H. Hendus, *Z. Naturforsch.*, vol. 2a, p. 505, 1947.

[6] O. Kleppa, *J. Am. Chem. Soc.*, vol. 72, p. 3346, 1950.

Similarly, the deviations in the curves of partial molar entropy vs. composition in liquid Cd-Sb and Zn-Sb alloys (Seltz and DeWitt[1]) are interpreted by Kleppa as evidence for short-range order in the liquid state of these alloys, related to the low-coordination compounds that exist in the solid state in the Cd-Sb and Zn-Sb systems.

Thermodynamic data for the liquid system Ag-S, measured by Rosenqvist[2] by means of the escaping tendency of sulfur into a hydrogen atmosphere, indicate that sulfur atoms attract each other, a tendency counteracted by thermal agitation at high temperatures, but leading at lower temperatures to segregation into two liquid phases, one low in sulfur and one rich in Ag_2S. The latter phase is presumed to resemble the structure of solid Ag_2S, in which (at least in modification II) Ag atoms are almost randomly distributed in a lattice of S atoms (the 4 Ag atoms per unit cell can occupy 42 positions). Since most metal-sulfur systems show either immiscibility between a metal-rich and a sulfur-rich melt, or miscibility with a pronounced deviation from Raoult's law, short-range order in the liquid is also expected in these systems. Careful X-ray work can yield distribution curves that serve as useful bases for theoretical calculations. Entropy, heat of fusion, and heat of vaporization are quantities which have been calculated with considerable success for sodium[3] and potassium[4] from such curves.

Noncrystalline Solids. If the grain size of a solid is reduced until each grain is only a few unit cells in diameter, the regular repetition of the atomic arrangement is destroyed, the diffraction pattern (even the electron-transmission diffraction pattern) becomes diffuse and it is reasonable to call the structure amorphous (though there may still remain, perhaps, a close approximation to the normal crystalline arrangement of atoms). For further discussion see also Chap. XXIII. This state has been reached with Sb deposited electrolytically, and with many elements deposited from the vapor in vacuum,[5] including B, Ga, In, Tl, Si, Sn, Pb, P, As, Sb, Bi, S, Se, Te, and I. The amorphous state differs from the liquid state in that the atoms are far less mobile and the interatomic bonds do not continuously change as they do in a liquid.

Some substances, *e.g.*, silica, can be prepared in a glassy state. A glass can be understood, according to Zachariasen,[6] as a network in which nearest neighbor bonds are normal, but the bonds do not have the long-

[1] H. Seltz and B. J. DeWitt, *J. Am. Chem. Soc.*, vol. 60, p. 1305, 1938; vol. 61, p. 3170, 1939.

[2] T. Rosenqvist, *Trans. AIME*, vol. 185, p. 451, 1949.

[3] C. N. Wall, *Phys. Rev.*, vol. 54, p. 1062, 1939.

[4] N. S. Gingrich and C. N. Wall, *Phys. Rev.*, vol. 56, p. 336, 1939.

[5] H. Richter, *Physik. Z.*, vol. 44, p. 406, 1933. W. E. McCormick and W. P. Davey, *Phys. Rev.*, vol. 47, p. 330, 1935. J. A. Prins, *Trans. Faraday Soc.*, vol. 33, p. 110, 1937.

[6] W. Zachariasen, *J. Am. Chem. Soc.*, vol. 54, p. 3841, 1932.

range regularity of a crystal; e.g., in a silicate glass each Si atom is surrounded by four O atoms at the corners of a tetrahedron having the Si atom at its center, but the SiO_4 tetrahedra are linked together in a random fashion. The ability to form a glass is thus related to the fact that silicates, when crystalline, can have various crystal structures based on different linkage schemes in which the silicate tetrahedra may share corners and edges in various ways.

It is typical of diffraction patterns from most liquids and glasses that there is no scattering at very small angles; this means that there are no large-scale inhomogeneities in the sample, no "crystallites" separated by voids. In silica gel, on the other hand, there is very strong small-angle scattering as a result of the existence in the gel of colloidal particles 10 to 100 A in size with voids between them (cf. page 159). In the colloidal state it is possible to have all sizes of crystallites. As the particles become smaller, the diffraction lines broaden continuously and merge until at crystallite sizes of about 10 A there remain only the typical halos of the amorphous state.

It is commonly stated that metals cannot be reduced to an amorphous state by cold work. This appears to be true with regard to cold rolling, but with extremely severe shearing strains under high compressive stress Bridgman[1] has reduced crystalline fragments to a state giving typical amorphous patterns.

[1] P. W. Bridgman, Phys. Rev., vol. 48, p. 825, 1935.

CHAPTER XII

SUPERLATTICES

In an ordinary solid solution the different species of atoms are arranged at random on the atomic positions of the lattice. At the composition AB, for example, any given lattice point is occupied indifferently by either A or B atoms, and there is a constant interchange of atoms of both species at each lattice point. There are many solid solutions, however, in which a different atom distribution can be induced. Atoms of one kind can be made to segregate more or less completely on one set of atomic positions, leaving atoms of the other kind to the remaining positions. The resulting arrangement can be described as a lattice of A atoms interpenetrating a lattice of B atoms. The segregation of atoms to particular atom sites may take place with little or no deformation of the lattice, creating an ordered solid solution, or *superlattice*, out of a random solid solution.

In a disordered solid solution every plane of atoms is identical (statistically) with every other, but in an ordered superlattice this is no longer true. For example, alternate planes of a set may become A-rich and B-rich planes, respectively, and the distance between identical planes may become twice the distance between identical planes of the disordered alloy (or some other multiple of this distance). Diffraction patterns of the alloy will then contain reflections ("superlattice lines") from the new and larger spacings which are not present in patterns of the disordered alloy. An example is reproduced in Fig. 1. Bain[1] in 1923 and Johansson and Linde[2] in 1925 were the first to observe these lines with X-ray diffraction, though the possibility of ordering had been considered some years earlier by Tammann.[3]

The formation of superlattices takes place at relatively low temperatures and at compositions expressed by a simple formula like AB or AB_3, or at compositions near these. At all temperatures above a certain critical temperature the usual randomness persists; when the temperature is lowered through the critical point, order sets in and increases as the temperature drops, approaching perfection only at low temperatures.

[1] E. C. Bain, *Chem. & Met. Eng.*, vol. 28, pp. 21, 65, 1923; *Trans. AIME*, vol. 68, p. 625, 1923.
[2] C. H. Johansson and J. O. Linde, *Ann. Physik*, vol. 78, p. 439, 1925.
[3] G. Tammann, *Z. anorg. Chem.*, vol. 107, p. 1, 1919.

The intensive study of superlattices that followed their discovery has provided a remarkably clear view of the dynamic conditions within metallic crystals, the balance between the tendency of the atoms to take up regular positions and the opposing tendency of thermal agitation to maintain a chaotic arrangement. The main features of the order-disorder transformation have been worked out theoretically with marked success and confirmed by experiment.[1]

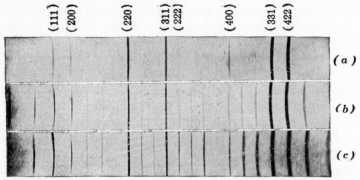

Fig. 1. Powder-diffraction patterns of the superlattice AuCu₃. (a) Disordered, (b) partially ordered, (c) highly ordered. (*From C. Sykes and H. Evans, J. Inst. Metals, vol.* 58, *p.* 255, 1936.)

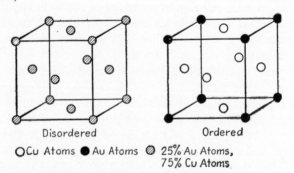

Disordered   Ordered

○Cu Atoms ●Au Atoms ⊘ 25% Au Atoms, 75% Cu Atoms

Fig. 2. The superlattice of AuCu₃ (cubic).

Common Types of Superlattices. Copper-gold alloys of about 25 atomic per cent gold (AuCu₃) were among the first investigated. In the disordered state, which exists at high temperatures, AuCu₃ has a random array of Au and Cu atoms on a face-centered cubic (f.c.c.) lattice (Fig. 2). If the alloy is annealed below a critical temperature, about 400°C (750°F), the atoms segregate as shown in the drawing of the ordered structure, Au atoms going to the cube corners and Cu atoms to the face

---

[1] An extensive review has been published by F. C. Nix and W. Shockley, *Rev. Modern Phys.*, vol. 10, p. 1, 1938, and shorter ones by F. C. Nix, *J. Applied Phys.*, vol. 8, p. 783, 1937, C. S. Barrett, *Metals & Alloys*, vol. 8, p. 251, 1937, and F. Seitz, "The Modern Theory of Solids," McGraw-Hill, New York, 1940.

centers. This represents the condition when ordering is complete, the equilibrium condition at low temperatures.

This structure has been observed in the following alloys: $AuCu_3$, $PtCu_3$, $PdCu_3$,* $FeNi_3$, $MnNi_3$, $(MnFe)Ni_3$.

The superlattice in β-brass is illustrated in Fig. 3. The disordered crystal is body-centered cubic (b.c.c.) with equal probabilities of having Cu and Zn atoms at each lattice point; the ordered structure has Cu atoms and Zn atoms segregated to cube corners and centers, respectively, in a

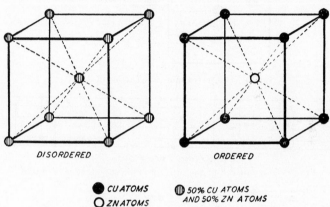

DISORDERED   ORDERED

● CU ATOMS   ◍ 50% CU ATOMS
○ ZN ATOMS   AND 50% ZN ATOMS

FIG. 3. The superlattice of β-brass (cubic, CsCl type).

structure of the CsCl type. This type of superlattice is characteristic of the following alloys of formula AB: CuZn, CuBe, CuPd; AgMg, AgZn, AgCd; AuNi, NiAl, FeCo.

In the Cu-Au system, from 47 to 53 atomic per cent a superlattice forms in which alternate layers of Cu and Au atoms form on (001) planes of the f.c.c. solid-solution lattice, distorting it into a tetragonal structure, illustrated in Fig. 4. The fourfold axis is normal to the alternating planes of Cu and Au atoms, and the axial ratio is approximately $c/a = 0.93$.†

Another superlattice in this composition range of the system Cu-Au has a surprising unit cell formed out of 10 cells of the disordered lattice,[1] as shown in Fig. 5. The structure is orthorhombic, with two axes nearly equal ($b/a = 1.003$ to 1.031 in different samples) and the third ten times as long. It is found when a 50 atomic per cent alloy is quenched from

* $PdCu_3$ has been shown to be actually tetragonal, slightly distorted from cubic [W. L. Bragg, C. Sykes, and A. J. Bradley, *Proc. Phys. Soc. (London)*, vol. 49, p. E96, 1937].

† C. H. Johansson and J. O. Linde, *Ann. Physik*, vol. 82, p. 449, 1927; vol. 25, p. 1, 1936. R. Hultgren and L. Tarnopol, *Trans. AIME*, vol. 133, p. 228, 1939.

[1] C. H. Johansson and J. O. Linde, *Ann. Physik*, vol. 25, p. 1, 1936.

about 420°C or when 36 to 65 atomic per cent alloys are annealed and quenched from somewhat lower temperatures.[1]

In the Cu-Pt system near 50 atomic per cent the f.c.c. disordered lattice takes up the ordered structure shown in Fig. 6a, consisting of

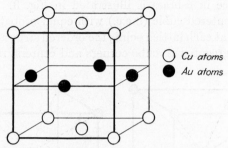

○ Cu atoms
● Au atoms

FIG. 4. The tetragonal superlattice of AuCu.

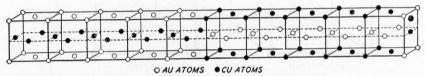

○ AU ATOMS ● CU ATOMS
FIG. 5. One unit cell of the orthorhombic superlattice of AuCu.

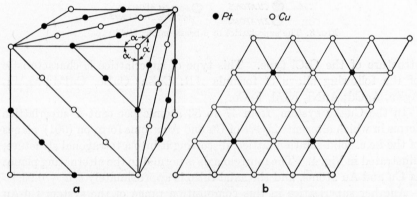

● Pt   ○ Cu

a   b

FIG. 6. The rhombohedral superlattice of CuPt. (a) Distribution of atoms at the composition CuPt. Alternate (111) planes are occupied by Cu and Pt atoms. (b) Distribution of atoms on a single (111) plane, at the composition Cu_3Pt_5.

alternating layers of Cu and Pt atoms on (111) planes. This form of ordering produces a lattice distortion from cubic to rhombohedral.[2] Copper atoms in excess of the 50-50 composition displace Pt atoms at random on the Pt (111) planes, but in alloys with Pt atoms in excess of the 50-50 ratio there is an interesting tendency for them to displace

[1] After quenching to room temperature the atomic structure undergoes a curious alteration: the ratio b/a increases, sometimes changing as much as from 1.018 to 1.031.

[2] J. O. Linde, *Ann. Physik*, vol. 30, p. 151, 1937.

certain atoms in the Cu (111) planes in the manner illustrated by the sketch of the (111) plane in Fig. 6b. Each Pt atom tends to be surrounded by Cu atoms; this arrangement would be complete in a Cu_3Pt_5 alloy.

In the Cu-Pd system one of the ordered structures (37 to 48 atomic per cent Pd) has the CsCl structure, although it forms from a f.c.c. disordered state. In spite of this change of lattice, however, it is probably a superlattice transformation, since the physical properties vary with temperature in a way similar to typical superlattices and since it can be shown that a relatively small adjustment of lattice dimensions is required in the transformation instead of an extensive rearrangement of atoms.[1]

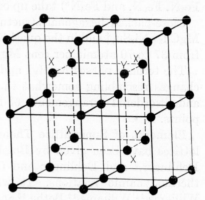

FIG. 7. The structure of Fe_3Al and FeAl. Al atoms fill the X positions in Fe_3Al and the X and Y positions in FeAl.

Bradley and Jay[2] have determined the superlattices in the system Fe-Al in detail. As Al is added to the body-centered lattice of Fe, at first the Al atoms replace Fe atoms at random, but beyond 18 atomic per cent they concentrate in certain positions and desert others. From 18 to 25 atomic per cent the Al atoms concentrate more and more in the positions labeled X in Fig. 7, this process being completed at the composition Fe_3Al. From 25 to 50 atomic per cent, increasing numbers of Al atoms go to Y positions until both X and Y positions are filled with Al atoms at the composition FeAl. The structure is then similar to the ordered structure in β-brass. In both Fe_3Al and FeAl the atom is surrounded by the maximum number of unlike atoms. A structure similar to Fe_3Al is found in Fe_3Si.[*]

The Heusler alloy Cu_2MnAl is ordered when in the ferromagnetic condition; the atoms are in a b.c.c. cell like that of Fig. 7, with the Al atoms in Y positions, the Mn atoms in X positions, and the Cu atoms at the remaining points.[3]

The ferromagnetic ordered phase Cu_2MnSn is isostructural with

[1] C. H. Johansson and J. O. Linde, *Ann. Physik*, vol. 78, p. 439, 1925; vol. 82, p. 449, 1927.

[2] A. J. Bradley and A. H. Jay, *Proc. Roy. Soc. (London)*, vol. A136, p. 210, 1932; *J. Iron Steel Inst. (London)*, vol. 125, p. 339, 1932.

[*] G. Phragmén, *Stahl u. Eisen*, vol. 45, p. 299, 1925.

[3] A. J. Bradley and J. W. Rodgers, *Proc. Roy. Soc. (London)*, vol. A144. p. 340, 1934.

Cu_2MnAl, the Sn atoms of the former taking the positions of the Al atoms of the latter,[1] and the same structure is found again at or near the compositions Cu_2MnIn and Cu_2MnGa, which are also ferromagnetic superlattices.[2] A structure of this type is also reported in the Ag-Mg-Sn system.[3] The structure of Ni_2Al_3 is also based on the FeAl structure, but contains vacant lattice points which increase in number and take up ordered positions as the Al content increases.[4] Thus not only substitutional atoms, but also holes and interstitial atoms (as in austenite, and in Fe_2N, Fe_3N, and Fe_4N[5]) take up ordered superlattice positions.

Close-packed hexagonal structures exist in superlattices of Mg_3Cd,* $MgCd_3$† Ni_3Sn,‡ and in the quasi-binary system $Mg-AgCd_3\|$ in the range, from 37 to 70 atomic per cent Mg.§

The ternary phases Ag_2HgI and Cu_2HgI show complex order-disorder changes resembling somewhat those in $AuCu_3$,¶ but involving ordered and disordered arrangements of both metal atoms and vacant lattice points.

Elements of Superlattice Theory. Theoretical treatments of superlattices have been given by Borelius,[6] Johansson and Linde,[7] Gorsky,[8] Dehlinger,[9] and Dehlinger and Graf,[10] chiefly on the basis of formal thermodynamic relations. It was considered anew by Bragg and Williams,[11] Williams,[12] Bethe,[13] and Peierls,[14] who as a group started with

[1] L. A. Carapella and R. Hultgren, *Trans. AIME*, vol. 147, p. 232, 1942.

[2] S. Valentiner and I. Pusicha, *Metallforschung*, vol. II-4, p. 127, 1947. F. A. Hames and D. S. Eppelsheimer, *Trans. AIME*, vol. 185, p. 495, 1949. B. R. Coles, W. Hume-Rothery, and H. P. Myers, *Proc. Roy. Soc. (London)*, vol. A196, p. 125, 1949.

[3] W. H. Hall, *J. Inst. Metals*, vol. 75, p. 805, 1949.

[4] A. J. Bradley and A. Taylor, *Proc. Roy. Soc. (London)*, vol. A159, p. 56, 1937.

[5] K. H. Jack, *Proc. Roy. Soc. (London)*, vol. A195, p. 34, 1948.

* U. Dehlinger, *Z. anorg. u. allgem. Chem.*, vol. 194, p. 223, 1930.

† K. Riederer, *Z. Metallkunde*, vol. 29, p. 423, 1937.

‡ P. Rahlfs, *Metallwirtschaft*, vol. 16, p. 640, 1937.

$\|$ F. Laves and K. Moeller, *Z. Metallkunde*, vol. 29, p. 185, 1937.

§ Atom positions in Mg_3Cd and similar structures are as follows: Mg: $0\,0\,0$, $\frac{1}{2}\,0\,0$, $0\,\frac{1}{2}\,0$, $\frac{1}{6}\,\frac{1}{3}\,\frac{1}{2}$, $\frac{2}{3}\,\frac{1}{3}\,\frac{1}{2}$, $\frac{2}{3}\,\frac{5}{6}\,\frac{1}{2}$; Cd: $\frac{1}{2}\,\frac{1}{2}\,0$, $\frac{1}{6}\,\frac{5}{6}\,\frac{1}{2}$.

¶ J. A. Ketelaar, *Z. physik. Chem.*, vol. B26, p. 327, 1934; vol. B30, p. 53, 1935; *Z. Krist.*, vol. 87, p. 436, 1934.

[6] G. Borelius, *Ann. Physik*, vol. 20, pp. 57, 650, 1934.

[7] C. H. Johansson and J. O. Linde, *Ann. Physik*, vol. 78, p. 439, 1925.

[8] W. Gorsky, *Z. Physik*, vol. 50, p. 64, 1928.

[9] U. Dehlinger, *Z. physik. Chem.*, vol. B26, p. 343, 1934.

[10] U. Dehlinger and L. Graf, *Z. Physik*, vol. 64, p. 359, 1930.

[11] W. L. Bragg and E. J. Williams, *Proc. Roy. Soc. (London)*, vol. A145, p. 699, 1934; vol. A151, p. 540, 1935.

[12] E. J. Williams, *Proc. Roy. Soc. (London)*, vol. A152, p. 231, 1935.

[13] H. A. Bethe, *Proc. Roy. Soc. (London)*, vol. A150, p. 552, 1935; *J. Applied Phys.*, vol. 9, p. 244, 1938.

[14] R. Peierls, *Proc. Roy. Soc. (London)*, vol. A154, p. 207, 1936.

simple assumptions about atomic forces and calculated quantitative results that compared very favorably with experiment. The point of view of this second series of papers is outlined here.

In a fully ordered alloy there are great distances within a crystal through which there is a perfect arrangement of A atoms on one set of lattice points and B atoms on another set. The ordering is consistent, "in step," through long distances. This long-distance order may be defined as to degree by a fraction, S, which varies from zero at complete disorder up to unity at complete order. The *degree of long-distance order* S, as defined for an AB superlattice, is the fraction of the atoms that are in their right positions minus the fraction that are in wrong positions. As a simple illustration, consider an alloy AB in which 100 A atoms and 100 B atoms are randomly arranged; just half of the A atoms are in the places they would occupy in the ordered structure, and the other half are in wrong positions; and the same would be true of the B atoms, giving $S = 0$. If 75 A atoms were right and 25 wrong, the order would be $0.75 - 0.25 = 0.50$.

This definition may be generalized to cover the condition in which n atomic positions of a total number N can be occupied by either kind of atom.[1] In the structure Fe_3Al the fraction $n/N = \frac{1}{2}$, since even in the completely disordered state one-half of the atom positions are still occupied exclusively by one kind of atom.[2] Suppose a fraction r of the n sites is occupied by A atoms in the state of perfect order; these rn sites are right positions for A atoms. In a partially ordered alloy, some of these positions are filled by A and some by B atoms. If p is the probability that a right position for an A atom is filled by an A atom, then the long-distance order is defined by the relation

$$S = \frac{p - r}{1 - r}$$

which varies from 0 to 1 as order increases.

In an alloy of A and B atoms the energy of the crystals will be a minimum when order is complete and will be increased an amount V if a pair of atoms is interchanged so that an A atom takes a place that should be occupied by a B atom, and a B atom moves to a position that should be occupied by an A atom. In other words, V is the net amount of work required to effect this interchange. Under thermal agitation an equilibrium will be reached such that the ratio of the number of atoms in the right positions to the number in wrong positions is proportional to Boltz-

---

[1] W. L. Bragg and E. J. Williams, *Proc. Roy. Soc. (London)*, vol. A145, p. 699, 1934.
[2] The Al atoms are confined to the X and Y positions in Fig. 7 even in the disordered alloy.

mann's factor $e^{-V/kT}$, where k is Boltzmann's constant, and T is the absolute temperature.

If V were a constant, say V_0, independent of the degree of order in the alloy, there would be a gradual increase in disorder with rising temperature along a curve plotted in Fig. 8 as a dashed line. This cannot be the case, however, for a decrease in order results in a decrease in the forces that tend to maintain order. The distinction between right and wrong positions for an atom, in fact, vanishes when disorder is complete, and the energy V to effect an interchange then drops to zero. This dependence of V on order is responsible for the decrease of order at an accelerating

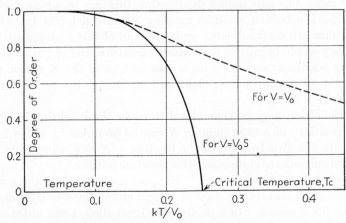

Fig. 8. Dependence of order on temperature according to the Bragg and Williams theory for long-distance order at equilibrium.

rate as the temperature is raised. As Bragg puts it, demoralization sets in, and there is a complete collapse of the ordered state.

To make a theoretical calculation of the degree of order in equilibrium at each temperature it is therefore necessary to assume a particular relation between V and the degree of order. For simplicity, Bragg and Williams[1] assumed that V is proportional to the degree of long-distance order, S, according to the relation $V = V_0 S$, where V_0 is a constant representing the interchange energy when the order is complete. The curve for equilibrium order vs. temperature is shown in Fig. 8 by the solid line. The curve is computed for a superlattice of composition AB, such as β-brass and AuCu; it also holds for Fe_3Al. Long-distance order decreases to zero at a critical temperature T_c that is directly analogous to the Curie temperature at which a ferromagnetic material loses its ferromagnetism.[2]

[1] W. L. Bragg and E. J. Williams, *Proc. Roy. Soc. (London)*, vol. A145, p. 699, 1934.

[2] Each point on the curve of equilibrium order satisfies two conditions that can be stated as follows: (1) The dependence of V upon S is assumed to be $V = V_0 S$ and it is assumed to be practically independent of temperature. (2) The dependence of

The critical temperature T_c is directly related to the ordering energy V_0; in a 50 atomic per cent alloy the relation is approximately $V_0 = 4kT_c$, where k is Boltzmann's constant.

A similar calculation for a composition like $AuCu_3$ gives a similar curve up to a certain temperature and then an abrupt drop to zero order, as indicated by the solid curve in Fig. 9.

Short-range Order. In Bragg and Williams's theory discussed above it is assumed that the ordering energy is proportional to the long-distance order in a crystal, yet it seems certain that the principal interactions in

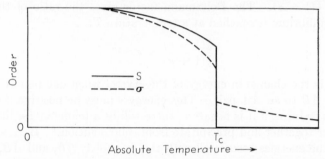

FIG. 9. Dependence of long-range order S and short-range order σ on temperature in an AB_3 superlattice.

crystals are between very close neighbors. A logical development of superlattice theory is therefore to consider a concept of order that concerns only nearest neighbors, and to compute ordering energies based on nearest neighbor interactions. Theories based on this point of view have been worked out by Bethe[1] and extended by Williams,[2] Peierls,[3] Easthope,[4] Kirkwood,[5] and Yang and Li.[6]

Short-range order is defined in terms of the number of "right pairs" of

equilibrium order upon V is dependent upon the Boltzmann factor $e^{-V/kT}$ in a way that leads to the relation $S = \tanh(V/4kT)$ when applied to a superlattice where $r = \frac{1}{2}$ (e.g., CuZn, Fe$_3$Al). Plotting S against V, the equilibrium degree of order is found at the intersection of the straight line of relation (1) with the curve of relation (2). At this intersection the interchange energy V caused by the amount of order present just balances the shuffling tendency of thermal agitation. As the temperature is raised, the intersection of (1) and (2) occurs at lower and lower S values until the intersection occurs at $S = 0$ at the critical temperature. Here $S = \tanh(V/4kT)$ is approximately equal to $S = V/4kT$, and by substituting relation (1) for this temperature, T_c, one obtains $V_0 = 4kT_c$.

[1] H. A. Bethe, *Proc. Roy. Soc. (London)*, vol. A150, p. 552, 1935.
[2] E. J. Williams, *Proc. Roy. Soc. (London)*, vol. A152, p. 231, 1935.
[3] R. Peierls, *Proc. Roy. Soc. (London)*, vol. A154, p. 207, 1936.
[4] C. E. Easthope, *Proc. Cambridge Phil. Soc.*, vol. 33, p. 502, 1937.
[5] J. G. Kirkwood, *J. Chem. Phys.*, vol. 6, p. 70, 1938.
[6] C. N. Yang, *J. Chem. Phys.*, vol. 13, p. 66, 1949. C. N. Yang and Y. Y. Li, *Chinese J. Phys.*, vol. 7, p. 59, 1947. Y. Y. Li, *J. Chem. Phys.*, vol. 17, p. 447, 1949.

atoms, just as long-distance order is defined in terms of the number of right atoms. A right pair is a pair of unlike atoms, an AB pair. At increasing temperatures the number of AB pairs diminishes and the number of AA and BB pairs (wrong pairs) increases until a disordered state is reached in which half the pairs are right and half are wrong. The local, or short-range, order σ may be defined as the probability of finding an unlike atom beside a given atom minus the probability of finding a like atom there. Considering a certain A atom, the probability that a nearest neighbor is a B atom is $\frac{1}{2}(1 + \sigma)$, while the probability that it is an A atom is $\frac{1}{2}(1 - \sigma)$. The Boltzmann factor gives the ratio of these two when equilibrium is reached at a temperature T:

$$\frac{\frac{1}{2}(1 - \sigma)}{\frac{1}{2}(1 + \sigma)} = e^{-v/kT}$$

where v is the change in energy of the crystal when one pair is changed from an AB to an AA pair. This energy v must be positive if a superlattice is to form; if it is negative, there will be a tendency for like atoms to cluster together and precipitate from solid solution.[1] If v_{AA}, v_{BB}, and v_{AB} are the energies associated with the pairs AA, BB, and AB, respectively, then

$$v = \frac{1}{2}(v_{AA} + v_{BB}) - v_{AB}$$

If v were a constant independent of the degree of order, we should find σ decreasing slowly toward zero at high temperatures and there would be no critical point. In Bethe's theory v is assumed to depend upon order in a manner he computes from the long-distance order that exists in the crystal, and this accounts for the accelerated decline toward zero as the temperature is raised toward the critical point.

The curve resembles the curve for Bragg and Williams's theory at low temperatures, as will be seen from Fig. 9, but at the critical temperature Bethe's theory predicts that σ does not fall entirely to zero but to a residual value greater than zero, a value which in turn gradually decreases as the temperature is still further increased. Thus even at high temperatures there are more than the random number of AB atom pairs; and while they are unable to link up together into a constant long-distance order in the crystal, they are able to form small domains within which there is order. At T_c the domains begin to hook together into long-distance order, and as the temperature is lowered the long-distance order increases toward perfection. Even at low temperatures, however, a

[1] The theory of precipitation from a simple binary eutectic system has been discussed by R. Becker, Z. Metallkunde, vol. 29, p. 245, 1937. See R. F. Mehl and L. K. Jetter, The Mechanism of Precipitation from Solid Solution, The Theory of Age Hardening, "Symposium on Age Hardening," American Society for Metals, Cleveland, Ohio, 1940.

crystal may be divided into domains "out of step" with each other in the manner indicated in Fig. 10. The energy for each degree of order may be computed by statistical mechanics from the number of different arrangements of atoms that will have that degree of order.

The existence of local order above the critical temperature has been confirmed by observations on specific heats of superlattices, as will be discussed later; it has also been shown by certain diffuse rings in electron diffraction patterns,[1] and by the diffuse scattering of X-rays.[2] Bethe's first treatment of the local-order problem was limited to simple structures of composition AB; this was extended to composition AB_3 by Peierls[3]

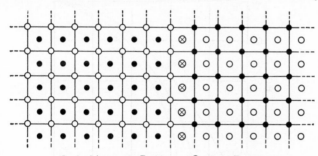

O–A Atom ●–B Atom ⊗–A or B Atom

FIG. 10. Out-of-step domains in a superlattice.

and generalized to compositions other than stoichiometric ratios by Kirkwood,[4] Easthope,[5] and others.

Dependence of T_c on Composition. Easthope's theory[5] for the variation of the critical temperature with composition indicates that T_c is a maximum at 50 atomic per cent for structures like the simple cubic or b.c.c. in which each atom has unlike atoms for nearest neighbors when fully ordered. His predictions for T_c vs. composition are plotted in Fig. 11 on a temperature scale expressed as fractions of T_c at 50 atomic per cent. The curve is symmetrical about this composition. He does not predict a maximum in T_c for f.c.c. lattices at the stoichiometric ratio AB_3.

Shockley[6] treats the f.c.c. lattice as four interpenetrating lattices of the simple cubic type and notes that in ordered AuCu two of these are pure Cu and two are pure Au, while in ordered AuCu$_3$ three of these are Cu and one is pure Au. By considering the degree of order on each of these inter-

[1] L. H. Germer, F. E. Haworth, and J. J. Lander, *Phys. Rev.*, vol. 61, p. 93, 1942.

[2] Z. W. Wilchinsky, *J. Applied Phys.*, vol. 15, p. 806, 1944. J. M. Crowley, *J. Applied Phys.*, vol. 21, p. 25, 1950.

[3] R. Peierls, *Proc. Roy. Soc. (London)*, vol. A154, p. 207, 1936.

[4] J. G. Kirkwood, *J. Chem. Phys.*, vol. 6, p. 70, 1938.

[5] C. E. Easthope, *Proc. Cambridge Phil. Soc.*, vol. 33, p. 502, 1937.

[6] W. Shockley, *J. Chem. Phys.*, vol. 6, p. 130, 1938. F. C. Nix and W. Shockley, *Rev. Modern Phys.*, vol. 10, p. 1, 1938.

penetrating lattices separately he is able to treat intermediate compositions and to compute the free energy as a function of composition for all
alloys of the system.   His theory predicts a phase diagram in which the
ordered tetragonal phase (AuCu), the ordered cubic phase (AuCu₃), and
the disordered phase are separated by two-phase regions (Fig. 12).   Both
ordered structures have a maximum T_c at 50 atomic per cent, and there is
symmetry around this composition.   Modifications of the theory are
necessary to account for the lack of symmetry that actually exists in the
Au-Cu system and to account for the fact that an orthorhombic rather

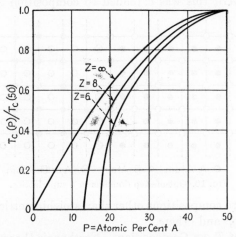

FIG. 11. Easthope's theoretical curves for critical temperature vs. composition for structures with coordination numbers 6, 8 and ∞ (the latter corresponding to the Bragg-
Williams theory).

than a cubic structure forms.   Further developments and generalizations
of the theory of superlattices, based on sublattices of various number and
geometrical arrangement by Yang and Li,[1] have led to a theory[2] for the
order-disorder characteristics and phase diagram of Au-Cu alloys with
results different from Shockley's theory.   Ordered structures are predicted at compositions near AuCu₃, AuCu, and Au₃Cu at low temperatures.   Compositions with less than 17 per cent of one kind of atom are
predicted to be disordered at all temperatures.   There are regions at the
edges of each of the ordered regions on the phase diagram where ordered
and disordered phases can coexist in equilibrium (even at the lowest
temperatures).   As with other theories based on the statistics of nearest
neighbor bonds, the phase diagram is symmetrical with respect to the
50-50 composition.   In another treatment of the problem, based on

[1] C. N. Yang, J. Chem. Phys., vol. 13, p. 66, 1945.   C. N. Yang and Y. Y. Li,
Chinese J. Phys., vol. 7, p. 59, 1947.

[2] Yin-Yuan Li, J. Chem. Phys., vol. 17, p. 447, 1949.

statistical mechanics, Mutō[1] employs methods analogous to those used in the theory of the condensation of an imperfect gas, based on nearest-neighbor interactions in clusters of atoms.

Cowley[2] has devised a theory in which the interactions of an atom with all atoms in the concentric shells around it are treated. Considering a certain B atom in an alloy of A and B atoms, there will be c_i atoms on the ith shell around it, of which n_i will be, on the average, A atoms. Then

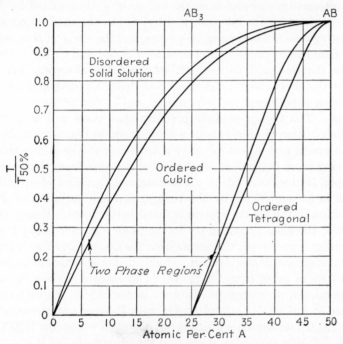

Fig. 12. Shockley's theoretical phase diagram for f.c.c. superlattices.

the short-range order may be considered in terms of the parameters $\alpha_i \equiv 1 - n_i/m_A c_i$, where m_A is the fraction of atoms in the alloy that are A atoms. These parameters are zero for the completely disordered state, but for the completely ordered state they may have various positive and negative values, depending upon the alloy structure. Cowley uses these parameters, α_i, because they can be determined experimentally by an analysis of the diffuse X-ray scattering. The probability that an atom at lmn will be an A atom is given by $p_{lmn} = m_A(1 - \alpha_{lmn})$, if a B atom is at the origin, and by $p_{lmn} = m_A + m_B \alpha_{lmn}$ if an A atom is at the origin, where m_B is the atom fraction of B atoms, and α_{lmn} has the same significance as α_i. These probabilities govern the X-ray scattering power, and,

[1] Y. Mutō, *J. Chem. Phys.*, vol. 16, p. 519, 1948.
[2] J. Cowley, *Phys. Rev.*, vol. 77, p. 669, 1950.

in fact, the α_{lmn} are the coefficients of the three-dimensional Fourier series that describes the intensity of the diffuse scattering throughout the reciprocal lattice. By expressing the configurational energy and the entropy of the structure in terms of α_i, m_A, m_B, kT, and energies of interaction of an atom with like and with unlike atoms in the ith shell, and by making certain approximations, the free energy is computed. The principle that the free energy is a minimum at equilibrium then enables a computation of the interaction energies from the values of α_i determined by X-rays. Then equations for the long-range order, S, are obtained by considering the limiting case of i becoming very large, and the curve of S vs. temperature is found to fit experimental data for Cu_3Au[1] and $CuZn$[2] better than previous theories, and, in fact, within experimental error. The curves of α_i for the short-range order vs. T are also computed, and when compared with experiment for the case of $AuCu_3$ the agreement again is excellent. The theory predicts properly that there will be a "liquid-like" distribution of atoms about a given atom, in that certain shells will have an excess and others will have a deficiency of like atoms, this tendency being more dependent on the radial distance from the given atom than upon lattice coordinates. The observed variation of α_i with composition is accounted for by the theory, and the variation of T_c with composition in the Cu-Au system is fitted better by this theory than by the earlier theories. Asymmetry in the phase diagram about the 50-50 composition is predicted; this stems from the assumption that interaction between neighbors depends on interatomic distance, which increases from 2.55 to 2.88 in going from Cu to Au. (An inverse sixth-power law for the dependence of energy on distance is assumed.) Superlattices are predicted at $AuCu_3$, $AuCu$, and Au_3Cu, with T_c being a maximum at each, but the Au_3Cu maximum—which is not observed—is so low (190°C) that sluggish diffusion may have prevented the observation of it.

Alternate Views on Superlattice Theory. An alternate basis has been neglected in theoretical work (or avoided because of inherent difficulties), viz., the principle that superlattice formation should reduce strain energy resulting from the atoms of a solid solution differing in radii.[3] There are two ways, in fact, for strain energy to be reduced, because not only ordering but also segregation should do this. An opposing factor that must be considered is the strain located at the boundaries of ordered nuclei or nuclei of a segregate.[4]

[1] J. M. Cowley, *J. Applied Phys.*, vol. 21, p. 25, 1950.

[2] B. E. Warren and C. Chipman, *Phys. Rev.*, vol. 75, p. 1629, 1949.

[3] C. Zener, private communication.

[4] If strain energy is an important factor in an alloy, it might be possible for local order to be found at elevated temperatures and yet for segregation to occur at lower temperatures. On the other hand, if bond energies between nearest neighbors are

A statistical mechanics treatment of simple binary diagrams has been given by Lawson.[1] The problem of calculating solubility limits vs. temperature even when these are not symmetrical about the 50-50 composition is solved with reasonable success by considering the entropy of mixing, vibrational entropy, and strain energy.

In addition to the factors that commonly govern superlattice formation, there are some that become of importance in special cases. Ferromagnetism is an example. For those structures in which a consistent antiferromagnetic arrangement of unpaired d-electron spins is possible, the energy associated with the antiferromagnetism may be a factor.

X-ray Determinations of Order vs. Temperature. The degree of long-distance order in a superlattice may be determined from the intensity of the superlattice lines. For example, if the equation for the intensity of reflection (Chap. IV) is evaluated for $AuCu_3$, where atoms with scattering power f_{Au} are at positions with coordinates 000 and atoms with scattering power f_{Cu} are at $\frac{1}{2}\frac{1}{2}0$, $\frac{1}{2}0\frac{1}{2}$, and $0\frac{1}{2}\frac{1}{2}$, it will be seen that there are two classes of reflections. The main reflections occur when indices are all odd or all even, and have intensities proportional to $|F|^2 = (f_{Au} + 3f_{Cu})^2$. The superlattice lines occur when indices are mixed odd and even, and have intensities proportional to $|F|^2 = (f_{Au} - f_{Cu})^2$ in a completely ordered alloy and proportional to $S^2(f_{Au} - f_{Cu})^2$ in a partially ordered alloy having S as the degree of long-distance order. Thus in a fully disordered alloy $S = 0$ and the superlattice lines vanish, since each lattice point then has, on the average, the same scattering power.

Measurements of long-distance order by reflected intensities, which require consideration of the geometry used, absorption, extinction, the multiplicity of the reflection, and the temperature factor, have been made for $AuCu_3$ using both powder[2] and single-crystal methods.[3] It has also been proposed that the axial ratio in tetragonal superlattices be used as an index of order.[4]

When long-range order is not complete the superlattice lines are widened, and careful applications of the particle-size formula have been made in an effort to determine the domain sizes from the broadening in

---

the controlling factor, this would not be expected, for if the bonds between like neighbors are of lower energy than the bonds between unlike neighbors, there should be a tendency toward segregation rather than ordering at both low and high temperatures.

[1] A. W. Lawson, *J. Chem. Phys.*, vol. 15, p. 831, 1947; *Trans. ASM*, vol. 42A, p. 85, 1950.

[2] Z. W. Wilchinsky, *J. Applied Phys.*, vol. 15, p. 806, 1944.

[3] B. E. Warren and D. Chipman, *Phys. Rev.*, vol. 75, p. 1629, 1949.

[4] G. Borelius, *J. Inst. Metals*, vol. 74, p. 17, 1947. A. H. Wilson, *Proc. Cambridge Phil. Soc.*, vol. 34, p. 81, 1938.

AuCu₃.[1] It was found, however, that the apparent domain sizes determined in this way varied from line to line in a given sample by as much as a factor of 2. Wilson[2] was able to obtain reasonable agreement between theory and experiment by assuming that the boundaries of domains occur in such a way that they do not bring Au atoms into contact. The shape of spots on oscillating-crystal patterns appeared to offer some support for this theory, in that they could be explained in terms of nodes in reciprocal space having the shape of disks with axes along [100], [010], and [001],[3] but somewhat different views have been proposed by others.[4]

The nature of the *short-range order* in alloys has been studied by investigating the intensity of the diffuse background between the main lattice reflections. Wilchinsky[5] showed that short-range-order parameters could be determined from powder photographs, but because of the difficulty in accurately correcting for the diffuse scattering from thermal motion of the atoms, powder methods are inferior to single-crystal methods. In single-crystal patterns, thermal diffuse scattering is concentrated near the main reflections and is well separated from the maxima of the diffuse scattering due to short-range order, which lie at the positions of the superlattice reflections of a fully ordered crystal. Cowley[6] measured and analyzed with marked success the diffuse scattering from short-range order in a single crystal of AuCu₃. Crystal-monochromatized radiation was used in a Geiger-counter spectrometer; the specimen was mounted in a furnace and held at constant temperature above T_c: the intensity of the scattering was measured at enough orientations of the crystal so that it could be plotted at 8000 points throughout a unit cell of the reciprocal lattice. A three-dimensional Fourier analysis of these data then yielded the α_{lmn} coefficients of short-range order mentioned on page 281. The analysis shows that there is a large excess of Cu atoms in the first shell around an atom of Au, a defect of Cu in the next three shells, an excess in the next three, and a defect in the following three, as compared with the number in each shell for a completely random arrangement. Since there is a tendency for unlike atoms to be nearest neighbors, the excess of

[1] C. Sykes and F. W. Jones, *Proc. Roy. Soc. (London)*, vol. A157, p. 213, 1936. F. W. Jones and C. Sykes, *Proc. Roy. Soc. (London)*, vol. A166, p. 376, 1938.

[2] A. J. C. Wilson, *Proc. Roy. Soc. (London)*, vol. A181, p. 360, 1943; "X-ray Optics," Methuen, London, 1949; *Nature*, vol. 160, p. 305, 1947.

[3] I. G. E. Edmunds, R. M. Hinde, and H. Lipson, *Nature*, vol. 160, p. 304, 1947.

[4] Other experiments and discussions have been published by C. H. MacGillavry and B. Stryk, *Physica*, vol. 11, p. 369, 1946; vol. 12, p. 129, 1946; A. Guinier and R. Griffoul, *Acta Cryst.*, vol. 1, p. 188, 1948; *Compt. rend.*, vol. 221, p. 555, 1945; vol. 224, p. 1168, 1947.

[5] Z. W. Wilchinsky, *J. Applied Phys.*, vol. 15, p. 806, 1944.

[6] J. M. Cowley, *J. Applied Phys.*, vol. 21, p. 24, 1950.

Cu atoms in the first shell is understandable. This principle also accounts for the defect of Cu atoms in the next three shells, for each of these three is composed of atoms that are nearest neighbors of those in the first shell; atoms in these three similarly have neighbors in the following three shells and tend to produce an excess of Cu in these. The analogy with the excess and defect of density at various distances from an atom in a liquid is striking. But the influence of an atom appears to extend to greater distances than had been previously supposed. The local-order parameters at 405°C indicate that with an atom of Au at the center there is an excess of one Cu atom among the 24 atoms of the fifth shell, and a defect of half a Cu atom among the 24 atoms of the tenth shell.

Guinier[1] has found X-ray evidence of short-range order in the system Ag-Au at the 50-50 composition, although no superlattice exists. That the same is true of other solid solutions is also certain. Short-range order may be deduced from thermodynamic-activity considerations,[2] and the values for alpha-brass and certain compositions in the Ag-Au, Ag-Zn, and Ag-Cd systems have been deduced from measurements of the vapor pressures of the components of the vapor in equilibrium with the solid solution. Negative deviations from ideal-solution behavior result in the formation of more A—B bonds at the expense of A—A and B—B bonds than would be found in truly random solutions, and in each of the three systems mentioned this appears to be the case.

The Order of Transformations. A transformation is said to be of first order, in the thermodynamic sense, if it is associated with a discontinuity in the first derivatives of the free energy with respect to temperature and pressure. If the free energy and its first derivatives are equal before and after transformation but there is a discontinuity in the *second* derivatives of the free energy during the transformation, it is said to be a second-order transformation. Similarly, an nth order transformation is one in which a discontinuity occurs in the nth derivative of the free energy but in no lower derivative. In a one-component system a second-order transformation will replace the usual first-order type only if the entropy and volume of the phases in equilibrium at the transformation temperature and pressure are equal. An example of this is the transformation in liquid helium. In two-component systems a second-order transformation requires not only equality of entropy and volume of the two phases in equilibrium, but identical composition of the two phases.[3] Thus a first-order transformation appears on a phase diagram as two lines bounding the region where

[1] A. Guinier, *Proc. Phys. Soc. (London)*, vol. 57, p. 310, 1945.

[2] Y. Takagi, *Proc. Phys. Math. Soc. Japan*, vol. 23, p. 44, 1941. C. E. Birchenall, *Trans. AIME*, vol. 171, p. 166, 1947. L. Guttman, *Trans. AIME*, vol. 175, p. 178, 1948. C. E. Birchenall and C. H. Cheng, *Trans. AIME*, vol. 185, p. 428, 1949.

[3] J. W. Stout, *Phys. Rev.*, vol. 74, p. 605, 1948.

two phases of different composition coexist in equilibrium, but a second-order transformation appears as a single line.   In distinguishing between these types in alloys by looking for a heat of transformation, one encounters the difficulty that this heat is spread over a temperature range (*i.e.*, the two-phase range).   If sufficient care is taken, the presence or absence of the two-phase region may be established by X-ray investigations of equilibrated alloys.   A third method is to determine by precision X-ray measurements whether there is a discontinuity in volume during transformation.   All the methods encounter the difficulty that equilibrium is reached very slowly in solid-solid reactions, particularly near transformation points.

The superlattice transformation in $AuCu_3$ must be first-order: there are discontinuous changes in order and in lattice constant[1] and there is a latent heat.   Rhines and Newkirk[2] have found X-ray patterns of two phases (partially ordered and disordered) existing together in equilibrium at a composition slightly different from $AuCu_3$ and at a temperature of 383°C.   Electrical resistance vs. temperature in this alloy and in beta-brass also appear to indicate the existence of a region in which segregation produces two phases of different composition.   The cubic to tetragonal change in CuAu is abrupt[3] as in Fig. 9, rather than continuous as in Fig. 8, and two phases appear to coexist in equilibrium at some compositions.[4] Two-phase regions indicative of first-order transformations have been found in the Co-Pt system at 53.8 atomic per cent Co in connection with the face-centered cubic to face-centered tetragonal change induced by ordering,[5] also in the Ni-Pt system near NiPt.[6]   Possibly some superlattice transformations act as second-order changes when segregation does not have time to occur, and become first-order under equilibrium conditions.

There appears reason to believe that cubic to tetragonal transformations in indium alloys (such as In–20 per cent Tl)[7] may be of the second order, since it occurs without change in volume and without a two-phase range being detected (as yet).   The axial ratio jumps abruptly from 1 to 1.023 at the transformation temperature in an alloy of 22.24 atomic per cent thallium.   This, however, does not appear to be an ordering reaction.

Superlattices have a close parallel in ferromagnetism.   Bragg and

[1] E. A. Owen and Y. H. Liu, *Phil. Mag.*, vol. 38, p. 354, 1947.

[2] F. N. Rhines and J. B. Newkirk, private communication.

[3] W. Gorsky, *Z. Physik*, vol. 50, p. 64, 1928.

[4] R. Hultgren and L. Tarnopol, *Trans. AIME*, vol. 133, p. 228, 1939.

[5] J. B. Newkirk, A. H. Geisler, and D. L. Martin, *J. Applied Phys.*, vol. 20, p. 816, 1949; *Trans. AIME*, vol. 188, p. 1249, 1950.   J. B. Newkirk and R. Smoluchowski, *Phys. Rev.*, vol. 76, p. 471, 1949.

[6] U. Esch and A. Schneider, *Z. Electrochem.*, vol. 50, p. 268, 1944.

[7] L. Guttman, *Trans. AIME*, vol. 188, p. 1472, 1950.

Williams's treatment of long-distance order S is analogous to Weiss's theory of ferromagnetism, S corresponding to the magnetization and V to the difference in potential energy for parallel and antiparallel electron spins. Similarly, the theories of local order are related to the modern theories of ferromagnetism, with interaction assumed between spins in near-neighboring atoms.

Another close analogy is the vibration and rotation of molecules in crystals such as the ammonium halides where there is a critical temperature above which all the ammonium radicals rotate and below which the rotation is gradually replaced by oscillation. Fowler has presented the

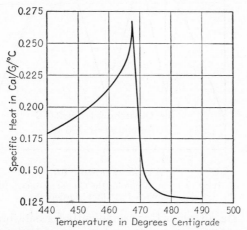

FIG. 13. Specific heat vs. temperature in β-brass (50.4% Zn).

theory of these transitions[1] in each of which there is a critical temperature, properly called a Curie temperature, resulting from an ordering force that decreases with decreasing order.

Specific Heats of Superlattices. The order-disorder transformation has a marked effect on the specific heat of an alloy. Energy must be supplied to interchange atoms from right to wrong positions, for the fully ordered state is the one of lowest energy. The specific heat during disordering is greater than the normal value that is given approximately by the law of Dulong and Petit; the value at each temperature depends upon the rate of decrease of order with increasing temperature. Just below the critical temperature the order drops most rapidly and the specific heat rises to a maximum and then drops precipitously, as shown in Fig. 13. However, the specific heat does not become infinite—*i.e.*, there is no latent heat—unless there is an infinitely sharp drop in order at the critical temperature T_c. Theory and experiment are in reasonable

[1] R. H. Fowler, *Proc. Roy. Soc. (London)*, vol. A149, p. 1, 1935.

agreement[1] for the total energy change from order to disorder but are divergent in predicting the maximum specific heat just below T_c.*

In all specific-heat curves for superlattices the effect of local order above the critical temperature is found—the curves continue to fall as the local order is further destroyed by thermal agitation. Sykes and Wilkinson's

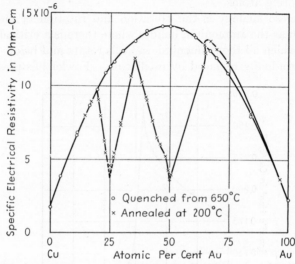

FIG. 14. Electrical resistivity vs. composition for the Cu-Au system. (o) Alloys quenched from 6.0°C (disordered), (x) alloys annealed at 200°C (ordered).

measurements[2] (Fig. 13) show this prominently for beta-brass. The long-distance order breaks up into small partially ordered domains that are out of step with one another, and at still higher temperatures the order approaches zero in each of these. Since the interactions among atoms

[1] F. C. Nix and W. Shockley, Rev. Modern Phys., vol. 10, p. 1, 1938.

* In Bragg and Williams's theory, the notation of the preceding pages being used, an increase in order from S to $S + dS$, which accompanies a fall of temperature $-dT$, involves an increase in the number of atoms in right positions from rnp to $rn(p + dp)$; and since $S = (p - r)/(1 - r)$, we have $dp = (1 - r) dS$. With the potential energy decreasing by $V = V_0 S$ at each atom interchange, the crystal gives off energy $dE = Vrn(1 - r) = V_0 rn(1 - r)S dS$. This integrated between any limits S_1 and S_2 gives the evolution of energy from ordering ("configurational energy"), which for the total change $S = 0$ to $S = 1$ is $V_0 nr(1 - r)/2$. For a superlattice of the AB type with $n = N$ and $r = \frac{1}{2}$, the equation reduces to $NV_0/8$ per mole. On Bethe's theory and Kirkwood's theory this energy of transformation from $\sigma = 1$ to $\sigma = 0$ is $3Nv/2$ for simple cubic AB structures and $2Nv$ for b.c.c. structures. The configurational specific heat is a maximum just below T_c; the predicted values on the different theories are as follows for b.c.c. AB superlattices: Bragg and Williams, $1.50R$; Bethe $1.78R$; Kirkwood $2.20R$; Cowley ∞. The observed value for beta-brass is $5.1R$. Mott [Proc. Phys. Soc. (London), vol. 49, p. 258, 1937] predicts values from a quantum mechanical computation of the energy in beta-brass.

[2] C. Sykes and H. Wilkinson, J. Inst. Metals, vol. 61, p. 223, 1937.

are largely between nearest neighbors, energies and specific heats are determined by the degree of local order.

Electrical Resistivity of Superlattices. Electrical resistivity, like X-ray diffraction, reveals long-distance order but is insensitive to local order. When the disordered state is retained at room temperature by quenching from above the critical temperature, the strains from the irregularity of the distribution are superimposed upon the distortions from thermal agitation, both contributing to the electrical resistance. Annealing below T_c induces order and removes the disordered component of resistance, sometimes lowering the resistivity of the alloy by as much as a factor of 3.

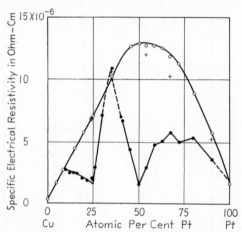

FIG. 15. Electrical resistivity vs. composition for the Cu-Pt system. (o) Alloys quenched and cold-worked (disordered), (+) alloys quenched from 900°C (nearly disordered), (●) alloys annealed at 300°C (ordered).

Measurements on Cu-Au alloys, reproduced in Fig. 14, show the maximum effect of ordering at compositions $AuCu_3$ and $AuCu$, where ordering is most complete. In the Cu-Pt system (Fig. 15) it will be recalled that the CuPt structure distributes excess Pt atoms differently from excess Cu atoms, the former taking ordered positions on (111) Cu planes of the face-centered lattice, the latter taking random positions. This doubtless accounts for the low resistivity of the ordered alloys above 50 atomic per cent compared with those below.

Disorder makes a large contribution to the electrical resistance, superimposed upon the resistance due to thermal vibrations. Bragg and Williams's calculated curve of resistivity vs. temperature for AuCu in equilibrium is reproduced in Fig. 16 and compared with measured values obtained during a slow cooling.[1] The experimental curve deviates from the theoretical because of the increasing sluggishness of diffusion at the

---

[1] N. S. Kurnakow and N. W. Ageew, *J. Inst. Metals*, vol. 46, p. 481, 1931.

lower temperatures, the alloy finally "freezing" into a state of partial order when atomic interchange becomes negligible.

There is an abrupt change in resistance at the critical temperature in AuCu₃, corresponding to the abrupt change in long-distance order from 0 to about 0.4. The abruptness is partly obscured, however, by sluggish diffusion, by the limited size of the domains in which order is coherent, and by strains introduced during the change from a cubic to a tetragonal

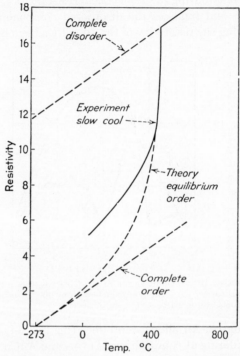

FIG. 16. Electrical resistivity of Au-Cu alloys during slow cooling from above the critical temperature.

lattice. These factors produce a hysteresis effect, making T_c appear at different temperatures on heating and on cooling.

Resistance changes at the critical temperature are relatively minor when the alloy constituents are neighbors in the periodic table. In FeCo,[1] for example, the change in slope of the resistance vs. temperature curve is barely noticeable, and in beta-brass the change in slope at the critical temperature is much smaller than in AuCu₃.[2] In Ni₃Mn there is no change of slope at the critical temperature, although there is one at a slightly lower temperature where ferromagnetism begins;[3] a similar break

[1] R. McGreary and S. Siegel, *Phys. Rev.*, vol. 65, p. 347, 1944.

[2] W. Webb, *Phys. Rev.*, vol. 55, p. 297, 1939.

[3] N. Thompson, *Proc. Phys. Soc. (London)*, vol. 52, p. 217, 1940.

in the resistance curve for FeCo occurs at the α-γ transformation temperature, where the alloy becomes ferromagnetic on cooling.

Plastic deformation tends to destroy long-distance order. It will be seen from Fig. 17 that an annealed $AuCu_3$ alloy reverted to the resistance of a fully disordered alloy when reduced 60 per cent in cross section by drawing through a die.[1] The disordered (quenched) alloy remained relatively unchanged, thus resembling pure metals and random solid solutions, most of which are increased only about 2 per cent in resistivity.

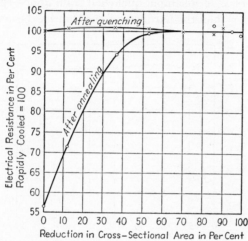

FIG. 17. Effect of cold work (wire drawing) on the electrical resistivity of $AuCu_3$.

Other Physical Properties of Superlattices. Mechanical properties are altered when ordering takes place. Hardness, tensile strength, and elastic limit generally increase.[2] Hardening associated with the ordering process occurs most markedly in those systems where the shape of the unit cell is altered by ordering,[3] *e.g.*, in AuCu, PtCu, and CuPd; it is negligible in $AuCu_3$ and $PtCu_3$, and in fact well-ordered $AuCu_3$ has a lower critical shearing stress when ordered than when disordered.[4] If the alloy AuCu is quenched to retain disorder and is then annealed at 150 to 300°C, the hardness increases with time much as in a precipitation hardening alloy (Fig. 18).[3] The microstructure suggests a martensitic transformation of lamellae.[5] Doubtless the formation of many nuclei of the ordered tetrag-

[1] O. Dahl, *Z. Metallkunde*, vol. 28, p. 133, 1936.

[2] G. Sachs, "Praktische Metallkunde," vol. III, pp. 68–81, Springer, Berlin, 1935.

[3] L. Nowack, *Z. Metallkunde*, vol. 22, p. 94, 1930. W. Köster, *Z. Metallkunde*, vol. 32, p. 277, 1940.

[4] G. Sachs and J. Weerts, *Z. Physik*, vol. 67, p. 507, 1930.

[5] N. Kurnakow, S. Zemczuzny, and M. Zasedatelev, *J. Inst. Metals*, vol. 15, p. 305, 1916. W. Gorsky, *Z. Physik*, vol. 50, p. 64, 1928. J. L. Haughton and R. J. M. Payne, *J. Inst. Metals*, vol. 46, p. 457, 1931. D. Harker, *Trans. ASM*, vol. 32, p. 210, 1944.

onal phase induces severe strains which are presumably responsible for much of the hardening, and the small size of the ordered regions may also be involved.

In beta-brass the ordering process takes place almost instantly. It cannot be prevented or even retarded by quenching. As expected of a super lattice having this rapid ordering, it is found that the conductivity of beta-brass is unaffected (within 1.5 per cent) by the rate of cooling from above the critical temperature (450 to 470°C) and by cold work. In spite of this, the *hardness* of a sample quenched from above the critical temperature is greater than the hardness of one that has been slowly cooled.[1]

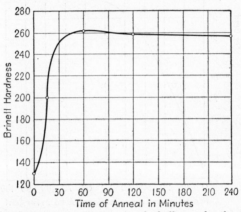

Fig. 18. Hardening of CuPt by annealing a quenched alloy under the critical temperature. (Annealing temperature 500°C.)

The additional hardness must have its origin in out-of-step domains. Hardness changes in beta-brass during aging[1] (Fig. 19) are also under-standable on this basis. An alloy quenched from 500°C presumably has many small out-of-step domains which rapidly coalesce during aging, quickly lowering the hardness. An alloy quenched from a temperature where ordering is about half complete (425°C) probably contains domains of larger size, which grow more slowly, and hence hardness decreases more slowly.

Dilatometric changes occur during ordering, for lattice constants are altered. Young's modulus increases with ordering in Cu_3Pd and $AuCu_3$ but decreases in AuCu and CuPd. The elastic moduli of single crystals are strongly influenced by the degree of order, local as well as long-range.[2]

Ordering affects magnetic properties in many alloys.[3] An outstanding

[1] C. S. Smith, *Trans. AIME*, vol. 152, p. 144, 1943.

[2] S. Siegel, *Phys. Rev.*, vol. 57, p. 537, 1940. W. A. Good, *Phys. Rev.*, vol. 60, p. 605, 1941.

[3] Reviews of the subject have been published by F. C. Nix and W. Shockley, *Rev.*

example occurs in $MnNi_3$, which is paramagnetic when disordered and ferromagnetic when it becomes ordered with the $AuCu_3$ structure. The saturation magnetization is a maximum at about the composition for complete order. A slight increase in saturation magnetization occurs with ordering in FeCo, and in the Fe-Ni system near $FeNi_3$ (permalloy). The Heusler alloys are ferromagnetic ordered structures. Cu_2MnAl has the Fe_3Al-type superlattice when quenched from 800°C, and is ferromagnetic in this state; but when annealed at 500°C and slowly cooled it takes a

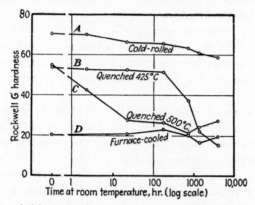

FIG. 19. Hardness of β-brass aged at room temperatures. (*A*) Samples annealed at 425°C, slowly cooled to room temperature, and cold-rolled 15 per cent reduction. (*B*) Annealed 1 hr at 500°C, furnace-cooled to 425°C, held 1 hr at 425°C, and quenched. (*C*) Annealed 1 hr at 500°C and quenched. (*D*) Annealed 1 hr at 425°C and furnace-cooled. (*C. S. Smith.*)

different structure, similar to that of gamma-brass, and is nonmagnetic.[1] Analogous alloys in the Cu-Mn-Ga system are also magnetic when quenched and undergo a transformation that destroys the magnetic quality when either slowly cooled or quenched and aged.[2] A transformation is not found, however, in the analogous ferromagnetic ordered alloy Cu_2MnIn.[2] The saturation moments of some binary alloys of iron, including Fe-Si alloys at 12.5 and 25 atomic per cent silicon, have been attributed to ordering.[3] Pt-Cr alloys containing 20 to 50 atomic per cent chromium are also ferromagnetic, but the composition with highest

Modern Phys., vol. 10, p. 1, 1938; and J. E. Goldman, *J. Applied Phys.*, vol. 20, p. 1131, 1949.

[1] A. J. Bradley and J. W. Rodgers, *Proc. Roy. Soc. (London)*, vol. A144, p. 340, 1934.

[2] F. A. Hames and D. S. Eppelsheimer, *Trans. AIME*, vol. 185, p. 495, 1949. B. R. Coles, W. Hume-Rothery, and H. P. Myers, *Proc. Roy. Soc. (London)*, vol. A196, p. 125, 1949.

[3] M. Fallot, *Ann. Physik*, vol. 6, p. 305, 1936.

saturation magnetization (about 30 per cent) is not that for which the superlattice lines are strongest in X-ray patterns.[1]

In an ordered crystal of $FeNi_3$ the [111] direction is the direction of easiest magnetization, and the [110] and [100] directions follow in order, as in nickel, with marked anisotropy. But in the disordered state this magnetic anisotropy drops to zero.[2] The highest initial and maximum permeabilities occur in the composition range of the $FeNi_3$ superlattice when the ordering is suppressed. Ordering brings about a doubling of the magnetostriction of Permalloy,[3] a 40 per cent increase with FeCo,[4] and increases with Fe-Al alloys.[3]

These various ferromagnetic properties are accounted for theoretically by theories based on the interactions between pairs of atoms (nearest neighbors or these together with more remote atoms); consequently the alteration of atom pairing by ordering may be expected to alter the properties.

The coercive force of some superlattices is strongly influenced by heat treatment. When FePt (also CoPt) becomes ordered during rapid cooling it transforms from face-centered cubic to face-centered tetragonal with $c/a = 0.968$ and forms lamellae parallel to $\{110\}$ planes of the original cubic lattice.[5] The extremely high coercive force of this finely laminated structure has been attributed[5] to strains caused by the transformation—strains resulting from a forced coherency at the interfaces between cubic and tetragonal lamellae. But since yield stress, hardness, and brittleness are altered to a minor extent compared with the changes in permeability and coercive force, doubt has been expressed[6] that the strain theory is adequate, unless consideration is also given to the magnetic anisotropy and magnetostriction. It seems not unlikely, too, that the fine state of subdivision of the crystallites may play a part, particularly if they reach the size of a single magnetic domain.

The Rate of Approach to Equilibrium. Bragg and Williams have made some interesting calculations of the rate at which an alloy will approach its equilibrium degree of order at any temperature. They assumed that the rate of approach is directly proportional to the discrepancy between the actual and the equilibrium order. The constant of proportionality was taken as $1/\tau$, where τ is the "time of relaxation" of the alloy, the time required for the departure from equilibrium to be reduced to $1/e$ (or

[1] E. Friederich and A. Kaussmann, *Physik. Z.*, vol. 36, p. 183, 1935.

[2] E. M. Grabbe, *Phys. Rev.*, vol. 57, p. 728, 1940.

[3] J. E. Goldman, *Phys. Rev.*, vol. 76, p. 471, 1949.

[4] J. E. Goldman and R. Smoluchowski, *Phys. Rev.*, vol. 75, p. 140, 1949.

[5] H. Lipson, D. Shoenberg, and G. V. Stupart, *J. Inst. Metals*, vol. 67, p. 333, 1941.

[6] J. E. Goldman, *J. Applied Phys.*, vol. 20, p. 1131, 1949.

0.368) of its initial amount. A reasonable expression for τ is then $\tau = Ae^{W/kT}$, where A is roughly of the order of 10^{-12} and W is the "activation energy" that a pair of neighboring dissimilar atoms must have in order to surmount their potential barrier and exchange positions.

This expression for the relaxation time permits an estimate of the range of states that can be produced in an alloy by different heat-treatments. Rapid quenching will retain a degree of order characteristic of a high temperature, and annealing for several days will produce a degree of order characteristic of a lower temperature; but the calculations indicate that these two temperatures will differ by only about 30 per cent (on the absolute-temperature scale) because of the rapid change of τ with T. Bragg and Williams estimate from resistance curves that, for $AuCu_3$, τ is 1 sec at about 550°C (a temperature above the transition point), which accounts for the fact that complete disorder can be maintained by quenching. Because of sluggish diffusion, prolonged annealing at temperatures below 270°C, on the other hand, could not be expected to produce degrees of order corresponding to temperatures much below 270°C where the equilibrium order S is approximately 0.75. In the case of Cu-Zn the rate of diffusion is so fast (τ so small) that it is impossible to retain the disordered structure by quenching, and the alloy at room temperature is always highly ordered.

It appears, however, that this treatment of the problem overlooks some important complications. There is much reason to believe that as an alloy is cooled below T_c a number of nuclei start to grow independently of one another and with a noncoherent relation to one another. They probably spread out rapidly until they touch, then grow slowly by some absorbing others.[1,2,3] The integrated intensities of the superlattice reflections increase during this process, and the lines sharpen (apparently simultaneously[2]), until limiting values are reached when the nuclei have absorbed the unordered material and have grown larger than about 1000 A. After large domains have been grown, subsequent changes in order within the domains may occur very rapidly.[1] Bragg[4] has emphasized the similarity between interdomain boundaries and the intergranular boundaries of polycrystalline metals, in structures that have *four* different kinds of out-of-step domains that can meet at a point, as in $AuCu_3$, and not just *two*, as in CuZn.

Compounds, Superlattices, and Solid Solutions Compared. The interactions among atoms may be so strong (V so great) as to cause the virtual value of the critical temperature T_c to lie above the melting point. Such

[1] C. Sykes and H. Evans, *J. Inst. Metals*, vol. 58, p. 255, 1936.
[2] E. A. Owen and G. McA. Sim, *Phil. Mag.*, vol. 38, p. 342, 1947.
[3] J. M. Cowley, *J. Applied Phys.*, vol. 21, p. 24, 1950.
[4] W. L. Bragg, *Proc. Phys. Soc. (London)*, vol. 52, p. 105, 1940.

is the case in phases that are ordered at all temperatures in the solid state. An example seems to be Cu_3Sb (with Fe_3Al structure), and AuZn is another (with the CsCl structure). Alloys with these characteristics closely resemble true chemical compounds.

It will be seen that the whole range of intermetallic structures can be considered from this point of view. When atomic interactions are strong, they may retain order, as in a compound, up to a temperature at which another phase has a lower free energy and begins to form; taking as an example AgZn, the new phase is another solid of different crystal structure, while in AuZn the new configuration is the liquid phase. With less intense ordering forces between the atoms the ordered arrangement may decrease gradually to a low value or to zero at the critical temperature. Finally, if V is very small—and this must be true at low concentrations in terminal solid solutions, since any ordered array would put the solute atoms far apart on the lattice—the critical temperature will be below room temperature, or at least so low that the atoms will not diffuse appreciably into their ordered positions.

The behavior of an alloy will thus be governed largely by two constants, the interaction energy V_0, which is the net amount of work necessary to switch a pair of atoms into disordered positions in the fully ordered alloy, and the activation energy W that the atoms must acquire in order to make the exchange. Approximate values[1] for these in AuCu, expressed in electron volts, are $V_0 = 0.3$, $W = 1.85$. The value W may also be converted to calories, Q ($Q = 23,066W$), and will then be seen to be of the same order as the heats of activation for diffusion in solid solution.[2] It is also of the same order of magnitude as the heats of activation for recovery from cold work; for example, in experiments[3] on permalloy the rate of sharpening of broadened X-ray diffraction lines has yielded the value $W = 1.7$ electron volts.

[1] W. L. Bragg and E. J. Williams, *Proc. Roy. Soc. (London)*, vol. A145, p. 699, 1934.

[2] R. F. Mehl, *Trans. AIME*, vol. 122, p. 11, 1936. See also "Progress in Metal Physics," vol. I, 1949, Interscience Publishers, New York.

[3] J. F. Dillinger, *Phys. Rev.*, vol. 49, p. 863, 1936.

CHAPTER XIII

THE ELECTRON THEORY OF METALS AND ALLOYS

The physicists who in recent years have applied the mathematics of quantum mechanics to the problems of the metallic state have greatly increased our understanding of the phenomena of physical metallurgy, including conductivity, magnetism, specific heat, lattice energy, and alloy structure. The details of the theories they have developed are often of great complexity and are presented in a mathematical language to which most people are allergic, but the results can be presented in a simple manner. A summary of certain results of general interest is given below, with a minimum outline of the reasoning by which they were derived. For details and comprehensive treatments the reader is referred to the books of Mott and Jones[1] and Seitz,[2] and to the review articles.[3]

Metallic Binding. It is now well established that the atoms in metal crystals are ionized and that a metal should be thought of as an assemblage of positive ions immersed in a cloud of electrons. The electrons of this cloud are relatively "free": they are not bound to any particular ion but move rapidly through the metal in such a way that there is always an approximately uniform density of them throughout the interior between the ions. Metal crystals are held together by the electrostatic attraction between this "gas" of negative electrons and the positively charged ions. The binding forces in metals are thus in contrast to those in nonmetallic substances, where the predominating forces are from one atom to another or from positive to negative ions.

Cohesive and Repulsive Forces in Metals. Wigner and Seitz[4] have shown a convenient way to calculate the attractive forces between the positive ions and the electrons of a metal. Planes are drawn bisecting the lines joining an atom to each of its neighbors; these planes then form polyhedra surrounding each atom of the crystal. The polyhedra are

---

[1] N. F. Mott and H. Jones, "The Theory of the Properties of Metals and Alloys," Oxford, New York, 1936.

[2] F. Seitz, "The Modern Theory of Solids," McGraw-Hill, New York, 1940; "The Physics of Metals," McGraw-Hill, New York, 1943.

[3] J. C. Slater, *Rev. Modern Phys.*, vol. 6, p. 209, 1934. N. F. Mott, *Science Progress*, vol. 31, p. 414, 1937. F. Seitz and R. P. Johnson, *J. Applied Phys.*, vol. 8, pp. 84, 186, 246, 1937. W. Shockley, *Bell System Tech. J.*, vol. 18, p. 645, 1939.

[4] E. Wigner and F. Seitz, *Phys. Rev.*, vol. 43, p. 804, 1933; vol. 46, p. 509, 1934. E. Wigner, *Phys. Rev.*, vol. 46, p. 1002, 1934.

convenient units for the calculation of the energy of the lattice, for each polyhedral cell contains one ion and, on the average, one free electron (in monovalent metals). The potential energy of the lattice consists of (1) the energy arising from the positive and negative charge in each polyhedron and (2) the energy of the interaction of each polyhedron with its neighbors. The second of these two energies is very small, since each cell is electrically neutral and is nearly the shape of a sphere; this term can therefore be treated as a small correction—amounting to 1 per cent or less—to the calculation of the energy of interaction between the positive and negative charges in one cell. The polyhedra, which are rhombic dodecahedra in face-centered cubic lattices, can be replaced by spheres for approximate calculations since they are nearly spherically symmetrical.

Balanced against the attraction of each positive ion for the negative electrons that happen to be within its electrostatic field are two principal repulsive forces: (1) the mutual repulsion of the electrons in the electron gas (this may be termed the "pressure" of the gas) and (2) the repulsion between ions that are in contact. Calculations show that the pressure of the gas is not inversely proportional to its volume V, as with an ordinary gas, but is proportional to $1/V^{\frac{5}{3}}$.

The free electrons thus contribute two opposing terms to the potential energy of the lattice. The attractive force is furnished by the potential energy of the electrons in the electric field of the ions; this energy varies inversely as the mean distance between ions, therefore as $-1/V^{\frac{1}{3}}$. The repulsive force derives from the kinetic energy of the electron gas; this energy varies as $1/V^{\frac{2}{3}}$. Summing these two terms gives

$$E = \frac{A}{V^{\frac{2}{3}}} - \frac{B}{V^{\frac{1}{3}}} \tag{1}$$

where A and B are constants and V is the volume of the metal.

It has been shown[1] that for monovalent crystals this energy E is approximately equal to the total energy of the crystal, other terms being negligible. If computations are carried out for various assumed values of the lattice constant of a metal, E is found to vary in the manner illustrated in Fig. 1 (a plot for sodium). The minimum on a curve of this type gives the theoretical prediction of the lattice constant. The difference in energy between this minimum and the value of E for an infinitely large lattice constant is the energy that would be required to remove the atoms from the crystal and scatter them to infinity; this is the heat of sublimation. The curvature of the curve at the minimum is directly

[1] For details, see N. F. Mott and H. Jones, "The Theory of the Properties of Metals and Alloys," Chap. IV, Oxford, New York, 1936; Frederick Seitz, "The Modern Theory of Solids," Chap. X, McGraw-Hill, New York, 1940.

related to the compressibility of the crystal. Bardeen's[1] theoretical values of lattice constant, heat of sublimation, and compressibility are compared with observed values in Table XII.

TABLE XII

Physical property	Lithium	Sodium
Lattice constant, (Å):		
Observed...	3.46	4.25
Calculated...	3.49	4.53
Heat of sublimation, k-cal. per gram atom:		
Observed...	39	26
Calculated...	34	23
Compressibility, sq. cm. per dyne:		
Observed...	7.4×10^{-12}	12.3×10^{-12}
Calculated...	8.4×10^{-12}	12.0×10^{-12}

For the noble metals the atom cores as well as the valence electrons must be taken into account, or otherwise the predicted compressibility would be too high. It appears that with the metals Cu, Ag, and Au—and probably many others—the inner shells of the atoms come into con-

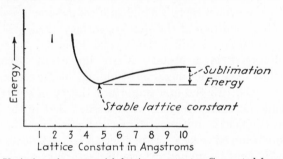

Fig. 1. Variation of energy with lattice constant. Computed for sodium.

tact and begin to overlap before the lattice constant is reduced to the minimum point on the curve corresponding to Fig. 1. A strong repulsion then sets in, and the energy curve turns upward more steeply than in Fig. 1; therefore, the compressibility is lower. One may properly think of these metals as composed of hard spheres in contact. The spherical ions are held in their tight-packed array by the attraction between them and the electron gas in which they are immersed.

The theoretical prediction of what type of crystal structure will be the most stable for any element is a task too difficult for quantum mechanics in its present state. In the first place, its proper method of attack would be to calculate the energy of every possible crystalline

[1] J. Bardeen, *J. Chem. Phys.*, vol. 6, pp. 367, 372, 1938.

arrangement of atoms to see which has the lowest energy. But even if this infinitely laborious task were possible, the results would be unreliable, for the best of the present methods of calculation can yield an accuracy of only about 5 kcal per mole, and the difference between a stable structure and an unstable one may be much less than this. Some theories have succeeded, however, in bringing out *differences* in energies between different structures in such a way as to give useful results in spite of the uncertainties about the total energies; these are discussed in a subsequent section (page 312).

The resistance of metals to cleavage may be understood as arising from electrostatic attraction, since any force tending to pull the ions apart also tends to increase the average distance between ions and their neighboring electrons. Cleavage at grain boundaries is resisted by the same attractive force, since the electron gas is presumed to be substantially the same at a boundary as elsewhere. Most of the energy of the lattice arises from the interactions within each polyhedron; *i.e.*, it depends on electrostatic attraction over very short distances, a fact which suggests that disarranged atoms at a grain boundary should not appreciably reduce cohesion across the boundary. This point of view also provides an answer to the question, "Why does a metal not fall apart when slip is occurring?" For even if there is a high state of disorder possibly approximating a molten condition at the slipping surface, there still remains the electrostatic attraction holding the crystal together.

Electron Energies in a Metal. Many important advances in the theory of metals have been made by studying the movement of valence electrons in metals. In the first important theory of electrical conduction, the Drude-Lorentz theory, it was assumed that in the interior of a metal the electric field is uniform. The conduction electrons in this uniform field were believed to be a sort of gas that is free to drift about whenever an electric field is applied externally, as, for example, when wires from a battery touch the metal. The drift of electrons creates an electric current, and the collisions of the electrons with the ions of the metal interfere with the flow and cause electrical resistance.

The general outlines of this theory are still valid, but it has been so elaborated from its early form as to be almost unrecognizable. The modern theories are based on the fact that a moving electron does not act as if it were a small hard particle but behaves as if it were a system of waves. These waves that constitute the electron (or, better, that describe the motion of the electron) have a definite wavelength that depends upon the velocity of the electron according to the relation

$$\lambda = \frac{h}{mv} \tag{2}$$

where λ is the wavelength, v is the velocity of the electron, m is the mass of the electron, and h is a constant known as Planck's constant.

The problem was undertaken of calculating the velocities that a wave-like electron could have as it moved around in a metal within which the electric field was assumed to be uniform. The problem is analogous to that of calculating what various modes of elastic vibration are possible for the solid block of metal, *i.e.*, its natural frequencies. In both the sound-wave problem and the electron-wave problem a series of modes of vibration are found with different wavelengths, like the fundamental tone and the overtones of a vibrating string. Each mode of vibration corresponds to a definite wavelength according to the relation given in Eq. (2). As a consequence of this, the electron is permitted to have only certain discrete velocities in the metal. If an electron were made to go faster and faster through a crystal, it would increase its velocity by jumps, not continuously, and if we could hear the waves belonging to this electron we should hear a scale composed only of the harmonics of some fundamental tone, not the continuously ascending wail of a siren. The kinetic energies of the electrons are related to their velocities by the equation

$$E_{\text{kin}} = \tfrac{1}{2}mv^2 \qquad (3)$$

and by Eq. (3) this may be written in terms of electron wavelengths:

$$E_{\text{kin}} = \frac{h^2}{2m\lambda^2} \qquad (4)$$

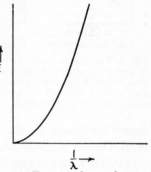

Fig. 2. Energy of an electron moving in a uniform field of force.

The energy thus varies with wavelength as in Fig. 2, along a parabolic curve. This curve could be properly drawn as a string of closely spaced dots representing the closely spaced energy values that are permitted an electron in a crystal.

There are a great many energy values—*energy levels*, as they are called —that are permitted an electron in a crystal; in fact, there are more levels than there are electrons. To determine which of these possible energy levels will actually be occupied by electrons, it is necessary to make use of *Pauli's exclusion principle*, which states that only two electrons can exist in any one energy level in the entire crystal. The two electrons in one energy level must be spinning in opposite directions. Suppose we were to build a crystal by starting with a lattice of positive atom nuclei and adding the electrons one by one until the crystal became electrically neutral. The first electrons added would fill the lowest energy levels, where they would be tightly bound to the individual nuclei. These would be the ones that would take part in the processes of X-ray emission, discussed in Chap. III. As these levels became filled, two electrons going to each level, succeeding additions would go to higher levels. When all the electrons had been placed, we should find all the lower levels up to some maximum energy completely filled and all the levels above this empty.

The theory just outlined is more successful than the earlier Drude-Lorentz theory in explaining certain physical properties of metals, particularly their specific heats. The earlier theory postulated a gas of free electrons in a metal; if each particle of this gas were to behave as a particle of an ordinary gas, it would have a heat capacity of $\frac{3}{2}k$, where k is the gas constant. But the total contribution to the specific heat of the metal from the conduction electrons when computed on this basis is much too great, about a hundred times greater than the observed value. The newer concept removes this discrepancy, for only a small proportion of the electrons contribute to the specific heat. When the temperature of a metal is raised, the electrons in the lower energy levels cannot accept any thermal energy because for them to do so would require that they move up to a level that is slightly higher than the one they are in and there are no available empty spaces in the tightly filled band of levels that would permit this. Only the electrons at or near the very top of the layer of filled levels are able to find vacant levels above them and are able, therefore, to accept additional energy. This may be represented schematically by the sketches in Fig. 3 for a crystal at a low temperature (Fig. 3a) and at a high temperature (Fig. 3b). The number, $N(E)$, of allowed energy levels in each interval on the energy scale is indicated by the horizontal distance out to the curve; the number of levels in each interval that are actually filled—the *Fermi distribution*—is indicated by the lengths of the horizontal lines. The electrons near the top of the filled region may be said to be "splashed" up to higher energies by the heat waves. Since the thermal energy available for "splashing" an electron is of the order of magnitude of kT, where T is the absolute temperature and k is 1.38×10^{-16} ergs per degree, only electrons with energies within kT (approximately) from the top of the filled region are affected; the maximum energy of the filled region is about $100\ kT$.

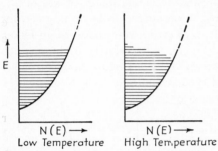

N(E) ⟶   N(E) ⟶
Low Temperature   High Temperature

FIG. 3. Effect of temperature on distribution of electron energies, E, in a metal. Curve gives allowed number of levels, $N(E)$, in each energy interval; horizontal lines give actual number (schematic).

The Zone Theory of Solids. An extremely important advance in this theory was made by discarding the assumption that the electrons move in a uniform electric field within a crystal and investigating the problem of electrons moving in a periodically varying field. The crystalline array of positive charges (the positive ions) produces a crystallographically varying field which interacts with the wave of the electron. Under these circumstances, the electrons can be diffracted by the lattice of ions just as X-rays are diffracted, and in fact the condition for diffraction is the same as the Bragg condition for reflection, viz., $n\lambda = 2d \sin \theta$, where λ is now the electron wavelength. The reflection of electrons within the crystal changes the relation between wavelength and energy sketched in Fig. 2. There can be no electrons in the crystal that have an energy just correct for reflection (if they also have a direction of motion that is correct for reflection). In other words, there is a gap in the allowed energy levels, as indicated in Fig. 4. It will be seen from the figure that electrons having wavelengths slightly greater than the critical wavelength for Bragg reflection have their energies depressed below the value of the smooth parabolic curve, while those having wavelengths slightly less than the critical wavelength have their energies raised, leaving a gap in energy.

The gaps in the allowed energy levels depend upon reflection of the electrons and therefore upon the direction of motion of electrons, and they will occur at different energy values for electrons going in different directions. In some crystals the gaps for differently directed electrons happen to coincide and leave a range of energy that is forbidden to electrons whatever their velocity and direction of motion. In other crystals the gaps for one direction of electron motion overlap the curves for another direction, and the gaps are effectively closed. Davisson and Germer's electron-diffraction experiments which proved the wave nature of the electron also indicated the existence of these gaps, for when critically directed and accelerated electrons were directed at a nickel crystal the electrons did not penetrate the crystal but reflected from it. The gaps divide the spectrum of energies into *zones*, or *bands* (*Brillouin zones*).

The energy levels just discussed are represented mathematically by the various solutions of Schrödinger's wave equation.[1] If the equation is set

---

[1] Schrödinger's equation for an electron of mass m moving with constant total energy E in a potential field $V(x,y,z)$ is

$$\frac{\partial^2 \psi}{\partial x^2} + \frac{\partial^2 \psi}{\partial y^2} + \frac{\partial^2 \psi}{\partial z^2} + \frac{8\pi m}{h^2}(E - V)\psi = 0$$

where h is Planck's constant and m is the electronic mass. To give physical significance to ψ, the wave function or amplitude, it was first assumed that ψ^2 at any point is the electron density at that point; later, ψ^2 was seen to be the *probability* of an elec-

up for a crystal conceived as a box, with abrupt boundaries on all sides
and a uniform potential everywhere within the box, the solutions of the
wave equation lie along the curve of Fig. 2; this was the model on which
Sommerfeld's theory of electrical conduction was based. Now if the
wave equation is written for a periodic field, such as must exist in a
crystal composed of a periodic array of atoms or ions, the solutions have
the discontinuities shown by the full line in Fig. 4.

These discontinuities are small when the electrostatic forces between
the electrons and the ions of the lattice are small, as in the monovalent
alkali metals, but the discontinuities are larger
with elements of higher valence. They are
larger, also, for electrons moving so as to
reflect from atomic planes of large structure
factor than for those that reflect from planes
of small structure factor. Let us see how
these zones and gaps are related to the energy
levels of isolated atoms.

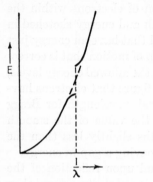

In an isolated atom the energy levels of an
electron are relatively few and are represented
on a diagram such as has been drawn to explain
X-ray emission (page 53).[1] When a number,
N, of atoms are brought together to form a
solid, each individual level of the atom
becomes spread into a series of N levels clustering in a band about the original level, a

Fig. 4. Energy of an electron
moving in the periodic field
of a crystal. Gap in curve
results from diffraction of
electrons with critical direction and velocity.

Brillouin zone. Grains of ordinary size contain so many atoms (roughly
10^{17}) that the levels in the band form almost a continuum. The upper
limit of a band is marked by a gap of the type illustrated in Fig. 4. The
calculations of the distribution of levels in these zones, the extent to
which they overlap or have gaps between them, and the extent to which
they are filled with electrons are of first importance in predicting the
physical properties of crystals.

---

tron being at a given point at a given instant. A "time exposure" of an electron in
motion in an atom or a crystal would be a photograph of ψ^2.

Values of ψ that are finite, single valued, and continuous throughout space exist
only for certain values of E. It is these values that are the allowed energies for
electrons in an atom or a crystal.

[1] The energy states of an atom are defined in terms of four quantum numbers,
n, l, m, and m_s. The energy level is fixed chiefly by the *principal quantum number*, n.
The size of the orbit increases with n, which may have any positive integral value; n
has the values 1,2,3, . . . for the K,L,M, . . . electrons, respectively. The *angular
momentum quantum number*, l, has a smaller effect on the energy levels; for those
levels belonging to a given n, the number l may have any positive integral value from
0 to $n - 1$. Following the notation introduced by spectroscopists, the letters s, p, d,

Zones in Conductors and Insulators. Figure 5*a* is a schematic plot of two zones in a crystal that is an insulator. The plot indicates the density of the levels, *i.e.*, the number of energy levels $N(E)$ between energy E and $E + \Delta E$, and shows two zones separated by an energy interval. The first zone is shaded to indicate that it is filled with electrons, while the second zone contains none. If an electric field is applied to this crystal, the field would tend to change the energy of the electrons by a small amount, causing the net drift in one direction that constitutes

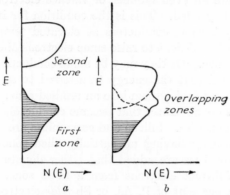

FIG. 5. (*a*) Illustrating gap between zones characteristic of an insulator; first zone filled. (*b*) Possible zone configuration in a metal; partially filled and overlapping zones.

an electric current. But since every level in the zone is occupied, no electron can be transferred from one level to another in the zone. Furthermore, the electrons at the top of the first zone cannot move into the vacant levels of the second zone because the gap between the zones is large compared with the energy they can receive from the field. With all electrons anchored to their former energy states the application of an electric field is without effect, and the crystal is an insulator.

Consider now Fig. 5*b*, which represents a metal in which each atom sup-

---

$f, g, h, \ldots$ are used to stand for $l = 0,1,2,3,4,5, \ldots$ A quantum state having $n = 3$ and $l = 2$ is known as a "$3d$" state and an electron occupying that state is a "$3d$ electron." The *magnetic quantum number*, m, has a very small influence on energy levels. The *spin quantum number*, m_s (sometimes written S), is related to the direction of rotation of the spinning electrons. This quantum number may be either $+\frac{1}{2}$ or $-\frac{1}{2}$; electrons occupying quantum states with $m_s = +\frac{1}{2}$ are rotating oppositely to those with $m_s = -\frac{1}{2}$. The number of electrons in each state is commonly written as an exponent above the letter giving the angular-momentum quantum number. The electron configuration of helium, for example, is written $1s^2$ since there are two electrons in the state $n = 1$, $l = 0$, while for lithium it is written $1s^2 2s^2$ to indicate two additional electrons in the $2s$ state for which $n = 2$, $l = 0$. Pauli's principle states that no two electrons in an isolated atom can have the same set of four quantum numbers.

plies one valence electron. The first band is only half filled because the N atoms of the crystal have each contributed one valence electron to the zone of N levels and two electrons have gone into each level. An electric field can now move any of the many electrons at the top of the filled portion of the band into one of the many vacant levels immediately above it in either band, and the electrons can have a net motion through the lattice in the direction of the field. The metal is therefore a conductor. Homopolar and ionic crystals possess narrow zones separated by gaps, and since there are an even number of valence electrons per atom all zones are completely filled. This is the condition for insulators.[1]

Insulators may become conductors at elevated temperatures if the thermal agitation is sufficient to raise some electrons above the gap into the empty zone above. Or they may be made conducting by irradiation with light, provided that the energy transferred to some electrons by light quanta suffices to raise them into an unfilled zone.

There is a class of substances that become conductors only when they contain certain impurities. Silicon and germanium are such *semiconductors*. Silicon, normally having no partially filled zones, becomes conducting when impurities are added that either donate electrons to an empty zone or subtract electrons from a filled zone. Adding a few thousandths of a per cent of P, As, or Sb *adds* electrons, which go to empty zones (these atoms have five valence electrons while silicon atoms that they replace have only four). The added electrons in unfilled zones convert the silicon into what is called an n-type semiconductor, the name implying conduction by negative carriers. On the other hand, adding traces of B or Al, of lower valence than silicon, *subtracts* electrons from a filled zone, leaving holes.[2] The movement of electrons of the zone then has the effect of moving the holes in the opposite direction; they act as if they were *positive* carriers of current; hence a semiconductor of this type is called a p-type semiconductor.[3] An understanding of the wave mechanics of semiconductors has led to various practical applications, including the development of the "transistor."[4] Conductivity in semi-

---

[1] Electrons in insulators are actually able to penetrate potential barriers (to "tunnel" through them in the "tunnel effect") in a way understandable on the basis of wave mechanics. This does not lead to conductivity, however, for electrons moving in one direction are always balanced by electrons moving in the opposite direction; there is no *net* flow.

[2] W. Shockley, "Electrons and Holes in Semiconductors," Van Nostrand, New York, 1950.

[3] J. H. Scaff, H. C. Theuerer, and E. E. Schumacher, *Trans. AIME*, vol. 185, p. 383, 1949.

[4] The type A transistor, developed by the solid-state research group at the Bell Telephone Laboratories, uses three properly arranged and electrically biased electrodes, on an n-type germanium semiconductor. The "emitter" contact point emits

conductors may involve the movement of ions instead of electrons; for example, conductivity in the silver halides is accompanied by transport of the silver. Ionic conductivity in semiconductors may occur by movement of interstitial ions, or vacant lattice sites, or both.[1]

Factors Affecting Electrical Resistance of Metals. The electron theory accounts for all the factors that alter the electrical resistance of metals.[2]

1. The resistance of metals increases with temperature. This is interpreted as the result of thermal vibrations of the atoms interfering with the motion of conduction electrons. Thermal motions of atoms in a crystal can be analyzed as the superposition of many sets of elastic waves of varying amplitude and wavelength. When an electron going in the right direction and with the right speed encounters one of these sets of waves, it is deflected (diffracted) from its normal path. As the number and amplitude of these elastic waves increase with temperature, scattering becomes more pronounced, the electron paths become more frequently interrupted, and the resistance increases.

2. Resistance increases with impurities and alloying. When atoms dissolve in a metal to form a random solid solution, the resistance is always increased. This is accounted for by the distortions produced in the lattice by the foreign atoms. The disturbances cause scattering of the conduction electrons, thereby hindering electron flow and increasing resistance, both at low temperatures and at elevated temperatures.[3]

3. Resistance increases with increasing randomness in a superlattice. A well-ordered superlattice possesses a low electrical resistance, but the irregularities introduced when disorder begins cause increased scattering of electrons.

4. Cold work increases electrical resistance. This may be attributed to the presence of locally distributed internal strains, including disturbances at boundaries between grain fragments, and disturbances

---

holes into the germanium; these are drawn to the negatively biased "collector" point and add to its current. The transistor can rectify and can amplify currents. J. Bardeen and W. H. Brattain, *Phys. Rev.*, vol. 75, p. 1208, 1949. See W. Shockley, "Electrons and Holes in Semiconductors," Van Nostrand, New York, 1950.

[1] F. Seitz, *J. Applied Phys.*, vol. 16, p. 553, 1945; "The Modern Theory of Solids," McGraw-Hill, New York, 1940. N. F. Mott and R. W. Gurney, "Electronic Processes in Ionic Crystals," Oxford, New York, 1940. A. H. Wilson, "Semi-conductors and Metals," Cambridge University Press, New York, 1939. F. Seitz, in "Imperfections in Nearly Perfect Crystals," Wiley, New York, 1952. J. C. Slater, *J. Applied Phys.*, vol. 22, p. 237, 1951.

[2] F. Seitz, "The Modern Theory of Solids," McGraw-Hill, New York, 1940; "The Physics of Metals," McGraw-Hill, New York, 1943. W. Hume-Rothery, "Atomic Theory for Students of Metallurgy," Institute of Metals, London, 1946

[3] Superconductivity, the abrupt drop in resistance to nearly zero which occurs in many metals at temperatures near absolute zero, is not covered by any well-developed theory at the present time.

around the imperfections or places of misfit in the lattice, the "dislocations." The local disturbances scatter the electrons and increase the resistance.[1]

5. Precipitation from solid solution during aging is also believed to set up internal strains which scatter the electrons as well as harden the alloy. Another possible origin of resistance during age hardening is the scattering of electrons from precipitated crystals, especially when these are very small. Local inhomogeneities in composition, prior to precipitation, should also contribute to resistivity.

Increased resistivity is observed when metals and alloys are subjected to high-energy radiation (neutrons, protons, deuterons, ions, electrons, alpha particles, fission fragments) from a particle accelerator or a chain-reacting pile. Many of the individual factors listed above are believed, in these cases, to combine their effects.[2] Superlattices may be disordered; high temperatures may be reached and quickly lost along the path of the invading particle and the path of atoms recoiling from collision with the invader, or along the paths of fission fragments if the invader causes fission, possibly altering the state of precipitation in an alloy; fission fragments may be retained interstitially or substitutionally, altering the composition locally (their range is short). In semiconductors (Si, Ge, Se, Te, Cu_2O, etc.) resistivity is changed by bombardment; it generally increases, though in n-type germanium it first increases, then decreases as the germanium becomes converted to p type. In ionic compounds color centers are produced—positive or negative ion vacancies distributed singly or in combination, in which electrons are trapped that color the crystal by absorption of certain wavelengths of light. Other effects that have been detected in bombarded insulators are the raising of atoms to excited states, producing "excitons" that can migrate through the substance, and the ionization of atoms.

Energy Levels and Ferromagnetism.[3] A metal that is strongly attracted by a magnet is "ferromagnetic." Slater[4] has advanced a theory

---

[1] Current quantitative theories of resistivity in cold-worked, radiation-damaged, and alloyed crystals are—because of the complexities of these states—of necessity highly simplified as to the assumptions made, the model assumed, and often the mathematical development. Some current treatments will be found in: J. S. Koehler, *Phys. Rev.*, vol. 75, p. 106, 1949; J. K. Mackenzie and E. H. Sondheimer, *Phys. Rev.*, vol. 77, p. 264, 1950; J. Bardeen and W. Shockley, *Phys. Rev.*, vol. 80, p. 69, 1950; Rolf Landauer, *Phys. Rev.*, 82, p. 520, 1951; D. L. Dexter, *Phys. Rev.*, 1952 (in press, two papers). Some of these consider the scattering from edge dislocations, others consider models based only on regions of abnormal electron charge density.

[2] J. C. Slater, *J. Applied Phys.*, vol. 22, p. 237, 1951.

[3] For extensive reviews and bibliographies on magnetism the reader is referred to R. Bozorth, "Ferromagnetism," Van Nostrand, New York, 1950; *Bell System Tech. J.*, vol. 19, p. 1, 1940. W. Shockley, *Bell System Tech. J.*, vol. 18, p. 645, 1939.

[4] J. C. Slater, *J. Applied Phys.*, vol. 8, p. 385, 1937.

of ferromagnetism in the elements near iron in the periodic table, based on a calculation of the zones in the element copper.[1]

In Fig. 6 the $N(E)$ curves are plotted for two zones of Cu, those known[2] as $4s$ and $3d$. Assuming that these $N(E)$ curves do not change appreciably throughout the ferromagnetic elements, iron, cobalt, nickel, and their

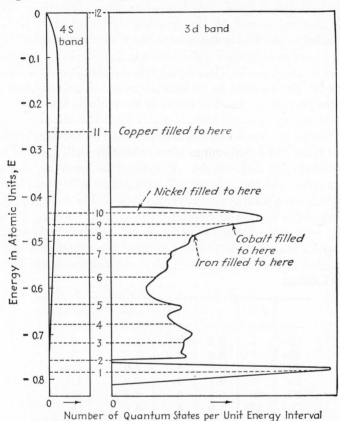

Fig. 6. Zone configuration in copper and iron-group elements. (*Krutter, Slater.*)

alloys, it is possible to indicate the top of the filled levels for the various metals on a single plot. This is done in Fig. 6 by dotted lines that are labeled with the number of $3d$ and $4s$ electrons per atom. The outer shell of electrons, $4s$, which forms the "gas" of free electrons, is filled to the line numbered 11 in copper and to the lines numbered 10, 9, and 8, respectively, in nickel, cobalt, and iron. The next inner shell of electrons, $3d$, is completely filled in copper but is only partly filled in the transition elements from nickel (line 10) to scandium (line 1). All these elements,

[1] H. M. Krutter, *Phys. Rev.*, vol. 48, p. 664, 1935.
[2] The nomenclature is given in the footnote, p. 304.

therefore, have zones only partly filled with valence electrons and for this reason are conductors.

Figure 6 serves as a basis for an understanding of ferromagnetism. The elementary magnets of a ferromagnetic material are the electrons which act as if they are spinning about an axis through their center. In a magnetic field the electrons are limited to two orientations only: the magnetic moment caused by the spinning electricity must be directed either parallel to the field or opposite to the field, "antiparallel." When there are two oppositely directed electrons in a given shell, their moments cancel and there cannot be a large magnetic moment in one direction as is necessary for the material to be ferromagnetic. This condition of balanced spins prevails for most elements in the periodic table. The ferromagnetic elements, however, contain partly filled $3d$ shells as indicated by Fig. 6. The $3d$ band of levels can accommodate 10 electrons per atom, 5 with plus spins and 5 with minus spins, which we shall speak of as $+3d$ and $-3d$ electrons, respectively. In general, as many as possible will have plus spins, and the balance will have minus spins; for example, in cobalt, which has a total of nine electrons in $3d$ and $4s$ shells, the distribution is deduced to be, on the average, 0.7 in $4s$, 5 in $+3d$, and 3.3 in $-3d$. Those in $-3d$ spin states cancel an equal number in $+3d$, leaving $5 - 3.3 = 1.7$ unpaired electrons to produce the ferromagnetism. The corresponding number of outer electrons in other elements are distributed about as follows:

	Total	$4s$	$+3d$	$-3d$	Unpaired $3d$
Cr	6	0.6	2.7	2.7	0
Mn	7	0.6	3.2	3.2	0
Fe	8	0.6	4.8	2.6	2.2
Co	9	0.7	5	3.3	1.7
Ni	10	0.6	5	4.4	0.6
Cu	11	1.0	5	5	0

The number of unpaired electrons can be altered at will by forming a solid solution of one of these elements with an element of different valency. It should then be possible to predict the saturation magnetization of any alloy by figuring out the number of unpaired electrons, which one would expect to vary in a simple way with the valence electron-atom ratio.[1] Actually there *is* a simple relation of this sort for some alloys composed of atoms only one or two atomic numbers apart, such as Fe-Cr, Fe-Ni, and Ni-Cu. But modifications of the theory must be brought

---

[1] Pauling has arrived at somewhat different figures (see pp. 241, 242) that account for the maximum of 2.44 unpaired spins for properly chosen alloys (a magnetic moment of 2.44 Bohr magnetons per atom).

in to account for the magnetization in many systems, particularly those with atomic numbers farther apart, such as Cr-Ni, Cr-Co, and V-Ni.[1]

The mechanism by which the unpaired $3d$ electrons of one atom bring about alignment of those in a neighboring atom has been generally supposed to be by direct interaction,[2] an "exchange interaction" supposed to be favorable to parallel alignment of spins when the ratio of the diameter of the $3d$ shell to the interatomic spacing falls within favorable limits. This has been questioned and an alternate theory has recently been proposed,[3] based on the interactions between s electrons and d electrons, an interaction which tends to produce parallel alignment of s and d electrons in isolated atoms and may therefore do so also in solids. This theory postulates that unpaired d electrons are brought into ferromagnetic (parallel) alignment by their interaction with the s electrons, which migrate from atom to atom without change of spin direction. On the other hand, if there are no conducting electrons, the *direct* interaction of unpaired d electrons is presumed to produce opposite orientation (antiparallel spins) and therefore lead to antiferromagnetism.[4]

The tendency to align the electron spins in neighboring atoms is opposed by the tendency of thermal agitation to induce disorder. It will be recalled that an analogous battle between opposing tendencies goes on in superlattices. The balance between ordering and disordering forces produces a net amount of alignment, in either ferromagnetic or antiferromagnetic materials, that falls with increasing rapidity as the temperature is raised, along a curve very similar to a superlattice order curve, reaching zero at the critical temperature known as the Curie point.

Ferromagnetic Domains. The magnetic ordering force in ferromagnetic metals fails to align the electrons of all atoms in a crystal into a uniform "long-distance order." The magnetic moments of atoms in a small portion of a grain are aligned one way and those in the adjoining portions are aligned in the opposite way, forming alternating bands across a crystal. When one magnetizes a ferromagnetic crystal, the properly oriented domains grow at the expense of the others. The direction of magnetization in each domain is parallel to an important crystal direction — $<100>$ in Fe, $<111>$ in Ni, and [001] in Co—and the domain boundaries array themselves so that the directions of magnetization on each side

---

[1] R. M. Bozorth, *Phys. Rev.*, vol. 79, p. 887, 1950.

[2] J. C. Slater, *Phys. Rev.*, vol. 36, p. 57, 1930.

[3] C. Zener, *Phys. Rev.*, vol. 81, p. 440, 1951.

[4] In support of this idea is the fact that compounds of perovskite structure, with the composition $(La_{1-x}A_x)MnO_3$, where A represents either Ca, Sr, or Ba, are ferromagnetic only in the range of x between 0.2 and 0.4, and it is only in this range that they are good conductors. Similarly, the Heusler alloys are ferromagnetic and have conducting electrons, whereas MnF_2 is antiferromagnetic and nonconducting, as Zener points out. C. Zener, *Phys. Rev.*, vol. 82, p. 403, 1951.

of a boundary make equal angles with the boundary, a condition that avoids magnetic poles at the boundary. The position and movement of the domain boundaries is revealed by patterns made by colloidal magnetic powders on the surface.[1]

Paramagnetism and Diamagnetism. Substances that are very weakly attracted by a magnet are called paramagnetic and substances that are repelled, diamagnetic. Paramagnetism is dependent upon the tendency of a permanent magnet to align itself parallel to a magnetic field in which it is placed. The elementary magnets that undergo alignment are the individual spinning electrons. It will be recalled that in each energy level there are two electrons with oppositely directed spins. When a magnetic field is applied, there is a tendency for some of these to shift the direction of their spins into parallelism with the field. However, this shifting involves a slight change in energy and cannot take place unless there are vacant levels into which the shift can be made. Whenever there are bands that are only partly filled, such appropriately located levels will be found; this is the situation, we have seen, in all conductors. From this point of view all the common metals, which are good conductors, should be paramagnetic unless the conditions in their 3d bands happen to be right for ferromagnetism. Furthermore, an insulator should be neither ferromagnetic nor paramagnetic, for the bands in an insulator are crowded to capacity and are separated by gaps from all unfilled bands.

It is, in fact, the rule for insulators to be diamagnetic, but the prediction that conductors should be paramagnetic breaks down about half the time. Diamagnetism in insulators and in conductors is due to the motion of the electrons in their orbits around the atom nuclei, this motion being altered by an applied field in a manner such as to set up a repulsive force. This closed-orbit magnetic effect sometimes overbalances the magnetic moment from reversed spins and makes a conductor diamagnetic instead of paramagnetic, a situation most likely to happen when the 3d band is just filled.

Theories of Alloy Phases. To the extent that the electron concentration factor governs the structure type and homogeneity range of alloy phases it is to be expected that theories based on the distribution of electron energies will account for them. As has been emphasized in Chap. XI, electron concentration appears to be the controlling factor in many metallic phase equilibria, though other influences modify it and sometimes prevail.

The zone theory of alloy structures can be summarized by saying that

[1] E. Bitter, *Phys. Rev.*, vol. 38, p. 1903, 1931. W. C. Elmore, *Phys. Rev.*, vol. 53, p. 757, 1938. H. J. Williams, R. M. Bozorth, and W. Shockley, *Phys. Rev.*, vol. 75, p. 155, 1949. For reviews see C. Kittel, *Rev. Modern Phys.*, vol. 21, p. 541, 1949; R. M. Bozorth, *Physica*, vol. 15, p. 207, 1949.

an alloy will assume that type of crystal structure in which there are enough *low-energy* states to accommodate all the electrons. Given the structure of a phase, it is possible to calculate at least approximately the zones and how they are filled. If the electrons fill the levels of one zone and must spill over into the lower levels of another zone which is separated from the first by a gap, they will have an abnormally high energy; the crystal as a whole may then have higher energy than some other structure in which this does not occur. When the ratio of valence electrons to atoms in an alloy is gradually increased by adding successive amounts of a higher valence metal, the upper limit of the filled levels moves up slowly until a zone is nearly filled. Further additions then result in a rapid increase in the energy (particularly if the next zone is separated from the first by a gap). Jones[1] has found that at this point a new phase begins to appear in the alloy. The predicted values for the electron-atom ratios in the structurally analogous phases (see Chap. XI, page 235) agree with the

TABLE XIII

Phase	Hume-Rothery's value	Jones's value
α	. . . .	1.362
β	$\frac{3}{2} = 1.5$	1.480
γ	$\frac{21}{13} = 1.615$	1.538
η	$\frac{7}{4} = 1.75$	1.7

observed values as well as could be expected in view of the approximate nature of the calculations, and the probable influence of other factors discussed in Chap. XI; Jones's value for the limit of solubility of the α phase, 1.362, is in satisfying agreement with the observed limits in cases where other factors would not be expected to modify the solubility (see Table XIII).

Referring to Fig. 6, it will be seen that a rapid increase in energy per added electron will occur when there are about 9.5 electrons present—in other words, even before the $3d$ band is completely filled. It is at any such point, where the number of energy states available to added electrons begins to diminish rapidly, that the zone theory would anticipate a change of phase; thus a complete filling of a band is not required.

The solubility limits of the β phase as a function of temperature have been computed by Zener[2] on the basis of thermodynamic properties of the structure. Fitting the equations to the observed boundaries in the

[1] H. Jones, *Proc. Roy. Soc. (London)*, vol. A144, p. 225, 1934; vol. A147, p. 396, 1934. N. F. Mott and H. Jones, "The Theory of the Properties of Metals and Alloys," Oxford, New York, 1936.

[2] C. Zener, *Phys. Rev.*, vol. 71, p. 846, 1947; "Elasticity and Anelasticity of Metals," University of Chicago Press, Chicago, 1948.

Cu-Zn system above 500°C, Zener predicts that the $\alpha/(\alpha + \beta)$ and $\beta/(\beta + \gamma)$ boundaries would come together near 100°C and would make the β phase unstable below this temperature if the stability were not increased by the phase becoming ordered. Zener suggests that all body-centered structures tend to be unstable with respect to a simple (110) [1$\bar{1}$0] shear; the elastic constant for this shear, $(c_{11} - c_{12})/2$, is, in fact, very low in β Cu-Zn, a condition ascribed to a near balance between the attraction of electrons and ions, and the repulsion between ions with filled shells. An unusually large amplitude of vibration in shear should therefore be expected, giving a large entropy term at high temperatures, but as temperature is lowered this term becomes small. The free energy of the phase depends on the entropy through the well-known relation $F = U - TS$, so when the temperature T is lowered in a structure with large entropy S, the free energy F increases rapidly and may become greater than the free energy of another structure. Zener suggested that a transformation might be expected to the face-centered cubic when some body-centered cubic metals with filled inner shells are cooled. The theory led to the discovery of the transformation of b.c.c. lithium at low temperatures.[1]

The interplay of electron-atom ratio, electrochemical, and size factors in determining alloy structures and lattice constants has been discussed in some detail.[2] The solubility of B subgroup elements in magnesium is understandable on the zone theory.[3] As mentioned on page 229, lattice spacings appear to depend on the "apparent atomic diameter" of the solute, and this, in turn, is affected by "Brillouin zone overlap." If the second zone of valence electron energy levels contains energy levels below the highest levels of the first zone, it "overlaps" the first. Overlaps may occur for electrons moving only in certain directions in a crystal; for example, a close-packed hexagonal crystal with c/a greater than 1.63 has the greatest overlap for electrons moving along c; but if c/a is less than 1.63 the greatest overlap is for electrons moving normal to c. Zone theory states that as electrons are added progressively to a structure by alloying and reach a region of overlap two results are expected: (1) more levels become available for the electrons so that their energy is less than normal, thus increasing the stability of the structure and extending the solubility limit; and (2) overlap along c tends to expand the lattice in the c direction. The latter is believed to account for the fact that the c/a

[1] C. S. Barrett, *Phys. Rev.*, vol. 72, p. 245, 1947. C. S. Barrett and O. Trautz, *Trans. AIME*, vol. 175, p. 579, 1948. C. S. Barrett in "Phase Transformations in Solids," Wiley, New York, 1951.

[2] W. Hume-Rothery, "Atomic Theory for Students of Metallurgy," Institute of Metals, London, 1946. K. W. Andrews and W. Hume-Rothery, *Proc. Roy. Soc. (London)*, vol. A178, p. 464, 1941. W. Hume-Rothery, P. W. Reynolds, and G. V. Raynor, *J. Inst. Metals*, vol. 66, p. 191, 1940.

[3] W. Hume-Rothery and G. V. Raynor, *J. Inst. Metals*, vol. 63, p. 227, 1938.

ratio of Mg-In solid solutions abruptly begins to increase more rapidly when an electron concentration of about 2.007 is passed.[1] The effect is found in many magnesium systems,[1,2] superimposed on changes of unit cell size that are proportional to electron concentration. Some influence of differences in atomic radii is also superimposed.[3]

[1] G. V. Raynor, *Proc. Roy. Soc. (London)*, vol. A174, p. 457, 1940; vol. A180, p. 107, 1942. W. Hume-Rothery and G. V. Raynor, *Proc. Roy. Soc. (London)*, vol. A177, p. 27, 1940.

[2] R. S. Busk, *Trans. AIME*, vol. 188, p. 1460, 1950.

[3] If the overlap theory is correct, there should be an effect of temperature on the electron concentration at which c/a abruptly begins to increase, since thermal energy raises the electron energies of some electrons at the top of the filled levels. This is, in fact, observed by R. S. Busk, *Trans. AIME, J. Metals*, vol. 4, p. 207, 1952. Mg alloyed with Al, Ag, or Sn retains approximately invariant c/a up to a temperature T_0 that depends on the electron concentration in the following way: $T_0 = 435°K$ for concentration 1.998, $T_0 = 140°K$ for 2.009, and values between these are given by linear interpolation.

CHAPTER XIV

STRESS MEASUREMENT BY X-RAYS

X-ray diffraction as a means of determining stresses is finding increasing application. For some problems it offers definite advantages over all other types of strain gauges. It is the only method by which stresses can be determined without making measurements on the structure in the unstressed condition. Consequently it is the only method of determining residual, "locked-up" stresses in an object without cutting up the object so as to relieve the stresses—it is the only truly nondestructive test for residual stresses. The method detects elastic strains only, while other strain gauges are affected by both elastic and plastic strains. This is a result of the fact that the X-ray method is fundamentally a measure of interatomic spacings, which are altered by elastic stresses but not by plastic flow. The X-ray beam that is employed strikes an area roughly $\frac{1}{8}$ in. in diameter and determines the strain within this area as contrasted with the usual strain gauge, which employs a gauge length of 1 in. or more. This is a useful feature of the method in the study of localized stresses and steep stress gradients.

The peculiarities of the method are not all to its advantage. It can be applied to specimens of large grain size only by taking care to provide suitable oscillation of specimen and film, and this requires mechanical devices in addition to the usual X-ray equipment. It requires equipment more costly and more cumbersome than the competitive devices. It registers only the stresses in the *surface* of a metallic object because the radiation does not penetrate appreciably into the interior; it therefore deals always with a biaxial stress since the stress component perpendicular to the surface is always zero. Perhaps the most unfortunate characteristic of the method is that it is satisfactory only for metals that yield reasonably sharp diffraction lines. With fine-grained annealed steel it is capable of the very satisfactory accuracy of 2000 or 3000 psi, but with cold-worked or quenched steels that give diffuse lines the error is four or five times this and the method (in its present state of development) is seldom of value.

The pioneer work on the method was done by Lester and Aborn[1] in 1925. It was shown that the spacing d of the atomic planes is altered by

[1] H. H. Lester and R. H. Aborn, *Army Ordnance*, vol. 6, pp. 120, 200, 283, 364, 1925–1926.

applied stresses.   The distance d acts as a gauge length, and changes in this length enable the elastic strains to be measured and the stresses to be computed.   The strain can be determined by Bragg's law

$$n\lambda = 2d \sin \theta$$

from measured values of the diffraction angle θ.   When back-reflection cameras were applied to the problem in 1930,[1] it became apparent that under favorable conditions the X-ray strain gauge could compete in accuracy with other types of strain gauges.

In the first applications only the *sum* of the principal stresses existing at the surface was determined.   Later it was shown that the principal stresses can be determined individually[2] and that an exposure of the material in the unstressed state was unnecessary[3] since the unstressed value of d can be computed from two measurements on the stressed metal. Numerous techniques and methods of computation have been proposed, but only the more satisfactory ones will be presented here.   While the equations for some of these are complex, it should be understood that in routine work it is almost always possible to reduce the computations to simple slide-rule operations requiring but a minute or two.   Some fundamental principles of stress and strain in elastic bodies will first be reviewed.

Elastic Stress-Strain Relations.   Strain, ϵ, is defined by the relation

$$\epsilon = \frac{\Delta l}{l} \tag{1}$$

where Δl is the change in length of a line in a stressed body having the original length l.   If this is produced by a stress σ (a force divided by the area over which it is applied) and if the stress acts in a single direction, Hooke's law states that the strain will be proportional to the stress,

$$\epsilon = \frac{\sigma}{E} \tag{2}$$

The constant of proportionality, E, is Young's modulus.   Consider a rectangular coordinate system with tension σ_x applied in the X direction, and assume that the body is isotropic.   That is, assume that the elastic properties are the same in all directions through the material.   There will then be a contraction in all directions at right angles to X, and if

[1] G. Sachs and J. Weerts, *Z. Physik*, vol. 64, p. 344, 1930.

[2] C. S. Barrett and M. Gensamer, *Phys. Rev.*, vol. 45, p. 563, 1934 (abstract); *Physics*, vol. 7, p. 1, 1936.   R. Glocker and E. Osswald, *Z. tech. Physik*, vol. 16, p. 237, 1935.

[3] F. Gisen, R. Glocker, and E. Osswald, *Z. tech. Physik.*, vol. 17, p. 145, 1936.

strains parallel to Y and Z are ϵ_y and ϵ_z, respectively, then

$$-\epsilon_y = -\epsilon_z = \nu\epsilon_x = \frac{\nu\sigma_x}{E} \tag{3}$$

where ν is Poisson's ratio and negative signs denote contraction.

In addition to the strains produced by stresses normal to a surface, the *normal strains* mentioned above, there are *shear strains*. The magnitude of a shear strain, γ, is defined by the lateral displacement of a plane

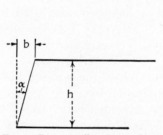

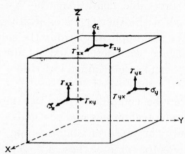

FIG. 1. Diagram illustrating shear strain.

FIG. 2. Diagram illustrating equilibrium of shear stresses, τ, and normal stresses, σ, on an element of volume.

relative to another parallel plane per unit distance separating the planes. Referring to Fig. 1,

$$\gamma = \frac{b}{h} = \tan\alpha$$

The proportionality between shear strain and the shear stress, τ, that produces it may be written

$$\gamma = \frac{\tau}{G} \tag{4}$$

where the constant G is the modulus of elasticity in shear, the torsion modulus. In a rectangular coordinate system, shear stresses and shear strains require subscripts to designate their directions; a shear stress acting on a plane perpendicular to the X direction and along the Y direction is written τ_{xy}, and a shear strain on a plane perpendicular to X and acting in the direction of Y is written γ_{xy}.

If an infinitesimal parallelepiped, say a cube, is inscribed in the stressed body and the cube edges are taken as coordinate axes, there will be in general three components of stress acting on each face, as in Fig. 2, but in ordinary conditions of equilibrium many of these are equal (for example, $\tau_{yz} = \tau_{zy}$ and $\sigma_x = \sigma_{-x}$). It requires, in fact, no more than six of these components of stress to specify completely the state of stress at a point in an isotropic solid: σ_x, σ_y, σ_z, τ_{xy}, τ_{yz}, and τ_{zx}.

A simplification results if the coordinate axes of Fig. 2 are directed in such a way that the shear stresses on all faces are zero. This is always possible, regardless of the complexity of the stress system. The stresses normal to the cube surfaces are then the *principal stresses* σ_1, σ_2, and σ_3, and these are related to the principal strains in isotropic bodies by the equations

$$\left.\begin{array}{l} \epsilon_1 = \dfrac{1}{E}\left[\sigma_1 - \nu(\sigma_2 + \sigma_3)\right] \\[2mm] \epsilon_2 = \dfrac{1}{E}\left[\sigma_2 - \nu(\sigma_1 + \sigma_3)\right] \\[2mm] \epsilon_3 = \dfrac{1}{E}\left[\sigma_3 - \nu(\sigma_1 + \sigma_2)\right] \end{array}\right\} \tag{5}$$

Equations (2) and (3) are special cases of these relations. Individual grains of a polycrystalline material are usually anisotropic, E varying with crystallographic direction, but if there is no preferred orientation of the grains the material may still follow closely the laws for an isotropic medium.

Method for Sum of Principal Stresses $(\sigma_1 + \sigma_2)$. An X-ray method of stress analysis suitable for determining uniaxial stresses and the sum of the principal stresses in the plane of the surface requires one photograph of the stressed specimen and another of the same material in the stress-free state.[1] If we assume that the material is elastically isotropic and is subjected to principal stresses σ_1 and σ_2 lying in the plane of the surface, the normal strain perpendicular to the surface will be $\epsilon_3 = -(\sigma_1 + \sigma_2)\nu/E$, where ν is Poisson's ratio and E is Young's modulus. (At a free surface the *stress* normal to the surface is zero; thus $\sigma_3 = 0$.) For simple tension, $\sigma_2 = 0$ and the sign of σ_1 is positive; this produces a strain in the Z direction which is a contraction (indicated by the negative sign). The spacing of the atomic planes lying parallel to the surface will thereby be altered from d_0 (the unstressed value) to $d_\perp$, so that $\epsilon_\perp = (d_\perp - d_0)/d_0$. Therefore, measurements of $d_\perp$ and d_0 give the sum of the principal stresses,

$$\sigma_1 + \sigma_2 = -\frac{E}{\nu}\left(\frac{d_\perp - d_0}{d_0}\right) \tag{6}$$

Strain measurements by X-rays require precision technique, which means that back-reflection cameras must be employed. (These cameras have been discussed in Chap. VII, page 130.) Figure 3 illustrates a back-reflection camera set for determining stresses by this method. An X-ray beam passes through a pinhole placed at the focusing position, goes through a hole in the film, and strikes the specimen perpendicularly,

[1] G. Sachs and J. Weerts, *Z. Physik*, vol. 64, p. 344, 1930. F. Wever and H. Möller, *Arch. Eisenhüttenw.*, vol. 5, p. 215, 1931–1932.

reflecting from planes that are nearly parallel to the surface (N_1 and N_2 are the reflecting-plane normals). Using cobalt $K\alpha$ radiation for an iron or steel specimen, reflection will occur from (310) planes with $\theta = 80°37.5'$, and the strain measured along the (310) plane normals will closely approximate the desired strain $\epsilon_\perp$ and can be used in the above equations. Copper $K\alpha$ radiation is suitable for aluminum and duralumin since the (511) reflection occurs at about 81°. Cobalt reflects from copper at $\theta = 81°46.5'$ (400 reflection) and from brass (68 per cent copper) at 75°30'. Nickel reflects from cartridge brass (331) planes at 79°, and iron reflects from magnesium (105) planes at 83°.

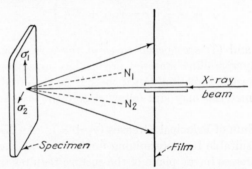

FIG. 3. Back-reflection camera set up for stress determination with beam normal to surface. Reflecting plane normals are N_1 and N_2.

The best accuracy to be expected of this method is about $\pm 1 \times 10^{-4}$ A for the spacing of atomic planes, corresponding to ± 2 kg per sq mm or about 3000 psi in stress for iron and steel specimens.[1] Owing to the fact that the reflecting planes are not exactly parallel to the surface, Eq. (6) is only an approximate expression; the computed stress ($\sigma_1 + \sigma_2$) will be on the average about 7 per cent too small.[2] The film is usually rotated about its center during the exposure to smooth out spottiness in the lines.

The distance between the film and the specimen surface can be determined by placing a powdered calibrating substance on the specimen. The lattice spacing of this substance is known, and so one can compute the specimen-to-film distance from a measurement of a Debye ring produced by it. Annealed gold or silver powder is suitable for iron, aluminum, duralumin, and brass samples.[3]

The distance from specimen to film can also be measured directly, permitting exposure times only half as long as those when calibration sub-

[1] H. Möller and J. Barbers, *Mitt. Kaiser-Wilhelm-Inst. Eisenforsch., Düsseldorf*, vol. 16, p. 21, 1934. H. Möller, *Mitt. Kaiser-Wilhelm-Inst. Eisenforsch., Düsseldorf*, vol. 21, p. 295, 1939.

[2] R. Glocker, "Materialprüfung mit Röntgenstrahlen," Springer, Berlin, 1936.

[3] The Au 333 reflection with copper $K\alpha_1$ is at $\theta = 78°56'$ and with cobalt $K\alpha_1$ the 420 reflection is at $\theta = 78°46'$; a_0 for Au is 4.0700 A; a_0 for Ag is 4.077 A.

stances are used. The distance can be measured by inside micrometers or can be set at a predetermined value, say 5.00 cm, by a metal pointer attached to the hub of the camera.[1] A feeler gauge slipped between the end of the pointer and the specimen enables one to determine when the camera is adjusted to the proper distance. The pointer is then removed during the exposure. A suitably inscribed circle on the film, concentric with the axis of rotation of the film, facilitates accurate measurement. Thomas states that film shrinkage errors amount to about 1 part in 84,000 in lattice-constant measurement and may be neglected; in any event, a circle inscribed on the film before development can be used to calibrate for shrinkage, or photographic plates that have been drilled for the passage of the beam can be employed to eliminate shrinkage.

At a standard distance the displacement of the diffracted line corresponds directly to a certain stress; for example, for a distance which gives a gold ring 50.0 mm in diameter, a shift of $\frac{1}{10}$ mm in the position of one side of the 310 line from iron corresponds to $(\sigma_1 + \sigma_2) = 9.2$ kg per sq mm (13,000 psi), assuming $E = 21,000$ kg per sq mm $(30 \times 10^6$ psi) and $\nu = 0.28$. With aluminum, assuming $E = 7200$ kg per sq mm $(10.3 \times 10^6$ psi) and $\nu = 0.34$, the same shift would indicate $(\sigma_1 + \sigma_2) = 2.4$ kg per sq mm (3420 psi).

Since only $(\sigma_1 + \sigma_2)$ is determined, this method gives a limited view of the stress situation, and in fact the method cannot detect torsional stresses in the surface since these have $\sigma_1 = -\sigma_2$. The unstressed reading can be obtained by removing the load, or in an internally stressed piece it sometimes can be had by cutting out a small piece of the specimen with saw cuts or with a hollow drill. Stress-relief annealing can also be resorted to, but at some risk of dissolving or precipitating some elements from the diffracting matrix, which would change the unstressed value of the lattice spacings.

Equations for the Ellipsoid of Strain and of Stress. Before taking up other procedures for stress analysis the fundamental equations on which all are based will be presented.

Under homogeneous elastic deformation a spherical element of volume in an isotropic solid is deformed into an ellipsoid. The normal strain, ϵ, in any chosen direction is given by the approximate equation for the ellipsoid of strain

$$\epsilon = a_1^2\epsilon_1 + a_2^2\epsilon_2 + a_3^2\epsilon_3 \tag{7}$$

where ϵ_1, ϵ_2, and ϵ_3 are the principal strains (Fig. 4) and a_1, a_2, and a_3 are the direction cosines of the chosen direction with respect to the directions of the principal strains.[2] In terms of the coordinates ϕ, ψ of Fig. 4, the

[1] D. E. Thomas, *J. Sci. Instruments*, vol. 18, p. 135, 1941.

[2] A derivation of elastic-theory formulas will be found in S. Timoshenko, "Theory of Elasticity," McGraw-Hill, New York, 1934.

direction cosines may be written

$$\left.\begin{array}{l} a_1 = \sin \psi \cos \phi \\ a_2 = \sin \psi \sin \phi \\ a_3 = \cos \psi = \sqrt{1 - \sin^2 \psi} \end{array}\right\} \qquad (8)$$

If the direction cosines are substituted in (7) together with the values of the principal stresses ϵ_1, ϵ_2, and ϵ_3 from (5) and if we set $\sigma_3 = 0$ (since the

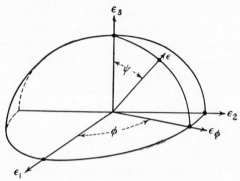

Fig. 4. The ellipsoid of strain. Principal strains are ϵ_1, ϵ_2, and ϵ_3.

stress normal to a free surface is zero), then Eq. (7) may be written

$$\epsilon - \epsilon_3 = \frac{1 + \nu}{E} (\sigma_1 \cos^2 \phi + \sigma_2 \sin^2 \phi) \sin^2 \chi \qquad (9)$$

Now the approximate equation for the stress ellipsoid is

$$\sigma = a_1^2 \sigma_1 + a_2^2 \sigma_2 + a_3^2 \sigma_3 \qquad (10)$$

where a_1, a_2, and a_3 are the direction cosines of the stress σ with respect to the principal axes of stress. When $\psi = 90°$, this becomes

$$\sigma_\phi = \sigma_1 \cos^2 \phi + \sigma_2 \sin^2 \phi \qquad (11)$$

which gives the component of stress in the direction ϕ. Substitution of (11) in (9) leads to the relation

$$\sigma_\phi = (\epsilon - \epsilon_3) \cdot \frac{E}{1 + \nu} \cdot \frac{1}{\sin^2 \psi} \qquad (12)$$

Let d_0 be the spacing of atomic planes in the unstressed condition, $d_\perp$ the spacing in the stressed metal perpendicular to the surface, and d_ψ the spacing in the direction ψ, ϕ; then

$$\epsilon - \epsilon_3 = \frac{d_\psi - d_0}{d_0} - \frac{d_\perp - d_0}{d_0} = \frac{d_\psi - d_\perp}{d_0} \qquad (13)$$

To a close approximation this may be written

$$\epsilon - \epsilon_3 = \frac{d_\psi - d_\perp}{d_\perp} \tag{14}$$

and Eq. (12) may be reduced to the convenient form

$$\sigma_\phi = \frac{d_\psi - d_\perp}{d_\perp} \cdot \frac{E}{1 + \nu} \cdot \frac{1}{\sin^2 \psi} \tag{15}$$

Two-exposure Method for σ_ϕ. The component of stress in any desired direction in the surface can be determined from two exposures, one with the beam normal to the surface giving $d_\perp$, and one with the beam inclined in the plane of the normal and the component σ_ϕ, giving σ_ϕ in Eq. (15).[1]

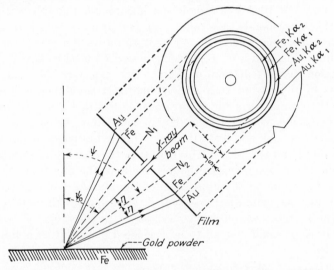

FIG. 5. Back-reflection camera inclined at $\psi_0 = 45°$, and type of film obtained with cobalt radiation, iron specimen, and gold calibrating powder on surface.

No exposure of the material in the unstressed state is necessary. The usual practice is to make the inclined exposure with the beam 45° from the perpendicular. It is necessary to use rings of a comparison substance (usually gold, silver, or brass) on the surface of the specimen to determine the effective distance from the irradiated spot to the film, as illustrated in Fig. 5 where r is the radius of a gold calibrating ring and $r - s$ the radius of a specimen ring. Measurement of the distance s between the rings on the side nearest the specimen gives a calculation of d at the angle $\psi = \psi_0 + \eta$, which is different from the value of d on the other side of the rings at $\psi = \psi_0 - \eta$. Both measurements may be computed independently in Eq. (15), or the more sensitive one, $(\psi_0 + \eta)$, may be used.

[1] F. Gisen, R. Glocker, and E. Osswald, *Z. tech. Physik*, vol. 17, p. 145, 1936.

Direct measurement of the distance from specimen to film is possible if sufficient care is taken and if a circle is put on the film concentric with the axis.[1]

A convenient procedure is to calculate a relationship between stress and the ring displacement rather than to apply Eq. (15) to every reading. For this purpose one finds the multiplying factor that will bring the diameter of the calibration ring $(2r)$ to some standard value, say 50 mm, and the measured s is also multiplied by this factor. This value can then be compared with a prepared table or chart relating s to σ_ϕ for the given experimental conditions.

Möller and Gisen[2] conclude that visual measurement of the films gives about the same accuracy as measurement with a recording micropho-tometer, *viz.*, 1×10^{-4} A in atomic spacings for photographs with sharp lines. This corresponds to about 1.7 kg per sq mm (2400 psi) in stress with a steel specimen when $\psi_0 = 45°$. With diffuse lines the error is four or five times this, and a microphotometer can be used to advantage.

Correction for Oscillation of Film (Two-exposure Method). The spottiness of rings from large-grained material should be removed by rotating the film in perpendicular exposures, but this is not advisable in inclined exposures where the rings deviate more from the circular. How-ever, oscillation back and forth through a limited range of angles may be used to smooth out the lines. This decreases the average angle of inclina-tion of the planes reflecting to the lower side of the film from $\psi_0 + \eta$ to $\psi_0 + \eta - \Delta\psi$, while on the upper side of the film $\psi_0 - \eta$ is increased to $\psi_0 - \eta + \Delta\psi$; the azimuthal position, ϕ, also changes through a range. The errors in stress computations decrease with the range of oscillation and can be kept small enough to be neglected if oscillation is limited to $\pm 30°$ or less.[3]

[1] D. E. Thomas, *J. Sci. Instruments*, vol. 18, p. 135, 1941.

[2] H. Möller and F. Gisen, *Mitt. Kaiser-Wilhelm-Inst. Eisenforsch., Düsseldorf*, vol. 19, p. 57, 1937.

[3] The value of $\Delta\psi$ is small—for iron specimens with cobalt radiation $\Delta\psi$ is only 0.1° for a range of oscillation $\delta = \pm 10°$, 1.3° for $\delta = \pm 30°$, and 2.8° for $\delta = \pm 45°$. Oscillation of the film also alters ϕ through a range $\pm \Delta\phi$. In a photograph of iron with $\psi_0 = 45°$, $\pm \Delta\phi = 2.0°$ for $\delta = \pm 10°$, 5.9° for $\delta = \pm 30°$, and 8.5° for $\delta = \pm 45°$, provided that the diffraction lines are measured on the lower side where $\psi = \psi_0 + \eta$. On the upper side the range $\pm \Delta\phi$ is larger, being 2.8, 7.9, and 10.8° for $\delta = \pm 10$, 30, and 45°, respectively. (R. Glocker, B. Hess, and O. Schaaber, *Z. tech. Physik*, vol. 19, p. 194, 1938.) If a stress component, θ_ϕ, is determined from a perpendicular and an inclined exposure (iron with cobalt radiation, $\psi = 45° + \eta$), an oscillation of $\delta = \pm 30°$ requires corrections that depend upon the stress ratio defined by the rela-tion $\sigma_{\phi+90} = k\sigma_\phi$, the percentage correction being as follows:

k	-6	-3	0	$+3$	$+6$
Percentage	$+3.4$	$+2.5$	$+1.4$	$+0.5$	-0.5

Single-exposure Method for σ_ϕ. A stress component may be determined from a single inclined exposure if the diffraction rings are measured at two positions on their circumference.[1] The beam is inclined toward the direction in which the component σ_ϕ is to be measured; that is, the beam lies in the plane containing the normal and the component to be measured, thus at the angle ϕ, and is ψ_0 from the normal. The ring from the specimen is measured with reference to the ring from the calibration substance, both at the top of the ring where $\psi_1 = \psi_0 - \eta$ and at the bottom where $\psi_2 = \psi_0 + \eta$, giving spacings d_1 and d_2, respectively. Equation (12) is written for each set of measurements, giving two simultaneous equations whose solution is

$$\sigma_\phi = \left(\frac{E}{1+\nu}\right)\left(\frac{d_1 - d_2}{d_0}\right)\frac{1}{\sin 2\psi_0 \sin 2\eta} \tag{16}$$

For the incident beam at $\psi_0 = 45°$, this reduces to

$$\sigma_\phi = \left(\frac{E}{1+\nu}\right)\left(\frac{d_1 - d_2}{d_0}\right)\frac{1}{\sin 2\eta} \tag{17}$$

In this formula, d_0 need not be determined accurately on each individual specimen for the normal lattice constant for unstressed metal may be used (2.8610 for steel). This is a rapid method but is less accurate than the method employing a perpendicular exposure in addition to the inclined one, for an error of $\pm 1 \times 10^{-4}$ A in d in Eq. (17) introduces an error of ± 3.5 kg per sq mm (5000 psi) for steel specimens, twice the error of the two-exposure method.[2]

Methods for Determining σ_1 **and** σ_2 **When Their Directions Are Known.** When the directions of the principal stresses are known (for example, in a cylinder containing quenching stresses), Eq. (15) can be applied to give the principal stresses σ_1 and σ_2. For this purpose the perpendicular exposure is combined with an inclined exposure in which the beam is tipped toward σ_1 and also with an exposure in which the beam is tipped toward σ_2. Thus, three exposures, all of them on the stressed material, serve to determine completely the surface stresses.

If d_0 is obtained by an exposure of the specimen in the stress-free state, then two inclined exposures of the stressed material will serve, one giving the spacing d_ψ at the angle ψ from the normal and at the azimuth ϕ, the other giving $d_{\psi'}$ at the same angle from the normal and at azimuth

[1] R. Glocker, B. Hess, and O. Schaaber, *Z. tech. Physik*, vol. 19, p. 194, 1938. An alternate method of computation is given by D. E. Thomas, *J. Sci. Instruments*, vol. 18, p. 135, 1941.

[2] The correction to be introduced if the film is oscillated is small. For a photograph of iron with $\psi_0 = 45°$ and an oscillation of $\pm 15°$ the correction for σ_ϕ is 1.1 per cent; for $\pm 30°$ it is 4.5 per cent.

$\phi + 90°$.* Equations (2), (3), and (7) for these conditions lead to the relations

$$\left.\begin{array}{l} \sigma_1 + \sigma_2 = \left(\dfrac{d_\psi + d_{\psi'} - 2d_0}{d_0}\right)\dfrac{E}{(1 + \nu)\sin^2\psi - 2\nu} \\[3mm] \sigma_1 - \sigma_2 = \left(\dfrac{d_\psi - d_{\psi'}}{d_0}\right)\dfrac{E}{(1 + \nu)\sin^2\psi} \end{array}\right\} \qquad (18)$$

The sum of these equations gives σ_1 while the difference gives σ_2.

If one uses the single inclined exposure method for σ_ϕ, with the beam inclined toward σ_1 and again with the beam tipped toward σ_2, the two principal stresses may be determined with only two exposures.[1] However, this shorter method, based on Eqs. (16) or (17), has lower accuracy than three-exposure methods. A still less accurate method has been proposed[2] in which the diffraction ring of a single inclined photograph is measured in four places.

The various equations of this chapter can be solved to give the unstressed lattice spacing, d_0, from three or more measurements of the stressed state. For example, a perpendicular exposure combined with two inclined exposures at azimuths ϕ and $\phi + 90°$ will give d_0 by simultaneous equations of types (6) and (15).

Method Giving Magnitude and Direction of Principal Stresses. Both the magnitudes and directions of σ_1 and σ_2 can be determined if the components of stress are computed for three directions in the surface. The maximum accuracy can be obtained if one uses a perpendicular exposure paired with three inclined exposures at azimuth angles ϕ, $\phi + 60°$, and $\phi - 60°$.† An error of $\pm 1 \times 10^{-4}$ A in spacing then corresponds to ± 2.3 kg per sq mm (± 3300 psi) in the principal stresses in steel and an error in their direction that is given by the relation $\pm 65°/(\sigma_1 - \sigma_2)$ where the stresses σ_1 and σ_2 are given in kilograms per square millimeter. These figures are computed for beams at an angle of inclination of $45°$ and for stress directions that would give minimum accuracy.

The stress components in the plane of the surface at angles ϕ, $\phi + \alpha$, $\phi - \alpha$ (Fig. 6) are given by the relations[3]

$$\left.\begin{array}{l} \sigma_\phi = \tfrac{1}{2}(\sigma_1 + \sigma_2) + \tfrac{1}{2}(\sigma_1 - \sigma_2)\cos 2\phi \\[2mm] \sigma_{\phi+\alpha} = \tfrac{1}{2}(\sigma_1 + \sigma_2) + \tfrac{1}{2}(\sigma_1 - \sigma_2)\cos 2(\phi + \alpha) \\[2mm] \sigma_{\phi-\alpha} = \tfrac{1}{2}(\sigma_1 + \sigma_2) + \tfrac{1}{2}(\sigma_1 - \sigma_2)\cos 2(\phi - \alpha) \end{array}\right\} \qquad (19)$$

* C. S. Barrett and M. Gensamer, *Physics*, vol. 7, p. 1, 1936.

[1] R. Glocker, B. Hess, and O. Schaaber, *Z. tech. Physik*, vol. 19, p. 194, 1938.

[2] H. Möller and H. Neerfeld, *Mitt. Kaiser-Wilhelm-Inst. Eisenforsch., Düsseldorf*, vol. 21, p. 289, 1939.

† H. Möller, *Mitt. Kaiser-Wilhelm-Inst. Eisenforsch., Düsseldorf*, vol. 21, p. 295, 1939.

[3] See, for example, C. E. Fuller and W. A. Johnston, "Applied Mechanics," vol. II, art. 42, Wiley, New York, 1913.

Solving for σ_1, σ_2, and ϕ with $\alpha = 60°$, we have

$$\sigma_1 = \tfrac{1}{3}\left[\sigma_\phi + \sigma_{\phi-60} + \sigma_{\phi+60} + \sqrt{(2\sigma_\phi - \sigma_{\phi-60} - \sigma_{\phi+60})^2 + 3(\sigma_{\phi-60} - \sigma_{\phi+60})^2}\right]$$

$$\sigma_2 = \tfrac{1}{3}\left[\sigma_\phi + \sigma_{\phi-60} + \sigma_{\phi+60} - \sqrt{(2\sigma_\phi - \sigma_{\phi-60} - \sigma_{\phi+60})^2 + 3(\sigma_{\phi-60} - \sigma_{\phi+60})^2}\right]$$

$$\tan 2\phi = \frac{\sqrt{3}\,(\sigma_{\phi-60} - \sigma_{\phi+60})}{2\sigma_\phi - \sigma_{\phi-60} - \sigma_{\phi+60}} \tag{20}$$

The components of stress σ_ϕ, $\sigma_{\phi+60}$, and $\sigma_{\phi-60}$ are determined by inclined beam exposures at azimuth angles ϕ, $\phi + 60$, $\phi - 60$, each exposure being combined with an exposure prependicular to the surface, using Eq. (15). Alternatively, this four-exposure technique may be shortened by merely using three inclined exposures and Eq. (16), but the accuracy is then cut to about half. The simultaneous equations relating stress components to the principal stresses can be solved graphically if desired.[1]

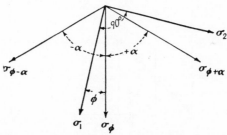

Fig. 6. Arrangement of principal stresses (σ_1, σ_2) and stress components in the specimen surface.

Values of the Elastic Constants. Anisotropy. The elastic constants that are measured mechanically do not necessarily apply accurately to X-ray determinations of stress. Each grain is anisotropic, and the strain is measured always along a certain crystallographic direction (along [310] for iron). Therefore, the grains that reflect have only certain orientations with respect to the axes of stress, and the effective values of E and ν in these orientations may differ from the over-all average orientations, the latter being measured in a mechanical test.

The theoretical treatment of the problem has been carried out on the assumptions both that the grains are stressed equally and deform independently of one another and that they all are strained equally.[2] Com-

[1] W. R. Osgood and R. G. Sturm, *J. Research Natl. Bur. Standards*, vol. 10, p. 685, 1933 (three components). W. R. Osgood, *J. Research Natl. Bur. Standards*, vol. 15, p. 579, 1935 (four components). A. H. Stang and M. Greenspan, *J. Research Natl. Bur. Standards*, vol. 19, p. 437, 1937 (four components). "Handbook of Experimental Stress Analysis," Wiley, New York, 1950.

[2] R. Glocker, *Z. tech. Physik*, vol. 19, p. 289, 1938. H. Möller and G. Martin, *Mitt. Kaiser-Wilhelm-Inst. Eisenforsch., Düsseldorf*, vol. 21, p. 261, 1939. H Möller and J. Barbers, *Mitt. Kaiser-Wilhelm-Inst. Eisenforsch., Düsseldorf*, vol. 17, p. 157, 1935. H. Möller and G. Strunk, *Mitt. Kaiser-Wilhelm-Inst. Eisenforsch., Düsseldorf*, vol. 19, p. 305, 1937.

parison of the predictions of these theories with X-ray measurements of specimens subjected to known stresses led Möller and Martin[1] to conclude that neither of these two assumptions is correct. They suggest that effective elastic constants be determined empirically by X-raying a specimen with known stresses; Hauk concludes that the X-ray values differ from the mechanical values by an amount that depends on the wavelength used.[2] Other investigators[3] agree that it is permissible, in general, to use the mechanical values of the elastic constants, without correction for

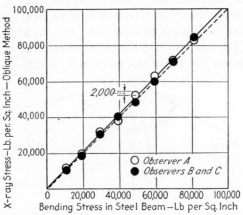

FIG. 7. Comparison of stresses determined by X-rays (two-exposure method) and stresses computed from the curvature of a bent beam. Annealed mild steel. (*Norton and Loring.*)

anisotropy. In precise work it is advisable to check apparatus, technique, and effective values of the constants by calibration experiments, using a specimen under a known load, or a beam bent to a known curvature.

A typical calibration experiment is illustrated by Fig. 7. The calculated stresses on the surface of a bent beam are plotted as abscissas and X-ray stresses (obtained with the two-exposure method) are plotted as ordinates. The points for different observers who read the films agreed satisfactorily and fell close to the dotted line that was computed on the basis of ordinary mechanical values of the elastic constants.[4]

Equipment for Stress Measurement. Equipment for stress measurement usually consists of a portable X-ray tube mounted in a ray-proof

[1] H. Möller and G. Martin, *Mitt. Kaiser-Wilhelm-Inst. Eisenforsch.*, Düsseldorf, vol. 21, p. 261, 1939.

[2] V. Hauk, *Z. Metallkunde*, vol. 36, p. 120, 1944.

[3] R. Glocker and O. Schaaber, "Ergebnisse der technische Röntgenkunde," vol. VI, p. 34, Akademische Verlagsgesellschaft m.b.h., Leipzig, 1938. H. Möller and G. Strunk, *Mitt. Kaiser-Wilhelm-Inst. Eisenforsch.*, Düsseldorf, vol. 19, p. 305, 1937. L. Frommer and E. H. Lloyd, *J. Inst. Metals*, vol. 70, p. 91, 1944. J. T. Norton, *Experimental Stress Analysis*, vol. 2, p. 157, 1944.

[4] J. T. Norton and B. M. Loring, *Welding J.*, Research Supplement, June, 1941.

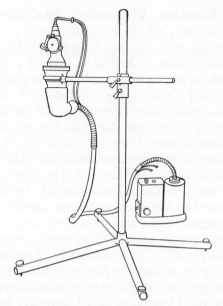

FIG. 8. Portable X-ray stress-measuring apparatus.

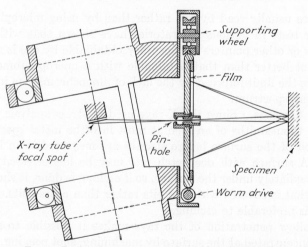

FIG. 9. Back-reflection camera clamped to X-ray tube.

and shockproof housing (the smaller the better) and supported on an
adjustable stand, as, for example, in Fig. 8.   The tube may be connected
to the portable power source by an insulated cable.   A back-reflection
camera is essential and should be mounted on the X-ray tube itself, somewhat in the fashion sketched in Fig. 9.   The film is mounted on a small
film holder that can be rotated or oscillated in its own plane to remove
spottiness from the rings, with the beam passing through an adjustable

pinhole system at its center. The smallest pinhole should be placed at the focusing position, *viz.*, on the circumference of a circle that passes through the Debye ring on the film and is tangent to the irradiated spot on the surface of the specimen. The film is covered with black celluloid (black paper is likely to leave a radiograph of the paper fiber on the film).

Tests have indicated[1] that varying the distance from the film to the specimen makes no appreciable difference in the accuracy of measurements, but decreasing the pinhole size from 1 to 0.3 mm decreases the error in a set of measurements from $\pm 2.5 \times 10^{-4}$ A to $\pm 0.6 \times 10^{-4}$ A.

Exposure times vary from a few hours to a fraction of an hour, depending on pinholes, focal-spot size, and absorption in the window of the X-ray tube. Much time can be lost in adjusting the tube to the proper distance and angle with respect to the object unless one provides convenient distance and angle gauges. Some European equipment has been designed so that the tube and camera snap quickly from a perpendicular position to a position inclined at 45°. When a specimen is coarse-grained, it may be necessary not only to oscillate the film, as mentioned on page 324, but also to oscillate the specimen slightly about an axis normal to the X-ray beam, as Frommer and Lloyd have done,[2] to obtain smooth diffraction lines.

Films are usually read by eye rather than by using microphotometer traces, for tests in various laboratories have shown that with suitable cross hairs or other pointers the accuracy obtainable by eye is at least as good, if not better than that obtainable with a microphotometer,[3] and approaches the limit imposed by the lack of monochromatism in the lines of the X-ray spectrum.

Surface Stresses. Since the X-rays used in stress analysis penetrate but a few thousandths of an inch at most into the metal specimen, the preparation of the surface before stresses are measured is an important matter. A surface with deep etch pits may be less stressed than the metal immediately under the surface, so if etching is done, it should leave a surface that is covered with fine pits rather than coarse pits. Electropolishing is preferable to etching.

The shallow penetration of the rays makes it possible to study the stresses concentrated at the surface by machining, shot peening, abrasion, etc. For example, Wever and Möller[4] found that the machined surface of a piece of steel contained a layer less than 0.010 in. deep in which the

[1] F. Wever and A. Rose, *Mitt. Kaiser-Wilhelm-Inst. Eisenforsch., Düsseldorf*, vol. 17, p. 33, 1935.

[2] L. Frommer and E. H. Lloyd, *J. Inst. Metals*, vol. 70, p. 91, 1944.

[3] See, for example, H. Ekstein and S. Siegel, *Acta Cryst.*, vol. 2, p. 99, 1949.

[4] F. Wever and H. Möller, *Mitt. Kaiser-Wilhelm-Inst. Eisenforsch., Düsseldorf*, vol. 18, p. 27, 1936,

stresses ($\sigma_1 + \sigma_2$) differed from the stress in underlying layers by 60,000 psi. An investigator must be on guard against assuming that, on the one hand, the stresses detected by X-rays extend well into a specimen, and, on the other hand, that mechanical methods of stress measurement can be relied on for disclosing conditions at the surface (where stress corrosion, season cracking, and other damage may originate).

Because diffraction is limited to surface layers, there is no nondestructive method for determining stresses at interior points. Norton and Rosenthal,[1] however, devised a method that involves cutting out rectangular blocks from a stressed plate and then slicing layers from them, with X-ray stress measurements being made after each cut. The method yields the distribution of longitudinal and transverse stresses throughout the interior. This method becomes less reliable as stress gradients become steeper, and as the plate thickness increases.

Measurements of Stress Alterations during Service. The nondestructive nature of the X-ray method makes it applicable to the problems of changing stresses. X-rays reveal only the elastic component of strain, not the plastic, whereas strain-gauge measurements concern the sum of the elastic and plastic components. Therefore it is possible to trace the gradual relaxation of stresses during fatigue stressing or other conditions encountered in service.

In one early application of the method by Gisen and Glocker,[2] the changes in the residual stresses around a drilled hole were measured during the life of the specimen in a fatigue test. The slight plastic flow accompanying the cyclic stressing made major changes in the stress pattern adjacent to the hole, even though the specimen withstood more than 10^7 cycles.

Norton and Rosenthal have made X-ray measurements on the effect of external loading upon residual stresses.[3] A biaxial state of residual stress was introduced into mild-steel strips by squeezing them between two round electrodes of a butt-welding machine and heating locally with a current of 3000 amp for a few seconds. The results on one of the plates are reproduced in Fig. 10, where the curves marked I show, respectively, the longitudinal and the transverse components of the stresses after the heating, measured along a line through the center of the electrodes. The electrodes contacted the strip from −0.5 to 0.25 on the scale of inches, and it will be noted that the heated zone was left with stresses approximating the tensile yield point for the steel (which was 35,000 psi). Curves II, III, IV, and V give the history of these residual stresses after

[1] D. Rosenthal and J. T. Norton, *Welding J.*, Research Supplement, vol. 24, pp. 295-s, 307-s, 1945.

[2] F. Gisen and R. Glocker, *Z. Metallkunde*, vol. 30, p. 297, 1938.

[3] J. T. Norton and D. Rosenthal, *J. Am. Welding Soc.*, vol. 22, no. 2, p. 63S, 1943.

loading and unloading the strip successively to 7200, 16,000, 29,500, and 38,300 psi. Loading to the yield point relieved all the stresses and replaced them with compressive stresses in the direction of the applied load. Since the stresses left after tensile loading were uniformly compressive over both front and back surfaces, the interior of the strip (which was 0.3 in. thick and 3 in. wide) must have been under residual tension. The relief of stresses by fatigue and by bending was also studied by these investigators. Plastic flow induced by applied loads always tends to reduce the residual stresses, and these stresses do not affect the safety of a structure provided that the material of which the structure is composed is

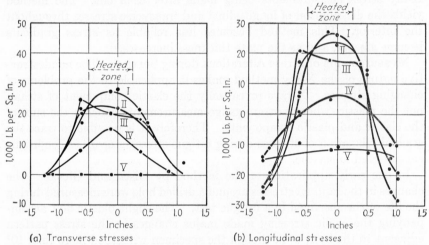

(a) Transverse stresses   (b) Longitudinal stresses

FIG. 10. Residual stresses in a mild-steel strip after local heating and after subsequent straining in tension. (I) Directly after heating and cooling. (II) After applying 7,200 psi tensile stress. (III) After applying 16,000 psi tensile stress. (IV) After applying 29,500 psi tensile stress. (V) After applying 38,300 psi tensile stress. (*Norton and Rosenthal.*)

ductile and that the ductility is not decreased by severe triaxial stresses (such as are introduced by notches). Whether the stresses left after tensile loading were balanced by opposing stresses in neighboring grains or, on the other hand, by stresses in the interior of the specimen remains uncertain. Abnormal values of interplanar spacings have been found in tensile specimens that have been stressed beyond the yield point. For example, Wood and Smith[1] have reported spacings of (310) planes of iron that were as much as 0.04 per cent above normal. This may be a result of residual stresses or of some more fundamental change in the structure. When there is uncertainty in the unstressed value of the lattice spacings,

[1] W. A. Wood and S. L. Smith, *Nature*, vol. 146, p. 400, 1940. S. L. Smith and W. A. Wood, *Proc. Roy. Soc.* (*London*), vol. A176, p. 398, 1940; vol. A178, p. 93, 1941; vol. A179, p. 450, 1942. W. A. Wood and S. L. Smith, *J. Inst. Metals*, vol. 67, p. 315, 1941.

as in this case or in cases where precipitation from solid solution may be involved, it is advisable to determine the unstressed value by the two-exposure technique rather than by preparing a stress-free sample.

Other Applications. X-rays have been used for determining residual stresses in castings, such as valve bodies and engine parts, and have been employed in investigations of the relation of such stresses to foundry technique, design, welding technique, and heat-treatment. They have been used by McCutcheon in the study of steel (SAE 1045) having a hardness as high as Rockwell C 49—only, however, with careful measurement of densitometer traces,[1] and with errors estimated at ±8000 psi. A review of industrial applications of X-ray methods together with the many other methods is to be found in the "Handbook of Experimental Stress Analysis."[2]

Do X-rays Register the Average Stress? The discussion presented in this chapter suggests a reliability in stress measurement by X-rays that may be considered to be much greater than has actually been established, particularly when applied to specimens in which plastic strain has occurred. The following experiments suggest the need for caution.

Bohlenrath and Scheidt[3] subjected low-carbon steel bars, in the annealed condition, to a series of increasingly severe bends. The stresses in the outer fibers were measured by the perpendicular-beam X-ray method, both under load and after the bending couples were removed. The X-ray stresses at load increased in proportion to the load throughout the elastic range, but when the outer fibers began to flow plastically the X-ray values, measured under load, began to fall and continued to fall as the load was further increased. The results of tests on bars with rectangular, triangular, and trapezoidal cross section were all essentially similar and may be represented by the curve in Fig. 11. In one experiment the X-ray stress value fell to 15 kg per sq mm from a maximum of 65; in another it fell to 10 from a maximum of 22. Neerfeld[4] found the same effect in notched flat bars of low-carbon chromium-manganese steel. The effect has also been confirmed in a bar of low-carbon stress-relieved steel by Nicholson.[5]

[1] D. M. McCutcheon, *Ind. Radiography*, spring, 1946, p. 9.

[2] "Handbook of Experimental Stress Analysis," M. Hetényi, Editor, Wiley, New York, 1950.

[3] F. Bohlenrath and E. Scheidt, *Metal Treatment*, vol. 4, p. 110, 1938.

[4] H. Neerfeld, *Mitt. Kaiser-Wilhelm-Inst. Eisenforsch., Düsseldorf*, vol. 27, p. 13, 1944.

[5] M. E. Nicholson, private communication. The two-exposure method was used, with the X-ray beam at 90° and at 45° to the surface. The outer fiber stress fell from a maximum of 40,000 psi at a strain (measured by a strain gauge) of 14.5×10^{-4} to 29,000 psi at a strain of 19.8×10^{-4}. S. Maloof, Thesis, (S. M.), MIT, 1945, also found a discontinuity at the yield point, but found the X-ray stress remained constant as bending increased beyond the beginning of yielding.

All the observers cited found that upon release of the bending moment the outer fibers went into compression whenever the previous strain had entered the plastic range, the residual compressive stress being proportional to the amount of plastic strain.

Smith and Wood[1] found closely related effects even in simple tensile experiments, and not only with ferrite, but with aluminum. They reflected a beam from planes that were approximately parallel to the tensile axis; the spacings of these should contract as the tensile load increases. Up to the yield point this occurred, but with increasing stress above the yield point the spacing remained approximately constant. When the load was released, the spacings returned to normal only when stressing had remained within the elastic range; the spacings became abnormally large if there had been plastic flow, becoming larger approximately in proportion to the amount of the plastic flow (or the maximum stress that had been applied).

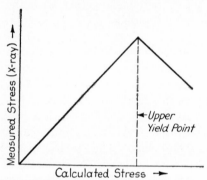

Fig. 11. Stresses as measured by X-rays in the outer surface of a bent beam vs. stresses calculated from the formula for the bent beam.

Some of the explanations that have been advanced to account for these observations should be mentioned. It has been proposed that the lattice constant is greater in cold-worked metal than in annealed metal, and that it increases as the amount of cold work increases. In Smith and Wood's experiment the expanded lattice constant, on this basis, would be the one that is measured when the load is released.

Another view is that the surface grains have a lower yield point than the interior grains (because they are less constrained). Thus they elongate plastically under loads that are still carried elastically by grains in the interior. When the load is released they find themselves too long to return to their previous unstressed length, so are thrown into compression.

Another suggestion, one that brings the validity of X-ray measurements of residual stresses into question for metals in which there has been plastic flow, is that the X-rays do not register the average grains, but register chiefly the grains or portions of grains that are under the least stress, regions we may call "indicator grains."[2] While neighboring grains carry

---

[1] S. L. Smith and W. A. Wood, *Proc. Roy. Soc. (London)*, vol. A179, p. 450, 1942 (mild steel); vol. A178, p. 93, 1941 (iron). W. A. Wood and S. L. Smith, *J. Inst. Metals*, vol. 67, p. 315, 1941 (aluminum).

[2] We are indebted to L. R. Jackson for a discussion of this possibility.

the load and strain-harden by plastic flow, the indicator grains are the ones that have remained free from the heterogeneous distortions that lead to work hardening, and that consequently have remained at low stress. The distorted, work-hardened grains yield blurred and broadened reflections that are not noticed when superimposed on the sharper reflections from the indicator grains.   This suggestion is in accord with the fact that Smith and Wood found a sharp drop in the apparent intensity of the diffraction lines when the yield point was passed, and with the fact that cold work reduces a grain to "fragments" only a few of which reflect at a given orientation.   The indicator grains are the ones that are thrown into compression upon release of the load (and cause the Bauschinger effect if the stress is reversed).   They cause X-rays to indicate compressive stresses even when the average stress may be zero.

CHAPTER XV

THE PLASTIC DEFORMATION OF METALS

The present chapter concerns the crystallography of slip, twinning, and fracture in metals, including the stresses necessary for these operations, and how the laws of flow in single crystals are modified by conditions in polycrystalline metals. Subsequent chapters take up current theories of plastic flow, the structure of deformed metal, the nature and theories of preferred orientations generated by plastic flow, and directional properties resulting from preferred orientations.

SLIP IN METAL CRYSTALS

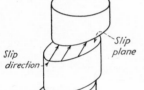

Slip direction

Slip plane

FIG. 1. Sketch of movement on crystallographic slip planes.

Slip Planes and Directions. Plastic deformation in a crystal occurs by the movement of lamellae of the crystal over one another. The movement is concentrated in a succession of planes, or at least in very thin sheets, as in Fig. 1, leaving the intervening blocks undeformed, like the movement of cards in a pack when the pile is distorted. The displacement takes place along a crystallographic plane, the *slip plane* or *glide plane*, and in a crystallographic direction, the *slip direction*. As details of this mechanism are fundamental to an understanding of plastic flow, strain hardening, cold work, and preferred orientations, a great amount of research has been devoted to the subject in the last twenty years.[1] A summary of slip planes and slip directions is given in Table XIV.

In face-centered cubic (f.c.c.) metals the slip plane is normally the plane in the lattice that is most densely packed with atoms, (111), and the same is true of the close-packed hexagonal (c.p.h.) metals, which have the basal plane (0001) as the slip plane. Other planes may become active at elevated temperatures, but these are also planes of relatively high atomic

[1] E. Schmid and W. Boas, "Kristallplastizität," Springer, Berlin, 1935; and English translation, Hughes, London, 1950. C. F. Elam, "The Distortion of Metal Crystals," Oxford, New York, 1935. H. J. Gough, Edgar Marburg Lecture, *ASTM, Proc.*, vol. 33, pt. 2, p. 3, 1933. Report of a Conference on Internal Strains in Solids, *Proc. Phys. Soc. (London)*, vol. 52, 1940. "International Conference on Physics, vol. II, The Solid State of Matter," Physical Society, London, 1935. D. Kuhlman, *Z. Metallkunde*, vol. 41, p. 129, 1950.

Table XIV. Slip in Metals*

Structure	Metal	Low temperatures		High temperatures	
		Plane	Direction	Plane	Direction
F.c.c.	Al	(111)	$[10\bar{1}]$	(100)	$[10\bar{1}]$
	Cu	(111)	$[10\bar{1}]$		
	Ag	(111)	$[10\bar{1}]$		
	Au	(111)	$[10\bar{1}]$		
	Ni	(111)	$[10\bar{1}]$		
	Cu-Au	(111)	$[10\bar{1}]$		
	α-Cu-Zn	(111)	$[10\bar{1}]$		
	α-Cu-Al	(111)	$[10\bar{1}]$		
	Al-Cu	(111)	$[10\bar{1}]$		
	Al-Zn	(111)	$[10\bar{1}]$		
	Au-Ag	(111)	$[10\bar{1}]$		
B.c.c.	α-Fe	(110)	[111]		
		(112)	[111]		
		(123)	[111]		
	Mo	(112)	[111]	(110)	[111]
	W	(112)	[111]		
	K	(123)	[111]	(123)	[111]
	Na	(112)	[111]	(110)	[111]
				(123)	[111]
	β-Cu-Zn	(110)	[111]		
		(112)(?)			
	α-Fe-Si; 5% Si	(110)			
C.p.h.	Mg	(0001)	$[2\bar{1}\bar{1}0]$	$(10\bar{1}1)$	$[2\bar{1}\bar{1}0]$
		$(10\bar{1}1)$(?)		$(10\bar{1}2)$(?)	
				(0001)	$[2\bar{1}\bar{1}0]$
	Cd	(0001)	$[2\bar{1}\bar{1}0]$		
	Zn	(0001)	$[2\bar{1}\bar{1}0]$		
	Be	(0001)	$[2\bar{1}\bar{1}0]$		
	Zn-Cd	(0001)	$[2\bar{1}\bar{1}0]$		
	Zn-Sn	(0001)	$[2\bar{1}\bar{1}0]$		
	Te	(0001)			
Rhombohedral	Bi	(111)	$[10\bar{1}]$		
	Hg	(100) and Complex			
Tetragonal	β-Sn (white)	(110)	[001]	(110)	[111]
		(100)	[001]		
		(100)	[011](?)		
		$(10\bar{1})$	[101]		
		(121)	[101]		

* [Note added in proof:] Alpha uranium has slip predominantly on (010) [100] of the orthorhombic structure, with rare and faint evidence of (110) slip, and with predominant cross slip on (011) and (013), according to R. W. Cahn, *Acta Cryst.*, vol. 4, p. 470, 1951.

density.   In the body-centered cubic (b.c.c.) and tetragonal lattices, slip can occur on several planes, most of which are among the most densely packed ones.   Data are somewhat inconclusive for beta-brass, Te, Hg, and Sn.[1]   Investigation of Bi and Sb* failed to reveal evidence of slip when deformed at room temperature in tension, for all the deformation was by the process of twinning.   However, by compression or by elevating the temperature it is possible to produce slip.[2]

Many metals probably change their slip planes when deformed at unusually high or low temperatures.   Examples that have been noted to date include Al,[3] Mg,[4] β-Sn,† Mo,[4] Na,‡ K,‡ and Fe-Si alloys.§   Andrade[5] has correlated the operative slip planes in b.c.c. materials with the temperature relative to the melting point.   If T is the absolute temperature at which slip takes place and T_m the melting point, then the results may be arranged as in Table XV.   This correlation does not seem to apply, however, to iron and Fe-Si alloys, for all three planes, (110), (112), and (123), are active at room temperature in iron[6] and in Fe-Si alloys § containing less than 4 per cent silicon.   At low temperatures or with silicon contents above 4 per cent only (110) is an active slip plane in these silicon alloys,§ whereas (112) would be expected from Table XV.   The correlation also fails with Mo, according to Chen and Maddin, who find (110) [1$\bar{1}$1] slip at room temperature.[7]

It is evident that the slip plane chosen in any lattice is rather easily influenced by temperature and chemical composition and perhaps by the amount of previous deformation, but the slip direction is not so fickle. In f.c.c., b.c.c., rhombohedral, hexagonal, and tetragonal crystals the most closely spaced row of atoms in the lattice is always the direction of

[1] H. Mark and M. Polanyi, *Z. Physik*, vol. 18, p. 75, 1923.   I. Obinata and E. Schmid, *Z. Physik*, vol. 82, p. 224, 1933.   E. N. da C. Andrade and P. J. Hutchings, *Proc. Roy. Soc. (London)*, vol. A148, p. 120, 1935.

* H. J. Gough, Edgar Marburg Lecture, *ASTM, Proc.*, vol. 33, pt. 2, p. 3, 1933.

[2] E. N. da C. Andrade, "International Conference on Physics, vol. II, The Solid State of Matter," p. 173, Physical Society, London, 1935.   W. F. Berg, "International Conference on Physics, vol. II, The Solid State of Matter," p. 178, Physical Society, London, 1935.

[3] R. Karnop and G. Sachs, *Z. Physik*, vol. 41, p. 116, 1927; vol. 42, p. 283, 1927. W. Boas and E. Schmid, *Z. Physik*, vol. 71, p. 703, 1931.

[4] E. Schmid, *Z. Elektrochem.*, vol. 37, p. 447, 1931.   P. W. Bakarian and C. H. Mathewson, *Trans. AIME*, vol. 152, p. 226, 1943.

† E. Schmid and W. Boas, "Kristallplastizität," Springer, Berlin, 1935.

‡ E. N. da C. Andrade and L. C. Tsien, *Proc. Roy. Soc. (London)*, vol. A163, p. 1, 1937.

§ C. S. Barrett, G. Ansel and R. F. Mehl, *Trans. ASM*, vol. 25, p. 702, 1937.

[5] E. N. da C. Andrade, Report of a Conference on Internal Strains in Solids, *Proc. Phys. Soc. (London)*, vol. 52, p. 1, 1940.

[6] H. J. Gough, *Proc. Roy. Soc. (London)*, vol. A118, p. 498, 1928.

[7] N. K. Chen and R. Maddin, *J. Metals*, vol. 3, p. 937, 1951.

slip. In iron, where (110), (112), and (123) all function as slip planes, the direction of slip is always the close-packed direction, [111], which is common to all three sets of planes;[1] and the choice of slip direction is less sensitive to the amount of deformation, the temperature at which deformation is carried out, and the composition than is the slip plane. In ionic lattices of the sodium chloride type, slip is also along the lines of greatest atomic density, [1$\bar{1}$0], although the slip plane, (110), is not the plane of greatest density.[2]

A plane of slip and a direction of slip lying in that plane constitute a *slip system*. Face-centered cubic metals, having four (111) planes and

TABLE XV

Metals	T/T_m	Slip plane
W, Mo, Na	0.08–0.24	(112)
Mo, Na, β-brass	0.26–0.50	(110)
Na, K	0.80	(123)

three [101] directions in each, possess 12 slip systems; body-centered iron has four [111] directions around each of which are arranged 12 slip planes having the slip direction as their zone axis, thus giving 48 slip systems.

Slip Lines. Slip is an abrupt movement, sometimes accompanied by an audible tick when the total deformation is small, as was first observed by Joffé and Ehrenfest.[3] In transparent crystals the intermittent nature of the process is evident from observations with polarized light. When a crystal is placed between crossed nicols, individual slip movements cause streaks of light to appear along the slip planes, a result of double refraction from the strains left in the crystal along the slip plane after the slip has occurred.[4]

Slip is most commonly recognized by the presence of slip lines formed by the intersections of slip planes with the surface of a crystal. When the slip direction lies parallel to the surface, there is, of course, no upward displacement of one portion with respect to another, and the lines are nearly invisible. (This fact has been used to determine the slip directions in cylindrical specimens.[5]) As a rule it is difficult to see traces of slip lines after a specimen has been polished and etched subsequent to their

[1] H. J. Gough, *Proc. Roy. Soc. (London)*, vol. A118, p. 498, 1928.

[2] An extensive discussion of the geometry of slip and its relation to atomic configuration, particularly in minerals, has been published by M. J. Buerger, *Am. Mineral.*, vol. 15, pp. 45, 174, 226, 1930.

[3] Abram F. Joffé, "The Physics of Crystals," McGraw-Hill, New York, 1928.

[4] J. W. Obreimow and L. W. Schubnickow, *Z. Physik*, vol. 41, p. 907, 1927. W. Schütze, *Z. Physik*, vol. 76, p. 135, 1932.

[5] H. J. Gough, Edgar Marburg Lecture, *ASTM, Proc.*, vol. 33, pt. 2, p. 3, 1933.

formation, and this is sometimes used to distinguish slip from twinning. However, there are disturbances left on planes where slip has occurred and suitable etching will bring these out—at least in some metals, notably alpha-brass.[1] The disturbances concentrated along slip planes have been "photographed" by making use of their effect on the reflecting power of X-rays, in the X-ray reflection micrograph method of page 96.

When slip is on a single set of planes, the slip lines can be very straight. Figure 2 is the appearance of a polished surface of an iron-silicon crystal deformed on two slip planes of the type (110), and Fig. 3 shows an iron crystal deformed on an indefinite number of slip planes. The wavy slip

FIG. 2. Slip lines from two sets of (110) slip planes in silicon ferrite. Black markings at upper left are twins. ×250.

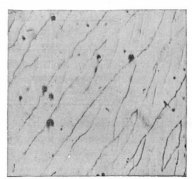

FIG. 3. Waxy slip lines in α-iron. ×200.

lines of iron are characteristic of slip in this material and were attributed at first to a glide process, "banal glide," in which the slip direction but not the slip planes was considered to be crystallographic, but later investigations showed that the waviness was merely the result of many slip systems operating simultaneously and using a common slip direction.[2] Greenland also observed wavy slip in mercury (viewed along the slip direction), provided that the crystals were handled with great care prior to straining, but in crystals that had been slightly bent the lines became straight.[3] Wavy slip occurs on $\{10\bar{1}1\}$ planes in magnesium at elevated temperatures.[4] "Cross slip," observed by Maddin, Mathewson, and Hibbard in crystals of alpha-brass, is another example of different slip planes oper-

[1] Strained or reoriented material may be responsible, and in some cases it is likely that twin faults [improperly stacked (111) layers] are involved; see C. H. Mathewson, *Trans. ASM*, vol. 32, p. 38, 1944; J. E. Burke and C. S. Barrett, *Trans. AIME*, vol. 175, p. 106, 1948, and discussion of this paper; C. S. Barrett, *Trans. AIME*, vol. 188, p. 123, 1950.

[2] H. J. Gough, Edgar Marburg Lecture, *ASTM, Proc.*, vol. 33, pt. 2, p. 3, 1933.

[3] K. M. Greenland, *Proc. Roy. Soc. (London)*, vol. A163, p. 28, 1937.

[4] P. W. Bakarian and C. H. Mathewson, *Trans. AIME*, vol. 152, p. 226, 1943.

ating simultaneously that use the same slip direction.[1]   Increased waviness of slip lines in aluminum (99.9 per cent pure) has been noted by Lacombe and Beaujard in crystals deformed at 450°C, probably as a result of (100) planes becoming active along with (111),[2] and Cahn[3] has noticed cross slip on (100) and (212) as well as (111) planes even at room temperature, in single crystal strips of aluminum.

If the movement along slip planes is concentrated on a single plane, the contour of the surface after deformation should appear as in Fig. 4a for compression or Fig. 4b for tension.   By electroplating a layer of copper on an iron crystal and then cutting and polishing a section at right angles to the surface, Rosenhain found a saw-tooth contour, as expected from Fig.

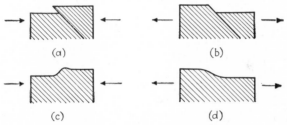

(a)   (b)

(c)   (d)

Fig. 4. Sketches (a) and (b) represent contour expected of surface after slip from compressive and tension stresses, respectively; (c) and (d) illustrate contours found by Greenland on mercury.

4b.   Greenland,[4] however, found that single crystals of mercury had contours like Fig. 4c or 4d at a slip line, suggesting that movement had occurred on a series of closely grouped planes rather than on a single one. Hoyt[5] has discussed similar features in the deformation of zinc.   It is common to find that slip bands appearing as single lines at low magnification will resolve into groups of closely spaced lines at high magnification, while the regions between the bands, which appear undeformed at low magnification, may contain minute lines that become visible when the resolving power and magnification are increased.   Clustering of slip lines within a band that appears to be a single line at low magnifications is seen in Fig. 5.[6]   In this sample of alpha-brass the minimum distance between individual lines resolved by the microscope is approximately 2000 atom diameters, and the displacement of the horizontal scratch

[1] R. Maddin, C. H. Mathewson, and W. R. Hibbard, *Trans. AIME*, vol. 185, p. 527, 1949.

[2] P. Lacombe and L. Beaujard, *J. Inst. Metals*, vol. 74, pt. 1, p. 1, 1947.

[3] R. W. Cahn, *Trans. AIME*, vol. 188, p. 1037, 1950; *J. Inst. Metals*, vol. 79, p. 129, 1951.

[4] K. M. Greenland, *Proc. Roy. Soc. (London)*, vol. A163, p. 28, 1937.

[5] S. L. Hoyt, *Trans. AIME*, vol. 74, p. 116, 1927.

[6] R. G. Treuting and R. M. Brick, *Trans. AIME*, vol. 147, p. 128, 1942.

indicates an average movement of about 700 atom diameters per visible slip plane.   The width of the clusters increases linearly with the strain.[1]

The condition of the surface layers of a crystal has a marked influence on the spacing of the lines: mechanically polished or abraded surfaces show coarse lines; electropolished strain-free surfaces, fine lines, closely spaced, not only with f.c.c. metals (Al, Cu, Pb, Au)[2] but also with b.c.c. iron.[3]   Coarse slip tends to be replaced by fine slip, also, in the neighborhood of a grain boundary.[3]

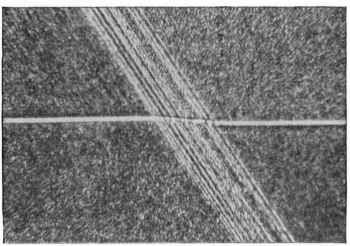

Fig. 5.   Cluster of slip lines in alpha-brass cutting across a scratch.   ×800.   (*Treuting and Brick.*)

Heidenreich and Shockley,[4] using electron microscopy, found that slip lines are clustered extremely closely into bands in aluminum single crystals of the highest purity.   The spacing between individual lines of a band is about 200 A, and the relative displacement of lamellae at each line in a cluster is about 2000 A.   In a similar investigation, Brown[5] deformed polycrystalline aluminum at different temperatures.   At all temperatures one-line bands are first formed and increasing deformation creates new bands until a minimum spacing is reached that depends on temperature. Subsequent deformation results in adding to the number of lines per band.

[1] R. Maddin, C. H. Mathewson, and W. R. Hibbard, *Trans. AIME*, vol. 185, p. 527, 1949.

[2] A. F. Brown and R. W. K. Honeycombe, *Phil. Mag.*, vol. 42, p. 1146, 1951.

[3] H. W. Paxton, M. A. Adams, and T. B. Massalski, *Phil. Mag.*, vol. 43, p. 257, 1952.

[4] R. D. Heidenreich and W. Shockley, "Report of a Conference on Strength of Solids," p. 57, Physical Society, London, 1948.

[5] A. F. Brown, *Nature*, vol. 163, p. 961, 1949.

After 15 per cent elongation the electron micrographs showed the following structures:

Deformation temperature, °C	Spacing between bands, μ	Lines per band
−180	$\frac{1}{2}$–1	1–2
20	2	3–4
250	4	5–6
500	10	12

Brown found displacements of about 2000 A (0.2 μ) per line in all cases, and line spacings of 200 to 800 A.   Electron micrographs of copper and of monel metal deformed at room temperature failed to reveal clustering.[1]

At the present time it is not known in how many metals this fine-scale clustering occurs; when slip lines or slip bands are referred to it will be realized that what appears to be a single line may be an unresolved cluster of lines.

Rosenhain[2] measured the displacement at an individual slip line in iron and found the value 0.5 μ.   Andrade[3] states that the displacement may amount to as much as 0.1 mm in metals.   It is clear that slip lines visible in optical and electron microscopes are made by movements amounting to hundreds or thousands of atom diameters.

Investigations with the optical microscope on slip-line spacings include the following.   Andrade and Roscoe[4] found a probability distribution around a spacing of 4.2 μ for parallel lines in lead, and noted that the spacing was independent of temperature (between 0 and 100°C), diameter of the crystal, and rate of stretch (varied by a factor of 3000).   The spacing did not change with increasing deformation in crystals of lead, cadmium, or mercury for a considerable extension, which indicates that deformation proceeded at slip lines already formed.   In aluminum, on the other hand, Yamaguchi[5] observed that the slip bands in aluminum crystals increased in number and became more closely spaced as deformation continued.

Crussard[6] confirmed this and reported specimen elongations of about

[1] C. S. Barrett, *Trans. AIME*, vol. 156, p. 62, 1944.

[2] W. Rosenhain, "Introduction to Physical Metallurgy," Van Nostrand, New York, 1916.

[3] Report of a Conference on Internal Strains in Solids, *Proc. Phys. Soc. (London)*, vol. 52, p. 1, 1940.

[4] E. N. da C. Andrade and R. Roscoe, *Proc. Phys. Soc. (London)*, vol. 49, p. 152, 1937.

[5] K. Yamaguchi, *Sci. Papers Inst. Phys. Chem. Research (Tokyo)*, vol. 8, p. 289, 1928.   C. F. Elam, "Distortion of Metal Crystals," Oxford, New York, 1935.

[6] C. Crussard, *Rev. mét.*, vol. 42, p. 286, 1945.

0.5 μ per slip line at slow strain rates and about 3 μ in constant-load creep tests (in 99.995 per cent Al). He concluded that in single crystals of aluminum the spacings average about 5 or 6 μ at 15 per cent elongation, and as deformation continues, new ones form, reducing the spacing to 1 to 2 μ at 40 per cent elongation. The number of lines seems to be roughly proportional to the applied stress in some crystals, and to increase more rapidly than this in others. In polycrystalline grains the average number in the various grains may be taken as proportional to $(\sigma - \sigma_0)^{0.30}$ where σ is the applied stress and σ_0 the elastic limit. In alpha-brass, Burghoff and Mathewson[1] found a direct proportionality between the number of lines and the strain in creep deformation at room temperature.

The behavior of different metals with regard to whether continued flow occurs on old planes or by adding new ones is presumably related to whether strain hardening results within the slipping regions. If hardening is sufficient to divert subsequent slip to undeformed regions that are softer, new lines will form. But if the material deforms without appreciable hardening further slip will continue in the same location. Thus the stress-strain curve of aluminum shows marked strain hardening at room temperature and this metal deforms by adding to the number of slip lines, while lead, cadmium, and mercury, when stretched at temperatures where little strain hardening results, deform on the previously active planes.[2] The number of new lines that appear per increment of strain decreases as the temperature is raised and the displacement at each slip line increases.[3] Andrade and coworkers have noted that also in Na, K, and Mo the slip lines become fewer, broader, and more contrasty as the deformation temperature is raised. Crussard notes a tendency, however, for fine lines to develop in the *initial* (transient) stage of creep deformation at elevated temperatures in aluminum, though only a few of the lines continue to widen in the subsequent stages.[4] There remains an uncertainty as to whether slip of the usual type occurs between the visible slip lines, either at high temperatures or otherwise. Experiments in which strain hardening occurs without visible slip[5] may indicate either slip lines too fine to be seen, or some unknown mechanism of flow.

Critical Resolved Shear Stress for Slip. There is a rather clearly defined stress at which a given crystal will begin to flow at an appreciable rate. Below this stress the rate of strain is so slow it requires long-time tests to measure it. In this range the flow is called *creep*. In the neigh-

---

[1] H. L. Burghoff and C. H. Mathewson, *Trans. AIME*, vol. 143, p. 45, 1941.

[2] E. N. da C. Andrade, *Proc. Phys. Soc. (London)*, vol. 52, p. 1, 1940.

[3] E. N. da C. Andrade and S. Chow, *Proc. Roy. Soc. (London)*, vol. A175, p. 290, 1940. D. Hanson and M. A. Wheeler, *J. Inst. Metals*, vol. 45, p. 229, 1931.

[4] C. Crussard, *Rev. mét.*, vol. 42, p. 286, 1945.

[5] R. D. Heidenreich and A. Shockley, "Report of Conference on Strength of Solids," p. 57, Physical Society, London, 1948.

borhood of the critical stress the rate of strain increases rapidly and becomes easily measurable with comparatively crude equipment; it is this type of flow that is commonly referred to as *slip*. Many investigations have shown that differently oriented crystals of a given metal will begin to slip when different stresses are applied to their cross section but that *the stresses resolved on the slip plane and in the slip direction are always the same*, the critical resolved shear stress. This is readily computed from the applied load. Referring to Fig. 6, suppose a force F is applied to a crystal having a cross section of area A. If the slip plane is inclined at an angle ϕ to the cross-section plane, its area will be $A/\cos\phi$, and consequently the stress per unit area acting on the slip plane will be

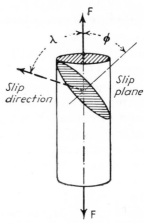

FIG. 6. Coordinates for calculating resolved shear stresses.

$F/(A/\cos\phi)$. This stress is directed along the axis of the crystal, and to resolve this along the slip direction one must multiply by the cosine of the angle λ between the axis and the direction of slip. The resolved shear stress is then

$$\tau = \frac{F}{A}\cos\phi\cos\lambda$$

The loads that are required to stretch differently oriented crystals of magnesium are shown in Fig. 7.[1] It will be seen that they vary by more than a factor of 5. The abscissa of this plot is the function $\cos\phi\cos\lambda$ computed from the known orientations of the crystals, and the curve that is plotted is the variation in load that would be expected if a *constant resolved shear stress* were required for slip in the different crystals. The experimentally determined points follow the curve within the limit of error of the experiments and verify the law. There would have been a systematic trend in the observed values away from the curve if the compo-

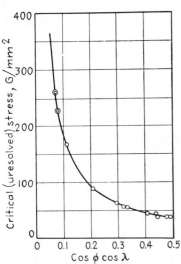

FIG. 7. Variation of yield stress with orientation for single crystals of 99.999 + per cent zinc tested at 25.0°C. Curve is computed for constant resolved shear stress of 18.4 g/mm². (*Jillson*).

---

[1] D. C. Jillson, *Trans. AIME*, vol. 188, p. 1129, 1950. Confirms the conclusions of E. Schmid, *Z. Electrochem.*, vol. 37, p. 447, 1931.

nent of stress *normal* to the slip plane influenced the slip, and it will be seen that this is not the case. Hydrostatic tests up to 40 atm have also failed to disclose any influence of normal stress on the resolved shear stress required for slip.[1] The constant-resolved-shear-stress law has been found not only with hexagonal crystals but with cubic and with lower symmetry crystals and appears to be generally applicable.[2]

Hexagonal crystals usually have only one slip plane, the basal plane; the resolved shear stress for a given load is a maximum when this plane is not far from an inclination of 45° to the axis. When this plane is either flatly or steeply inclined to the axis, the resolved stress approaches zero (*cf.* equation above). Face-centered cubic crystals, on the other hand, have so many slip systems that the resolved shear stress in the most *highly stressed* plane for a given load can vary only by a factor of 2, and with iron the variation is even less. The orientation dependence has been computed and plotted stereographically and otherwise.

Experiments have repeatedly shown that, when there are several crystallographically equivalent slip systems in a crystal, the one having the greatest resolved shear stress will become active; or if two are stressed equally, there will be slip on both. The critical shearing stress is different for nonequivalent planes of the same crystal, and it differs greatly with different metals, different degrees of purity of a given metal, different temperatures at which deformation is carried out, and different degrees of prior strain. A summary of measured values is given in Table XVI. If it were possible to inhibit slip on all planes but one, this one could be made the active slip plane regardless of its indices or the density of atomic packing on the plane. It seems certain that planes of higher indices than those of Table XVI are prevented from becoming active merely by the fact that the planes of easy slip operate and relieve the applied stress before the critical value of the stress is reached on any other planes. In magnesium during a tensile test at 330°C, for example, Bakarian and Mathewson[3] found a critical resolved shear stress of 0.400 kg per sq mm for slip on {101} planes and 0.0655 for slip on the basal plane. For {101} slip to be observed under these conditions the stress on a {101} plane must exceed six times that on (001), and this can occur only if the axis of tension is within 5° of (001). Opinsky and Smoluchowski[4] found that the critical shear stresses for slip on (123), (112), and (110) are related as follows in crystals of Fe containing 3.3 per cent Si: at room temperature,

. M. Polanyi and E. Schmid, *Z. Physik*, vol. 16, p. 336, 1923.

[2] The law (Schmid's law) appeared not to be even approximately obeyed, however, in 99.5 and 99.99 per cent aluminum single crystals tested by K. Lücke and H. Lange, *Z. Metallkunde*, vol. 43, p. 55, 1952.

[3] P. W. Bakarian and C. H. Mathewson, *Trans. AIME*, vol. 152, p. 226, 1943.

[4] A. J. Opinsky and R. Smoluchowski, *J. Applied Phys.*, vol. 22, p. 1488, 1951.

TABLE XVI. CRITICAL RESOLVED SHEAR STRESS FOR SLIP IN CRYSTALS[1]

Metal	Temperature, °C (20°C unless specified)	Impurity content, per cent	Slip plane	Direction	Critical stress, kg per sq mm
Cu	...	0.1	(111)	[10$\bar{1}$]	0.10
Ag	...	0.01	(111)	[10$\bar{1}$]	0.060
Au	...	0.01	(111)	[10$\bar{1}$]	0.092
Ni	...	0.2	(111)	[10$\bar{1}$]	0.58
Mg	...	0.05	(0001)	[11$\bar{2}$0]	0.083
Mg[2]	...	0.02	(0001)	[11$\bar{2}$0]	0.0778
Mg[2]	330	0.02	(0001)	[11$\bar{2}$0]	0.0655
Mg[2]	330	0.02	(10$\bar{1}$1)	[11$\bar{2}$0]	0.400
Zn[3]	...	0.001	(0001)	[11$\bar{2}$0]	0.000
Zn[4]	...	< 0.001	(0001)	[11$\bar{2}$0]	0.030
Zn	...	0.04	(0001)	[11$\bar{2}$0]	0.094
Zn[5]	25	0.00088	(0001)	[11$\bar{2}$0]	0.0184
Cd	...	0.004	(0001)	[11$\bar{2}$0]	0.058
Cd	...	0.004	(11$\bar{2}$0)	.....	0.03
Cd[6]	...	0.0006	......	.....	0.0098
Cd[6]	...	0.0006	......	.....	0.0171
β-Sn	...	0.01	(100)	[001]	0.19
		0.01	(110)	[001]	0.13
		0.01	(101)	[10$\bar{1}$]	0.16
		0.01	(121)	[10$\bar{1}$]	0.17
Bi	...	∼ 0.1	(111)	[10$\bar{1}$]	0.221
Hg	...	∼ 10^{-6}	(100)	.....	0.007
NaCl	...	....	(110)	[1$\bar{1}$0]	∼ 0.2
AgCl	...	....	(110)	[1$\bar{1}$0]	∼ 0.1

[1] Values are for 20°C and from E. Schmid, "International Conference on Physics, vol. II, The Solid State of Matter," Physical Society, London, 1935, unless otherwise noted. [Note added in proof:] Al with 0.004 per cent impurity has a critical stress of 0.104 kg/mm^2 at room temperature, 0.092 at 80°C, and 0.421 at −185°C, according to F. D. Rosi and C. H. Mathewson, *Trans. AIME*, vol. 188, p. 1159, 1950. Ni with less than 0.1 per cent impurity has a critical stress of 1.04 at 17°C, 1.36 at −180°C, 0.97 at 235°C, and 0.90 at 560°C; gold with 10^{-5} impurities varies linearly with temperature from 0.059 at −180°C to 0.0275 at 214°C, according to E. N. da C. Andrade and C. Henderson, *Phil. Trans. Roy. Soc. (London)*, vol. 244, p. 177, 1951.

[2] P. W. Bakarian and C. H. Mathewson, *Trans. AIME*, vol. 152, p. 226, 1943.

[3] R. F. Miller and W. E. Milligan, *Trans. AIME*, vol. 124, p. 229, 1937 (creep test).

[4] S. Harper and A. H. Cottrell, *Proc. Phys. Soc. (London)*, vol. 63, p. 331, 1950; for rate of strain of 10^{-2} sec^{-1}; for 10^{-5} sec^{-1} the corresponding value (0.05 per cent extension) was 21 g per sq mm.

[5] D. C. Jillson, *Trans. AIME*, vol. 188, p. 1129, 1950.

[6] D. F. Gibbons, Dissertation, University of Birmingham, 1949.

$$\tau_{123} = 1.11\tau_{110} \text{ to } 1.07\tau_{110}, \ \tau_{123} = 0.99\tau_{112}; \text{ at } 190°C$$

$$\tau_{123} = 1.06\tau_{110} = 0.99\tau_{112};$$

and at −140°C, only (110) slip occurred, and so $\tau_{123} > 1.13\tau_{110}$ and $\tau_{112} > 1.16\tau_{110}$. They concluded that in beta brass $\tau_{123} = 1.05\tau_{110}$.

Wu and Smoluchowski found that slip does not always occur on the slip system of maximum resolved shear stress. They found that in aluminum crystals having the dimensions 0.2 by 2 by 20 mm there was a tendency for those slip directions to become active that provided the shortest path of slip across the crystal.[1] If the sample is approximately square or round in cross section the usual resolved-shear-stress criterion was believed adequate.

Surface conditions have an important effect on the critical shear stress of crystals. An oxide film of the order of 1000 atoms thickness raises the critical shear stress of cadmium crystals to 2.5 times that of freshly cleaned crystals.[2] An oxide film may double the yield strength of a zinc

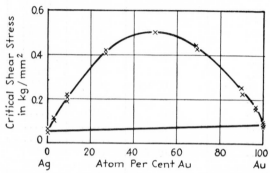

Fig. 8. Variation in critical shear stress with composition in Ag-Au alloys. (*Sachs and Weerts.*)

crystal.[3] Surprising softening effects have been observed when a crystal is immersed in certain liquids,[4,5] for example, when crystals of zinc and tin were tested in paraffin oil containing 0.2 per cent oleic acid their yield strength was halved and their creep rates at constant stress were accelerated.[4] Harper and Cottrell found, however, that these effects can only be expected when an oxide film is present that has already increased the yield strength appreciably above the normal value for an oxide-free surface; they apparently are caused by the liquid penetrating through cracks in the film and lifting the oxide away from the metal surface.[3] Furthermore, the effects appear to concern the rate of strain hardening, not the initial yield stress.[6]

[1] T. L. Wu and R. Smoluchowski, *Phys. Rev.*, vol. 78, p. 468, 1950.

[2] R. Roscoe, *Phil. Mag.*, vol. 21, p. 399, 1936; confirmed by A. H. Cottrell and D. F. Gibbons, *Nature*, vol. 162, p. 488, 1948. Marked hardening from surface films on silver crystals has been noted by E. N. da C. Andrade and C. Henderson, *Phil. Trans. Roy. Soc. (London)*, vol. 244, p. 177, 1951.

[3] S. Harper, Dissertation, University of Birmingham, 1949; S. Harper and A. H. Cottrell, *Proc. Phys. Soc. (London)*, vol. 63, p. 331, 1950. See footnote 2, p. 360.

[4] P. Rehbinder, V. I. Lichtmann, and V. M. Maslenikov, *Compt. rend. acad. sci. U.R.S.S.*, vol. 32 (2), p. 125, 1941.

[5] E. N. da C. Andrade and R. F. Y. Randall, *Nature*, vol. 162, p. 890, 1948.

[6] In Cd and Pb the effect is unaccompanied by changes in electrical resistance. E. N. da C. Andrade, R. F. Y. Randall, and M. J. Makin, *Proc. Phys. Soc. (London)*, vol. B63, p. 990, 1950.

The critical shear stress in the Ag-Au alloys, which form a complete series of solid solutions, is plotted in Fig. 8. The maximum occurs at about the 50 atomic per cent composition.[1] A very similar variation with composition is found with Cu-Ni alloys.[2]

The critical shearing stress of Zn-Cd and Zn-Sn alloys, shown in Fig. 9,[3] illustrates the general rule that the hardening effect of a *soluble* impurity is greater than that of an *insoluble* one, for cadmium is soluble to the extent of roughly 1.5 per cent in zinc (at 250°C), whereas tin is soluble to less than 0.1 weight per cent. Greenland's results[4] on crystals of high-purity distilled mercury are particularly interesting (Fig. 10). The presence of an impurity in concentra-

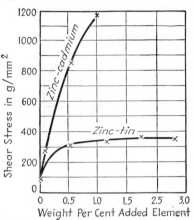

Fig. 9. Critical shearing stress of Zn-Cd and Zn-Sn alloys. Cadmium is soluble, tin almost insoluble, in the concentrations shown. (*Rosbaud and Schmid.*)

tions of 1 part in 10^6 or 10^7 has an important effect on the critical shearing stress. (The tests were made at $-60°C$, about 23° below the melting point.)

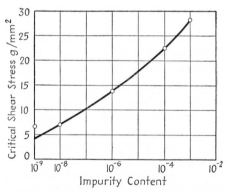

Fig. 10. Critical shearing stress of single crystals of mercury containing silver as an impurity. Tested at $-60°C$. (*Greenland.*)

Much evidence is accumulating to indicate that the presence of interstitial atoms of carbon or nitrogen is responsible for causing a sharp yield point in both single crystals and polycrystalline metals. Iron acquires a

---

[1] G. Sachs and J. Weerts, *Z. Physik,* vol. 62, p. 473, 1930.

[2] E. Osswald, *Z. Physik,* vol. 83, p. 55, 1933.

[3] P. Rosbaud and E. Schmid, *Z. Physik,* vol. 32, p. 197, 1925.

[4] K. M. Greenland, *Proc. Roy. Soc. (London),* vol. A163, p. 28, 1937.

yield point if either of these elements is present in amounts greater than 0.003 per cent;[1] nitrogen produces a yield point in molybdenum,[2] cadmium,[3] and zinc.[4]

Aging of an aluminum alloy containing 5 per cent copper increased the critical stress from 1.9 up to 9.3 kg per sq mm. The former value was

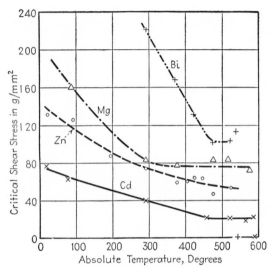

Fig. 11. Effect of temperature on critical shear stress of metal cystals. (*Schmid and Boas.*)

measured in a crystal slowly cooled from 525 to 300°C, the latter after quenching from 525°C and aging at 100°C for 1 hr.[5]

Dependence on Temperature. The critical resolved shear stress for a metal decreases with increasing temperature and drops abruptly to zero at the melting point (at the solidus temperature in alloys). Experimental data for hexagonal metals (Fig. 11) indicate a rather small dependence on

[1] J. R. Low and M. Gensamer, *Trans. AIME*, vol. 158, p. 207, 1944. There is an increase in the yield strength of iron, however, whenever the carbon content exceeds 0.0001 weight per cent; the solubility limit for carbon at room temperature, as determined by internal friction methods, is 10^{-7} weight per cent. C. A. Wert, *Trans. AIME.*, vol. 188, p. 1242, 1950.

[2] P. Túry and S. Krausz, *Nature*, vol. 138, p. 331, 1936; vol. 139, p. 30, 1937.

[3] C. L. Smith, *Nature*, vol. 160, p. 466, 1947. A. H. Cottrell and D. F. Gibbons, *Nature*, vol. 162, p. 488, 1948.

[4] H. L. Wain and A. H. Cottrell, *Proc. Phys. Soc. (London)*, vol. B63, p. 339, 1950. A yield point is also found under certain conditions in alpha and beta brass. In single crystals of these alloys, as well as in zinc, the presence of a yield point appears to be associated with a jerky type of plastic flow. (Private communications from A. H. Cottrell, G. W. Ardley, and M. J. Dumbleton).

[5] R. Karnop and G. Sachs, *Z. Physik*, vol. 49, p. 480, 1928.

temperature, particularly in the neighborhood of the melting point.[1] This is also true of aluminum and tungsten.[2] The critical shear stress even near absolute zero is still of the same order of magnitude as at room temperature, and much ductility remains in crystals of cadmium, zinc, and many other metals at these low temperatures. The fact that different slip systems are observed at different temperatures (*e.g.*, aluminum and magnesium) indicates that the alteration in shear strength with temperature is not uniform on all planes of a lattice. The ratio τ_{123}/τ_{110} in silicon ferrite depends upon temperature and accounts for the slip being confined to (110) at low temperatures (see page 338); similar explanations account for changes of slip planes in aluminum and tungsten.

In creep tests with a sensitive extensometer, Miller and Milligan[3] found that the resolved shear stress for plastic flow was even greater at elevated temperatures than at room temperature, in single crystals of high-purity silver and aluminum—provided that the recrystallization temperature was not exceeded.[4] Creep in alpha-brass starts at a resolved shear stress that is independent of temperature in tests at 300, 500, and 700°F.[5] These observations have led Zener[6] to suggest that perhaps the frequently observed apparent decrease in critical resolved shear stress with increase in temperature might be due to the effect of temperature on *strain hardening* in the first stages of plastic flow, rather than the effect on the initial resolved shear stress.

Strain Hardening. The shear stress necessary to cause slip is always increased by prior cold work. If a crystal of zinc is sheared by as much as 500 per cent, which is possible for suitably oriented crystals, the shear stress necessary to continue slip on the basal plane will have increased by a factor of about 7. An even more rapid strain hardening is observed with f.c.c. metals than with hexagonal metals, as is seen in the curves of Fig. 12, where the resolved shear stress is plotted against the amount of shear strain for the f.c.c. metals Ni, Cu, Ag, Al, and Au, the hexagonal metals Mg, Zn, and Cd, and tetragonal Sn.* The data of Fig. 12 indicate that strain hardening in some crystals (*e.g.*, zinc) increases linearly with

[1] E. Schmid and W. Boas, "Kristallplastizität," Springer, Berlin, 1935.

[2] "International Conference on Physics, vol. II, The Solid State of Matter," Physical Society, London, 1935.

[3] R. F. Miller and W. E. Milligan, *Trans. AIME*, vol. 124, p. 229, 1937.

[4] However, Andrade and Henderson find that the thickening of oxide films on silver with increasing temperature is a cause of marked strengthening in tests at elevated temperatures. E. N. da C. Andrade and C. Henderson, *Phil. Trans. Roy. Soc. (London)*, vol. 244, p. 177, 1951.

[5] H. L. Burghoff and C. H. Mathewson, *Trans. AIME*, vol. 143, p. 45, 1941.

[6] C. Zener, "Elasticity and Anelasticity of Metals," p. 140, University of Chicago Press, Chicago, 1948.

* E. Schmid, and W. Boas, Kristallplastizität, Springer, Berlin, 1935.

the amount of strain.   According to Taylor's results, Fig. 13, aluminum
hardens with a different curve.   Both the tensile tests (dots) and the
compression tests (crosses) follow the parabolic curve $\sigma = c\sqrt{S}$, where σ
is the resolved shear stress, S is the shear strain on the slip plane, and c is
a constant.   Obviously, the normal stress, which is different in the two
tests, does not affect the curve.   The whole of the strain-hardening curve,
including the initial critical stress, is a function of the rate of deformation.

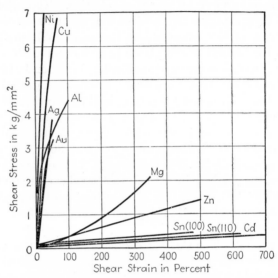

FIG. 12. Shear-stress–shear-strain diagrams for single crystals.   (*Schmid and Boas.*)

The shape of the curve can be dependent, for example, on whether the
stress or the strain is increased uniformly with time,[1] and if the crystal is
tested rapidly the stresses will always be higher than if the test is run
slowly.   The influence of time is further discussed on page 359.

Strain hardening appears to be very small (sometimes negligible)
when slip is confined to one system, but is greater when two systems operate simultaneously and is still greater when three or more operate.[2]

[1] R. Houwink, "Elasticity, Plasticity and Structure of Matter," University Press,
Cambridge, Mass., 1937 (especially the chapter by W. G. Burgers).

[2] P. L. Pratt has observed striking differences in strain hardening rates in rock
salt, confirming this principle (private communication, to be published).   It is also
indicated by tests on aluminum crystals.   A long extension is possible before rapid
strain hardening sets in, for aluminum crystals having the tensile axis near [110];
moderate extensions without rapid hardening are also found for many other orientations (a behavior Andrade calls "easy glide").   Presumably these are crystals in
which slip on a single slip system is predominant at first, since contrasting with this
are crystals with orientations near [100] and [111], which harden very rapidly as soon
as plastic deformation starts, and which presumably slip on two or more slip systems
simultaneously.   K. Lücke and H. Lange, *Z. Metallkunde*, vol. 43, p. 55, 1952 (99.99

Single slip (together with cross slip) is not accompanied by strain harden-ing in alpha brass crystals (30 per cent Zn) but hardening is rapid when crystal rotation causes multiple slip to start.[1]

Cottrell suggests that, by analogy with fluid flow, the single slip con-dition be called "laminar flow" and the other (rapid strain-hardening) conditions "turbulent flow." After much importance had been attached to subdivision of crystals into deformation bands during plastic flow (see page 372) it now appears that these are relatively unimportant in

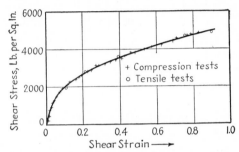

Fig. 13. Strain hardening in aluminum compression specimens (+) and tensile specimens (O). (*Taylor.*)

causing strain hardening: they may be present when hardening is slight and they may be absent when hardening is rapid—at least in f.c.c. single crystals. Cottrell points out that the stress field from the boundary of a deformation band must not extend far away from the boundary, hence cannot be expected to harden the major portion of a crystal.[2]

PLASTIC FLOW IN POLYCRYSTALLINE METAL

The purpose of much of the experimental work on single crystals has been to understand the mechanism of flow in a polycrystalline metal. When the data from single crystals are applied to the polycrystalline case, however, many new complicating factors enter. The most impor-tant of these are the grain boundaries and the constraints imposed on the flow of a grain by the flow of the aggregate and by the variously oriented neighboring grains. The homogeneous strain of the single crystal is

per cent Al, and 99.5 per cent Al crystals). See also G. Masing and J. Raffelsieper, *Z. Metallkunde*, vol. 41, p. 65, 1950. The effect was probably first detected by G. I. Taylor, *Proc. Roy. Soc. (London)*, vol. A116, p. 39, 1927. I am indebted to A. H. Cottrell, R. W. Cahn, and P. L. Pratt for helpful discussions of this field.

[1] R. Maddin, C. H. Mathewson, and W. R. Hibbard, *Trans. AIME*, vol. 185, p. 527, 1949. See also F. von Göler and G. Sachs, *Z. Physik*, vol. 55, p. 581, 1929.

[2] A. H. Cottrell, private communication; to be published in a monograph on dis-locations and plastic flow in crystals. Since a band boundary is merely a wall of dislocations, the stress field extends a distance comparable to the interdislocation distance.

replaced by an inhomogeneous strain that varies from grain to grain and from point to point within a grain. Additional complexities arise from the different properties of the phases in polyphase alloys, and from their distribution. It is not surprising that investigators have reached a less satisfactory understanding of the conditions within the aggregate than within a single crystal.

Grain Boundaries and Their Effect on Plastic Flow. Aston[1] measured the amount of strain at various distances from the grain boundary in large-grained tensile specimens and found that near a boundary there is less deformation than in the center of a grain. Similar observations of the effect of boundaries in restraining plastic flow have been made by others.[2] In general there tends to be an equalizing of the strains on the two sides of a boundary, so the deformation of a grain near a boundary can exceed the deformation at the center if the neighboring grain has a lower yield point.[3]

Chalmers[4] conducted an interesting experiment with tensile specimens composed of two crystals of tin in which the boundary between the pair of crystals extended longitudinally throughout the specimen. His results show that the critical stress depends upon the difference in orientation between the two crystals, being a minimum when the lattices in the two crystals are similarly oriented and a maximum when the orientations differ the most. This indicates that when slip planes in two adjacent grains are not parallel it is difficult for the block movement in one grain to cross the boundary into the next grain.

There seems no need to assume that there exists an amorphous cement along the boundaries which imparts additional strength to the whole, although this was a favored theory of early investigators, notably Rosenhain. It now appears more likely that there is merely a transition region at the boundary, where the atom positions represent a compromise between the crystalline arrangements in the two adjoining grains. The thickness of this layer of disturbed crystallinity can be roughly estimated. Various theories indicate that the preponderant forces between atoms in solids extend only between nearest neighbors or at most only a few atom diameters. Because of this localization of forces the transition layer at a boundary must be exceedingly thin. One estimate puts the upper limit for the thickness of the layer at five interatomic distances,[5] too narrow to

[1] R. L. Aston, *Proc. Cambridge Phil. Soc.*, vol. 23, p. 549, 1927.

[2] D. Hanson and M. A. Wheeler, *J. Inst. Metals*, vol. 45, p. 229, 1931. H. C. H. Carpenter, *J. Iron Steel Inst. (London)*, vol. 107, p. 175, 1923. R. F. Miller, *Trans. AIME*, vol. 111, p. 135, 1934. G. Seumel, *Z. Krist.*, vol. 93, p. 249, 1936. W. R. Hibbard, *Trans. AIME*, vol. 180, p. 52, 1949.

[3] W. Boas and M. E. Hargreaves, *Proc. Roy. Soc. (London)*, vol. A193, p. 89, 1948.

[4] Bruce Chalmers, *Proc. Roy. Soc. (London)*, vol. A162, p. 120, 1937.

[5] F. Seitz and T. A. Read, *J. Applied Phys.*, vol. 12, p. 538, 1941.

be seen on photomicrographs made with optical or electron microscopes. More recent estimates of the range through which boundaries extend their influence are based on the theory of dislocations, discussed in Chap. XVI. Boundaries are viewed as a wall of dislocations, and the range of stresses is comparable to the spacing between dislocations. In addition, there is a hardening resulting from the presence of a neighboring grain of different orientation if the grains are elastically anisotropic, or if the neighboring grain is of a different phase and therefore has different elastic constants.

The irregular atomic array at the boundary appears to be less stable than grain interiors. Chalmers[1] showed that in tin of high purity the grain-boundary material has a melting point about 0.14°C below the melting point of the bulk material. Additional evidence for lattice

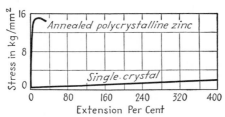

Fig. 14. Stress-strain curves for zinc. (*Elam.*)

imperfection at the boundary is obtained from numerous observations that atoms diffuse into many polycrystalline metals more rapidly along grain boundaries, where the potential barriers that must be overcome during diffusion are lower than those in the interior of grains. In many practical instances the properties of the boundaries are influenced by impurities that segregate at these places during freezing and by the penetration of oxygen and corrosive elements along the boundaries.

The Effect of Grain Size on Plastic Flow and Hardness. Polycrystalline metal generally offers more resistance to deformation than single crystals. This is particularly true of zinc, as the stress-strain curve of Fig. 14 shows, and of magnesium.[2] Contrasted with this are the results[3] with aluminum, a f.c.c. metal with four slip planes in contrast to the single plane of easy slip in hexagonal metals. In aluminum the curve for the aggregate is similar to some of the single crystal curves.

Indentation hardness increases with increasing fineness of the grains in polycrystalline metals.[4] Figure 15 illustrates the effect in copper.

---

[1] Bruce Chalmers, *Proc. Roy. Soc. (London)*, vol. A175, p. 100, 1940.

[2] C. F. Elam, "The Distortion of Metal Crystals," Oxford, New York, 1935. E. Schmid and W. Boas, "Kristallplastizität," Springer, Berlin, 1935.

[3] R. Karnop and G. Sachs, *Z. Physik*, vol. 41, p. 116, 1927.

[4] W. H. Bassett and C. H. Davis, *Trans. AIME*, vol. 60, p. 428, 1919. H. T. Angus and P. F. Summers, *J. Inst. Metals*, vol. 33, p. 115, 1925.

Hardness and resistance to deformation in iron[1] and aluminum[2] likewise increase as grain size is reduced. The yield strength in some alloys can be taken as proportional to $\sqrt{1/D}$ where D is the average grain diameter.[3]

The Hardness of Solid Solutions. Norbury[4] found that the indentation hardness of copper increased linearly with the atomic per cent of any metal dissolved in it. He also compared the hardening effects of different solutes and found that the hardening effect of 0.1 atomic per cent of an

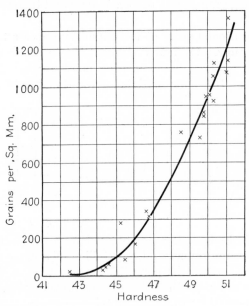

Fig. 15. Variation of hardness with grain size in copper. (*Angus and Summers.*)

alloying element added to copper or to lead was in almost direct proportion to the difference in atomic radii of the solute and solvent atoms. This relationship may also be expressed in terms of hardening vs. change of lattice parameter or vs. the extent of solid solubility, since these characteristics are all interrelated. Figure 16 illustrates the relationship in copper alloys of controlled grain size.[5] Nickel has nearly the same atomic radius as copper, expands the copper lattice only slightly, is soluble

[1] C. A. Edwards and L. B. Pfeil, *J. Iron Steel Inst. (London)*, vol. 112, p. 79, 1925. T. Ishigaki, *Sci. Repts., Tôhoku Imp. Univ.*, vol. 16, p. 285, 1927.

[2] J. E. Dorn, P. Pietrokowsky, and T. E. Tietz, *Trans. AIME*, vol. 188, p. 933, 1950.

[3] C. Zener, *Phys. Rev.*, vol. 69, p. 128, 1946.

[4] A. L. Norbury, *Trans. Faraday Soc.*, vol. 19, p. 586, 1924.

[5] R. M. Brick, D. L. Martin, and R. P. Angier, *Proc. ASM*, vol. 31, p. 675, 1943. This principle has been confirmed and studied in detail by J. H. Frye and J. W. Caum, *Trans. AIME*, vol. 152, p. 83, 1943; and by J. H. Frye and W. Hume-Rothery, *Proc. Roy. Soc. (London)*, vol. A181, p. 1, 1942.

up to 100 per cent, and hardens it the least of any of the elements plotted in the figure. Antimony and tin differ the most in atomic radii, expand the copper lattice the most per atom dissolved, have the most restricted solubility (0.6 and 1.0 atomic per cent, respectively), and exert the greatest hardening effects. The capacity of any of these alloys to be hardened by cold work is linearly proportional to its hardening by solution; an element that confers great solution hardening to the matrix also confers correspondingly great work-hardening properties.

Indentation hardness is itself largely a measure of work hardening for it is effectively a weighted average of the stress-strain curve from zero strain up to the maximum value encountered under the penetrator. This

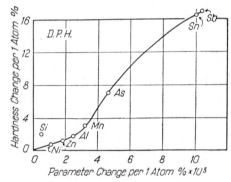

FIG. 16. Comparative solid-solution hardening of copper alloys as related to alteration of lattice parameter. (*Brick, Martin, and Angier.*)

is recognized in Meyer's analysis of the Brinell impressions made with penetrator balls of various sizes and loads. If L is the load on a ball that makes an impression of diameter d, then $L = ad^n$ where the constant n is an index of the work-hardening capacity of the metal.

From studies of true stress-strain curves derived from tensile tests further data have been obtained on solution hardening. In binary alloys of iron, prepared with constant ferrite grain size, Gensamer compared the strengthening effect of various solute elements, and concluded that the strengthening effect per atom per cent of the dissolved element decreased in the order Be, Ti, W, Si, Mo, Mn, Ni, Al, V, Co, and Cr.[1] The greater the difference in valence between the added element and iron the greater the effect in many of these alloys, but not in all. There is fair correlation, also, with the solubility, greater strengthening going with lower solubility. By expressing the effect of each element in terms of the amount of dissolved nickel that would produce a similar stress-strain curve, it was possible to predict successfully the curves obtained with ternary alloys. In ternary alloys the nickel equivalents of the individual

[1] M. Gensamer, *Trans. ASM*, vol. 36, p. 30, 1946.

solutes were found to be additive. A similar study of controlled grain-size aluminum alloys by Dorn, Pietrokowsky, and Tietz[1] indicated that the strengthening effect was related both to the difference in valence of solute and solvent, and to the change in lattice constant per one atom per cent solute. Quantitatively, the atom per cent dissolved copper that would be equivalent to N atom per cent of any of the elements tested (Ge, Ag, Cu, Zn, Cr, Mg) could be computed from the empirical expression

$$\{102|\Delta a| + 15|\Delta v| + 7000|\Delta a||\Delta v|\}N$$

where $|\Delta a|$ is the absolute value of the change in lattice constant per one

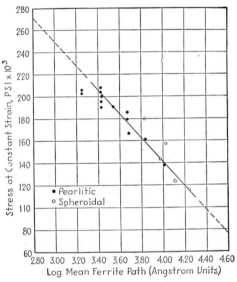

Fig. 17. Stress at a constant amount of elongation as related to mean straight path through ferrite in steel of 0.80 per cent C, 0.74 per cent Mn with both pearlitic and spheroidal microstructures. (*Gensamer, Pearsall, Pellini, and Low.*)

atom per cent solute and $|\Delta v|$ is the absolute value of the change in the number of electrons per atom upon addition of one atom per cent of the solute, provided that aluminum is considered to contribute two electrons per atom.

The Effect of Fineness of Microstructure in Steels. Gensamer and his collaborators[2] studied the quantitative relation between the fineness of the microstructures in steel and the tensile properties. By causing the steel to react at different temperatures in the subcritical range they produced

[1] J. E. Dorn, P. Pietrokowsky, and T. E. Tietz, *Trans. AIME*, vol. 188, p. 933, 1950.

[2] M. Gensamer, E. B. Pearsall, W. S. Pellini, and J. R. Low, Jr., The Tensile Properties of Pearlite, Bainite and Spheroidite, *Trans. ASM*, vol. 30, p. 983, 1942. M. Gensamer, E. B. Pearsall, and G. V. Smith, *Trans. ASM*, vol. 28, p. 380, 1940.

pearlite and spheroidite of varying fineness. Plotting the resistance to deformation at a constant value of strain against a measure of the fineness gave the linear relation shown in Fig. 17. The measure of fineness used was the logarithm of the mean straight path through the continuous phase (ferrite) from one hard cementite particle or lamella to another. It was found that a given value of mean path, along which slip occurs, corresponds to the same flow resistance regardless of the shape of the carbide particles—whether they are lamellae as in pearlite or globules as in spheroidite.

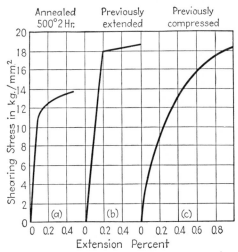

Fig. 18. The Bauschinger effect in polycrystalline brass. Resistance to elongation is increased by prior elongation, from curve (a) to curve (b), and is lowered to curve (c) by prior compression. (*Sachs and Shoji.*)

The Effect of Strain Rate. Determinations of the resistance to deformation are made at a controlled rate of straining, for the rate varies the resistance. The effect of rate is slight, however, at ordinary rates.[1] For example, as the rate is increased, Nádai has found a 10,000-fold increase in rate merely doubles the flow resistance in 0.35 per cent carbon steel at 455°C. The resistance increases in proportion to the logarithm of the rate of straining, and there is a greater increase in the soft metals than in the hard ones.

The Bauschinger Effect and the Elastic Aftereffect. A stress-strain curve is strongly influenced by any previous compression or extension the

---

[1] For a review of this subject see M. Gensamer, "Strength of Metals under Combined Loads," American Society for Metals, Cleveland, Ohio, 1941; G. V. Smith, "Properties of Metals at Elevated Temperatures," McGraw-Hill, New York, 1950; A. L. Nádai, "Theory of Flow and Fracture of Solids," vol. I, McGraw-Hill, New York, 1950.

specimen has undergone.   Prior compression raises the yield strength for further compression but lowers it for tension, as will be seen from Fig. 18. Straining of either kind, in fact, raises the ability of the metal to withstand further stressing of the same kind and lowers its strength to stresses of the opposite kind.

This Bauschinger effect in polycrystalline material can be ascribed to the state of stress existing within the metal after the first deformation.[1] If some grains of the aggregate have an orientation such that they have a high yield strength to an applied tensile load while others have a low yield strength, then when the load is removed the latter will be brought into a compressive strain by the tensile stresses in the former and the final state is an equilibrium between compressive and tensile stresses in many small regions.   Consider now the state of stress upon reapplication of the tensile load to the grains that were originally the weak ones and that are now the compressed ones.   They must first be reduced to zero stress from their elastically compressed state, then raised to their yield strength in tension, before flow can begin.   The material has consequently been work-hardened for stresses in this direction.   But if a *compressional* stress is applied, the grains that were left in a state of residual compression are already part way to their yield point in compression and slight additional stresses in this direction will start plastic flow.   In fact, the compressional stress already existing is sufficient to cause a limited amount of flow, for after the tensile load is released there is a small additional contraction that takes place rather slowly (the elastic aftereffect).   This contraction diminishes in rate in the way that the stresses in a bent beam diminish when they are relaxed by annealing.   The flow is sufficiently rapid so that it is observed during a tensile test, where it causes the stress-strain curve during unloading to differ from the curve for reapplication of the load (at a given value of the load the strain is greater during the unloading than during the subsequent reloading).

Since the Bauschinger and elastic aftereffects are observed in single crystals as well as in polycrystalline samples, the above explanation is incomplete.   A more fundamental point of view, which accounts for the effects in both single crystals and polycrystalline specimens, is that the effects are due to the stresses that surround the individual slip bands where relative displacement of the two sides of the slip band has occurred.[2]

---

[1] G. Masing, *Wiss. Siemens Konzern*, vol. 3, p. 231, 1924; vol. 4, pp. 74, 244, 1925; vol. 5, pp. 135, 142, 1926.

[2] See discussion by C. Zener in "Symposium on the Cold Working of Metals," American Society for Metals, Cleveland, 1949, p. 180.   The presence of these effects in single crystals of zinc has been observed by the author, who has also observed an aftereffect of *reversed sign* (experiments at the University of Birmingham, to be published).   This abnormal aftereffect is caused by the escape from the metal of disloca-

Theories of Flow in Aggregates. When a single crystal is elongated in a tensile test, the central portion of the crystal remote from the influence of the grips is subjected to a uniform stress and is free to deform on a single slip plane, altering its shape in accord with this mechanism. A grain in an aggregate, on the other hand, is constrained on all sides by neighboring grains and cannot change its shape in an arbitrary manner since the grain boundaries do not pull apart during the deformation. Each grain undergoes approximately the same strain as the aggregate; *i.e.*, it tends to elongate in proportion to the elongation of the bulk material and to contract laterally in proportion to the lateral contraction of the aggregate. An arbitrary change of shape of this type requires a minimum of five different slip systems to operate continually. Taylor[1] has shown that the principle of least work limits the number to five and has computed which five will operate for a f.c.c. crystal of given orientation. Then assuming that the shear-hardening curve for each of the five is similar to that for a slip plane in a single crystal he has computed the stress-strain curve for polycrystalline aluminum from the curve for a single crystal. The computed curve agrees well with the observed. Taylor's theory also predicts the direction of rotation of the grains during deformation. However, actual experimental determination of the direction of rotation has shown that about one-third of the grains rotate in ways not predicted by the theory.[2] This is attributed to the fact that each grain and each fragment of a grain deform inhomogeneously in a manner influenced by ever-changing flow of its neighbors, whereas Taylor's theory assumes uniform strain in all the grains. The theory does not predict a grain-size effect in tensile properties or hardness when there are many grains in the cross section of the specimen under test.

Kochendörfer[3] has proposed a different manner of predicting the flow curve of an aggregate from the characteristics of flow in single crystals. He assumes that a properly corrected average of the flow curves for single crystals of the various orientations should give the flow curve for the aggregate. As a first approximation he considers that each grain attempts to flow as it would when isolated, using slip planes of maximum resolved shear stress, undergoing hardening by slip only, without interaction with the neighboring grains. Then he assumes that another hardening is added to this, *viz.*, the hardening from stresses near grain

---

tions that have been held up at the metal-oxide interface, when the oxide is suddenly removed by etching.

[1] G. I. Taylor, *J. Inst. Metals*, vol. 62, p. 307, 1938; "Stephen Timoshenko 60th Anniversary Volume," Macmillan, New York, 1938.

[2] C. S. Barrett and L. H. Levenson, *Trans. AIME*, vol. 137, p. 112, 1940.

[3] A. Kochendörfer, "Plastische Eigenschaften von Kristallen und Metallischen Werkstoffen," Springer, Berlin, 1941.

boundaries. The boundary effect, arising from grains being forced to remain in contact, is assumed to be relatively minor in metals with many slip systems, such as f.c.c. metals and alloys, but very important in metals with few slip systems (*e.g.*, magnesium) in which it should be relatively difficult to provide the kinds of deformation that are necessary to keep the grains in contact.[1]

Dependence of Strain Hardening on Temperature. Stress-strain curves for magnesium are reproduced in Fig. 19 to show the effect of the

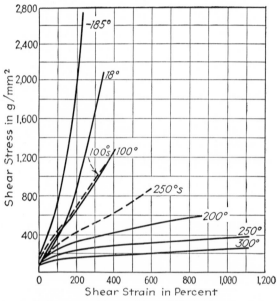

FIG. 19. Strain hardening in magnesium crystals at different temperatures. Dashed curves 100°*S* and 250°*S* are for a rate of test a hundred-fold faster than the others. Temperatures in degrees centigrade. (*Schmid and Siebel.*)

temperature at which the test is run.[2] The amount of strain hardening decreases markedly as the temperature is raised. The dashed curves marked 100° *S* and 250° *S* were for a rate of test about a hundredfold faster than the others. It will be noted that, while the rate was not an important factor at 100°C, it exerted a profound effect at 250°. Other metals show a temperature dependence of strain hardening of much the same sort. Curves for aluminum are reproduced in Fig. 20.[3]

The effect of holding a metal at a given temperature for a length of

[1] Further discussion of the flow stress in polycrystalline aggregates will be found in recent publications of J. F. W. Bishop and R. Hill in *Phil. Mag.* (1951 and in press). It is held that the work of actual deformation is the same as the work that would be predicted by G. I. Taylor's theory.

[2] E. Schmid, *Z. Elektrochem.*, vol. 37, p. 447, 1931.

[3] W. Boas and E. Schmid, *Z. Physik*, vol. 71, p. 703, 1931.

time is to anneal the metal and bring about a softening, a *recovery* from
the strain hardening. In this process a short time at a high temperature
is equivalent to a long time at a low temperature. Stress-strain curves
at temperatures where recovery is rapid may be considered to be the

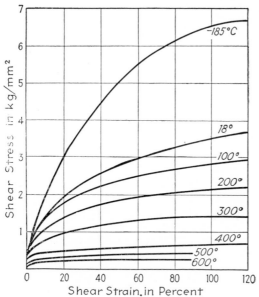

FIG. 20. Strain hardening in aluminum crystals at different temperatures. (*Boas and Schmid.*)

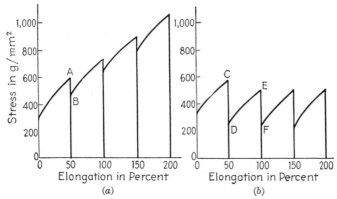

FIG. 21. Partial recovery (*a*) and complete recovery (*b*) in zinc crystals at room temperature. Tests interrupted for ½ min in (*a*) and for 1 day in (*b*). (*Haase and Schmid.*)

result of a balance between two opposing tendencies, strain hardening
and recovery. At low temperatures, the hardening predominates and
the stress-strain curve rises steeply. At elevated temperatures, recovery
is proceeding at a rate comparable with the rate of strain hardening, and

eventually a temperature is reached at which recovery almost wholly prevents strain hardening. The stress-strain curve is then horizontal (see Figs. 19 and 20).

The separate effects of hardening and recovery can be distinguished more easily if successive stress-strain curves are run with annealing treatments interposed. Figure 21 gives the result of such an experiment on zinc,[1] which partly recovers from the effects of cold work in a rest interval of $\frac{1}{2}$ min and completely recovers in an interval of a day. The yield strength is lowered from A to B (Fig. 21a) by a $\frac{1}{2}$-min rest, whereas it drops from C to D or from E to F (Fig. 21b) during a day's rest.

The temperature dependence of the flow curve is not, however, entirely due to recovery. Even at temperatures too low to permit recovery the hardening produced by a given strain continues to increase as the temperature of deformation is lowered.[2]

A specimen is hardened more by a given elongation at low temperatures than at room temperature. The effect of hardening during low-temperature straining is retained at room temperature and raises the course of a subsequent stress-strain curve at room temperature throughout a strain of several per cent. Similarly, metal strained at room temperature retains a memory of this through the initial stages of a low-temperature test, and flows at lower stresses but strain-hardens more rapidly than metal strained entirely at the low temperature.[2,3] This effect occurs[3] in many metals, including copper, commercial-purity aluminum, high-purity aluminum, alpha-brass, austenitic (18-8) stainless steel, annealed low-carbon steel, and silicon steel; the magnitude of the effect is smaller, however, in the body-centered cubic specimens than in the face-centered cubic. An analogous effect is noted in recovery rates, for recovery of high-purity aluminum from strain hardening is faster when prestraining is at low temperatures. Although the observations mentioned were made on polycrystalline samples, they probably apply also to single crystals. Experiments on naphthalene crystals have, in fact, shown clearly the dependence of the strain-hardened state on the prior thermomechanical history.[4]

The desirability of having a mathematical expression for the combined effect of temperature and strain rate on the flow curve led to a proposal of a function that holds for a considerable range of strain rates and tem-

[1] O. Haase and E. Schmid, Z. Physik, vol. 33, p. 413, 1925.

[2] E. Orowan, J. West Scot. Iron Steel Inst., vol. 54, pp. 45–96, 1946–1947.

[3] J. E. Dorn, A. Goldberg, and T. E. Tietz, Trans. AIME, vol. 180, p. 205, 1949. E. J. Ripling and G. Sachs, Trans. AIME, vol. 185, p. 78, 1949. T. E. Tietz, R. A. Anderson, and J. E. Dorn, Trans. AIME, vol. 185, p. 921, 1949.

[4] A. Kochendörfer, Z. Krist., vol. 97, p. 263, 1937.

peratures in various metals.[1] Since the function involves only the instantaneous values of the variables, and thus is a "mechanical equation of state," it was objected to by those who have noted the "memory" of samples for prior conditions of straining. It appears that the "mechanical equation of state" should therefore be regarded as valid only with restrictions, an approximation rather than a fundamental law.

CREEP

Continuing slow plastic flow under constant conditions of load or stress is termed creep. It is a property of outstanding importance in materials used for high-temperature applications. The engineering aspects of this property, which cannot be covered here, are related to certain fundamentals that are within the scope of this book and will be briefly reviewed here.

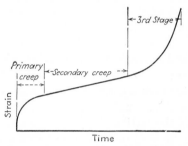

The curve of strain vs. time in a constant-load creep test is normally of the type illustrated in Fig. 22. When the load is first applied there is an instantaneous elongation (elastic strain), then a "primary stage" of transient nature in which the creep rate

Fig. 22. First, second, and third stages of creep.

gradually slows to a minimum, followed by a "secondary stage" in which creep continues at an approximately constant minimum rate. If the stress is sufficiently high, this steady-state creep is followed by a "tertiary stage" in which creep accelerates until fracture occurs. Extensive discussions of these stages will be found in the literature.[2]

Transient Effects and Equations for Creep. Andrade[3] showed that when a load is applied at the beginning of a creep test the instantaneous (elastic) elongation is followed by the transient state in which strain varies with time according to a $t^{\frac{1}{3}}$ law, and finally the steady state in which a constant rate of creep is reached (under constant effective stress). These states can be represented by three terms in a single equation, which for

[1] Originally proposed by P. Ludwik ("Elements der Technologischen Mechanik," Springer, Berlin, 1909), it was developed by C. Zener and J. H. Hollomon (*J. Applied Phys.*, vol. 15, p. 22, 1944), and J. H. Hollomon (*Trans. AIME*, vol. 171, p. 535, 1947).

[2] G. V. Smith, "Properties of Metals at Elevated Temperatures," McGraw-Hill, New York, 1950. A. L. Nádai, "Theory of Flow and Fracture of Solids," vol. I, McGraw-Hill, New York, 1950. E. Orowan, "The Creep of Metals," West Scotland Iron and Steel Institute, February, 1947. D. Hanson, *Trans. AIME*, vol. 133, p. 15, 1939. W. Kauzmann, *Trans. AIME*, vol. 143, p. 57, 1941.

[3] E. N. da C. Andrade, *Proc. Roy. Soc. (London)*, vol. A84, p. 1, 1910; vol. A90, p. 327, 1914.

single crystals can be written[1] as

$$\gamma = \gamma_0 + \beta t^{\frac{1}{3}} + \kappa t$$

where γ is the shear strain and γ_0 the instantaneous strain. Andrade found the β coefficient (for transient flow) and κ (for steady-state flow) to be temperature-dependent, the transient flow term being the more important in low-temperature creep and the steady-state term more important at high temperatures. These laws apply both to polycrystalline metals and to single crystals and are not limited to metals of a particular crystal structure, but appear to apply quite generally. Transient effects occur not only when load is applied or released, but also when it is altered,[2,3,4] or when the temperature is suddenly changed.[3]

Transient (β) creep is accompanied by the appearance of slip bands, and in single crystals of zinc, also by twinning.[5] Steady-state creep also occurs by slip to some extent,[6] but the higher the temperature the more the flow is concentrated into the grain boundaries,[7,8] the more prominent is the formation of subboundaries ("cells") within grains,[5,8] and the less is the lattice distortion revealed by asterism in Laue photographs.[6,8]

In polycrystalline metals the strain that occurs in the transient stage is "recoverable" in the sense that, by removing the load and waiting a time about equal to the duration of the original transient, a flow in the reverse direction occurs that is about equal to the amount of the original transient strain. While transient flow occurs in both single crystals and polycrystalline metals, recovery of the transient creep in single crystals of tin seems not to occur,[9] and recoverable strain is absent, also, if the original strain rate is high, or if a low rate is followed by a high rate.[6]

Recoverable primary creep is understandable in terms of grain-boundary flow: it could be the amount of flow that occurs before it is brought to a stop by the keying points at grain junctions. It is recoverable because residual stresses, built up during this flow, cause reversed

---

[1] A. H. Cottrell and V. Aytekin, *J. Inst. Metals*, vol. 77, p. 389, 1950.

[2] M. Gensamer and R. F. Mehl, *Trans. AIME*, vol. 131, p. 372, 1938 (single crystals of iron). H. L. Burghoff and C. H. Mathewson, *Trans. AIME*, vol. 143, p. 45, 1941 (single crystals of brass).

[3] R. P. Carreker, J. G. Leschen, and J. D. Lubahn, *Trans. AIME*, vol. 180, p. 139, 1949 (polycrystalline lead, copper, and aluminum).

[4] A. W. McReynolds, *Trans. AIME*, vol. 185, p. 32, 1949 (stress-strain curves of polycrystalline aluminum alloys; accompanying strain waves and aging).

[5] A. H. Cottrell and V. Aytekin, *J. Inst. Metals*, vol. 77, p. 389, 1950.

[6] C. Crussard, *Rev. mét.*, vol. 42, p. 286, 1945 (high-purity aluminum).

[7] D. Hanson and M. A. Wheeler, *J. Inst. Metals*, vol. 45, p. 229, 1931.

[8] G. R. Wilms and W. A. Wood, *J. Inst. Metals*, vol. 75, p. 693, 1948–1949.

[9] B. Chalmers, *Proc. Roy. Soc. (London)*, vol. A156, p. 427, 1936.

flow in the boundaries when the external load is removed. Some recoverable flow can be expected on slip bands as well as grain boundaries and this may occur even when grain-boundary flow is negligible. The residual stresses left around the slip bands that have operated cause "aftereffects" if they relax, and if they remain until a reversed stress is applied they cause the "Bauschinger effect," *i.e.*, the lowered yield stress when plastic strain in tension is followed by compressive stressing or vice versa.

Relaxation theories of transient creep, creep recovery, and anelastic deformation (time-dependent, nonpermanent deformation) have been developed by Zener and his coworkers, and the fundamental relations have been developed between internal friction, dynamic and static elastic moduli, and aftereffects.[1]

The *exhaustion theory* of transient creep is based on the idea that slip starts first at localities where flow resistance is low, and as these are used up "exhaustion hardening" takes place. Barriers to flow are surmounted with the aid of thermal fluctuations, even at low temperatures, in this theory, and with suitable assumptions as to one glide process initiating others a $t^{\frac{1}{3}}$ law can be obtained.[2] The exhaustion theory seems applicable only at low temperatures and low stresses and is held to be unable to account for the fact that the total amount of transient flow usually exceeds the instantaneous strain.[3]

A *nucleation theory* of the transient flow considers the origin of individual slip events as a problem in nucleation.[4] The theory postulates that the slipped region on a slip plane is a stable nucleus of slip that tends to propagate only when it has exceeded a critical size; otherwise it is an unstable embryo that tends to disappear. The free energy of the embryos depend on their size, and it is assumed that a metal tends to approach a state in which there is a Boltzmann distribution of these free energies at each stress and temperature. Sudden changes of stress or temperature then initiate a change toward the new equilibrium and account for the transient flow, whether it exceeds the steady-state rate (*e.g.*, when stress or temperature is increased) or is less than the steady rate (as when stress or temperature is reduced).

[1] C. Zener, "Elasticity and Anelasticity of Metals," University of Chicago Press, Chicago, 1948; "Cold Working of Metals," p. 180, American Society for Metals, Cleveland, Ohio, 1949.

[2] E. Orowan, *J. West Scot. Iron Steel Inst.*, vol. 54, p. 45, 1946–1947.

[3] N. F. Mott and F. R. N. Nabarro, "Report of Conference on Strength of Solids," p. 1, Physical Society, London, 1948. A. H. Cottrell, "Progress in Metal Physics," vol. 1, p. 77, Interscience, New York, 1949.

[4] J. G. Leschen, R. P. Carreker, and J. H. Hollomon, *Trans. AIME*, vol. 180, p. 131, 1949. J. H. Hollomon, "Cold Working of Metals," p. 148, American Society for Metals, Cleveland, Ohio, 1949.

Steady-state Creep. A discussion of the advantages and limitations of theories of steady plastic flow under creep conditions has been presented by Cottrell and Aytekin.[1] The *constant-barrier* theory proposes that the rate of flow of a single crystal, $d\gamma/dt$, is given by

$$\frac{d\gamma}{dt} = \nu e^{U(\tau)/RT}$$

where ν is a frequency, τ is the shear stress, and the activation energy $U(\tau)$ for the barrier is assumed to have the form $U - a\tau$ or perhaps $U(\tau_0) - a(\tau - \tau_0)$. The *recovery theory* proposes that steady-state creep is a balance between strain hardening, $\partial\tau/\partial\gamma$, and thermal softening (recovery), $\partial\tau/\partial t$, the balance occurring when the expression

$$d\tau = \frac{\partial\tau}{\partial\gamma} d\gamma + \frac{\partial\tau}{\partial t} dt$$

is set equal to zero. The barrier in a constant-barrier theory is presumably related to internal stresses created by previous plastic flow and it is objected that these stresses should increase as deformation progresses, thus gradually stopping flow. The recovery theory, on the other hand, overlooks the fact that the flow stress depends not only on strain hardening and thermal softening, but also on the rate of straining. A *unified theory* is proposed[1] that develops out of both: it makes use of a barrier, but instead of having the barrier constant has it dependent on both strain hardening and thermal softening. The theory thus relates steady-state creep rates and the rates of softening of a strain-hardened specimen at different temperatures, and is successful in that the activation energy calculated from creep data on zinc crystals agrees well with the activation energy computed from recovery experiments; also the transient effects that occur when load is suddenly reduced last about the length of time demanded by the theory.

Objections have been raised that the entire concept of a constant-rate secondary creep stage may be illusory,[2] perhaps resulting from the superposition of an anelastic strain that dies out after a time and a plastic strain that may not be at a constant rate. If the plastic component of the total strain occurs at a steadily decreasing rate because of strain hardening and if this is counterbalanced by the increasing stress caused by thinning of the specimen in a constant-load creep test, a constant creep rate may be observed that is of no fundamental significance. Yet a constant strain rate *is* observed in some creep tests in which constant

[1] A. H. Cottrell and V. Aytekin, *J. Inst. Metals*, vol. 77, p. 389, 1950.

[2] J. D. Lubahn, Creep of Metals in "Cold Working of Metals," American Society for Metals, Cleveland, Ohio, 1949.

stress rather than constant load is maintained, so it is proper to consider constant-rate creep as a problem that must be explained.

The accelerating flow rate of *tertiary creep* must be associated with the beginning of processes that lead to fracture.   In some cases this appears to be merely local necking of the test specimen in a constant-load test. On the other hand, it may signify the initiation of cracking, under some conditions.

Creep does not occur by a single mechanism.   In addition to slip and twinning, there may be flow at grain boundaries and subboundaries, recrystallization, and precipitation or phase change.   An understanding of creep is possible only when the components that make up the total flow are recognized and given individual attention.

REORIENTATION FROM SLIP

Lattice Rotation with Simple Slip.   When a crystal slips on a single set of planes, as in Fig. 23, it shears

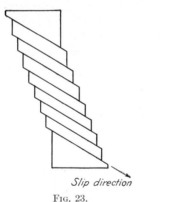

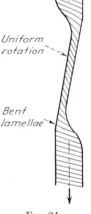

Uniform rotation

Bent lamellae

Slip direction

Fig. 23.   Fig. 24.

Fig. 23. Deformation of a crystal by slip without constraint.
Fig. 24. Rotation and bending in a single crystal elongated in a testing machine.   Homogeneous rotation of the necked-down region ends in bend gliding near the grips.   The slip direction approaches the tension axis.

"sideways" without altering its orientation, but when it is strained in an ordinary tensile machine it is not free to do this.   The constraints of the tensile grips keep the ends in line, and the crystal is forced to deform as in Fig. 24.   The central necked-down portion is therefore altered in orientation in such a way that the slip direction becomes more nearly parallel to the axis of tension.

In the compression test another kind of rotation occurs which is easily understood with reference to Fig. 25.   The slip planes, indicated by the diagonal lines, rotate toward a position parallel to the plane of the compression plates.   The axis about which this rotation takes place is indicated by A_r and is obviously parallel to the intersection of the slip planes with the compression plates.

The amount of rotation increases as deformation proceeds and can be computed from simple formulas.[1] For tension the relation is

$$\sin \chi_1 = \frac{l_0}{l_1} \sin \chi_0$$

where χ_0 and χ_1 are the initial and final angles between the slip plane and the tension axis, while l_0 and l_1 are the initial and final lengths of the specimen. By X-ray determination of the orientations before and after deformation it is thus possible to learn the type of rotation a crystal has undergone and thus to determine the indices of the slip system that operated. (This has been useful for hexagonal and f.c.c. crystal studies but is not reliable when many slip systems are active, as in b.c.c. metals or in grains of an aggregate.)

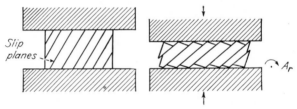

Fig. 25. Homogeneous lattice rotation in compression. Rotation is around axis A_r. The slip plane approaches the compression plane.

Duplex Slip. As a slip plane rotates away from a position for maximum resolved shear stress (approximately 45° from the axis of tension), the resolved shear stress on the plane diminishes, whereas another potential slip plane in the same crystal—if one exists—is subjected to an increasing component of the stress. Ultimately, the two planes will receive equal components of shear stress, and there will be slip on both planes simultaneously or alternately (duplex slip).

It is found experimentally that crystals tend to rotate slightly past the orientation where duplex slip should start before the second slip plane begins to function. This is more pronounced in alloy crystals than in pure metals—for instance, it is prominent with crystals of alpha-brass.[2] A reasonable interpretation of this is that the critical resolved shear stress for slip becomes greater on the inactive plane than on the active one. Since there is strain hardening on the active one, this implies that there is even greater strain hardening on the latent slip planes. In seeking an understanding of this it should be remembered that slip on the second

[1] E. Schmid and W. Boas, "Kristallplastizität," Springer, Berlin, 1935.

[2] V. Göler and G. Sachs, Z. *Physik*, vol. 55, p. 581, 1929.

plane must *cut through* the active slip planes, whereas for slip to continue on a plane parallel to those that originally operated it is necessary merely to fit a new slip plane *between* the planes on which slip has previously occurred. If one assumes that strain hardening is localized largely in the vicinity of the slip planes, it would be expected that continued slip on the first set of planes would follow the relatively soft material between slip planes, whereas slip on the second set of planes would have to cut across the relatively harder material around the already existing slip planes.

Tension tests of alpha-brass crystals by Maddin, Mathewson and Hibbard[1] showed that strain hardening and X-ray evidence of lattice distortion are absent when slip is confined to a single set of parallel slip planes, or two nonparallel sets that use a common slip direction, whereas both hardening and distortion become severe as soon as slip commences to "cut through" previously slipped regions, using a different slip direction (dislocations cutting through dislocations). This effect, which is another aspect of the hardening of latent slip planes, may be accounted for by assuming that faults (stacking disorders) are left where slip has occurred, the bands of faulted material resisting the passage of slip on the second set of planes.[2,3] The theory that faults are a major cause of latent slip-plane hardening leads to a prediction that there should be a close correlation of this hardening with the faulting tendency[3] in f.c.c. alloys. This appears to be true, though data are meager at present.[4]

Rotation from Duplex Slip. Taylor and Elam[5] showed that single crystals of aluminum when elongated in tension deform by slip on (111) planes in [110] directions, with an accompanying rotation of [110] toward the axis of tension, until duplex slip starts. The lattice then rotates so as to maintain the axis of tension in a plane symmetrical to the two acting slip planes—*i.e.*, so as to keep equal stresses on the two active systems. Duplex slip and its corresponding rotation continue until the two active slip directions lie in the same plane as the axis of tension and on opposite sides of it. Further elongation does not then cause rotation, and this position is retained until fracture. The nature of these rotations is conveniently shown in stereographic projection, with the axis of tension indicated by a point which moves over a standard projection of the cubic

[1] R. Maddin, C. H. Mathewson, and W. R. Hibbard, *Trans. AIME*, vol. 185, p. 527, 1949.

[2] R. D. Heidenreich and W. Shockley, "Report of Conference on Strength of Solids," p. 55, Physical Society, London, 1948.

[3] C. S. Barrett, *Trans. AIME*, vol. 188, p. 123, 1950.

[4] C. S. Barrett, "Imperfections in Almost Perfect Crystals," Wiley, New York, 1952. The relative importance of various possible causes of strain hardening is difficult to judge at present. It would be surprising if many of the current ideas and current appraisals of them were to gain permanent acceptance.

[5] G. I. Taylor and C. F. Elam, *Proc. Roy. Soc. (London)*, vol. A102, p. 643, 1923.

lattice (Fig. 26). The rotation of the axis along the great circle toward [110] can be noted, as well as the rotation along the symmetrical plane between slip directions [011] and [110] to the stable end position, in which [121] is parallel to the axis.[1]

In deformation by compression, single slip in f.c.c. crystals brings the specimen axis into the plane symmetrical to the poles of the active slip planes; then double slip causes the specimen axis to move in this plane until it reaches the [110] position that lies in the plane containing the poles of the active slip planes and midway between them. This is a position which is stable throughout the remainder of the deformation.[2]

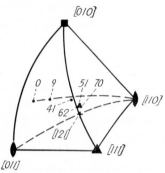

FIG. 26. Rotation of axis of aluminum single crystal during elongations up to 70 per cent. Initial rotation is along a great circle toward the active slip direction [110]; then duplex slip moves the axis toward [121]. (*Taylor and Elam.*)

Hexagonal metals slipping only on the basal plane (0001) rotate so as to bring the basal plane toward the plane of compression or parallel with the axis of tension and cannot exhibit duplex slip. The rotation is eventually stopped, however, by the onset of slip on other planes or, more generally, by twinning.

Swiveling of Glide Lamellae. A single crystal rod of zinc can be deformed in torsion so that longitudinal scratches form a spiral along the rod, provided that the basal planes are nearly parallel to the cross-section plane.[3] This type of deformation appears to be a swiveling of slip planes about their normal, a mechanism of flow that has frequently been proposed.[4]

Deformation Bands. A common feature of the structure of cold-worked metal is the banded appearance of individual grains. The bands are formed in both single crystals, where their widths may be a millimeter or more, and grains of an aggregate, where they have microscopic dimensions as in Fig. 27. They are visible on a polished and etched surface as twins are, but they differ from twins in that they appear with varying contrast after varying degrees of cold work. Rosenhain[5] believed them

[1] G. I. Taylor and C. F. Elam, *Proc. Roy. Soc. (London)*, vol. A108, p. 28, 1925.

[2] G. I. Taylor and W. S. Farren, *Proc. Roy. Soc. (London)*, vol. A111, p. 529, 1926. G. I. Taylor, *Proc. Roy. Soc. (London)*, vol. A116, p. 39, 1927.

[3] D. C. Jillson, *Trans. AIME*, vol. 188, p. 1009, 1950.

[4] See, for example, H. Wilman, *Nature*, vol. 165, p. 321, 1950; R. D. Heidenreich and W. Shockley, "Report of Conference on Strength of Solids," p. 57, Physical Society, London, 1948; J. A. Collins and C. H. Mathewson, *Trans. AIME*, vol. 137, p. 150, 1940.

[5] W. Rosenhain, *Engineering*, vol. 96, p. 30, 1913.

to be amorphous metal left on slip planes after slip had taken place. Howe was unsatisfied with this theory and devoted an entire chapter of his book[1] to the "X-bands," as he called them. He regarded them as regions in which the lattice orientation had changed without reaching a twinned orientation but remarked that their nature had yet to be discovered. Pfeil[2] made a detailed study of them in iron and surmised that they consisted of lamellar regions within which differing orientations have arisen as a result of slip. We now know that this view is correct and that this progressively increasing contrast with increasing degrees of cold work is the result of a progressive growth of orientation differences between adjoining bands.[3] The rotation in individual bands creates new grain boundaries within crystals and must therefore contribute to work hardening though perhaps in a minor way (see page 352). The development of deformation bands is an important cause of asterism in X-ray photographs; it is also important in the development of preferred orientations[4] and will be discussed in later chapters in this connection.

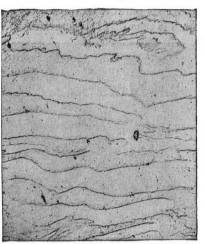

Fig. 27. Deformation bands in a grain of iron. Section perpendicular to axis of compression, polished and etched after 68 per cent reduction in thickness. ×100.

Deformation bands occur in many metals. Mathewson and Phillips[5] observed strain markings in alpha-brass that resemble the deformation bands of iron in that their prominence increases with increasing cold work. Probably all f.c.c. metals exhibit them. Johnson[6] has reported them in rolled copper and alpha-brass, Adcock[7] in rolled cupronickel (80 per cent copper, 20 per cent nickel), Elam[8] in rolled silver, and Rosenhain[9] in

[1] H. M. Howe, "The Metallography of Steel and Cast Iron," McGraw-Hill, New York, 1916.

[2] L. B. Pfeil, *J. Iron Steel Inst., Carnegie Scholarship Mem.*, vol. 15, p. 319, 1926; vol. 16, p. 153, 1927.

[3] C. S. Barrett, *Trans. AIME*, vol. 135, p. 296, 1939.

[4] C. S. Barrett, *Trans. AIME*, vol. 135, p. 296, 1939. C. S. Barrett and L. H. Levenson, *Trans. AIME*, vol. 135, p. 327, 1939; vol. 137, p. 112, 1940; vol. 147, p. 57, 1942.

[5] C. H. Mathewson and A. Phillips, *Trans. AIME*, vol. 54, p. 608, 1916.

[6] F. Johnson, *J. Inst. Metals*, vol. 21, p. 335, 1919; vol. 27, p. 93, 1922.

[7] F. Adcock, *J. Inst. Metals*, vol. 27, p. 73, 1922.

[8] C. F. Elam, *J. Inst. Metals*, vol. 27, p. 94, 1922.

[9] W. Rosenhain, *J. Inst. Metals*, vol. 27, p. 96, 1922.

cupronickel manganese. They make a striking appearance on the surface of large grains of copper after cold rolling (Fig. 28). Body-centered cubic iron exhibits deformation bands after all types of deformation and with both homogeneous and heterogeneous strain, and it is not unlikely that bands are produced in all other b.c.c. metals. The tendency for a crystal or a grain to develop bands depends upon the orientation of the grain with respect to the direction of flow. For example, an iron crystal having a [100] axis parallel to the axis of compression will form no bands, and the same is true if [111] is parallel to the axis of compression; crystals of all other orientations become banded.

The crystallography of the bands has not been extensively studied. It is known, however, that in iron during elongation the boundaries first form on {100} and {111} planes, and in aluminum during compression they form on {100} planes and perhaps others in addition to these. Honeycombe[1] has observed deformation bands in aluminum single crystals extended in tension. These were spaced about 0.05 mm apart and were parallel to (110) planes; they could be detected after as little as 1 per cent elongation. It appears to be a general rule that the bands

FIG. 28. Deformation bands in large grains of copper after rolling. ×1.

in single-crystal aluminum specimens form on planes normal to the active slip direction, which is [110], and that bands do not form if the tension axis is near [111].[2] As deformation increases there is a greater tendency for slip lines to come to an end as they approach the boundary of a band. Crystals of cadmium do not contain deformation bands after a tensile strain of 20 per cent elongation.[1] Some "twinlike" bands reported by Elam[3] in beta-brass, which formed on {100} and {111} planes, were probably deformation bands.

Lattice Bending. Not all the distortion of the lattice in crystals is so regular as the type discussed in the preceding section. The lattice within a single deformation band often exhibits a large range of orienta-

[1] R. W. K. Honeycombe, *Proc. Phys. Soc.* (*London*), vol. 63A, p. 673, 1950; *Trans. AIME*, vol. 188, p. 1039, 1950; *J. Inst. Metals*, vol. 80, p. 45, 1951–52.

[2] N. K. Chen and C. H. Mathewson, *Trans. AIME, J. Metals*, vol. 3, p. 653, 1951. Bands seem to develop in crystals with the more regularly dispersed (not clustered) slip lines.

[3] C. F. Elam, *Proc. Roy. Soc.* (*London*), vol. A153, p. 273, 1936.

tions from one side to another, and even in the absence of clearly defined bands there is usually a spread in orientation from point to point within a crystal or grain. Figure 24 illustrates a simple case of this in which the lamellae between slip planes have been bent by the constraints imposed by the grips of the tensile machine. The axis of bending lies in the slip plane normal to the slip direction. In polycrystalline material the constraints of neighboring grains cause the inhomogeneities of stress that produce the bending.

Kink Bands. When a single crystal rod of cadmium or zinc is compressed longitudinally it may collapse in the manner shown in Fig. 29, forming what Orowan has termed a "kink band."[1] This happens when the basal plane is nearly parallel to the rod axis, provided that a uniform bending of the entire rod is prevented. A detailed study[2] showed that the kinks could properly be regarded as a particularly simple type of deformation band. Plastic flow is confined largely or wholly to the region within the outer boundaries of a band, and causes severe but regular bending of the glide lamellae around an axis that is initially in the slip plane and normal to the slip direction. As flow continues, reorientation of the central part progressively increases, but the sharp grooves

Fig. 29. Zinc kink. ×1.

that mark the boundaries do not move along the rod. Thus the lattice is bent to progressively smaller radii in the two symmetrical boundary regions, as may be seen by cleaving the rod after kinking. When slip occurs on a single system the boundaries are initially planes that are normal to the slip direction. Less symmetrical types of bands are also observed if the stress conditions are less simple. There is evidence of at least occasional deformation bands, analogous to these, in polycrystalline zinc; but they would not be expected in hexagonal metals or alloys having an axial ratio c/a greater than 1.732, since these would deform by twinning (see below) when compressed along the basal plane. Many unusual appearances of deformed zinc crystals discussed by Jillson[3] are fundamentally equivalent to kinking, in that they are due to bending of the crystal around an axis in the basal plane normal to the slip direction.

It cannot be doubted that there is much fundamental similarity between bend planes, kink bands, and deformation bands; but it would be unwise to assume that all deformation bands are alike, since Honeycombe finds evidence of multiple slip systems operating in some and single slip systems in others. Perhaps S types should be distinguished

[1] E. Orowan, *Nature*, vol. 149, p. 643, 1942.

[2] J. B. Hess and C. S. Barrett, *Trans. AIME*, vol. 185, p. 599, 1949.

[3] D. C. Jillson, *Trans. AIME*, vol. 188, p. 1009, 1950.

from Z types, also, the latter having sharply defined boundaries, the former only gradual curvatures. "Polygonization" may create stepped or Z type bands from S type during annealing.[1]

TWINNING

Crystals are said to be twinned if they are composed of portions that are joined together with a definite mutual orientation. When a twin forms in a crystal, as a result of either deformation or conditions during crystal growth, the orientation of the twin is either a mirror image of the orientation of the parent crystal in a plane called the twinning plane, or an orientation that could be derived from the parent by rotation about an axis termed the twinning axis. Twins with the rotation relationship are usually also reflection twins. If a crystallographer makes goniometric measurements on a crystal that is twinned he may conclude that the crystal belongs to a class with higher symmetry than the proper one, so it is important to have twin-free crystals in structure determinations.

Deformation Twins. An important mechanism of plastic flow in many metals is deformation twinning, consisting of shearing movements of the atomic planes over one another. The shearing appears to be homogeneous under the microscope, for it results in a uniform tilting of the surface in the twinned region; but in many crystals it is not true homogeneous shear in the sense that every atom shifts a distance proportional to its distance from the twinning plane.[2]

The development of deformation twins is illustrated by Fig. 30, which shows the metallographic appearance of polycrystalline zinc at successive stages of a tensile test. Thin lamellae first appear quickly, then grow slowly in width. The lenticular shape is characteristic not only of twins, but also of martensitic transformations in which there is a similar shear or shearlike distortion.

Iron and alloyed ferrites are twinned by impact at room temperature and by slower deformation at lower temperatures to form the narrow lamellae known as Neumann bands, shown in Fig. 31.[3] These have small

---

[1] A. Guinier and J. Tennevin, "Progress in Metal Physics," vol. 2, Butterworths, London, 1950. R. W. Cahn, *J. Inst. Metals*, vol. 79, p. 159, 1951.

[2] For example, in Mg, Zn, white Sn, Bi, and Sb the dimension changes of twinned regions correspond to simple homogeneous shear, but atom movements on the whole do not—only half the atoms in the close-packed hexagonal structures are displaced in the homogeneous fashion. *Cf.* G. Kolesnikow, *Physik. Z. Sowjetunion*, vol. 4, p. 651, 1933; B. Chalmers, *Proc. Phys. Soc. (London)*, vol. 47, p. 733, 1935; C. S. Barrett, "Symposium on Cold Working of Metals," American Society for Metals, 1949.

[3] That these are twins has been proved by K. Harnecker and E. Rassow, *Z. Metallkunde*, vol. 16, p. 312, 1924; C. H. Mathewson and G. H. Edmunds, *Trans. AIME*, vol. 80, p. 311, 1928. Confirmation has also been obtained by measuring the tilt of twinned portions of the surface of iron crystals containing Neumann bands: the

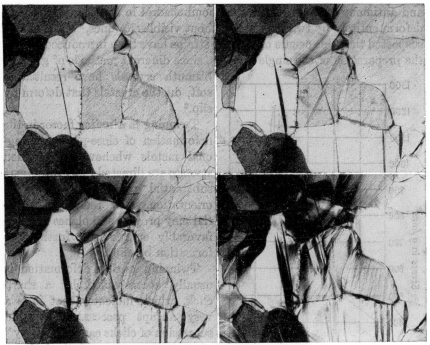

FIG. 30. Growth of twins in zinc during tensile elongation.   (*J. E. Burke.*)

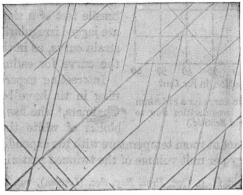

FIG. 31. Twins (Neumann bands) in a crystal of ferrite.   Photomicrograph of a polished and etched grain.   ×100.

but readily visible widths, unlike slip lines, and appear prominently after polishing and etching. A small fraction of the volume is reoriented by twinning in body-centered cubic crystals, but in close-packed hexagonal crystals almost any fraction can be converted to twins. Some bismuth

angles of tilt agree with theory to within an experimental error of a few degrees (H. W. Paxton, experiments at the University of Birmingham, to be published).

and antimony crystals, which are rhombohedral in structure, appear to deform entirely by twinning and without visible slip lines,[1] but it is now suspected that this occurs only when strains have been introduced during the preparation of the single crystals, since different methods of growing bismuth crystals have resulted in soft, ductile crystals that deform by slip.[2]

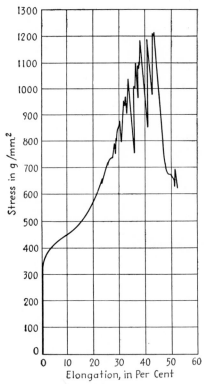

Twinning is a major factor in the deformation of close-packed hexagonal metals whenever the applied stresses are directed so as to convert substantial portions into a twin orientation. The reoriented material may provide slip planes that are favorably oriented for further deformation by slip.[3]

Twinning during deformation is usually accompanied by a sharp click, which indicates that it is a very abrupt process. The rapid succession of clicks causes the "cry" of tin when a bar of tin is bent. When twinning occurs during a tensile test of a single crystal, there are jagged irregularities in the stress-strain curve, as in the later stages of the curve for cadmium in Fig. 32.

Fig. 32. Stress-strain curve for a cadmium single crystal with irregularities due to twinning. (*Boas and Schmid.*)

Interesting experiments on twinning in tin have been reported by Chalmers,[4] who has found that large blocks of white tin (tetragonal β) twin during impact at room temperature with the expenditure of a definite amount of energy per unit volume of the twinned material. This energy

[1] H. J. Gough and H. L. Cox, *Proc. Roy. Soc. (London)*, vol. A127, p. 431, 1930; *J. Inst. Metals*, vol. 48, p. 227, 1932.

[2] W. F. Berg and L. Sander, *Nature*, vol. 136, p. 915, 1935. The Czochralski method produced soft crystals; the Bridgman method (with melting in glass) produced hard crystals that twinned.

[3] C. H. Mathewson and A. J. Phillips, *Trans. AIME*, vol. 74, p. 143, 1927. G. Edmunds and M. L. Fuller, *Trans. AIME*, vol. 99, p. 175, 1932. E. Schmid and G. Wassermann, *Z. Physik*, vol. 48, p. 370, 1928. H. Mark, M. Polanyi, and E. Schmid, *Z. Physik*, vol. 12, p. 58, 1922.

[4] Bruce Chalmers, *Proc. Phys. Soc. (London)*, vol. 47, p. 733, 1935.

TABLE XVII. CRYSTALLOGRAPHY OF TWINNING IN METALS

Lattice	Metal	Twinning plane (k_1)	Twinning direction (n_1)*
B.c.c.	α-Fe	(112)	[111]
	β-Cu-Zn	(112)	[111]
	W	(112)	[111]
C.p.h.	Cd	$(10\bar{1}2)$	
	Zn	$(10\bar{1}2)$	$[10\bar{1}\bar{1}]$
	Zn-Cd	$(10\bar{1}2)$	
	Zn-Sn	$(10\bar{1}2)$	
	Be	$(10\bar{1}2)$	
	Mg	$(10\bar{1}2)$	
F.c.c. (Growth twins)	Al	(111)	$[11\bar{2}]$
	Cu	(111)	$[11\bar{2}]$
	Ag	(111)	$[11\bar{2}]$
	Au	(111)	$[11\bar{2}]$
	Cu-Zn	(111)	$[11\bar{2}]$
	Cu-Al	(111)	$[11\bar{2}]$
	Al-Cu	(111)	$[11\bar{2}]$
	Al-Zn	(111)	$[11\bar{2}]$
	Au-Ag	(111)	$[11\bar{2}]$
	Cu-Au	(111)	$[11\bar{2}]$
Rhombohedral‡	Bi	(011)	
	As	(011)	
	Sb	(011)	
Tetragonal	β-Sn (white)	(301)†	$[\bar{3}01]$

* See p. 383.
† B. Chalmers, *Proc. Phys. Soc.* (*London*), vol. 47, p. 733, 1935; the indices refer to the axes of length $a = 5.81$, $c = 3.17$ A, rather than a set 45° from these, which would give twinning indices (331).
‡ Rhombohedral cell indices are given above. The hexagonal indices of twinning elements in As, Sb, and Bi are $K_1 = (\bar{1}012)$, $K_2 = (10\bar{1}1)$, and $n_1 = [10\bar{1}1]$. The angle between K_1 and K_2, and the twinning shear s is: As, 82°42′, $s = 0.2562$; Sb, 85°49′, $s = 0.1463$; Bi, 86°38′, $s = 0.1176$. This hexagonal unit cell has $c/a = 1.304$ for Bi whereas the rhombohedral cell has $\alpha = 57°14.2′$. See H. Tertsch, "Die Festigkeitserscheinungen der Kristalle," p. 56, Springer, Berlin, 1949. (Twinning elements for many minerals are given).

is 8×10^5 ergs per cc. Since the potential energy of the lattice after twinning is the same as before, this twinning energy appears in the crystal after twinning as heat, save for slight losses. It corresponds to a rise in temperature of 0.05°C, which was approximately what Chalmers observed. It is possible by subsequent impacts either to extend the twinned portion or to untwin the crystal.

Crystallography of Twins. The observations of twinning in metals have been summarized by Mathewson,[1] by Schmid,[2] and by Gough[3] and are presented in Table XVII. It will be noticed that invariably the twinning plane in f.c.c. metals is {111}, in b.c.c. metals {112}, in c.p.h.

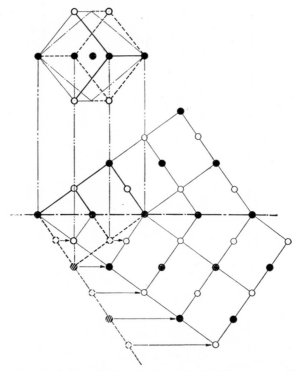

FIG. 33. Shear movements for twinning a body-centered cubic crystal. Twinning plane is normal to the paper, intersecting it along the heavy dot-dash line in the lower drawing. Shear of atoms below this is indicated by arrows. Position of (211) plane in unit cell is indicated by dot-dash line in upper drawing.

metals {10$\bar{1}$2}, and in rhombohedral metals {011}.* In the cubic metals, {111} and {112} twinning both yield the same orientations: a total of four new "first-order" twin orientations, and if each of these is

---

[1] C. H. Mathewson, *Trans. AIME*, vol. 78, p. 7, 1928.

[2] E. Schmid, *Z. Metallkunde*, vol. 20, p. 421, 1928.

[3] H. J. Gough, Edgar Marburg Lecture, *ASTM, Proc.*, vol. 33, pt. 2, p. 3, 1933.

* Referred to hexagonal axes, this is {01$\bar{1}$2}. Twinning on {10$\bar{1}$1} in Mg, reported by E. Schmid (*Z. Elektrochem.*, vol. 37, p. 447, 1931) has not been confirmed by the careful investigation conducted by P. W. Bakarian (*Metals Technol., Tech. Pub.* 1561, 1943). Deformation twins in orthorhombic uranium appear to be of four types, with K_1 and η_1 as follows: (130) [3$\bar{1}$0]; (112) [irrational]; (irrational) [312]; (121) [irrational]. R. W. Cahn, *Acta Cryst.* vol. 4, p. 470, 1951.

twinned, a total of 12 new "second-order" twin orientations, etc.[1]   Data have been published for accurately plotting {100} poles of four orders of twins for cubic crystals.[2]

Atom Movements in Twinning.   In many lattices the movement required to produce a twin is a simple homogeneous shear, each plane moving a distance proportional to its distance from the twinning plane. An example of this type is sketched in Fig. 33, the b.c.c. lattice.   In the unit cube drawn in the upper part of the figure, the twinning plane, (211), is indicated by dot-dash lines; this plane stands perpendicular to the paper in the lower part of the figure,

and the atom movements to form a twin are indicated by arrows.   The movement of an atomic layer to produce a twin is rather similar to the movement to produce slip.   This is readily seen in the f.c.c. lattice, for which the twinning movements are shown in Fig. 34.   The shear of one (111) layer, indicated by filled circles, over the underlying layer, indicated by open circles, is one-third the identity distance in the direction of motion, which is 30° from the closest packed direction that is the direction

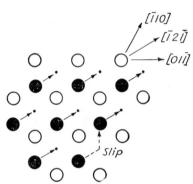

Fig. 34. Movement of atoms in adjacent (111) layers of face-centered cubic lattice during twinning.   Dashed arrow is corresponding movement in slip.

of net motion in slip.   (Two such motions along a zigzag path would give the type of movement that occurs in slip, as indicated by the dashed line in the lower right of the figure.)

The reason one plane serves as composition plane in preference to another probably lies in the strain energy of the twin interface, and this can be judged roughly by noting to what extent the interatomic bonds are distorted from their usual lengths.[3]

If the close-packed (111) layers of a f.c.c. crystal were displaced in a homogeneous (111) [$\bar{1}2\bar{1}$] shear, a deformation twin would be produced. There is no evidence, however, that deformation twins of appreciable thickness occur in any f.c.c. crystals.[4]   A point of view that makes this

[1] First-order cubic twins have one {111} plane, three {110} planes, and three {112} planes, and many others in common with the parent crystal.   A. B. Greninger, *Trans. AIME*, vol. 120, p. 293, 1936.

[2] C. G. Dunn, *Trans. AIME*, vol. 161, p. 90, 1945.   Projections of twins in zinc have been published by C. H. Mathewson, *Trans. AIME*, vol. 78, p. 7, 1928.

[3] L. W. McKeehan, *Nature*, vol. 119, pp. 120, 392, 1927.   G. D. Preston, *Nature*, vol. 119, p. 600, 1927.   C. S. Barrett, "Cold Working of Metals," p. 65, American Society for Metals, Cleveland, Ohio, 1949.

[4] J. E. Burke and C. S. Barrett, *Trans. AIME*, vol. 175, p. 117, 1948.

understandable is based on the forces that tend to make a shifting layer stop in the twin position rather than in the normal position of ideal slip.[1] Since the atoms of the moving layer find the usual number of nearest neighbors at normal distances in both stopping places, there must be a rather small net force favoring the untwinned arrangement rather than the twin of this. And if one layer stops in the twin position, the net force favoring a systematic continuation of the twin by the adjacent layers is likewise small. It seems more probable that the shifting layers would be irregularly spaced and that they would stop in unpredictable positions, leaving faulty stacking rather than a twin.[2]

Plots of atom movements in the twinning of hexagonal metals, on the other hand, show clearly that twin interfaces having strained nearest-neighbor bonds are unavoidable. Therefore the creation of many randomly spaced twin faults would result in relatively high strain energy; hence the number of twin boundaries should remain small and deformation should continue chiefly by the widening of twins already present rather than by the creation of many new twins or twin faults. In body-centered cubic metals, also, the atomic arrangement suggests that if any one layer shifts to the twinned position, the next layer that shifts will add less to the total strain energy if it is adjacent to the first than if it is at a distance from the first.

Critical Stress for Twinning. The existence of a critical resolved shear stress for twinning has been suspected for many years,[3] although the experimental evidence for it has not been very satisfactory. Recent work seems now to have convincingly established it for cadmium.[4] Crystals of 99.966 per cent purity twinned at a resolved shear stress of 422 g/mm², and 99.999 purity at a stress of 434, the probable error in measurements of 50 crystals being of the order of ± 50 g/mm². Since the initial critical resolved stress for slip was reduced from about 70 to 30 g/mm² by changing from the lesser of these purities to the greater, it

[1] C. S. Barrett, "Cold Working of Metals," p. 65, American Society for Metals, Cleveland, Ohio, 1949.

[2] C. H. Mathewson suggested many years ago that "twin faults" should be found in cold-worked f.c.c. metals, but until recently the evidence for them has been ambiguous and indirect.

[3] N. N. Davidenkov, A. F. Kolesnikov, and K. N. Fedorov, *J. Exptl. Theoret. Phys. (U.S.S.R.)*, vol. 3, p. 350, 1933. R. F. Miller, *Trans. AIME*, vol. 122, p. 176, 1936. Bruce Chalmers, *Proc. Phys. Soc. (London)*, vol. 47, p. 733, 1935. H. J. Gough and H. L. Cox, *Proc. Roy. Soc. (London)*, vol. A127, p. 431, 1930.

[4] R. King, *Nature (London)*, vol. 169, p. 543, 1952. Fuller publication by R. King, S. W. Gumbell, and M. J. Makin is in preparation. Recent experiments at the University of Bristol also indicate that there is a twinning stress in cadmium; first tests yielded 138 ± 50 g/mm² at room temperature for crystals of 99.98 per cent purity (N. Thompson, private communication).

appears that the *twinning* stress is relatively insensitive to purity; it is increased by a factor of about 1.3 by an extension sufficient to raise the slip resistance by a factor of 2.5 (*i.e.*, shear of 4 on the single set of active slip planes (0001) at room temperature); the presence of an oxide film caused maximum increases of about 130 g/mm² in twinning stress (with no previous glide) in both purities, and 30 g/mm² in initial slip resistance in both purities. The strain-hardening curves for slip and twinning are affected differently by the presence of an oxide film. Twinning in ferrite is complicated by the fact that several twins appear simultaneously in a "burst" analogous to a burst of martensite crystals.[1]

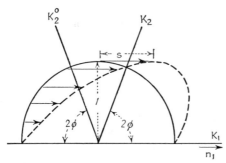

FIG. 35. Homogeneous shear in twinning. Undeformed planes K_1 (the twinning plane) and K_2 are normal to the paper and their intersection is normal to the direction of shear n_1.

Deformation by Twinning. Schmid and Wassermann[2] have analyzed the change in shape that a crystal can undergo by twinning. Referring to Fig. 35, there are two important reference planes to be considered. These are the ones which remain undistorted by the shearing process— *i.e.*, planes on which inscribed circles would remain unchanged. One of the undistorted planes, K_1, is the twinning plane or glide plane and contains the glide direction, n_1; the second undistorted plane is K_2^o before twinning, K_2 after twinning. This is located at an angle from the first that is determined by the magnitude of the shear. The shear is defined by the distance s through which a point moves that lies a unit distance from the plane K_1, and if 2ϕ is the acute angle between the planes K_1 and K_2^o it follows that tan $2\phi = 2/s$.

The reference sphere on which the orientation of the axes of a crystal is plotted will be divided into four regions by these two undistorted planes K_1 and K_2^o. A specimen whose longitudinal axis lies in one of the two regions in the *acute* angle between K_1 and K_2^o will be shortened by the

[1] H. W. Paxton, private communication.

[2] E. Schmid and G. Wassermann, *Z. Physik*, vol. 48, p. 370, 1928. For summaries of this treatment see E. Schmid and W. Boas, "Kristallplastizität," Springer, Berlin, 1935, and English translation, Hughes, London, 1950. C. F. Elam, "The Distortion of Metal Crystals," Oxford, New York, 1935.

formation of a twin, while a specimen in the *obtuse* angle between the undeformed planes K_1 and K_2° will be lengthened.[1]

The homogeneous shear varies with the axial ratio of the hexagonal crystal from about 0.186 for metals with c/a near 1.585 (Be, Ti, Zr, Hf, Ru) and 0.131 for Mg with $c/a = 1.624$ ($\cong$ Co, Cr, La, Ce, Pr, Er, Ca) to zero for $c/a = 1.732$; it becomes a shear in the opposite direction for ratios above this, reaching 0.143 and 0.175 for Zn and Cd of $c/a = 1.856$ and 1.886, respectively.

The magnitude of this homogeneous shear governs the maximum amount of deformation that can be provided by twinning alone. For example, the elongation of a zinc crystal when completely converted to a twin can amount to 7.39 per cent at most. The direction of shear controls whether a stress applied in a given direction will cause twinning or not. Thus compression parallel to the basal plane of magnesium, beryllium, or titanium will cause twinning because twinning leads to shortening of the axis of compression. A rolled (or rolled and recrystallized) plate of any of these metals is twinned by edgewise compression, since the grains in the plate lie with their basal planes parallel to the plane of the plate. Bending such a plate will twin the metal on the inside of the bend. (Unbending will also untwin this region.)[2] On the other hand, compression *normal* to a plate of rolled zinc or cadmium tends to twin it.

The deformation that accompanies twinning leads to intense local stresses in polycrystalline materials. The formation of a twin will be accompanied by slip in the surrounding metal regions and sometimes will cause twins in neighboring grains. As a consequence of these local strains, the regions around twin bands are favored positions for nuclei of recrystallization. If a twin forms entirely across a single crystal, however, internal strains at its boundaries are small or absent and recrystallization is not promoted there—at least in tin.[3]

FRACTURE

There are several processes by which metals fracture and much has been written about each. Many of the earlier points of view have been

---

[1] The new length l will be related to the length of the axis in the original untwinned crystal, l_0, by the formula

$$\frac{l}{l_0} = \sqrt{1 + 2s \sin \chi \cos \lambda + s^2 \sin^2 \chi}$$

where χ and λ are the angles between the specimen axis and the glide plane K_1 and the glide direction n_1, respectively, in the untwinned crystal. This is the same formula that applies to the elongation of a single crystal by shear during translation gliding (slip).

[2] C. S. Barrett and C. T. Haller, *Trans. AIME*, vol. 171, p. 246, 1947.

[3] Bruce Chalmers, *Proc. Phys. Soc. (London)*, vol. 47, p. 733, 1935. X-ray micrographs show the local strains of the deformation twins nicely. C. S. Barrett, *Trans. AIME*, vol. 161, p. 15, 1945.

discredited in favor of later ones, but many uncertainties still remain. Space does not permit a comprehensive critical survey, but some of the principal facts and theories will be presented.[1]

Cleavage. Under certain conditions single crystals fracture by cleavage on crystallographic planes of low indices. This may occur in a brittle manner or after some prior slip has occurred. It is easily studied in hexagonal and rhombohedral crystals by choosing orientations such that

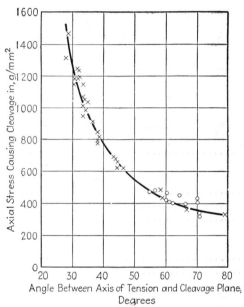

Fig. 36. Dependence of stress causing brittle cleavage upon orientation for bismuth crystals. Testing temperatures −80°C (×) and 20°C (○). (*M. Georgieff and E. Schmid, Z. Physik, vol.* 36, *p.* 759, 1926.)

the resolved stress tending to cause slip is only a small component of the applied stress. The applied stress at which cleavage occurs varies with crystal orientation, as, for example, in Fig. 36, and this variation has been accounted for by assuming that cleavage occurs at a critical value, N, of the stress that is resolved normal to the cleavage plane. In this figure the curve is drawn to correspond with constant N. A particular value of N may be assumed to exist for cleavage on any plane of a crystal, only the value for the one or two planes of lowest cleavage strength—the cleavage planes—being accessible to measurement.

[1] For summaries, see G. V. Smith, "Properties of Metals at Elevated Temperatures," McGraw-Hill, New York, 1950; E. Orowan, Fracture and Strength of Solids, in "Reports on Progress in Physics," vol. 12, p. 186, Physical Society London, 1948–1949; "Fracturing of Metals," American Society for Metals, Cleveland, Ohio, 1948; J. H. Hollomon, "The Problem of Fracture," American Welding Society, New York, 1946.

Table XVIII gives cleavage planes and measured values of N for several crystals and several temperatures of test.[1] These apply to fractures that result in a flat, plane surface of cleavage, the type of cleavage for which the constant-normal-stress law holds (see Shearing Fracture below). The variation of N with temperature, in the few cases that have been examined, is insignificant (see Table XVIII). The variation of N

TABLE XXVIII. CRITICAL NORMAL STRESS FOR BRITTLE CLEAVAGE OF SINGLE CRYSTALS

Metal	Cleavage plane	Temperature, °C	Critical normal stress, kg per sq mm
Zinc (0.03 per cent cadmium).........	(0001)	−80	0.19
	(0001)	−185	0.19
	(10$\bar{1}$0)	−185	1.80
Zinc + 0.13 per cent cadmium.........	(0001)	−185	0.30
Zinc + 0.53 per cent cadmium........	(0001)	−185	1.20
Bismuth...........................	(111)	20	0.32
	(111)	− 80	0.32
	(11$\bar{1}$)	20	0.69
Antimony..........................	(11$\bar{1}$)	20	0.66
Tellurium..........................	(10$\bar{1}$0)	20	0.43
Magnesium.........................	(10$\bar{1}$2)		
	(10$\bar{1}$1)		
	(10$\bar{1}$0)		
α-Fe..............................	(100)	−100	26
α-Fe..............................	(100)	−185	27.5
Rock salt (dry).....................	(100)	.....	0.44

with the amount of previous deformation is a matter of some uncertainty. Early experiments on zinc crystals at low temperatures seem to indicate that prior deformation lowers N;[2] deformation at higher temperatures seems to raise N, and when cold work is followed by recovery N decreases.

Studies on polycrystalline metals led various observers to postulate curves of "fracture stress" vs. amount of cold work that showed increasing fracture strength with increasing prior deformation, increasing alloying, and decreasing temperature. There is reason to doubt, however, as Zener points out,[3] that there is any real significance in a fracture-stress curve. Fracture is always or nearly always preceded by some plastic

[1] E. Schmid and W. Boas, "Kristallplastizität," Springer, Berlin, 1935, and translation, Hughes, London, 1950. C. F. Elam, "The Distortion of Metal Crystals," Oxford, New York, 1935. Abram F. Joffé, "The Physics of Crystals," McGraw-Hill, New York, 1928. L. Seigle and R. M. Brick, *Trans. ASM.*, vol. 40, p. 813, 1948.

[2] W. Fahrenhorst and E. Schmid, *Z. Physik*, vol. 64, p. 845, 1930.

[3] C. Zener, The Micromechanism of Fracture, in "Fracturing of Metals," American Society for Metals, Cleveland, Ohio, 1948.

flow, and Zener proposes that what is measured when a fracture-stress curve is determined is merely the stress required to produce *flow*—sufficient flow to initiate a crack. This is what would be expected if a microcrack is always initiated by the local stresses at the edge of a slip band, or deformation twin, or other locality where stress concentration results from local flow. Zener's view explains in a simple way why the factors that raise the stress for flow also raise the stress at which fracture occurs.

A few general rules[1] about cleavage in nonmetallic lattices may be mentioned here. It is always found that layer lattices (like graphite, MoS_2, $CdCl_2$, mica, $CaSO_4 \cdot 2H_2O$, and CdI_2) cleave parallel to the layers. In this group, Zn, Cd, As, Sb, and Bi can also be classed (although other cleavages are sometimes found in addition). Cleavages never break up radicals in ionic crystals or molecular complexes in homopolar crystals, but within the limits imposed by these two restrictions the cleavage planes are those most widely spaced. In ionic crystals which have no radicals, cleavage occurs so as to expose planes of anions, where such planes exist. Cubic crystals of the chemical formula AX cleave on $\{100\}$ planes.

Theories of Cleavage Strengths. The theoretical strength of an ideally perfect crystal has been calculated from the energy required to form two new surfaces at the break, with results much higher than the cleavage strengths normally observed (usually by a factor of 100 to 1000).[2] Much speculation has centered around the discrepancy between the calculated and observed strengths; it has been customary to ascribe it to imperfections, principally cracks. In this way Griffith[3] was able to account for the fact that fracture strengths found in freshly drawn glass fibers can reach the tremendous values of 1,000,000 psi[3] or even 3,500,000 psi.[4] Such unusual strengths were accounted for by the absence of cracks lying normal to the tensile stress. Cracks parallel to the tensile stress are not harmful;[5] so plastic flow that reorients cracks toward this position tends to raise the fracture strength in the tensile direction at the expense of strengths in other directions, not only in amorphous materials but also in metals.

[1] W. A. Wooster, "Crystal Physics," Cambridge University Press, London, 1938.

[2] M. Polanyi, *Z. Physik*, vol. 7, p. 323, 1921. F. Zwicky, *Physik. Z.*, vol. 24, p. 131, 1923. M. Born and R. Fürth, *Proc. Cambridge Phil. Soc.*, vol. 36, p. 454, 1940. F. Seitz and T. A. Read, *J. Applied Phys.*, vol. 12, p. 470, 1941. E. Orowan, "Reports on Progress in Physics," vol. 12, p. 185, 1948–1949, Physical Society, London; "International Conference on Physics, vol. II, The Solid State of Matter," Physical Society, London, 1935.

[3] A. A. Griffith, *Phil. Trans. Roy. Soc.*, vol. A221, p. 163, 1920; *First Intern. Conf. Applied Mech. (Delft)*, p. 55, 1924.

[4] F. O. Anderegg, *Ind. Eng. Chem.*, vol. 31, p. 290, 1939.

[5] W. Kuntze. *Z. Metallkunde*, vol. 22, p. 264, 1930. J. H. Hollomon, "Fracture of Metals," American Welding Society, New York, 1946.

Theories of the fracture strength of metals must take account not only of pre-existing microcracks and other structural inhomogeneities, but also of cracks appearing as the result of stress concentrations brought about by the deformation itself: cracks at the ends of slip bands, and at grain junctions. Since theories based on thermodynamics overlook inhomogeneities in structure and in flow they probably have little to offer toward further understanding of cleavage strengths in actual crystals.

Relative Stresses for Slip, Twinning, and Cleavage. It is often convenient to assume that the amount of deformation that can occur before twinning or fracture sets in is dictated by the relative values of the stresses required for slip, twinning, and cleavage. It will be recalled that there is a critical shearing stress for slip (which is increased by alloying, by decreasing temperature, and by plastic deformation). A similar critical shearing stress (also a function of the amount of prior strain) seems to exist for twinning. There is also evidence for a definite normal stress required to cleave crystals, which is little influenced by plastic flow and temperature. When a stress is applied to a crystal, it should cause slip, twinning, or cleavage, depending on whether the resolved stress on the slip plane in the slip direction, or on the twinning plane in the twinning direction, or normal to the cleavage plane is first to exceed the critical value for the process concerned.

Maurer and Mailänder[1] showed, for example, that the low-temperature brittleness of iron can be expressed in terms of the ratio of the cohesion across cleavage planes to the slip resistance. This ratio decreases with decreasing temperature and eventually reaches a value that results in a brittle failure by cleavage in preference to a ductile failure by slip. Heindlhofer[2] used these concepts to correlate temperatures of cold brittleness found in different tests of polycrystalline metals—notched bar, tensile, and torsion. Neglecting microscopically distributed stresses, the ratio of the greatest normal stress to the greatest shearing stress in a notched-bar "impact" specimen is considerably greater than 2:1 (but is somewhat indefinite); in a tensile specimen it is 2:1, and in a torsion specimen it is 1:1. Lowered plasticity would be expected in the tensile test, according to this theory, at a temperature where the ratio of cohesion to slip resistance is 2:1; in the torsion test at a lower temperature, where the ratio is 1:1; and in the notched-bar test, where the ratio exceeds 2:1, at a much higher temperature. A similar argument may be used to explain the relative prominence of twinning and slip.[3]

Slip, twinning, and cleavage in polycrystalline silicon-ferrite as a function of the temperature of deformation and the composition can be inter-

[1] E. Maurer and R. Mailänder, *Stahl u. Eisen*, vol. 45, p. 409, 1925.

[2] K. Heindlhofer, *Trans. AIME*, vol. 116, p. 232, 1935.

[3] C. H. Mathewson, *Trans. AIME*, vol. 78, p. 7, 1928.

preted along these lines.[1]   The resistance to slip increases with silicon content more on the (112) and (123) planes than on the (110) planes, and so only (110) slip remains when the composition includes 4 per cent or more of silicon. A similar effect is obtained with decreasing temperature. Brittle cleavage occurs below a certain temperature which increases with the silicon content, and twinning during slow deformation behaves similarly.

Similar considerations explain why the ductility of hexagonal crystals is so markedly dependent on orientation.[2]   From the measured values of critical stresses for slip, twinning, and cleavage (the latter on both (0001) and ($10\bar{1}0$) planes), it is possible to predict which processes will occur in a crystal of any given orientation. In polycrystalline magnesium the amount of twinning during deformation depends on temperature. It is reduced markedly by deforming slowly at 200°C and eliminated at 300°C, as if raising the temperature lowered the resistance to slip more than the resistance to twinning (additional slip planes may also become active, preventing the critical twinning stresses from being reached).[3]   Similarly, twinning is common in polycrystalline beryllium deformed slowly at temperatures below about 300°C, but is absent in the range 400 to 800°C; at temperatures above 200°C a general distortion ("twisting") of the grains is visible metallographically in polarized light, and above 400°C this, in turn, seems to be replaced by the formation of subgrain boundaries ("polygonization").[4]   Ductility increases rapidly with increasing temperature above 20°C, reaching a maximum at 400°C.

Rupture by Shear.   A mode of rupture distinctly different from cleavage is observed when a crystal separates by continued shear on a slip band (or on intersecting slip bands if conjugate slip is occurring). Tin, zinc, cadmium, and magnesium crystals, for example, fracture in this way in room-temperature tensile tests.   In some orientations of these hexagonal crystals the "shearing-off" process is preceded by a twinning process that brings a slip plane into a favorable orientation to operate. With zinc, cadmium, and magnesium crystals it is found that shear fracture occurs at an approximately constant value of the resolved shearing stress on the basal plane regardless of the initial orientation, provided that the basal plane is initially more than 15 to 20° from the axis of tension.[5]   (There is no similar rule for cubic crystals, which neck down

[1] C. S. Barrett, G. Ansel, and R. F. Mehl, *Trans. ASM*, vol. 25, p. 702, 1937.

[2] E. Schmid and W. Boas, "Kristallplastizität," Springer, Berlin, 1935, and translation, Hughes, London, 1950.

[3] C. S. Barrett and C. T. Haller, *Trans. AIME*, vol. 171, p. 246, 1947.

[4] A. R. Kaufman, P. Gordon, and D. W. Lillie, *Trans. ASM*, vol. 42, p. 785, 1950.

[5] E. Schmid and W. Boas, "Kristallplastizität," Springer, Berlin, 1935, and translation, Hughes, London, 1950.

and break after double slip sets in.) This limiting shear stress for the termination of basal slip decreases as the temperature of deformation increases. But at the same time the amount of elongation increases to an extent that makes the work of deformation (the area under the load-extension curve) practically a constant independent of initial orientation and of temperature.[1] Most of this work, of course, is dissipated as heat and is not retained in the crystal.

In polycrystalline metals both shear fractures and cleavage fractures are encountered. Cleavage surfaces are bright crystal facets, which exhibit many crystallographic and noncrystallographic markings when viewed under a microscope.[2] In contrast to these, shear fractures leave dull, velvety, fibrous surfaces (unless the surfaces are rubbed smooth as they separate). Bright fractures in mild steel, associated with brittle-ness, have been shown to be the result of cleavage on the {100} cleavage planes of ferrite.[3]

The brittle type of fracture is particularly destructive in welded struc-tures because the elastic energy stored in the structure prior to fracture is sometimes sufficient to cause the crack to propagate great distances at high speed. It is possible for a welded ship to crack completely in two with a loud report, from a crack running in a brittle manner through one plate after another in the ship's deck and hull. A mild-steel tensile test bar fails in this way at low temperatures, and at higher temperatures when it is notched.[4] At room temperature, however, steels usually fail in a ductile manner entirely by a shear fracture.[5]

The transition range of temperatures in which the fracture type changes from shear to mixed and then, at still lower temperatures, to cleavage, is an important characteristic of steels. It varies with deoxidation prac-

[1] E. Schmid and W. Boas, "Kristallplastizität," Springer, Berlin, 1935, and transla-tion, Hughes, London, 1950.

[2] Many photographs of the details on these surfaces have been published by C. A. Zapffe.

[3] E. R. Parker, H. E. Davis, and A. E. Flanigan, *ASTM, Proc.*, vol. 46, p. 1159, 1946. Shear fracture progresses in directions about 45° to the traces of {100} etch pits on a longitudinal section and therefore presumably follows slip planes, though whether or not the crack does follow slip planes was not definitely established by the experiment.

[4] E. R. Parker, H. E. Davis, and A. E. Flanigan, *ASTM Proc.*, vol. 46, p. 1159, 1946. H. E. Davis, E. R. Parker, and A. Boodberg, *ASTM Proc.*, vol. 47, p. 483, 1947.

[5] This is true even at the center of a tensile bar, where the crack runs a jagged course normal to the tension axis. The conical part of the fractured surface of a tensile bar may result from adiabatic conditions—heat generated where the deforma-tion is concentrated does not have time to flow away, so flow continues in the hot metal layer. C. Zener, "Fracturing of Metals," American Society for Metals, Cleveland, Ohio, 1948.

tice, composition, grain size, specimen size, severity of notches present, and other variables.[1]

Other Fractures. *Fatigue fracture* may occur if stresses are cyclically varied or reversed. In this process, slip bands may be seen to form and become progressively darker as cyclic stressing continues. Strain hardening takes place, and if the range of stresses and the number of cycles is great enough, a crack eventually forms and spreads. Cracks begin at stress concentrations, as at the ends of the slip bands that have been most active. Cracks in face-centered cubic crystals spread initially along the slip bands, in hexagonal crystals along twinning planes, and in rhombohedral crystals along twinning and cleavage planes.[2] At later stages the path of a crack tends to become less crystallographic and may, in fact, become more of a tensile crack than a fatigue crack. If strain hardening occurs sufficiently rapidly it may cause plastic deformation to cease, and may protect the metal from damage.[2,3,4] In ferritic steels, for example, flow finally ceases and damage is avoided if stresses do not exceed a value known as the "endurance limit," a value that is different from the yield point in static tests. The progressive hardening during fatigue stressing has been interpreted in a simple way in terms of tension-compression stress-strain curves by Orowan.[4] At sufficiently elevated temperatures and even at room temperature for some metals there appears to be no sharply defined endurance limit, since failure occurs at lower stresses the longer the stressing is continued (even after 10^6 cycles).

Intergranular fracture (cracks spreading along grain boundaries) replaces the transgranular fracture characteristic of ordinary temperatures when metals are strained slowly at elevated temperatures. Creep tests and creep rupture tests are more likely to terminate with intergranular fracture, with no necking down prior to fracture, the lower the strain rate at a given temperature, and the higher the temperature at a given strain rate.[5] The temperature (or range of temperature) above which ordinary transgranular fracture is replaced by intergranular was termed "equicohesive" by Jeffries, who showed that above this temperature coarse-grained metals are stronger, while below this, fine-grained are stronger.[6] Intergranular fracture seems to be characterized by many

[1] The many extensive research programs in this field cannot be summarized here.

[2] H. J. Gough, Edgar Marburg Lecture, *ASTM, Proc.*, vol. 33, pt. 2, p. 3, 1933.

[3] "Prevention of the Failure of Metals under Repeated Stresses," Wiley, New York, 1941.

[4] E. Orowan, in "Reports on Progress in Physics," vol. 12, p. 185, Physical Society, London, 1948–1949.

[5] G. V. Smith, "Properties of Metals at Elevated Temperatures," p. 142, McGraw-Hill, New York, 1950.

[6] Z. Jeffries, *J. Am. Inst. Metals*, vol. 11, p. 300, 1917; *Trans. AIME*, vol. 60, p. 474, 1919.

cracks forming simultaneously at the metal surface and spreading inward, each crack lying normal to the tensile stress. Because these cracks originate at the surface the fracture strength is influenced by the atmosphere surrounding the metals and is lowered if intergranular oxidation occurs.[1] This low-load creep fracture is believed to be connected with plastic flow becoming concentrated at grain boundaries, a phenomenon readily seen metallographically,[2] and revealed by the internal-friction and elastic-modulus studies of Zener[3] and Kê.[4] The flow at grain boundaries follows a viscous law, with flow rate proportional to stress at a given temperature, and dependent on temperature according to an activation-energy relationship such that it becomes increasingly predominant over ordinary slip as temperature increases.

The stress system at the junction of three grain boundaries under creep conditions may be responsible for the lowered ductility associated with intergranular cracking. If grain-boundary flow has relaxed the shear across each boundary, there can be no shear stress across any plane (except at the rare places where the boundaries happen to be at 90° to each other); in other words, regardless of the nature of the externally applied stress, the local stress at the junction is hydrostatic, and therefore will not be relieved by flow and must result in lowered ductility.[5] It is the misfits at grain junctions, also, that limit the total amount of viscous grain-boundary flow that can easily occur. Metals having irregular grain boundaries, with many "keying" points, creep at slower rates than metals with smooth boundaries (a principle that has been made use of in manufacturing nonsagging tungsten light filaments).

[1] G. V. Smith, "Properties of Metals at Elevated Temperatures," McGraw-Hill. New York, 1950. H. H. Bleakney, ASTM, Proc., vol. 47, 1947. R. H. Thieleman and E. R. Parker, Trans. AIME, vol. 135, p. 559, 1939.

[2] W. Rosenhain and J. Humfrey, Proc. Roy. Soc. (London), vol. A83, p. 200, 1909. D. Hanson and M. A. Wheeler, J. Inst. Metals, vol. 45, p. 229, 1931. H. F. Moore, B. B. Betty, and C. W. Dollins, Univ. Illinois Bull. 272, 1935.

[3] C. Zener, "Elasticity and Anelasticity of Metals," University of Chicago Press, Chicago, 1948.

[4] T. S. Kê, Phys. Rev., vol. 71, p. 533, 1947; vol. 72, p. 41, 1947; J. Applied Phys., vol. 19, p. 285, 1948; Trans. AIME, vol. 176, p. 448, 1948.

[5] C. Zener, in "Fracturing of Metals," American Society for Metals, Cleveland, Ohio, 1948. W. Siegfried, Trans. AIME, vol. 65, p. A202, 1943.

CHAPTER XVI

DISLOCATION THEORY

The data reviewed in the preceding chapter characterized the process of slip in crystals as a gliding of blocks over one another along slip planes and in slip directions. This, to be sure, explains the visible results of plastic flow, but as a model of the slipping process it is far from adequate to account for the stresses that are required to make metals flow. Suppose, for example, an ideal crystal containing no imperfections were to slip with a uniform movement of all the atoms in a plane, each atom being pushed over the atom beneath at the same time. The shear stress necessary to cause this to happen should be the stress required to shear the plane by about one-quarter of an atomic distance parallel to the underlying plane; having reached this point, the plane would then snap the rest of the way to the next position of equilibrium. The stress required for this amount of elastic displacement can be estimated by multiplying the shear by the shear modulus, and the result is about 1000 or 10,000 times the *observed* critical resolved shear stress for slip in single crystals. This discrepancy between calculated and observed yield strengths of crystals has stimulated much thought and has led to the development of a number of important theories of the plastic properties of crystalline materials.

Stress Concentrations. The earlier theories attempted to resolve the discrepancy between ideal and observed yield strengths by postulating that crystals contain cracks or other kinds of lattice flaws that set up local concentrations of stresses. Theories of this nature stemmed from the work of Griffith,[1] who showed the importance of cracks and other inhomogeneities in causing premature rupture of test specimens. Griffith calculated the stress at the edge of a thin transverse crack in a tensile specimen and found it many times larger than the average stress on the cross section. Smekal[2] suggested that stress concentrations of this sort around flaws in a crystal start plastic flow at stresses far below the stresses that would be required in perfect crystals. Smekal attributed many of the flaws, particularly places of misfit at the boundaries of mosaic blocks, to

[1] A. A. Griffith, *Proc. Intern. Congr. Applied Mechanics*, p. 55, Delft, 1924; *Trans. Roy. Soc. (London)*, vol. A221, p. 163, 1920.

[2] A. Smekal, "Report of the International Conference on Physics, vol. II, The Solid State of Matter," University Press, Cambridge, 1935; "Handbuch der Physik," vol. XXIV, p. 2, Springer, Berlin, 1933; *Z. Krist.*, vol. 89, p. 193, 1934, vol. 93, p. 161, 1936.

accidents of growth. He believed the approximate regularity in the spacings of slip planes was evidence of regularity in the arrangement of flaws and listed as possible flaws the following: gaps, variation in orientation, incorporated foreign atoms, inclusions, twins, and mosaic-block boundaries.

Becker-Orowan Theory. Becker[1] extended this line of thought by postulating that thermal vibrations help the applied stress overcome the resistance to flow, giving the effect of adding to the applied stress a stress sufficient to reach the value of the critical shear stress for slip at a temperature of absolute zero, τ_0. If the applied stress is τ, the amount added is then $(\tau_0 - \tau)$. This added stress increases the energy of the crystal by the amount E given by the equation

$$E = \frac{V(\tau_0 - \tau)^2}{2G}$$

where V is the volume subjected to the stress and G is the shear modulus. The probability that a region in the crystal will acquire the energy E as a result of thermal fluctuations is given by the Boltzmann function

$$\text{Probability} = e^{-E/kT}$$

where k is Boltzmann's constant and T is the absolute temperature.

It is assumed that the velocity D of the deformation process is proportional to this probability; hence

$$D = ce^{-V(\tau_0 - \tau)^2/2GkT}$$

where c is a constant of proportionality. For a constant rate of flow this predicts that the critical shearing stress will vary so that $(\tau_0 - \tau)^2/T$ is a constant, or, stated differently,

$$\tau = \tau_0 - aT^{\frac{1}{2}}$$

where a is a constant. The theory does not account for the very low value of the shearing strength compared with that expected for the simple model of the ideal crystal.

Orowan[2] extended this concept to include the effect of flaws acting as stress raisers, by substituting $q\tau$ for the applied stress τ, where q is the stress-concentration factor. Strain hardening is brought into the theory by adding to τ_0 a quantity that is dependent upon the amount of prior strain.

[1] R. Becker, *Physik. Z.*, vol. 26, p. 919, 1925.

[2] E. Orowan, *Z. Physik*, vol. 89, pp. 605, 614, 634, 1934; summarized by W. G. Burgers and J. M. Burgers, First Report on Viscosity and Plasticity, *Proc. Roy. Acad. Sci. Amsterdam*, vol. 15, p. 205, 1935; see also G. Masing, *Z. Metallkunde*, vol. 31, p. 235, 1939.

Theories of this type have difficulty in accounting for the fact that even at the temperature of liquid hydrogen or helium plastic flow occurs at stresses never more than three to five times those required at ordinary temperatures. Another objection that has been raised to such theories is their use of the assumption that the flow rate is a function only of the amount of deformation and the instantaneous values of stress and temperature. As mentioned in Chap. XV, this is only approximately true. Further, these theories do not specify a mechanism by which flow can leave a point of stress concentration and cross a region of average stress.

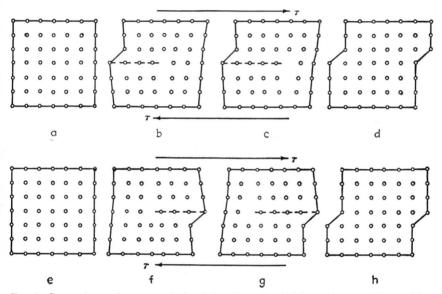

Fig. 1. Generation and movement of a dislocation. In sketches *a*, *b*, *c*, and *d* a positive dislocation moves to the right; in *e*, *f*, *g*, and *h* a negative one moves to the left; the resulting deformation is identical. (*Taylor.*)

The theory of dislocations that is reviewed briefly in the following pages has furnished a greater understanding of the nature of crystal plasticity than any prior theory in the field, and has served to relate the mechanism of flow to other characteristics of metals in useful ways. The concept of dislocations was first applied to slip by Orowan,[1] Polanyi,[2] and Taylor,[3] for the purpose of accounting for the low yield strength of crystals and other details of their plastic behavior, and subsequently was developed by many other investigators.

Types of Dislocations. The simplest type of dislocation, which was most frequently discussed in the early papers on the dislocation theory

[1] E. Orowan, *Z. Physik*, vol. 89, p. 634, 1934.
[2] M. Polanyi, *Z. Physik* vol. 89, p. 660, 1934.
[3] G. I. Taylor, *Proc. Roy. Soc. (London)*, vol. A145, p. 362, 1934.

of flow, is illustrated in Fig. 1, which represents a section through a crystal in the neighborhood of a slip plane as slip is taking place. In sketches b and c the upper side of the slip plane is compressed so that $n + 1$ atoms on this side are opposite n atoms on the lower side. Alternately, the compressed region may be on the lower side, as in sketches f and g, so that $n + 1$ atoms below are opposite n above. The former arrangement is designated as a *positive* dislocation and the latter as a *negative* one. If the dislocation starts at one side and runs through the crystal to the other side, it produces a shift of one portion with respect to the other a distance of one atomic spacing. The resulting displacement

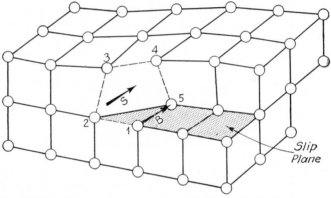

Fig. 2. A screw dislocation in a simple cubic structure. A right-hand screw dislocation passes through the block of crystal as indicated by S. If you follow a circuit around S as indicated by the dashed line 1-2-3-4-5, you move forward parallel to the screw dislocation by the amount of the Burgers vector B. The dislocation moves perpendicular to itself, and in the sketch it has already moved over the shaded area of the slip plane. (*D. F. Gibbons.*)

is the same whether a positive dislocation moves across a crystal toward the right or a negative dislocation moves across it toward the left.

Figure 1 is intended to represent a cross section of a three-dimensional crystal in which the dislocation is assumed to extend as a long line perpendicular to the plane of the drawing and to move to the right or left as shown. The resulting displacement may be represented by a vector that is one interatomic distance in length and that points horizontally to the right in the upper drawings of Fig. 1; this "slip vector" or "Burgers vector" is normal to the line of the dislocation, which is usually called an "edge" or "Taylor" dislocation.[1]

Burgers[2] noticed that a second type of dislocation, a "screw disloca-

[1] A raft of bubbles 1 mm or less in diameter floating on a soap solution forms an excellent two-dimensional model of dislocations, grain boundaries, and vacancies. W. L. Bragg and J. F. Nye, *Proc. Roy. Soc. (London)*, vol. A190, p. 474, 1947.

[2] J. M. Burgers, *Proc. Roy. Acad. Sci. Amsterdam*, vol. 42, pp. 293, 378, 1939; *Proc. Phys. Soc. (London)*, vol. 52, p. 23, 1940.

tion," or "Burgers dislocation," results when the displacement is *parallel* to the line of the dislocation. It is shown in Fig. 2, where a block of the crystal face is shown displaced by the amount indicated by the Burgers vector B, and where the misfits caused by this displacement are concentrated at the screw dislocation S. The block is supposed to be displaced one interatomic distance, so atomic planes normal to S are joined together again after the displacement. Suppose one moves from atom to atom on a plane normal to S and in so doing makes a circuit around the screw dislocation S. This will result in following a spiral path and returning not to the starting point but to a point displaced from the starting point by the amount of the Burgers vector B. A similar circuit around an edge dislocation on a plane normal to it also results in returning to a point displaced from the starting point by the vector B, which lies in the same plane. If a screw dislocation extends to the surface as in Fig. 2 and material is being deposited on this surface, the dislocation will continue as the crystal grows. Frank and his coworkers[1] proposed that the self-perpetuating step in the crystal surface at the point of emergence of a screw dislocation provides a place where growth can occur with almost arbitrarily low values of supersaturation or of undercooling. (The work of forming a nucleus of greater than critical size on a smooth face is thereby avoided.) This theory received emphatic confirmation when these points and the "growth spirals" radiating from them were recognized[2] on natural crystal faces of beryl ($Be_3Al_2Si_6O_{18}$), on long-chain paraffin crystals[3] ($C_{36}H_{74}$), on silicon carbide,[4] and on magnesium, PbI_2 and CdI_2 crystals.[5] The remarkable occurrence of various types of SiC crystals with periods up to 198 layers—far beyond the range of direct influence of interatomic forces—is accounted for by Frank as a period simply determined by the Burgers vector (the "strength") of the dislocation or dislocation cluster that dominates the growth.

Consider a slip plane on which slip is confined to a small patch inside the crystal. The slipped region will be surrounded by a *dislocation ring*. The portions of the ring that are normal to the Burgers vector will be of the edge type, those parallel to the Burgers vector will be of the screw type, and intermediate portions will be made up of segments of both types.

[1] F. C. Frank, *Discussion, Faraday Soc.*, vol. 5, pp. 48, 67, 186, 1949. W. K. Burton, N. Cabrera, and F. C. Frank, *Nature*, vol. 163, p. 398, 1949; *Phil. Trans. Roy. Soc.*, vol. A243, p. 299, 1951. F. C. Frank, "Advances in Physics," Quarterly Supplement to *Phil. Mag.*, vol. 1, p. 91, 1952.

[2] L. J. Griffin, *Phil. Mag.*, vol. 41, p. 196, 1950.

[3] I. M. Dawson and V. Vand, *Nature*, vol. 167, p. 476, 1951; *Proc. Roy. Soc. (London)*, vol. A206, p. 555, 1951.

[4] A. R. Verma, *Phil. Mag.*, vol. 42, p. 1005, 1951. S. Amelinckx, *Nature*, vol. 167, p. 939, 1951.

[5] A. J. Forty, *Phil. Mag.*, 1952 (in press) (Mg); vol. 42, p. 670, 1951.

Similarly, any wavy dislocation line in the slip plane consists of segments of edge and screw dislocations.   Such a line must either form a closed loop within the crystal, or must end at a crystal surface, for it is geometrically impossible for the line to end at any point within the crystal.

A still more general type of dislocation ring will occur if the dislocation line is not confined to a single slip plane, but has a component normal to the slip plane.   It is then useful to think of a column of material within the crystal, the surface of the column being the rows of atoms that touch

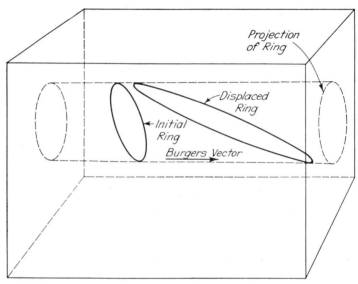

FIG. 3. A dislocation ring.   The ring may move along the surface of the column indicated by the dashed lines, parallel to the Burgers vector, and may become elongated in doing so, without requiring transport of atoms by diffusion.   (*Seitz.*)

the ring and that are parallel to the Burgers vector, Fig. 3.   Moving the ring along the surface of this column can readily occur since this is a movement parallel to the Burgers vector.   This involves no transport of atoms by diffusion.   But displacement of the ring from the surface of the column cannot occur unless there is diffusion of atoms to or from the point where such displacement occurs.[1]   This can be seen from the fact that the column can be produced by taking a layer of atoms of shape equal to the cross section of the column, and inserting it into the column, so that there is one more atom in every row of atoms within the column than there is in the rows outside.   The same reasoning holds if a layer of atoms is *removed* from the column so that rows in the column have a deficiency of atoms, or if "holes" (missing atoms) are diffusing around and migrate to the col-

[1] W. Shockley and W. T. Read, in "Imperfections in Nearly Perfect Crystals," Wiley, New York, 1952.

umn. Thus any dislocation ring maintains, during slip, a constant area projected on a plane normal to the Burgers vector and changes this projected area only if diffusion occurs. Two or more slip planes can use a common Burgers vector (*i.e.*, a common slip direction). Thus in f.c.c. crystals, where the vector is $\frac{1}{2}0\frac{1}{2}$ (or an equivalent), two {111} slip planes share the vector and the slip line on the surface may be a zigzag line made up of segments of each of the planes (this is termed "cross slip"). In body-centered cubic crystals, with the slip vector $\frac{1}{2}\frac{1}{2}\frac{1}{2}$, three {110}, three {112}, and six {123} planes share each slip vector, permitting wavy slip lines.

In discussing the edge and screw dislocations we have assumed that the displacement vector is a full identity distance in the lattice. This need not be the case if a partial displacement of a plane brings it to a place of metastable equilibrium. In the face-centered cubic structure, for example, we have seen that two successive displacements such as are needed to produce a twin add up to a slip displacement; referring to Fig. 34 on page 381, the displacement vector along $[\bar{1}2\bar{1}]$ added to one of the same length along $[\bar{2}11]$ yields the slip vector along $[\bar{1}10]$.[1] If an area of a f.c.c. (111) plane is displaced along the underlying plane by the amount of one of these partial vectors instead of the full Burgers vector, the area will be bounded by "partial dislocations" ("Shockley dislocations"), of edge and screw type, instead of the full edge and screw dislocations mentioned first. Shockley has proposed that a full dislocation on the f.c.c. (111) plane may not be stable and spontaneously decomposes into two partial dislocations that repel each other. The area between these is then a region in which the stacking is altered from the f.c.c. so that there is a thin layer of close-packed hexagonal stacking. If the c.p.h. structure is unstable, this area exerts a surface tension that tends to draw the partial dislocations together again. On the other hand, if a crystal having the f.c.c. structure is cooled into a temperature range where the c.p.h. structure is more stable, all dislocations should tend to dissociate into partial dislocations and separate as far as possible, thus increasing the amount of c.p.h. material. In more complex crystals there may be more than one intermediate position at which a shifting plane may come to rest, more than one type of partial dislocation.

Partial dislocations in f.c.c. structures can glide on (111) planes containing the dislocation line and its Burgers vector, but it cannot climb to another parallel (111) plane without considerably greater expenditure of energy, because of the higher energy surface it would produce in doing so.

Frank[2] has discussed still another type of dislocation, termed "sessile"

[1] R. D. Heidenreich and W. Shockley, "Report of a Conference on Strength of Solids," p. 57, Physical Society, London, 1948.

[2] F. C. Frank, *Proc. Phys. Soc.* (*London*), vol. A62, p. 202, 1949.

because it does not move in response to an applied stress. The (111) planes of a f.c.c. crystal are altered in their stacking sequence *ABCABC* . . . by removing a portion of the *A* plane and letting the *C* and *B* planes come together without lateral displacement. The line of misfit is then a sessile dislocation.

A lengthy review of the properties of dislocations and of the rapidly developing mathematical theories of their interactions cannot be given here,[1] but it may be useful to give a brief review covering the theories in a qualitative way. A most important property is that an edge or a screw dislocation can be made to move across a slip plane by very low stresses, thus accounting for the low critical shear strength of metal crystals.

Generation of Dislocations. The effect of moving an edge dislocation across a slip plane is to displace the material on one side of the plane with respect to that on the other. Expanding a ring dislocation until it covers the slip plane accomplishes the same result. Emerging from a surface of the crystal, an edge dislocation leaves a step that is one inter-atomic distance high. Since visible slip lines are thousands of times larger than this, some mechanism must exist for sending a succession of dislocations after one another across the slip plane or across neighboring planes in the slipping zone. Suggestions to account for this have been numerous. The suggestion has often been made that successive dislocations are generated in a local region of high stress concentration at the edge of a crack or suitable defect. The role of thermal fluctuations in generating dislocations is judged to be minor. Koehler,[2] Bragg,[3] Huntington[4] and Nabarro[5] have estimated the energy in a cylinder immediately surrounding a dislocation—say within 6×10^{-8} cm of it—as about $\frac{1}{2}$ to $1\frac{1}{2}$ electron volts per atom distance along the dislocation; additional energy must be supplied to expand a ring dislocation against the attraction of the opposite sides for each other until the ring becomes large enough to stay expanded.

---

[1] Reviews will be found in "Progress in Metal Physics," Interscience Publishers, New York, beginning in vol. I with A. H. Cottrell's chapter; "Report of a Conference on Strength of Solids," Physical Society, London, 1948. A detailed review of the mathematical theory of stationary dislocations and their interactions is given by F. R. N. Nabarro in "Advances in Physics," Quarterly Supplement to *Phil. Mag.*, 1952 (in press). Summaries of these and other imperfections will be found in "Imperfections in Nearly Perfect Crystals," Wiley, New York, 1952; F. C. Frank, *Phil. Mag.*, vol. 42, p. 809, 1951; A. H. Cottrell, monograph on dislocations and plastic flow in crystals (in press); F. Seitz, in "Advances in Physics," Quarterly Supplement to *Phil. Mag.*, vol. 1, p. 43; 1952; "Symposium on Plastic Deformation of Crystalline Solids," Carnegie Institute of Technology and Office of Naval Research, 1950.

[2] J. S. Koehler, *Phys. Rev.*, vol. 60, p. 397, 1941.

[3] W. L. Bragg, "Symposium on Internal Stresses," p. 221, Institute of Metals, London, 1947.

[4] H. B. Huntington, *Phys. Rev.*, vol. 59, p. 942A, 1941.

[5] F. R. N. Nabarro, *Proc. Phys. Soc. (London)*, vol. 59, p. 256, 1947.

Estimates place the total activation energy required in the range 1 to 5 electron volts per atom distance along the dislocation, so thermal fluctuations are judged to be incapable of generating rings of sufficient size, even in a stressed metal.

An entirely different mechanism for generation of successive dislocation rings on a plane has been pointed out by Frank and Read.[1] A dislocation line always moves normal to itself over a slip plane when subjected to an applied stress. If it is anchored to a certain point—as point A, Fig. 4a,

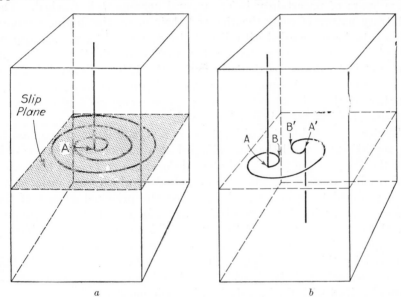

a   *b*

Fɪɢ. 4. The Frank-Read mechanism for generating dislocations. Dislocations are anchored at points A and A' where they leave the slip plane. They move perpendicular to their length and spiral outward on the slip plane, displacing the upper part of the crystal with respect to the lower. When anchored at two places (Fig. 4b) the points B and B' may touch, forming a dislocation ring; continued spiraling generates concentric rings.

a point where the dislocation jumps up to another parallel plane, for example—the dislocation pivots at the anchorage and swings around like the hand of a clock, producing slip of one atomic spacing at each revolution. The other end of the dislocation on this slip plane may be anchored at a boundary, as in Fig. 4a, in which case the clock-hand motion winds the dislocation into a spiral of increasing length; or the other end may be at another fixed point (A', Fig. 4b) where the dislocation leaves the slip plane, and where rotation in the opposite direction provides a means of sending out successive dislocation rings.

Strain Hardening. Dislocations exert a force on one another. Each dislocation sets up a stress field around it, of a type that had previously

[1] F. C. Frank and W. T. Read, *Phys. Rev.*, vol. 79, p. 722, 1950.

been calculated by elastic theory. Excluding the atoms within a few atom diameters of the dislocation, the elastic-theory computations can be transferred to the crystal problem so as to predict the forces caused by the interaction of dislocations. It should be possible to understand strain hardening in terms of these interactions, and many attempts have been made, but the problem is so complex, the number of facts to be accounted for is so great, and there are so many possible models of dislocation interaction and dislocation-barrier interaction, we must expect some years of uncertainty before general agreement is reached. The arbitrary nature of early theories and their many simplifying assumptions have been regarded with distaste by many and have been responsible in large measure for the reluctance of many scientists to think in terms of dislocations, particularly during the 1940s. Some dislocation concepts have now become accepted as indispensable, however, and the number of these is steadily growing; there seems no doubt but that detailed study of these is proving useful.

Taylor suggested that if dislocations in a crystal move in response to an applied stress until they are stopped at a barrier, their stress fields will then oppose the passage of other dislocations and strain hardening will result. Certain models were proposed[1] in which edge dislocations were assumed to form a superlattice, but the principal success of the theory—accounting for stress-strain curves in which stress is proportional to the square root of the strain—did not require the arbitrary assumption of a superlattice; and the weaknesses of the theory were not removed by this assumption.[2] The distance between barriers in this theory was deduced to be about 3×10^{-4} cm in aluminum, so the barriers were identified with the boundaries of mosaic blocks.

From the force required to move dislocations past each other on slip planes spaced at different distances, Koehler, Brown, and others have concluded that in cold-worked metal there are about 10^{12} dislocations per square centimeter normal to their length. If the energy of a dislocation per atom distance is taken as about 5 electron volts this dislocation density is of the right order of magnitude to account for measured values of the strain energy stored in cold-worked metal. Estimates of the dislocation

---

[1] G. I. Taylor, *Proc. Roy. Soc. (London)*, vol. A145, p. 362, 1934. J. S. Koehler, *Phys. Rev.*, vol. 60, p. 397, 1941; *Am. J. Phys.*, vol. 10, p. 275, 1942. W. F. Brown, *Phys. Rev.*, vol. 60, p. 139, 1941.

[2] The theory cannot convincingly account both for the *parabolic* strain-hardening curves of cubic crystals undergoing slip on multiple intersecting slip planes and for the *linear* strain-hardening curves of crystals (cubic or hexagonal) undergoing single slip (laminar flow, p. 353). No account is taken of the concentration of flow into slip bands. See A. H. Cottrell, monograph on dislocations and plastic flow in crystals (in press).

density in an annealed metal, based on observed yield strengths, suggest that it does not exceed 10^8 per sq cm.

Strain hardening must also result when a moving dislocation is forced to cut through dislocations that lie on other slip planes, for it produces a jog in each dislocation it cuts, lengthening these at an expenditure of energy.[1] A jog can move easily only in the direction of the slip vector;[1] if forced to move otherwise it must leave a trail of vacant lattice sites at the cost of further expenditure of energy. Strong interactions can likewise be expected to occur also between partial dislocations that cut across each other,[2] and as the number of points of interlocking must increase with increasing strain this may also provide another source of strain hardening, possibly accounting for the rapid strain hardening of solid solutions of Si in Cu (page 357). Recent strain-hardening theories are also employing Frank-Read sources (Fig. 4b) that become operative at stresses dependent upon the distance between anchor points, and that become inoperative when the back stresses from piled-up dislocations[3] neutralize the applied stresses or when some other mechanism causes them to cease. Current theories also use the concept that when screw dislocations cut across each other they are subsequently able to move only by creating a row of vacancies or of interstitial atoms.[4] Cottrell suggests[5] that the fundamental strain-hardening curve for a slipband is always linear during "laminar flow" and that nonlinear curves with intense work hardening arise from additional slipbands (particularly on intersecting slip systems) coming into action as stress is increased. He emphasizes that only with high-purity crystals, careful alignment of crystals, selected orientations, and freedom from oxide films can cubic metals be expected to flow in laminar fashion and that linear stress-strain curves have actually been found under these conditions.[6] Linearity presumably terminates when "turbulent" flow starts; the best confirma-

---

[1] W. T. Read and W. Shockley, in "Imperfections in Nearly Perfect Crystals," Wiley, New York, 1952.

[2] R. D. Heidenreich and W. Shockley, "Report of a Conference on Strength of Solids," p. 57, Physical Society, London, 1948.

[3] J. D. Eshelby, F. C. Frank, and F. R. N. Nabarro, *Phil. Mag.*, vol. 42, p. 351, 1951.

[4] A summary of these theories and a discussion of the possible effects of vacancies in crystals, including a postulated "spiral prismatic dislocation" formed by vacancies condensing on the lattice planes adjacent to a screw dislocation and also able to act as a generator, has been published by F. Seitz, in "Advances in Physics," Quarterly Supplement to *Phil. Mag.*, vol. 1, p. 43, 1952.

[5] A. H. Cottrell, monograph on dislocations and plastic flow in crystals (in press).

[6] This is the phenomenon of "easy glide" observed by E. N. da C. Andrade and C. Henderson, *Phil. Trans. Roy. Soc. (London)*, vol. 244, p. 177, 1951, and by Pratt in NaCl (see p. 352).

tion of this has been obtained with single crystals of brass (see page 353).[1]

Dislocation Theory of Age Hardening. Mott and Nabarro have developed a detailed theory of precipitation hardening making use of certain properties of dislocations.[2] The particles that precipitate from a supersaturated solid solution are too large or too small for the space they must occupy and consequently strain the matrix in their neighborhood. When a moving dislocation encounters a shearing stress unfavorable to its passage, as some of the stresses around these particles will be, the dislocation is stopped until a stress is applied that is capable of overcoming the local stress obstruction. Now if the dislocation is rigid and cannot bend, and if it is long compared with the average distance between particles, there will be nearly as many favorably directed stresses as there are opposing stresses along its length, hence little net obstruction to the motion of the dislocation will result. Mott and Nabarro then consider what happens if the dislocation is flexible. Since there is an energy of about 1 to 5 electron volts per atomic spacing along a dislocation, the dislocation tends to be as short as possible; there is effectively a tension along it. If the dislocation traverses a region with widely spaced local stress centers it will have a wavy form, following the contours of the stress field so as to have minimum energy, but with slight curvature. If a stress is applied the dislocation stretches into loops between the points where it is caught on stress centers. To free the wavy dislocation from the centers then requires a stress sufficient to pull the dislocation through the center, without aid from other stress centers, and the slip resistance will be high. This corresponds to the age-hardened condition. The theory for the quenched condition is that the centers are so close together that the dislocation cannot bend sharply enough to follow the stress contours, and consequently acts as a rigid dislocation, with aiding and opposing stresses canceling each other, and with slip resistance being low. Maximum hardness would come with a critical separation of the stress centers estimated to be in fair agreement with separations found experimentally (of the order of 100 atom spacings).

The softening accompanying overaging can be accounted for if the stress centers become so far apart that the dislocation can bulge out

[1] R. W. K. Honeycombe (private communication) suggests caution in attributing rapid hardening to slip on intersecting slip systems until it has been proven (with the high sensitivity of X-ray micrographs) that deformation bands are not responsible. It is not unlikely that bands play some role, especially when they are narrow.

[2] N. F. Mott and F. R. N. Nabarro, *Proc. Phys. Soc. (London)*, vol. 52, p. 86, 1940; *J. Inst. Metals*, vol. 72, p. 367, 1946; "Report of a Conference on Strength of Solids," p. 1, Physical Society, London, 1948. F. R. N. Nabarro, *Proc. Phys. Soc. (London)*, vol. 58, p. 669, 1946.

between them, the loops coming together behind them and passing on.[1] The greater the separation between obstructions, the larger the radius of curvature in this process and the lower the yield stress.

Segregation at Dislocations. Reference to the upper drawings of Fig. 1 will show that an edge dislocation is equivalent to inserting an extra plane of atoms, standing vertically and extending down to the slip plane but not below it. Thus the region *above* the slip plane and near the dislocation is in compression, that *under* the slip plane is in tension. Cottrell[2] has pointed out that the strain energy will be lessened if the natural lattice parameter of the compressed region is lessened or that of the extended region is increased. This will happen if segregation occurs in a solid solution; interstitial atoms or abnormally large substitutional atoms segregate in the region under tensile stress, and dissolved atoms that prefer smaller lattice parameters will segregate in the compressed region. An equilibrium concentration of solute atoms will soon be reached, for even with a dislocation density of 10^{12} per sq cm only about 0.1 atomic per cent of solute would be needed to supply one solute atom per dislocation on each atom plane, and with annealed metals of low dislocation density even high-purity metals could supply enough solute atoms to satisfy the segregation tendency.

If a dislocation surrounded by its atmosphere of segregated atoms is forced to move rapidly it can do so only at the expense of the increased strain energy required to break away from the atmosphere. If it does not break away it can move easily only with the rate at which the atmosphere can follow along by diffusion. Cottrell proposes that this is the mechanism of flow in *microcreep*, which Chalmers discovered[3] in crystals of tin.

Chalmers found that by using strain gauges reading to 10^{-7} per cm he could detect plastic flow at stresses less than 100 g per sq mm. The total creep at these stresses was limited to a total extension of about 10^{-5}. This microcreep starts at a rate that is proportional to stress and decreases to nearly zero after a strain of 10^{-5}. Microcreep appears to be caused by the movement of dislocations already present in the metal, and to be stopped by these being used up. It occurs at a rate sufficiently slow, Cottrell concludes, to permit diffusion of an atmosphere of segregated atoms along with a dislocation.[4]

[1] E. Orowan, "Symposium on Internal Stresses," p. 451, Institute of Metals, London, 1947.

[2] A. H. Cottrell, "Report of a Conference on Strength of Solids," p. 30, Physical Society, London, 1948; "Progress in Metal Physics," vol. I, p. 77, Interscience Publishers, New York, 1949.

[3] B. Chalmers, *Proc. Roy. Soc. (London)*, vol. A156, p. 427, 1936.

[4] A Cottrell atmosphere exerts a viscous drag on a dislocation; therefore the flow rate, when controlled by this drag, is proportional to the applied stress, according to

Cottrell's segregated atmospheres at dislocations provide a theory for the sharp yield point in iron and other metals. The force required to dislodge a dislocation from its atmosphere appears to be the right order of magnitude to account for the stress at the yield point,[1] and the stress to continue motion after the atmosphere is left behind would necessarily be less. The removal[2] of the yield point in iron by the removal of interstitial elements (carbon, nitrogen) and its return with reintroduction of carbon or nitrogen is thus accounted for, as well as the fact that cold work removes the yield point and aging brings a return of the yield point. The rate of return, according to Nabarro,[3] is consistent with that expected for the rate of formation of a carbon atmosphere. Facts regarding blue brittleness, strain aging, and jerky flow in nonferrous crystals (page 350) are accounted for by the theory. Thermal agitation aids the dislocations in breaking away from their condensed atmospheres,[4] and an additional marked reduction in yield strength is anticipated when temperatures are high enough to disperse the atmospheres from their condensed positions surrounding dislocations. Lack of yield points in some f.c.c. alloys at room temperature is sometimes due to their being above the critical temperature for condensation. In polycrystalline specimens Cottrell considers the yield point not to be the stress at which occasional dislocations begin to move but the stress at which enough dislocations pile up at a grain boundary so that their stress field forces dislocations in the adjoining grain to break away from their atmospheres.

Dislocation Models of Grain Boundaries and Subboundaries. The boundaries between differently oriented grains or subgrains are regions of misfit where planes of atoms come to an end; when the difference in orientation of the grains at a boundary is not too great the boundary can be accurately described as an array of dislocations. In the simplest cases an array of parallel edge dislocations may be present, which has the effect of tilting one grain with respect to its neighbor around an axis lying on the boundary, as in Fig. 5; in more complex situations there is a component of rotation about an axis normal to the boundary, and this

A. H. Cottrell and B. A. Jaswon, *Proc. Roy. Soc. (London)*, vol. A199, p. 104, 1949. Dislocation densities can be calculated from known values of critical velocities at which dislocations break away from their atmospheres, together with known diffusion rates. An early theory of microcreep is given in the review by F. Seitz and T. A. Read, *J. Applied Phys.*, vol. 12, pp. 100, 170, 470, 1941.

[1] A. H. Cottrell and B. A. Bilby, *Proc. Phys. Soc. (London)*, vol. A62, p. 49, 1949. A. H. Cottrell, "Symposium on the Plastic Deformation of Crystalline Solids," Carnegie Institute of Technology and Office of Naval Research, 1950.

[2] J. R. Low and M. Gensamer, *Trans. AIME*, vol. 158, p. 207, 1944.

[3] F. R. N. Nabarro, "Report of a Conference on Strength of Solids," p. 38, Physical Society, London, 1948.

[4] A. H. Cottrell and B. A. Bilby, *Proc. Phys. Soc. (London)*, vol. A62, p. 49, 1949.

requires an array of screw dislocations on the boundary.[1] Even though there are five degrees of freedom that must be specified to describe fully a plane grain boundary (three degrees in the relative orientation of the two grains and two in the orientation of the boundary), Shockley and Read[2] point out that dislocation models are possible and that the energy of the boundary can be computed from the attractive and repulsive forces of the dislocations comprising the boundary—provided that the dislocations are not too close together, *i.e.*, the orientation differences not too great. (The misfit at high angle boundaries is equivalent to a layer of liquid a few atoms in thickness.)

Shockley and Read have calculated the dependence of boundary energy upon orientation difference θ for a cubic lattice in which the relative orientation differs by a rotation of θ around the z axis. The energy per unit area when θ is less than $45°$ is

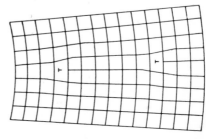

$$E = E_0\theta(A - \ln\theta)$$
$$= E_0\theta\left(1 - \ln\frac{\theta}{\theta_m}\right)$$

FIG. 5. A boundary composed of dislocations, indicated at the T symbols. The curved atom layers are plane at greater distances from the boundary.

where E_0 is a term that depends on the elastic constants and the orientation of the boundary; A is a term containing the energy of distortion that is concentrated close to the dislocations, which is difficult to evaluate theoretically, and also factors involving the boundary orientation; and θ_m is the angle at which E becomes a maximum. According to this theory, which assumes that the boundary is composed of edge dislocations only, without half dislocations and stacking faults, the boundary energy increases rapidly as θ increases from $\theta = 0$. To put the theory into a form that applies to many different experiments the energy is expressed as E/E_m where $E_m = E_0\theta_m$, and θ is expressed in terms of θ/θ_m. The formula then becomes

$$\frac{E}{E_m} = \frac{\theta}{\theta_m}\left(1 - \ln\frac{\theta}{\theta_m}\right)$$

and the curve is plotted in Fig. 6.

Experimental data on the orientation dependence of boundary energy have accumulated rapidly since C. S. Smith pointed out the importance

[1] J. M. Burgers, *Proc. Phys. Soc. (London)*, vol. 52, p. 23, 1940. W. L. Bragg, *Proc. Phys. Soc. (London)*, vol. 52, p. 54, 1940.

[2] W. Shockley and W. T. Read, *Phys. Rev.*, vol. 75, p. 692, 1949; vol. 78, p. 275, 1950; "Imperfections in Nearly Perfect Crystals," Wiley, New York, 1952.

of boundary energies in controlling microstructures.[1] The first data available to test the dislocation theory are summarized by Fisher and Dunn,[2] which include experiments by Aust and Chalmers on tin[3] and lead, and by Dunn and coworkers on silicon ferrite. There is excellent agreement between the curve (Fig. 6) and the measured values when the curve is adjusted to fit at θ_m. For ferrite grains having a common [100]

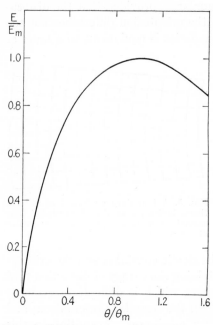

FIG. 6. Calculated dependence of grain-boundary energy upon difference in orientation for crystals of cubic symmetry. (*Read and Shockley.*)

axis θ_m is about 30°, and for a common [110] axis θ_m is about 26°; for grains of tin having c axes in common θ_m is about 10°. As the energy curve continues on beyond this maximum, certain orientation differences should be encountered that, according to dislocation models, should have abnormally low energy and the curve should dip down to a cusp at these orientations.[4] The cusps occur when the two grains are in register at the same atom at regular intervals of a few atom distances. There is, in fact, experimental evidence for such cusps, particularly for twin boundaries. Read and Shockley's calculated values of E_0 agree to within about 30 per cent with those derived from the available measurements on the absolute energy of a grain boundary of random orientation.

Dislocation theory provides a useful insight into the changes that occur in subboundaries of grains during annealing. Polygonization is clearly a movement of dislocations into planes that form subboundaries. The sub-

[1] Cyril S. Smith, *Trans. AIME*, vol. 175, p. 15, 1948.

[2] J. C. Fisher and C. G. Dunn, in "Imperfections in Nearly Perfect Crystals," Wiley, New York, 1952. See also W. T. Read and W. Shockley, same volume.

[3] B. Chalmers, *Proc. Roy. Soc. (London)*, vol. A196, p. 64, 1949. K. T. Aust and B. Chalmers, *Proc. Roy. Soc. (London)*, vol. A201, p. 210, 1950.

[4] W. Shockley and W. T. Read predict two b.c.c. grains to have cusps when the boundary orientations are as follows in grains 1 and 2, respectively: $(111)_1$ $(111)_2$; $(110)_1$ $(114)_2$; $(112)_1$ $(112)_2$; $(114)_1$ $(114)_2$; $(221)_1$ $(221)_2$, (the last three being twins or twinlike orientations) and at least some of these are actually found as low-energy boundaries. C. G. Dunn, F. W. Daniels, and M. J. Bolton, *Trans. AIME*, vol. 188, p. 369, 1950.

boundaries should be planes perpendicular to the active slip planes, a geometrical arrangement of low energy,[1] and this is actually observed in zinc,[2] silicon iron crystals,[3] and others. Dunn and Daniels found[3] that with bent silicon ferrite crystals a 10-min anneal at 950°C produced sub-grains a few microns wide that differed in orientation from their neighbors by a few hundredths of a degree; several hours of annealing at 1300°C increased their widths to 10 to 40 μ and the orientation difference to 0.2 to 0.3°. The driving force for this subgrain coarsening is easily understood from the dislocation theory, or from the observed curves of grain-boundary energy vs. orientation difference. The total energy of two subboundaries of 0.1° orientation difference is greater than that of one subboundary of 0.2°, so by subgrain coarsening the total energy of the metal is lowered.

Obstructions of Dislocations at Grain Boundaries. Dislocations encounter a barrier to their motion when they approach a grain boundary or an interphase boundary. Theoretical studies[4] have indicated several causes for this. If a dislocation finds different elastic constants in the material beyond the boundary, it will experience a force arising from this fact (a long-range force, computed as an "image force"). In isotropic single-phase metals this is absent, but there exist short-range forces from other causes. With small angle boundaries, the dislocations of which they are composed are surrounded by stress fields extending to distances comparable with the spacing of the dislocations. With other boundaries, Foreman and Jaswon have shown that there are forces resulting from the lack of continuation of the slip system across the boundary—the law of force on a dislocation altering as the boundary is approached. This is a short-range force, effective at 10 atom distances or less from the boundary.

Dislocations, Vacancies, and Interstitial Atoms. If two edge disloca-tions of opposite sign on the same slip plane come together they annihilate each other, leaving a perfect crystal. If they approach each other on adjacent slip planes and combine with an overlap, an extra row of atoms will be left that must be fitted into the lattice interstitially; on the other hand, if they combine when separated by a gap, they leave a row of vacant lattice sites. As has been mentioned earlier, displacement of a dislocation from its slip plane also involves addition or subtraction of atoms from the segment that is displaced. It is probable that atmos-

---

[1] J. M. Burgers, *Proc. Roy. Acad. Sci. Amsterdam*, vol. 42, pp. 293, 378, 1939; *Proc. Phys. Soc. (London)*, vol. 52, p. 23, 1940.

[2] R. W. Cahn, *J. Inst. Metals*, vol. 76, p. 121, 1949.

[3] C. G. Dunn and F. W. Daniels, *Trans. AIME*, vol. 191, p. 147, 1951.

[4] F. R. N. Nabarro, in "Some Recent Developments in Rheology," United Trade Press, London, 1950, p. 38. J. F. W. Bishop and R. Hill, *Phil. Mag.*, vol. 42, p. 1298. 1951. A. J. E. Foreman and M. A. Jaswon, *Phil. Mag.* (in press).

pheres of vacancies or interstitial atoms are an important factor in the structure and properties of cold-worked metal even if they perhaps have a very limited lifetime. Shockley and Read have shown, for example, that grain-boundary migration can occur in some boundaries by vacancy diffusion from one dislocation to another in the array at the boundary. Seitz accounts for the fact that the electrical resistivity of cold-worked crystals recovers (in part) very rapidly[1] by assuming that vacancies and possibly interstitial atoms are responsible and that these migrate rapidly into less effective clusters.[2]

Anelasticity. Hooke's law, that the deformation of a body is proportional to the stress applied to the body, does not apply even at low stress levels where no permanent strain results. The classical theory of elasticity must be modified to take account of "anelastic" effects that cause the deformation to be a nonunique function of the applied stress. A vibrating body exhibits "internal friction," *i.e.*, energy must be supplied to maintain vibration of constant amplitude; otherwise the vibration is damped out at a rate determined by the internal friction. There is a time lag between the application of a stress and the resultant strain. A wire that is suddenly subjected to a torque does not immediately twist to its full distortion, but approaches this asymptotically as "relaxation" processes occur in the wire. Sudden release of the torque, similarly, does not abruptly return the wire to its original position; it creeps back, exhibiting "recoverable creep" or the "elastic aftereffect." Consequently a measure of the modulus of the wire gives different results when it is carried out with and without time for relaxation.

Many different causes have been identified for these anelastic effects, largely as a result of the work of Zener and his coworkers[3] in measuring and analyzing the various relaxation times involved in the anelastic processes. Some anelasticity is the result of heat flowing back and forth from point to point in the specimen during cyclic stressing. Anelasticity results, also, from the diffusion of solute atoms, for a random distribution of solute atoms may not be the minimum energy configuration in the presence of an applied stress. The stress may tend to align pairs of solute atoms parallel to the axis of tension, for example.[4] In interstitial solid

---

[1] A. W. Stepanow, *Z. Physik.*, vol. 81, p. 560, 1933. J. Molenaar and W. H. Aarts, *Nature*, vol. 166, p. 690, 1950.

[2] F. Seitz, *Phys. Rev.*, vol. 80, p. 239, 1950; "Advances in Physics," Quarterly Supplement to *Phil. Mag.*, vol. 1, p. 43, 1952.

[3] For a summary of the field see C. Zener, "Elasticity and Anelasticity of Metals," University of Chicago Press, Chicago, 1948.

[4] C. Zener, *Trans. AIME*, vol. 152, p. 122, 1943; *Phys. Rev.*, vol. 71, p. 34, 1947. Estimates of the density of vacancies in Al-Ag alloys, based on the principle that atoms should change place most readily when adjacent to a vacancy, are referred to on p. 258, in connection with imperfections.

solutions the movement of the interstitial atoms into those interstices that are enlarged by the applied stress and out of those that are constricted causes marked anisotropy and provides a very sensitive test of the solute concentration and of the rate of precipitation. It also provides a remarkably effective way to determine the diffusion coefficients of the solute atoms.

Still other causes of anelasticity are concerned with relaxations that occur in highly localized regions. Viscous flow at grain boundaries is one such mechanism. This introduces a cause of internal friction that is absent in single crystals and that is dependent upon grain size, temperature, and frequency in a manner determined experimentally in a series of investigations by T. S. Kê.[1] This form of flow becomes particularly important at elevated temperatures, since there is a heat of activation associated with it that is approximately equal to the heat of activation for self-diffusion. It becomes the predominant flow mechanism in high-temperature creep and creep recovery tests of metals, and accounts for the difference between relaxed and unrelaxed modulus values at elevated temperatures. It also provides the mechanism for building up stress concentrations (hydrostatic tension) at grain corners that can lead to the initiation of cracks at these points. Movement of a twin interface or a twinlike interface in response to an applied stress can also produce anelastic effects, since here also there is a time lag between stress and resulting strain.[2] This type of deformation accounts for anelastic effects associated with domain boundary movement in ferromagnetic materials. Tetragonality is introduced into a cubic lattice when a ferromagnetic domain is formed (c/a is about 1.00003), and the low-energy twin or twinlike interfaces between the differently oriented tetragonal domains move in response to stress.

An important variety of internal friction occurs in metals that have been previously deformed; it increases with the amount of cold work, and is removed by annealing below the temperature of visible recrystallization. Read's experiments on single crystals of copper and zinc[3] established the fact that this internal friction introduced by cold work, unlike internal friction from other causes, increased with increasing strain amplitude, even with strain amplitudes as small as 10^{-6}. This has been confirmed by others.[4] Read observed that in the hexagonal crystals of zinc the

[1] T. S. Kê, *Phys. Rev.*, vol. 71, p. 533, 1947; vol. 72, p. 41, 1947; *J. Applied Phys.*, vol. 19, p. 285, 1948.

[2] F. T. Worrell, *J. Applied Phys.*, vol. 19, p. 929, 1948. A. V. Siefert and F. T. Worrell, *J. Applied Phys.*, vol. 22, p. 1257, 1951.

[3] T. A. Read, *Trans. AIME*, vol. 143, p. 30, 1941.

[4] A. S. Nowick, "Conference on Plastic Deformation of Crystalline Solids," Carnegie Institute of Technology and Office of Naval Research, 1950; *Phys. Rev.*, vol. 80, p. 249, 1950. Also J. Marx and J. S. Koehler, same volume.

internal friction depends upon the orientation of the crystals, approaching a maximum when the resolved shear stress on the basal slip planes is a maximum.

In ways incompletely understood at present, the anelasticity introduced by cold work must involve the movement of dislocations that are present in the cold-worked metal.[1,2,3] It appears likely that, when stress is applied, dislocations are pulled over the points at which they are locked, or are forced to pass through the gaps between these points, and that the number that pass the locking points increases with increasing stress, temperature, and time of application of the load (i.e., decreasing frequency). Another interpretation[4] is that the previously formed slip bands act as disks of viscous material that relax in the way viscous grain boundaries relax, the magnitude and rate of relaxation depending upon the size of the slip bands. The wide spectrum of relaxation times that is observed is ascribed, in this interpretation, to the range of sizes of slip bands. Another mechanism suggested by Kê is viscous flow at the boundaries of crystallites produced by deformation. In some of the low-temperature annealing experiments there may have been opportunity for polygonization, so perhaps the movement of the dislocations making up these subgrain boundaries is also involved.

Strain aging in body-centered cubic metals can be accounted for, as mentioned earlier, by Cottrell's atmospheres of interstitial carbon and nitrogen atoms segregating at the dislocations and locking them. Conversely, the stresses at the dislocations lock the interstitial atoms so that a small applied stress is no longer able to move them into different interstices. This immobilizing of the interstitial atoms lowers the internal friction caused by the solute atoms, for only the unlocked atoms respond to the stress. Measuring the internal friction at the vibration frequency and temperature for maximum internal friction from the unlocked atoms, Harper[5] has studied the strain-aging process in iron. He finds that the diffusion of carbon to the dislocations is at a rate expected by the theory[6] and with a normal activation energy for carbon diffusion. When the strain aging was induced by nitrogen, the activation energy of the process was in corresponding agreement with that for nitrogen diffusion. The

[1] T. A. Read, Trans. AIME, vol. 143, p. 30, 1941.

[2] A. S. Nowick, "Conference on Plastic Deformation of Crystalline Solids," Carnegie Institute of Technology and Office of Naval Reserch, 1950; Phys. Rev., vol. 80, p. 249, 1950. Also J. Marx and J. S. Koehler, same volume.

[3] T. S. Kê, Trans. AIME, vol. 188, p. 575, 1950.

[4] T. S. Kê and C. Zener, "Symposium on Plastic Deformation of Crystalline Solids," Carnegie Institute of Technology and Office of Naval Research, 1950.

[5] S. Harper, to be published.

[6] A. H. Cottrell and B. Bilby, Proc. Phys. Soc. (London), vol. A62, p. 49, 1949.

magnitude of the internal friction changes could be used to obtain an approximate value for the dislocation density. After 5 per cent extension of the iron the density of edge dislocations (disregarding any segregation at screw dislocations) was computed to be 1.8×10^{11} lines per sq cm. These values are compatible with other estimates of dislocation densities.

CHAPTER XVII

THE STRUCTURE OF COLD-WORKED METAL

The distortions that are introduced into metals by plastic deformation are of such complexity that they can be deduced only by using all that is known of the fundamental nature of the flow processes, which have been mentioned in earlier chapters, and all that can be contributed by the best diffraction techniques and analysis. The present chapter is a review of the X-ray diffraction investigations. First the Laue method is discussed; then a brief survey of the reciprocal lattice as affected by various disturbances related to cold work; this is followed by a review of measurements of line broadening, line intensities, and line shapes and the conclusions that have been drawn from these with regard to the cold-worked state and recovery from this during annealing. At the end is a section on a photoelastic investigation of bend gliding and one on X-ray studies of fatigue.

Asterism. The well-known analogy pointed out by W. L. Bragg between diffraction of X-rays by atomic planes and the reflection of light by plane mirrors extends also to the diffraction by *bent* planes of atoms and the corresponding optical reflection from curved mirrors. It also applies to the reflection from crystal fragments arranged on a curved surface, corresponding to reflection from small mirrors arranged on a curved surface.

The optical analogy thus provides a convenient way of interpreting Laue patterns of deformed metals. Visualizing the atomic planes as mirrors, one sees at once that the Laue spots from a perfect crystal should be sharp, their size determined by the size and divergence of the X-ray beam and the dimensions of the camera, whereas Laue spots from bent planes should be elongated. The direction and amount of the elongation would depend on the position of the axis of bending with respect to the X-ray beam and the film, and also on the range of orientation of the planes within the area struck by the beam. Figure 1 is a typical example of the phenomenon. The spots elongate chiefly in radial or nearly radial directions, giving rise to the appearance known as "asterism."

It is also clear from the optical analogy that asterism could be produced by a preferred orientation of small crystallites, as in Fig. 2. If the crystallites were sufficiently small or the beam insufficiently collimated, the individual reflections would overlap, and the asterism streaks would

414

resemble those from a bent crystal; there is thus an uncertainty as to whether in any particular case asterism is caused by bending of crystals or by grouping of small crystallites, or by both.

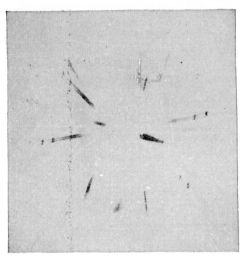

FIG. 1. Asterism from bending a thin crystal of ferrite cylindrically (molybdenum radiation, unfiltered).

Interpretation of Asterism in Terms of Range of Orientation. If a small crystal is placed in a beam of white radiation and rotated about an axis, the Laue spots will trace out curves on the film. When the axis of

FIG. 2. Pseudo asterism from preferred orientation in recrystallized rock salt. (*S. Konobejewski and J. Mirer, Z. Krist., vol.* 81, *p.* 69, 1932.)

rotation coincides with the axis of the primary beam, these curves will simply be arcs of circles concentric with the primary beam, but with all other orientations of the axis of rotation the Laue spots will follow curves having a complex form expressed by equations of the fourth degree. A number of charts giving these curves for special arrangement of axis and film have been published, a very complete collection appearing in the "International Tables for Crystal Structure Determination."[1] A more generally useful method is to plot the streaks on a stereographic projection.

From the lengths of asterism streaks one can determine the range of orientation within that portion of the material that lies in the primary beam. In practice, there are certain limitations that often prevent a streak from developing to the full length required by this orientation range. These result from the fact that each streak (unless it is an arc of a circle concentric with the primary beam) is a spectrum of the primary X-rays; *i.e.*, each part is formed by X-rays of different wavelength. For a streak formed by the (hkl) plane the wavelength of the ray forming any portion is given by Bragg's law $n\lambda = 2d_{hkl} \sin \theta$, and the streak must terminate abruptly at the short-wavelength limit of the spectrum (at θ corresponding to λ_{min}), irrespective of any additional length that would have been permitted by the orientation range. On the long-wavelength end a streak may be prevented from developing to its true length by the lack of intensity in the long-wavelength components of the general radiation. The intensity distribution along a streak is the combined result of the distribution in orientation of the diffracting material, the wavelength-intensity distribution of the primary beam, the efficiency of the photographic emulsion, and the absorption characteristics of the crystal. Abrupt changes in darkening will be found at λ values corresponding to the silver K absorption limit ($\lambda = 0.485$ A), the bromine K absorption limit ($\lambda = 0.918$ A), and critical-absorption limits of the elements in the crystal; and lines of intense blackening in the streaks will be found where characteristic radiation from the target is reflected. In the Laue pattern of Fig. 1 these points are illustrated. The thin crystal of alpha-iron was uniformly bent into a cylinder and mounted with the cylindrical axis vertical, normal to the primary beam; there was an approximately uniform distribution of material throughout the orientation range. The $K\alpha$ and $K\beta$ lines from the molybdenum target as well as sharp edges at the silver and bromine absorption limits are visible on some of the striae. The factors just enumerated have led many investigators to use methods based on monochromatic rays in preference to the Laue method to determine the distribution in orientation of deformed crystals.

The construction of a stereographic projection of a Laue spot or streak is very simple. If the projection plane is taken normal to the incident beam and parallel to the photographic film, the rules for its construction are as follows:[2]

[1] "Internationale Tabellen zur Bestimmung von Kristallstrukturen," vol. II, p. 631, Bornträger, Berlin, 1935.

[2] See Chap. IX, p. 170 , for a more detailed discussion.

1. The X-ray beam, the Laue spot, and its projection all lie in a plane. Therefore, the spot itself and the projection of the spot have the same angular position about the beam as an axis.

2. The value of the Bragg angle θ for a spot or portion of a streak is determined by the relation $r = R \tan 2\theta$, where r is the distance from the spot to the center of the film, and R is the distance from crystal to film. The angle θ can be read directly from a chart of concentric circles spaced according to this relation. The spot is then plotted at a distance of θ stereographic degrees measured inward from the outer circle of a stereographic net. (A polar net is most convenient for this purpose; but the equator of a Wulff net may be used as a scale.)

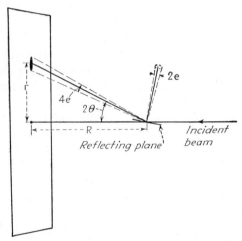

Fig. 3. Illustrating the radial character of asterism.

The predominantly radial direction of the streaks in forward-reflection Laue patterns is a direct consequence of the distorted angle relationships in the reflection projection. This will be understood if one considers the movement of a spot formed by reflection of a beam of light from a mirror that is rocked so that its normal moves within a small cone.[1] If the semivertical angle of this cone is e, the angle of incidence of a beam on a reflecting plane will vary through an angle $2e$, and the reflected beam through $4e$ (Fig. 3). This will elongate the reflected spot radially to a length $4eR$, where R is the distance from crystal to film. If the reflecting plane rocks around the beam as an axis, however, the reflected spot will move around the central beam through an angle $2e$. If the reflected beam is at an angle 2θ from the direct beam and the spot is at a distance r from the image of the direct beam, its lateral movement will be approximately $2er = 2e \times 2\theta R$. The ratio of major to minor axes of the elliptical spot

[1] W. L. Bragg, "The Crystalline State," vol. I, General Survey, Macmillan, New York, 1934.

will therefore be $4eR/4e\theta R = 1/\theta$. In the range of reflection of white radiation from the planes of greatest spacing, with θ values roughly 5 to 10° (0.08 to 0.17 radian), the major axis is six to twelve times the minor axis.

Asterism and Internal Stresses. The Laue method with its asterism streaks is definitely unsuited to the detection and measurement of internal stresses in metallurgical materials. The elastic distortions caused by internal stresses are negligible in comparison with the changes in orientation that result from plastic flow and are submerged by the latter. Numerous experiments have shown that Laue patterns from stressed and unstressed material are similar: single crystals loaded in tension give Laue patterns identical with the unstressed crystals as long as the load does not exceed the elastic range.[1] Elastically bent glide lamellae must be present in plastically deformed crystals, but asterism does not offer an attractive means of investigating the stresses in these, because of the complexities of the plastic distortions mentioned in the preceding chapters.[2] Some qualitative conclusions about the direction of bending are possible, however, from the shapes of Laue spots.[3]

Local Curvature. Homogeneous rotation of the lattice in a single crystal during either compression or tension is unusual. The constraints imposed by the grips of the testing machine or by the friction of the specimen on the compression plates cause bending of the glide layers in the lattice, the so-called "bend gliding."[4] In polycrystalline material the interference of neighboring grains having differently oriented slip systems gives rise to much of this bend gliding.[5] It is possible, however, to deform a single crystal so as to minimize all such bending moments.[6] This has been done in both tension and compression. If, for example, carefully prepared single crystals are squeezed between polished and greased compression plates, the slip planes rotate toward a position parallel to the plane of the compression plate; it would then be expected that the lattice would rotate homogeneously. Yet a considerable range of orientation is found in a crystal deformed in this way,[6] as is shown by asterism in Laue photograms and by reflections of monochromatic rays.

[1] Abram F. Joffé, "The Physics of Crystals," McGraw-Hill, New York, 1928. H. L. Cox and I. Backhurst, *Phil. Mag.*, vol. 7, p. 981, 1929. G. L. Clark and M. M. Beckwith, *Trans. ASM*, vol. 25, p. 1207, 1937.

[2] S. Konobejewski and I. Mirer (*Z. Krist.*, vol. 81, p. 69, 1932) attempted an analysis in rock salt.

[3] E. Orowan and K. J. Pascoe, *Nature*, vol. 148, p. 467, 1941.

[4] H. Mark, M. Polanyi, and E. Schmid, *Z. Physik*, vol. 12, pp. 58, 78, 111, 1922.

[5] F. Wever and W. E. Schmid, *Mitt. Kaiser-Wilhelm-Inst. Eisenforsch., Düsseldorf*, vol. 11, p. 109, 1929.

[6] G. I. Taylor and W. S. Farren, *Proc. Roy. Soc. (London)*, vol. A111, p. 529, 1926; vol. A116, p. 16, 1927.

The inhomogeneous character of deformed single crystals led Taylor, Yamaguchi, and Burgers to postulate distortions of a local character, "local curvature," arising from disturbances at the slipping surfaces and consisting of rotation of portions of the lattice about an axis lying in the glide plane and perpendicular to the glide direction, as shown in Fig. 4. The rotation is the same, in both direction and sense, as would be experienced by de-

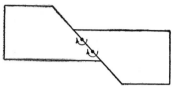

Fig. 4. Sketch illustrating local curvature at a slip plane.

tached portions of the lattice acting as rollers lying between the slipping surfaces and amounts to as much as 10, 20, or even 50° with severe deformation.

Another method of obtaining homogeneous deformation consists in pulling a long single crystal specimen in tension. In the center portion of the specimen at sufficient distances from the grips there should be no

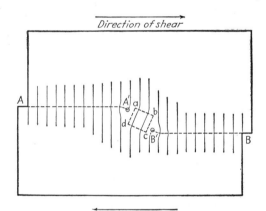

Fig. 5. Burgers's suggested mechanism for producing local curvature.

bending moments or bend gliding. The presence of asterism in photograms of this region has also been interpreted in terms of local curvature.[1]

Burgers has suggested that dislocations or slip movements approach each other, reaching the points A' and B' and creating local curvature in the region *abcd* in the manner indicated in Fig. 5.[2]

It cannot be safely concluded at the present time that the local curvatures postulated by Taylor, Yamaguchi, and Burgers actually exist.

[1] K. Yamaguchi, *Sci. Papers Inst. Phys. Chem. Research (Tokyo)*, vol. 11, p. 223, 1929.

[2] J. M. Burgers, *Proc. Phys. Soc. (London)*, vol. 52, p. 23, 1940.

Most of the experimental evidence for them would be equally well explained by macroscopic variations in orientation, and it is questionable whether the latter have been eliminated in their experiments. In fact, a series of studies[1] has shown that it is the rule, rather than the exception, for different portions of the crystal to rotate in different directions, forming deformation bands of differing orientation (see page 372). These bands are found even when great care is taken to provide homogeneous compression. They produce asterism much like that attributed to local distortion, as illustrated in Fig. 6. X-ray reflection micrographs of

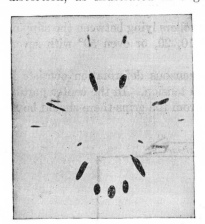

deformed rock salt by Berg[2] indicated rotation of narrow lamellae, but these, too, may have been deformation bands. An analysis of the directions of rotations in an aluminum crystal compressed in such a way as to avoid deformation bands did not confirm the predictions of the local curvature theory.[3] Some investigators fail to find asterism when crystals are homogeneously strained, provided slip is confined to a single slip system or to two slip planes using a common slip direction.[4] Laue photographs of an extended Al crystal with a microcollimated beam showed asterism only when the beam struck a kink band, which led Gay and Honeycombe to conclude that deformation bands are the cause of asterism.[5]

FIG. 6. Laue photograph showing asterism from deformation bands in a single crystal of aluminum compressed 28 per cent.

Nevertheless, there is direct evidence that some type of distortion is present along slip lines, for the reflecting power for X-rays is higher here, as shown by the black slip lines in X-ray reflection micrographs,[6] (Fig. 11, page 98).

[1] C. S. Barrett, *Trans. AIME*, vol. 135, p. 296, 1939. C. S. Barrett and L. H. Levenson, *Trans. AIME*, vol. 135, p. 327, 1939; vol. 137, p. 112, 1940.

[2] W. Berg, *Z. Krist.*, vol. 89, p. 286, 1934.

[3] C. S. Barrett, *Trans. AIME*, vol. 137, p. 128, 1940.

[4] R. Maddin, C. H. Mathewson, and W. R. Hibbard, *Trans. AIME*, vol. 185, p. 527, 1949 (alpha-brass elongated to a shear of 0.463). R. W. K. Honeycombe, *Proc. Phys. Soc. (London)*, vol. A63, p. 672, 1950 (cadmium crystals elongated 100 per cent, without deformation bands).

[5] P. Gay and R. W. K. Honeycombe, *Proc. Phys. Soc. (London)*, vol. A64, p. 844, 1951.

[6] C. S. Barrett, *Trans. AIME*, vol. 161, p. 15, 1945. R. W. K. Honeycombe, *Trans. AIME*, vol. 188, p. 1039, 1950.

Inhomogeneous Distortion in Polycrystalline Aggregates. In the deformation of grains of an aggregate it is difficult to separate the various factors causing spreading orientations in the grains, which produce asterism in Laue photograms. It is obvious that slip cannot proceed far without encountering interference from neighboring grains; severe bending and warping of the lattice then ensue; deformation bands form in many grains, and local curvature may also contribute to the inhomogeneity. Inasmuch as the average grain deforms by slip on several slip systems and is itself surrounded by several grains slipping in various ways, the average grain undergoes complex distortion. That this occurs can be shown clearly by plotting pole figures or by using an *oscillating-film technique*,[1] as illustrated in Fig. 7. In this camera the film and specimen are attached to the same carriage and rotate together; this permits

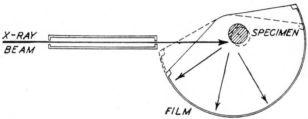

Fig. 7. X-ray camera in which film and specimen are mounted on an oscillating carriage Characteristic radiation is used.

the spreading of a Laue spot in all directions without altering the wavelength of the reflected beam. Figure 8 illustrates the results obtained in this camera and shows the gradually increasing complex spreading of spots from polycrystalline iron strained increasing amounts in tension.

The alterations in Laue photographs accompanying deformation are as follows: As deformation increases, there is first an elongation of spots chiefly in the radial direction, then an increase in the number of striae and a decrease in their sharpness, leading to an almost uniform blackening of Debye rings, and finally a grouping of the striae into intense spots, indicating a preferred orientation of steadily increasing perfection.

Factors That Broaden X-ray Reflections. The blurring and elongation of X-ray spots can be due to several causes in addition to the obvious one of a range of orientation within the diffracting crystal. These are first discussed briefly (the reader will find a detailed treatment of these in James's book[2]) and in subsequent sections the experimental data and the conclusions that have been drawn from them are reviewed. The nature of the effects can best be described by referring to the reciprocal lattice of

[1] C. S. Barrett, *Metals & Alloys*, vol. 8, p. 13, 1937.
[2] R. W. James, "The Optical Principles of Diffraction of X-rays," G. Bell, London, 1948.

the crystal, which consists of points at a distance r^* from the origin, where $r^* = 1/d_{hkl}$, the value d_{hkl} being the interplanar spacing represented by the point. Each point is located on a line through the origin normal to the crystal plane (hkl).

Orientation Range. As a crystal rotates, the reciprocal lattice rotates with it (since the points must remain on the plane normals). This means that, if a range of orientation exists in the crystal, as from a simple bend, it can be represented by a reciprocal lattice in which each point is elongated into an arc that is concentric with the origin; similarly, complex

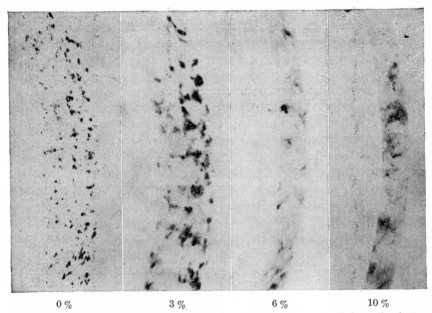

| 0 % | 3 % | 6 % | 10 % |

FIG. 8. Photographs of polycrystalline iron after increasing amounts of elongation in tension. Made with camera of Fig. 7 (Fe$K\alpha$ (110) reflections).

bending is equivalent in the reciprocal lattice to each point being spread out over a segment of a sphere concentric with the origin. Spots on Debye rings are elongated circumferentially by this distortion.

Stress. Consider a cubic crystal subjected to a tensile stress along one axis.[1] The reciprocal lattice will be compressed along the direction that the crystal is stretched, because of the reciprocal relationship; and because the crystal contracts laterally, the reciprocal lattice will expand in directions normal to the tensile stress. If the stress varies in magnitude throughout the crystal but is constant in direction, the points will be spread into lines, each point on a line corresponding to the position of a

[1] This discussion follows H. Lipson, "Symposium on Internal Stresses in Metals and Alloys," p. 35, Institute of Metals, London, 1948.

reciprocal point from a portion of the crystal that is under a certain stress. Along any row in the reciprocal lattice that extends out from the origin, the length of the lines will be proportional to their distance from the origin. If the stresses vary in direction as well as magnitude, each point will elongate into bundles of nonparallel lines that fill a small volume surrounding the point. This volume will not be spherical, in general, because even if the average stresses in the various directions were equal, the value of Young's modulus varies with orientation in the crystal. Even with volumes of irregular shape at each reciprocal lattice point, however, it will be true that the sizes of these volumes along any row extending radially from the origin will be proportional to their distance from the origin, r^*. Since $r^* = 1/d = (2 \sin \theta)/\lambda$ it follows that the spread in r^* at any point, δr^*, is proportional to r^* for the points in any such row; so if $\delta(2 \sin \theta)/\lambda$ is proportional to $(2 \sin \theta)/\lambda$ then $(\cos \theta \; \delta\theta)/\lambda$ is proportional to $(\sin \theta)/\lambda$ and, finally, $\delta\theta$ is proportional to $\tan \theta$ and independent of λ. There has been much discussion (see later) of the question of the $\tan \theta$ relation in actual experiments on line broadening.

Crystallite Size. We consider now the reciprocal lattice for crystals that are extremely thin in one dimension. Each reciprocal lattice point is elongated into a line, because of lack of resolving power (relaxation of one of the Laue conditions). All lines are of equal length and are normal to the plane of the crystal platelet. If more than one dimension is small the points become enlarged into three-dimensional volumes, but again are of equal size. Thus δr^* for points along a given row is a constant, so $(2 \cos \theta \; \delta\theta)/\lambda$ is a constant, and $\delta\theta$ is proportional to $\lambda/\cos \theta$. Thus line broadening from small crystallite size follows a different law from that produced by stresses.

Stacking Faults. Faulty stacking of planes in crystals having stacking disorders produces characteristic alterations of the reciprocal lattice. If faults occur on a single set of planes, such as the basal planes of hexagonal cobalt, certain reciprocal lattice points will be elongated normal to the faulted planes, and others will be left sharp, unlike crystallite-size broadening, which affects all points. The unaltered points correspond to reflecting planes that have structure factors unaltered by the fault displacements.[1] The various points that are elongated may belong to more than one class with regard to the effect of faulting upon their reflecting power, but all points in a given class are elongated equally, by an amount that increases with the density of the faults. Therefore, as in crystallite-size broadening, points along a given radial row in the reciprocal lattice that belong to the same class will have constant δr^* and, as in crystallite-size broadening, will have $\delta\theta$ proportional to $\lambda/\cos \theta$. If faulting occurs

---

[1] In hexagonal cobalt, 00l points remain sharp for any value of l, and also hkl points in which $h - k = 3n$ where n is any integer, including zero.

on several sets of planes, like the {111} planes of face-centered cubic crystals, several spikes may extend outward from individual reciprocal lattice points. The theory of intensity distribution in the reciprocal lattice of faulted structures has been presented in detail by Wilson,[1] Zachariasen,[2] and Jagodzinski.[3] Examples of stacking disorders are found in a steadily expanding list of crystals, including the micas,[4] graphite[5] and other layer structures, cobalt,[6] copper-silicon alloys,[7] and lithium.[8] Faults may arise as a result of processes in growth, or from plastic deformation, or from phase changes in the solid state.

Faulty Ordering in Superlattices. When a superlattice is only partially ordered the reflections from the planes that are unaffected by ordering remain sharp, but the superlattice reflections become diffuse. The results can be expressed in terms of a crystallite-size effect in the domains, but since different reflections give different effective domain sizes[9] this is an inexact approach. Different reciprocal lattice points are broadened in different ways. It is probably more appropriate to analyze the patterns by assuming that like atoms tend to avoid each other.[10] Further reference to this will be found in the chapter on superlattices. Since cold work can produce disorder in superlattices, the broadening of superlattice lines becomes a tool for investigating the structure of cold-worked metals.

Precipitation. Elongated reflections may be obtained when a phase precipitates from a supersaturated solid solution, especially when the precipitated crystals are coherent, along a certain plane, with the parent crystal. The reflections will be affected not only by the shape of the newly formed crystals, but by the coherent and strained lattice that extends across the matrix-precipitate interface, and also by the distribution of atoms of different scattering power. The diffraction patterns of Cu_4FeNi_3 and analogous alloys offer examples.[11] (See chapter on Precipitation and Transformation.) When glide movements are able to construct a stable or metastable phase from a parent phase, the diffraction

[1] A. J. C. Wilson, "X-ray Optics," Methuen, London, 1949; *Proc. Roy. Soc. (London)*, vol. A180, p. 277, 1942; *Acta Cryst.*, vol. 2, p. 245, 1949.

[2] W. H. Zachariasen, *Phys. Rev.*, vol. 71, p. 715, 1947; *Acta Cryst.*, vol. 1, p. 277, 1948. The formal theory for all disorders is given in W. Zachariasen, "Theory of Diffraction of X-rays in Crystals," Wiley, New York, 1945.

[3] H. Jagodzinski, *Acta Cryst.*, vol. 2, pp. 201, 208, 298, 1949.

[4] S. B. Hendricks, *Phys. Rev.*, vol. 57, p. 448, 1940.

[5] B. E. Warren, *Phys. Rev.*, vol. 59, p. 693, 1941.

[6] O. S. Edwards and H. Lipson, *Proc. Roy. Soc. (London)*, vol. A180, p. 268, 1942.

[7] C. S. Barrett, *Trans. AIME*, vol. 188, p. 123, 1950.

[8] C. S. Barrett in "Phase Transformations in Solids," Wiley, New York, 1951.

[9] F. W. Jones and C. Sykes, *Proc. Roy. Soc. (London)*, vol. A166, p. 376, 1938.

[10] A. J. C. Wilson, *Proc. Roy. Soc. (London)*, vol. A181, p. 369, 1943; "X-ray Optics," Methuen, London, 1949.

[11] V. Daniel and H. Lipson, *Proc. Roy. Soc. (London)*, vol. A182, p. 378, 1944.

patterns reveal this by the appearance of spots at positions corresponding to the new phase; elongated spots are to be expected both because the new phase consists of thin lamellae, and because stacking faults are likely.[1]

Thermal Vibrations of Atoms. The heat motion of atoms in crystals is responsible for diffuse reflections superimposed on the normal sharp reflections. The diffuse component is weak at ordinary temperatures, though visible on overexposed films; it is increased by raising the temperature of the sample and is reduced to negligible amount by cooling to liquid nitrogen temperature.[2,3] The diffuse patches are not spherical,[3] even with cubic crystals, but are elliptical or have spikes extending in simple crystallographic directions out from the reciprocal lattice point. The interpretation of these diffuse clouds in terms of the elastic waves of varying frequency and amplitude that make up the heat motions has been investigated in detail.[4]

If the intensity of the thermal diffuse scattering is measured (and related to the intensity of the primary beam) for a series of positions near the Bragg reflectors, it is possible to determine the elastic constants of the reflecting crystal for elastic waves of very short wavelength (down to about two unit cells in length).[5] The accuracies being obtained in these elastic constant determinations lie in the range 3 to 15 per cent.

Measurements of Line Broadening. Many investigators in the last 30 years have attempted to determine the nature of the distortions in cold-worked metals from analyses of the broadening of diffraction lines. As has been stated in earlier sections of this chapter, there are several factors that may contribute to the broadening, either singly or in combination, and the separate identification of these is extremely difficult. Only the most complete and precise X-ray data and the most thorough analysis of

---

[1] An example is the metastable γ' phase formed by cold working supersaturated copper-silicon alloys of 5 to 5.4 per cent silicon. C. S. Barrett, *Trans. AIME*, vol. 188, p. 123, 1950.

[2] G. D. Preston, *Proc. Roy. Soc. (London)*, vol. A172, p. 116, 1939; *Nature*, vol. 147, p. 467, 1941.

[3] K. Lonsdale and H. Smith, *Proc. Roy. Soc. (London)*, vol. A179, p. 8, 1941–1942. H. Jahn and K. Lonsdale, *Phys. Rev.*, vol. 61, p. 375, 1942. K. Lonsdale, *Repts. Progress Phys.*, vol. 9, p. 271, 1942–1943.

[4] M. Born and T. v. Kármán, *Physik. Z.*, vol. 13, p. 297, 1912; vol. 14, pp. 15, 65, 1913. H. Faxén, *Ann. Physik*, vol. 54, p. 615, 1917; *Z. Physik.*, vol. 17, p. 266, 1923. W. H. Zachariasen, *Phys. Rev.*, vol. 57, p. 597, 1940; vol. 59, p. 860, 1941. W. H. Zachariasen and S. Siegel, *Phys. Rev.*, vol. 57, p. 795, 1940. J. Weigel and Charles S. Smith, *Phys. Rev.*, vol. 61, p. 23, 1942. W. H. Zachariasen, "Theory of X-ray Diffraction in Crystals," Wiley, New York, 1945.

[5] I. Waller, *Z. Physik.*, vol. 17, p. 398, 1923; vol. 51, p. 213, 1928. J. Laval, *J. Phys. Radium*, vol. 4, p. 1, 1943. H. A. Jahn, *Proc. Roy. Soc. (London)*, vol. A179, p. 320, 1942. G. N. Ramachandran and W. A. Wooster, *Acta Cryst.*, vol. 4, pp. 335, 431, 1951.

it can be expected to lead to rigorous conclusions, and given these conclusions there is still the problem of interpreting them in terms of the fundamental types of lattice distortions that are thought to exist in cold-worked crystals. The process of assuming simple models, computing the diffraction effects from these, and comparing the computations with measured broadening has been used repeatedly in the past, and may have to be continued, but can scarcely be relied upon to arrive at a unique theory in the complicated situations encountered in actual crystals. The models used to predict broadening from cold work have been based chiefly on small crystallite size, microstresses, or faults; a brief discussion of the support for these various models is given below.

1. *Crystallite Size.* If cold work causes subdivision of grains into fragments that are smaller than 10^{-4} cm there will be a resultant broadening of the diffraction lines, analogous to the broadening of lines from a diffraction grating when the number of lines is reduced. A convenient measure of broadening from any cause is the "integral line width," which is obtained by dividing the area under the curve of intensity vs. θ by the peak height of the curve. After correction for the broadening arising in the diffraction equipment, the particle-size broadening B should vary with wavelength λ and diffraction angle θ according to the law

$$B = \frac{K\lambda}{L \cos \theta}$$

where L is the effective size of the crystallites and K is a constant.[1] On the basis of measurements he has made on films, Wood[2,3] has maintained for a number of years that broadening from cold-worked metal is due largely to this particle-size effect, cold work reducing the fragments to a limiting size that varies from metal to metal in the range between 10^{-4} and 10^{-6} cm. He proposes[3] that crystallite size is the only significant cause of broadening in samples strained homogeneously in tension or compression, with the metals Fe, Mo, Ta, and W. His proposal is based on measurements of widths on films exposed with different wavelengths, in which he found that observed widths, corrected in an approximate way for instrumental broadening, varied with wavelength as required by the crystallite-size theory. In view of the complexities of the microstress

---

[1] For detailed treatments of broadening theory see R. W. James, "The Optical Principles of Diffraction of X-rays," G. Bell, London, 1948; A. J. C. Wilson, "X-ray Optics," Methuen, London, 1949; A. R. Stokes and A. J. C. Wilson, *Proc. Cambridge Phil. Soc.*, vol. 38, p. 313, 1942; B. E. Warren and B. L. Averbach, *J. Applied Phys.*, vol. 21, p. 595, 1950. For particles of approximately spherical shape and for B expressed in terms of the angle 2θ, K is approximately 1.0.

[2] W. A. Wood, *Proc. Roy. Soc. (London)*, A172, p. 231, 1939; *Proc. Phys. Soc. (London)*, vol. 52, p. 110, 1940.

[3] W. A. Wood and W. A. Rachinger, *J. Inst. Metals*, vol. 75, p. 571, 1949.

distributions that must exist in cold-worked metal, it is difficult to agree with his assumption that homogeneous deformation of the specimen would not introduce heterogeneous internal stresses sufficient to widen the lines markedly, just as various investigators conclude that they do in inhomogeneous deformation (grinding, filing, etc.).

Brindley and Ridley[1] obtained line widths from filed rhodium that would indicate a crystallite size of 10^{-6} cm if it were the only cause of the widening, but the line widths did not vary with θ and λ as they should if particle size were the cause. Furthermore, there would be almost no primary extinction if the particles were small enough to explain the entire broadening; yet there is considerable extinction, and an estimate of crystallite size in rhodium from the extinction gives 6.5×10^{-5} cm. Averbach and Warren,[2] using crystal monochromatized rays and a Geiger-counter spectrometer, also observed extinction effects in the intensities of the strongest lines from cold-worked brass (30 per cent Zn). They assumed that the extinction was of the primary type and calculated particle sizes of about 10^{-5} cm from it. Hall and Williamson,[3] however, found better agreement with Geiger-counter data when the extinction in filed, annealed Al and in chemically precipitated Cu was assumed to be secondary rather than primary, and they suggested that dislocations were present to an extent that eliminated primary extinction and yet left effective particle sizes in the Al (of 99.997 per cent purity) of about 10^{-4} cm (judging by line widths) and in the Cu of 10^{-5} cm.

2. *Microstresses.* If individual grains or subgrain regions are stressed different amounts, so that the interplanar distances vary from region to region, a diffracted line from the metal as a whole will be the sum of many individual components that deviate slightly from one another. The composite line will therefore be broadened, even if the individual regions are larger than 10^{-4} cm so that no crystallite-size broadening is present. A test of this theory of line broadening that has been frequently applied is to see how broadening varies with the diffraction angle θ. Microstress broadening depends upon θ in a way that may be seen by taking the logarithmic derivative of Bragg's law, $n\lambda = 2d \sin \theta$, which gives

$$\frac{\delta d}{d} = \frac{\delta \theta}{\tan \theta}$$

The broadening for a given effective internal strain $\bar{e}$ should then be

$$B = \bar{e} \tan \theta$$

[1] G. W. Brindley and P. Ridley, *Proc. Phys. Soc. (London)*, vol. 50, p. 501, 1938.

[2] B. L. Averbach and B. E. Warren, *J. Applied Phys.*, vol. 20, p. 1066, 1949. B. L. Averbach, *Trans. AIME*, vol. 185, p. 491, 1949.

[3] W. H. Hall and G. K. Williamson, *Proc. Phys. Soc. (London)*, vol. B64, pp. 937, 946, 1951.

and should be distinguishable from crystallite-size broadening which is proportional to $\lambda/\cos\theta$. Studies of cold-worked metals by Smith and Stickley[1] and by Stokes, Pascoe, and Lipson[2] indicated that broadening varies with angle according to the theory for stresses, not crystallite size. Dehlinger and Kochendörfer[3] undertook the separation of broadening from crystallite size and from stresses by assuming that it could be separated into components proportional to $\lambda/\cos\theta$ and tan θ, respectively, and studied these components as a function of the amount of deformation, believing that both coexist.

Line widths measured by several investigators[4] were analyzed by Hall[5] using the principle that when line shapes are of the form $1/(1 + k^2x^2)$, broadening is additive (p. 158) and the particle size and strain equations combine to give

$$\frac{B \cos\theta}{\lambda} = \frac{K}{L} + \bar{e}\frac{\sin\theta}{\lambda}$$

and measurements can be plotted on a curve having a slope of $\bar{e}$ and an intercept of K/L.* Both types of broadening seemed to be present in the filings and rolled sheets analyzed; the mean effective particle size was found to be 10^{-5} cm.[6]

Comparison of theory and experiment in this field is hampered by the fact that most metals are anisotropic, Young's modulus varying with direction in the crystal. It cannot be taken for granted that the average normal stresses in the various directions in the crystal are equal, or that the average normal strains are equal, or that any one of many simplified models of stress distribution must obtain. Smith and Stickley noticed that the relative widths of $h00$ and hhh lines were as would be expected if the same average stress is assumed in the [100] and [111] directions, acting

[1] C. S. Smith and E. E. Stickley, *Phys. Rev.*, vol. 64, p. 191, 1943.

[2] A. R. Stokes, K. J. Pascoe, and H. Lipson, *Nature*, vol. 151, p. 137, 1943.

[3] U. Dehlinger and A. Kochendörfer, *Z. Krist.*, vol. 101, p. 134, 1939. A. Kochendörfer, *Z. Krist.*, vol. 105, p. 393, 1944.

[4] U. Dehlinger and A. Kochendörfer, *Z. Metallkunde*, vol. 31, p. 231, 1939; *Z. Krist.*, vol. A101, p. 134, 1939 (Cu). A. R. Stokes, K. J. Pascoe, and H. Lipson, *Nature*, vol. 151, p. 137, 1943 (Cu). W. H. Hall and G. K. Williamson, *Proc. Phys. Soc. (London)*, vol. B64, pp. 937, 946, 1951 (Al, Cu). J. A. Wheeler and M. A. Jaswon, *J. Iron Steel Inst.*, vol. 157, p. 161, 1947 (martensite). G. W. Brindley and P. Ridley, *Proc. Phys. Soc. (London)*, vol. 50, p. 501, 1938; vol. 51, p. 432, 1939 (Cu, Rh, Ni).

[5] W. H. Hall, *Proc. Phys. Soc. (London)*, vol. A62, p. 741, 1949. The principle is also used in the papers of Hall and Williamson.

*Assuming isotropic material. With Gaussian line shapes the curve would be asymptotic to a line of slope $\bar{e}$ at large distances from the origin and curve up to intercept K/L. (Hall and Williamson.)

[6] Attempts to discriminate between these two causes using one hkl and several wavelengths, or using several reflections with but one wavelength are ineffective. Hall and Williamson (private communication).

with the known values of Young's modulus in these two directions.   The anisotropic effects they observed in brass were absent in tungsten.   This would be expected on the stress theory since tungsten is isotropic.   Warren and Averbach,[1] using more precise data and a more detailed analysis, reached similar conclusions; they found the root-mean-square strains in various crystallographic directions in filings of brass to be roughly inversely proportional to the value of Young's modulus in these directions, as if normal stresses were about equal, on the average, in all directions. As Blackman[2] has pointed out, however, a great many different models of stress distributions can be invented and compared with observed line widths.   He finds that different models lead to different predictions of the relative widths, but the accuracy of the available measurements does not inspire great confidence in one's ability to distinguish between some of the models.

Paterson's study[3] of line widths of copper, nickel, and aluminum wires led him to suggest that stresses rather than crystallite size seem chiefly responsible for the broadening.   This conclusion rested largely on his finding that the stresses computed from the broadening varied with the temperature at which the cold work was done and paralleled quite closely the variation of the yield strength with temperature; the estimated stresses, also, were of the same order of magnitude as the measured yield stresses for each of the metals.   Megaw and Stokes[4] had previously concluded that the effective average stress calculated from line widths of filings is of the order of the ultimate strength in various metals, and a similar idea was proposed as early as 1925 by Van Arkel.[5]   Yet the apparent correlation of line breadths with yield strength might reflect some relation that is more fundamental, perhaps a relation with faulting tendency (see Section 3 below), or merely the ability of the cold worked metal to resist the tendency to recover at room temperature.[6]

Microstress models have formed the basis for computations of the residual strain energy in the cold-worked metal, and a number of investigators have made such computations from line widths.[7]   None of the

[1] B. E. Warren and B. L. Averbach, *J. Applied Phys.*, vol. 21, p. 595, 1950.

[2] N. Blackman, *Phys. Rev.*, vol. 70, p. 698, 1946.

[3] M. S. Paterson, Dissertation, Cambridge University, 1949.   M. S. Paterson and E. Orowan, *Nature*, vol. 162, p. 991, 1948.

[4] H. D. Megaw and A. R. Stokes, *J. Inst. Metals*, vol. 71, p. 279, 1945.

[5] A. E. Van Arkel, *Physica*, vol. 5, p. 208, 1925.

[6] W. H. Hall and G. K. Williamson, *Proc. Phys. Soc. (London)*, vol. B64, pp. 937, 946, 1951 (filed Al and W).   G. K. Williamson and R. E. Smallman, (filed Al and Fe) to be published.   Recovery of Al line widths was observed in a few minutes at room temperature.

[7] V. Cagliotti and G. Sachs, *Z. Physik*, vol. 74, p. 647, 1932.   W. Boas, *Z. Krist.*, vol. 96, p. 214, 1937.   F. E. Haworth, *Phys. Rev.*, vol. 52, p. 613, 1937.   G. W. Brindley and P. Ridley, *Proc. Phys. Soc. (London)*, vol. 51, p. 432, 1939.

early computations agreed even as to order of magnitude with the observed values of the residual energy in cold-worked metals. The measured values, in calories per gram in severely cold-worked metals, were Cu, 0.5; Fe, 1.2; Ni, 0.78; Al, 1.1, according to Taylor and Quinney,[1] and similar values were obtained by others.[2] The first computations were roughly one-thousandth of these measured values, later ones about one-tenth of these; but a recent one[3] seems to agree closely.

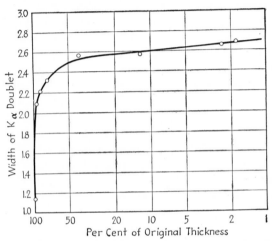

Fig. 9. Breadth at half-minimum intensity of the reflected $K\alpha$ doublet for permalloy reduced various amounts by cold rolling. (*Haworth.*)

The manner in which line width increases with plastic deformation has received extensive study.[4] Most observers find that plastic deformation widens the diffraction lines up to a limiting value that is essentially unchanged by further deformation of the same type. A typical curve, showing the usual leveling off at the limiting value, is reproduced in Fig. 9. It has been suggested that a definite limit of widening exists that is characteristic of the material,[5] but if a limiting value does exist it must

[1] G. I. Taylor and H. Quinney, *Proc. Roy. Soc.* (*London*), vol. A143, p. 307, 1934. H. Quinney and G. I. Taylor, *Proc. Roy. Soc.* (*London*), vol. A163, p. 157, 1937.

[2] W. S. Farren and G. I. Taylor, *Proc. Roy. Soc.* (*London*), vol. A107, p. 422, 1925. W. Rosenhain and V. H. Stott, *Proc. Roy. Soc.* (*London*), vol. A140, p. 9, 1933. L. M. Clarebrough, M. E. Hargraves, D. Mitchell, and G. West (to be published). G. Bockstiegel and K. Lüke, *Z. Metallkunde*, vol. 42, p. 225, 1951 (Cu wire reduced 99.97 per cent by cold drawing: 2.7 cal per gram).

[3] B. E. Warren and B. L. Averbach, to be published; see section on Fourier Analysis of Line Broadening.

[4] For an earlier review of the subject see C. S. Barrett, *Metals & Alloys*, vol. 5, pp. 131, 154, 170, 196, 224, 1934.

[5] H. J. Gough and W. A. Wood, *Proc. Roy. Soc.* (*London*), vol. A154, p. 510, 1936; summarized in lecture to Royal Aeronautical Society, Apr. 20, 1936, and in *Metal Progress*, vol. 30, p. 91, 1936.

certainly depend on the conditions of loading, the temperature of deformation, and the previous thermal and mechanical history of the specimen,[1] and it cannot be an invariant characteristic of a metal or alloy. Ludwik and Scheu,[2] in fact, have shown that line width at fracture depends upon the type of loading and heat-treatment and that the width at a brittle fracture is less than at a ductile fracture; others have shown a difference in maximum width from different kinds of deformation,[3] and from the same deformation at different temperatures.[4] The latter was shown[4] to be an effect that was not accounted for by self-annealing at the testing temperature, but a true effect of the temperature at which the deformation occurred.

The most severe cold-work broadening has been obtained by Bridgman[5] by applying shearing strains under tremendous pressure. Copper specimens were distorted to such a degree that only a single broad Debye line could be seen, the broadening being equivalent to that for crystallites of only about 10 A diameter. Lower melting metals like bismuth retained recognizable Debye patterns, perhaps because of room-temperature recovery of line sharpness; permalloy also retained patterns that did not approach those for amorphous materials.[6]

Analysing diffraction from bent lamellae, Wilson[7] concluded that broadening from bent glide lamellae should change continuously from crystallite-size broadening to stress broadening as the ratio $T^2/\lambda R$ increases, where T is the thickness of the lamellae, R is their radius of curvature, and λ is the wavelength of the radiation used. Also at small values of $\sin \theta/\lambda$ crystallite-size broadening should mask stress broadening, and for sufficiently large values of $\sin \theta/\lambda$ the stress broadening should predominate. The transition from one situation to the other will depend upon the nature of the distortion and the shape of the crystallites.

A shift in the mean lattice spacing has been reported in X-ray studies of rolled metals and elongated tensile specimens.[8] This cannot be accounted for by crystallite-size broadening, which would not shift the lines; it is probably due to stresses in the reflecting grains that do not have a mean value of zero in the direction concerned. The microstresses meas-

[1] C. S. Barrett, *Metals & Alloys*, vol. 8, p. 13, 1937.

[2] P. Ludwik and L. Scheu, *Metallwirtschaft*, vol. 13, pp. 257, 429, 1934.

[3] F. E. Haworth, *Phys. Rev.*, vol. 52, p. 613, 1937. U. Dehlinger and A. Kochendörfer, *Z. Metallukunde*, vol. 31, p. 231, 1939.

[4] M. S. Paterson and E. Orowan, *Nature*, vol. 162, p. 991, 1948.

[5] P. W. Bridgman, *J. Applied Phys.*, vol. 8, p. 328, 1937.

[6] F. E. Haworth, *Phys. Rev.*, vol. 52, p. 613, 1937.

[7] A. J. C. Wilson, *Acta Cryst.*, vol. 2, p. 220, 1949.

[8] W. A. Wood, *Phil. Mag.*, vol. 18, p. 495, 1934; *Proc. Phys. Soc. (London)*, vol. 52, p. 110, 1940. S. L. Smith and W. A. Wood, *Proc. Roy. Soc. (London)*, vol. A182, p. 404, 1944.

ured by X-rays might be balanced by stresses either in the interior, or in parts of the grains that are too distorted to diffract well, or in grains of nonreflecting orientation.[1]

3. *Faults (Stacking Disorders)*.   A third cause of line broadening that must be considered is faulty stacking of atomic layers.   If stacking errors are frequent, diffraction spots will have streaks extending out from them. (In the reciprocal lattice, spikes extend out from certain reciprocal lattice points in a direction normal to the faulted planes.)   The combined effect of the fault streaks is to widen the lines of a powder pattern.   The possibility that cold work introduces numerous faults into metals (at least into some f.c.c. and c.p.h. alloys) and that these make important contributions to the line broadening has been ignored in the early studies of broadening.

Oscillating-crystal studies have shown that cold work introduces numerous faults in Cu-Si alloys of f.c.c. structure containing 4 or 5 per cent Si.[2]   The powder diffraction lines from filings of these same alloys are extremely broad (when the filing is done at temperatures such that faulting occurs), and the same is true of an alloy of Ag plus 11 per cent Sn that is known to be subject to faulting by cold work, and an alloy of Ag plus 7 per cent Sb in which faulting is to be expected.[3]   Brass containing 30 per cent Zn also showed marked broadening, though independent proof of faulting is lacking for this alloy.   Contrasting with these samples that gave very wide lines, commercial aluminum (2S) gave narrow lines, when filed either at room temperature or at −195°C.   The aluminum alloy 24ST also gave narrow lines (when filed at room temperature), even though its yield strength is much greater than that of aluminum.   The results were interpreted to indicate that faulting is negligible in aluminum and 24ST,[*] and negligible or small in copper and silver.   It can scarcely be expected that the exact contribution of faulting to the broadening can be obtained by simple measurements of integral line widths.   But the results emphasize the need for caution by observers who ignore faulting in their analysis of broadening; and also those who point to the correlation between broadening and flow stress as support for the theory that broadening is due to microstress.   This correlation might in some instances be the result of flow stress being heavily dependent upon the number of faults rather than on microstresses or crystallite size.   Tests for faults are discussed further in the following section.

[1] G. B. Greenough, *Proc. Roy. Soc. (London)*, vol. A197, p. 556, 1949.

[2] C. S. Barrett, *Trans. AIME*, vol. 188, p. 123, 1950.

[3] C. S. Barrett and M. A. Barrett, *Phys. Rev.*, vol. 81, p. 311, 1951.   C. S. Barrett in "Imperfections in Nearly Perfect Crystals," Wiley, New York, 1952.

[*] J. E. Wilson and L. Thomassen (*Trans. ASM*, vol. 22, p. 769, 1934) as well as M. S. Paterson and E. Orowan (*Nature*, vol. 162, p. 991, 1948) found much wider lines after deforming aluminum at low temperatures (−76°C and −195°C, respectively) than at room temperature.   These investigators used massive samples, not filings.

Fourier Analysis of Line Broadening. The most promising approach to the nature of the distortion in a cold-worked metal should be an analysis that makes full use of precision data on the intensity distribution in each line of the pattern, not just a single index of the width of a few lines. This has been the object of a program started by Warren and Averbach[1] in which attempts are made to deduce as much as possible directly from X-ray data without making assumptions and using preconceived models. Line shapes are first measured with monochromatized X-rays and a Geiger counter; these are then corrected for instrumental broadening by the Fourier method of Stokes.[2] Each peak from the annealed sample is represented by a Fourier series; the corresponding peak from the cold-worked sample is also represented by a series, and from the coefficients of the two series a third set of coefficients is computed for a series that represents the shape of the corrected line. A general distortion is then considered in which the position of a unit cell $m_1 m_2 m_3$ is given by the vector **R**. In terms of the unit cell vectors a_1, a_2, and a_3,

$$\mathbf{R}_{m_1 m_2 m_3} = m_1 \mathbf{a}_1 + m_2 \mathbf{a}_2 + m_3 \mathbf{a}_3 + \delta_{m_1 m_2 m_3}$$

The displacement vector $\delta_m = X_m \mathbf{a}_1 + Y_m \mathbf{a}_2 + Z_m \mathbf{a}_3$, is different, in general, for each cell $m = m_1 m_2 m_3$. Let the direction of the primary and diffracted beams be represented by the unit vectors $\mathbf{S}_0$ and $\mathbf{S}$, so that their difference gives

$$\mathbf{S}_0 - \mathbf{S} = \lambda(h_1 \mathbf{b}_1 + h_2 \mathbf{b}_2 + h_3 \mathbf{b}_3)$$

where $\mathbf{b}_1$, $\mathbf{b}_2$, and $\mathbf{b}_3$ are the vectors of the reciprocal lattice and h_1, h_2, h_3 are continuous variables. The intensity from the crystal is then related to the displacement at *pairs* of cells—cells at $\mathbf{R}_{m_1 m_2 m_3}$ and $\mathbf{R}_{m_1' m_2' m_3'}$—by the relation

$$I(h_1 h_2 h_3) = F^2 \sum_{m_1} \sum_{m_2} \sum_{m_3} \sum_{m_1'} \sum_{m_2'} \sum_{m_3'} e^{(2\pi i/\lambda)(\mathbf{S}-\mathbf{S}_0)\cdot(\mathbf{R}_m - \mathbf{R}_{m'})}$$

This distribution of intensity in reciprocal space is then integrated throughout reciprocal space so as to give the power in the corrected plot of intensity distribution vs. 2θ in a diffraction line. For convenience, crystal axes a_1, a_2, and a_3 are chosen so that each reflection is of the type $00l$. The result of integration is expressed as a Fourier series

$$P_{2\theta} = K \sum_{n=-\infty}^{n=+\infty} A_n \cos 2\pi n h_3$$

---

[1] B. E. Warren and B. L. Averbach, *J. Applied Phys.*, vol. 21, p. 595, 1950; additional work to be published subsequently.

[2] A. R. Stokes, *Proc. Phys. Soc. (London)*, vol. 61, p. 382, 1948.

where $n = m_3 - m_3'$ and $h_3 = (2a_3 \sin \theta)/\lambda$; and the Fourier coefficients are

$$A_n = \; < \cos 2\pi l Z_n >_{av}$$

where the displacement is $Z_n = Z_{m_3} - Z_{m_3'}$ and the averaging is carried out over all pairs of cells separated n cell lengths apart in a given column of cells parallel to a_3, and over all such columns in the crystal. In practice, A_n is determined from the experimental data for $n = 0, 1, \cdots 15$ and plotted on a curve of A_n vs. n.

Several deductions can then be made from this curve, if it is established with sufficient precision. The shape of the curve should be different for different causes of line broadening, so it should be possible to deduce the causes that are contributing. For example, microstresses yield a curve that has zero slope at $n = 0$. Crystallite size gives a finite slope at $n = 0$, the slope being determined by the effective average size.[1] Microstresses and crystallite-size curves approach $A_n = 0$ with n large, whereas thermal vibrations yield a curve that starts at zero slope and falls to a constant value, greater than zero, with n large. Faults also give a curve with characteristic properties.[2] When the curve is of the shape that indicates microstress broadening it should be possible to determine the rms average of the strain components for the strains averaged over the columns of length L, and perhaps also a distribution function that gives the probability of finding a given average stress σ_L in a column of length L chosen at random in the crystal. Warren and Averbach conclude that stresses can alone account for the broadening in cold-worked alpha-brass (30 per cent Zn), and broadening from other causes is minor. The results are also interpreted to mean that the stresses are nonuniform over dis-

[1] This was concluded independently by M. F. Bertaut, *Compt. rend.*, vol. 228, p. 492, 1949.

[2] M. S. Paterson, *J. Applied Phys.*, vol. 23, p. 805, 1952. For faulty stacking produced by randomly spaced slip on a single set of f.c.c. (111) planes,

$$A_n = [\sqrt{1 - 3\alpha(1 - \alpha)}]^n$$

where α is the probability that a deformation fault will occur at any given layer of the crystal. Powder patterns for this case have lines widened and displaced by the faults as follows (L = widened and displaced to lower θ; H = widened and displaced to higher θ; U = unwidened and undisplaced): 111 line, 2 components U, 6 components H; 200, 6 L; 220, 6 U, 6 H; 311, 12 U, 6 H, 6 L; 222, 2 U, 6 L; 400, 6 H; 331, 6 L, 18 H; 420, 12 U, 12 L. This dependence upon hkl and the unsymmetrical nature of the displacement offers a possibility of distinguishing between faulting and other causes of widening, and the magnitudes of the displacements depend upon the value of α. If powder diffraction lines containing only one type of diffuse component are considered, such as 200 and 400, a plot of A_n against n for these will have a tangent at $n = 0$ of log $\sqrt{1 - 3\alpha(1 - \alpha)}$. In practice, faulting is usually expected on several intersecting slip systems, and on each of these it appears to be concentrated into bands, leaving much unfaulted material (C. S. Barrett, *Trans. AIME*, vol. 188, p. 123, 1950), and may be accompanied by a phase transformation.

tances of several unit cells, say 50 A.*   The magnitude of the short-range stresses appears to be adequate to account for the measured values of residual strain energy.[1]   Although this approach is far more powerful and rigorous than earlier work based solely on half widths and integral widths of lines, it, too, yields only limited information on the extremely complex distortions within cold-worked metal.   The interpretation of the X-ray information in terms of dislocations and other fundamental disturbances still remains a matter for postulating models and comparing them with the X-ray results, and interpretation of physical and mechanical properties in terms of the results would be even less direct, since disturbances that have minor effects on the diffraction pattern might have major effects on properties.

Line Intensities and Widths with Cold Working and Recovery.   A series of measurements of integrated intensities of cold-worked and annealed powders, using the photographic method, was made by Brindley and his collaborators.[2]   The conclusion was reached that the lines from copper, nickel, and rhodium were reduced in intensity by cold working, except for the strongest line, (111), which was increased by a reduction in extinction.   The intensity decrease was compared with the decrease due to thermal agitation and interpreted by analogy with the temperature factor in the standard formulas for X-ray scattering power.   It was concluded that the rms displacements of atoms from lattice positions were 0.083 and 0.106 A for filed nickel and copper, respectively, and 0.090 A for a Cu-Be alloy of 47 atomic per cent Be.   Computations[3] showed that strain energy computed from displacements of this magnitude was more than enough to account for measured values of residual cold-work energy.

Averbach and Warren,[4] however, with a Geiger-counter spectrometer and crystal monochromatized radiation reached very different conclusions from a detailed study of brass filings (30 per cent Zn).   Comparing cold-worked filings with filings subsequently annealed at various temperatures, the cold work apparently increased the intensity of the strong lines, such as 111 and 200, by changing primary extinction, and made practically no change in the weak lines, such as 400.   These results indicated no basis for a close analogy with heat motion.

---

* From the Fourier transform of the measured A_n values it is possible, at least in principle, to determine the distribution function for the strains Z_n.

[1] B. E. Warren and B. L. Averbach, private communication.

[2] G. W. Brindley and F. W. Spiers, *Phil. Mag.*, vol. 20, pp. 882, 893, 1935.   G. W. Brindley and P. Ridley, *Proc. Phys. Soc. (London)*, vol. 50, p. 501, 1938; vol. 51, p. 432, 1939.   G. W. Brindley, *Proc. Phys. Soc. (London)*, vol. 52, p. 117, 1940.

[3] W. Boas, *Z. Krist.*, vol. 96, p. 214, 1937.   F. E. Haworth, *Phys. Rev.*, vol. 52, p. 613, 1937.

[4] B. L. Averbach and B. E. Warren, *J. Applied Phys.*, vol. 20, p. 1067, 1949.   B. L. Averbach, *Trans. AIME*, vol. 185, p. 491, 1949.

Hall, Williamson, and Smallman,[1] however, also using a crystal mono-chromator and a monitored Geiger-counter spectrometer, concluded that extinction was entirely of the *secondary* type and that this masked the effect of cold work, which was to *reduce* the integrated intensity of all lines. The total corrected integrated intensity of the lines from filed Al (commercial and 99.997 purities), W, and Fe was about 7 per cent lower with each metal than in the annealed state, the missing energy appearing as an increase in the general background. The background has been found by Blin and Guinier to have abnormally high intensity below diffraction angles of about 7° in rolled Cu and Ni (but not in Al). This rise in intensity is attributed to imperfections in the nature of submicroscopic cavities.[2]

Line widths from cold-worked metals return to normal sharpness during annealing. The sharpening results from the process of *recovery* which may or may not proceed concurrently with *recrystallization* (the formation and growth of strain-free grains). In the work of Averbach and Warren on brass cited above, an abrupt drop in line width and in hardness occurred in 1 hr at 225°C, coincident with the change in extinction, although visible recrystallization was not seen until the annealing temperature was raised to 400°C. Other investigators have also found recovery of line sharpness at temperatures below the temperatures for visible recrystallization.[3] In tungsten the lines sharpen at temperatures of 600 to 1500°C (depending on the purity) while recrystallization begins at 800 to 2000°C—sometimes as much as 1000°C above the recovery temperature.[4] Recovery of line sharpness occurs simultaneously with loss of hardness in copper, nickel, various alpha-brasses, and several steels, according to Wilson and Thomassen,[5] as illustrated in Fig. 10. Yet, in general, recovery of various properties occurs at different rates, as extensive researches by Tamman and others have shown;[6] for example, elec-

[1] W. H. Hall and G. K. Williamson, *Proc. Phys. Soc. (London)*, vol. B64, pp. 937, 946, 1951. G. K. Williamson and R. E. Smallman, private communication, to be published. Correcting Averbach and Warren's data for secondary extinction brought these into agreement with the British measurements. It is difficult in this work to draw a suitable curve for background intensity, since the tails of the lines spread widely (at least 4° in the British experiments, and as much as 11° in the American); the utmost attainable accuracy in intensity measurements must be reached.

[2] J. Blin and A. Guinier, *Compt. rend.*, vol. 233, p. 1288, 1951.

[3] J. E. Wilson and L. Thomassen, *Trans. ASM*, vol. 22, p. 769, 1934. J. T. Norton, *Trans. AIME*, vol. 137, p. 49, 1940. F. Wever and B. Pfarr, *Mitt. Kaiser-Wilhelm-Inst. Eisenforsch., Düsseldorf*, vol. 15, p. 137, 1933. F. Wever, *Stahl u. Eisen*, vol. 53, p. 497, 1933.

[4] A. E. van Arkel and W. G. Burgers, *Z. Physik*, vol. 48, p. 690, 1928. For other references see C. S. Barrett, *Metals & Alloys*, vol. 5, pp. 131, 154, 170, 196, 224, 1934.

[5] J. E. Wilson and L. Thomassen, *Trans. AIME*, vol. 22, p. 769, 1934.

[6] W. G. Burgers, "Recrystallisation verformter Zustand und Erholung," Handbuch

ɹrical resistivity may be completely recovered before hardness falls appreciably. The different recovery rates for different properties may be ascribed to the different recovery rates for the imperfections to which each property is most sensitive. This idea is used by Dorn and collaborators[1] to interpret their flow-stress data on 2S-O aluminum, where one type of recovery seems to occur at a low temperature, lowering the *initial* flow stress after 90°C and 212°C annealing and is ascribed to easily moved imperfections, while another type, which lowers the flow stress at *all* strains, sets in when the annealing temperature is raised to 300 or 400°C and is ascribed to more tightly bound imperfections. These recovery effects take place so much more rapidly than recrystallization, and follow such a different time law that they are judged to be unrelated to recrystallization.

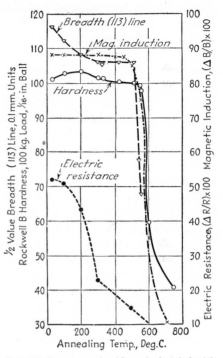

Fig. 10. Recovery of cold-worked nickel with 1-hour anneals (forged 75 per cent). (*Wilson and Thomassen.*)

An exact statement of the fundamental changes that occur during recovery cannot safely be made at this time. It appears highly probable that stresses are relieved during recovery by the straightening of bent glide lamellae. One mechanism that accomplishes this is polygonization[2] —the movement of dislocations into subgrain boundaries. The effect of polygonization on Laue patterns is to break up the continuous asterism streaks into discrete spots, producing the appearance shown in Fig. 2.

der Metallphysik, vol. III, Leipzig, 1941, and Edwards Brothers, Inc., Ann Arbor, Mich., 1944. R. F. Mehl, "Metals Handbook," p. 259, American Society for Metals, Cleveland, Ohio, 1948.

[1] T. V. Cherian, P. Pietrokowsky, and J. E. Dorn, *Trans. AIME*, vol. 185, p. 948, 1949. T. E. Tietz, R. A. Anderson, and J. E. Dorn, *Trans. AIME*, vol. 185, p. 921, 1949.

[2] A. Guinier and J. Tennevin, *Compt. rend.*, vol. 226, p. 1530, 1948. A. Guinier and P. Lacombe, *Métaux & corrosion*, vol. 23, p. 212, 1948. R. W. Cahn, *J. Inst. Metals*, vol. 76, p. 121, 1949. P. Lacombe, "Report on Conference on Strength of Solids," p. 91, Physical Society, London, 1948. See also reviews in "Progress in Metal Physics," vol. II, Interscience Publishers, New York, 1950.

However, Guinier and Tennevin report recovery of mechanical properties at 200 to 300°C in deformed aluminum crystals, whereas the first traces of polygonization were seen only at 450°C. Possibly submicroscopic polygonization precedes the visible type. This, or submicroscopic recrystallization, could account for the domains of 1 to 2 μ size seen by Heidenreich with electron microscopy[1] after recovery and before recrystallization of aluminum. Relaxation of stresses by viscous-like flow at previously formed slip bands may occur, as proposed by Kê and Zener for recoverable creep.[2] If very small stress-free blocks first form by rapid dislocation migration (polygonization) and if these undergo grain growth by a process analogous to ordinary grain growth, the latter could have an entirely different rate from the former, thus accounting for some of the observations of the inhomogeneous nature of the recovery process. Perhaps other mechanisms also come into play at different stages of recovery.[3]

Bragg[4] has proposed a theory for the strength of metals that correlates line widths with flow stress. But although the theory is based on an easily understood and simple model (the strain energy in a mosaic block before and after it is traversed by a unit slip displacement), Bragg points out that line broadening would be predicted from the model both on the basis of crystallite size and on the basis of strains within the blocks.

Stresses in Glide Lamellae by the Photoelastic Method. The most direct observations of residual stresses in plastically deformed crystals are made by viewing transparent crystals in a polarizing microscope.[5] If rolled sheets of silver chloride are recrystallized and then plastically strained, slip occurs much as in a metal and the lamellae between the slip planes become birefringent. Nye[6] has made a detailed study of the process and the resulting stresses. Slip is in [110] directions; the slip

---

[1] R. D. Heidenreich in "Cold Working of Metals," p. 57, American Society for Metals, Cleveland, Ohio, 1949.

[2] C. Zener in "Cold Working of Metals," p. 180, American Society for Metals, Cleveland, Ohio, 1949. T. S. Kê and C. Zener, "Symposium on Plastic Deformation of Crystalline Solids," Carnegie Institute of Technology, and Office of Naval Research, 1950 (in press).

[3] Note added in proof: Hall, Williamson, and Smallman (see p. 429) have observed that line widening from filings of Al, W, and Fe recovers more rapidly and at lower temperatures than line intensities. They conclude that long range strains responsible for the widening are less stable than highly localized strains responsible for the intensity changes. Migration of imperfections could account for this; for example, dislocations migrating into subboundaries.

[4] W. L. Bragg, Nature, vol. 149, p. 511, 1942; Proc. Cambridge Phil. Soc., vol. 45, pt. 1, p. 125, 1949; "Symposium on Internal Stresses," Institute of Metals, London, 1948.

[5] Rock salt has been investigated after deformation by N. A. Brilliantow and I. W. Obreinow, Physik. Z. Sowjetunion, vol. 6, p. 587, 1934; vol. 12, p. 7, 1937 (in English).

[6] J. F. Nye, Proc. Roy. Soc. (London), vol. A198, p. 190, 1949; vol. A200, p. 47, 1949.

lines, when viewed along the slip direction, are wavy, and the process is well described as "pencil glide" with movement like that of shearing a bundle of pencils, as proposed for alpha-iron by Taylor and Elam.[1] The slip surfaces lie near the plane on which the shear stress, resolved in the slip direction, is a maximum. Nye viewed the lamellae between the slip planes edge on, and by plotting the directions of polarization from point to point showed that the lamellae are elastically bent. The axis of bending, in simple cases, lies normal to the slip direction and parallel to the slip plane. The neutral axis of these bent layers is usually displaced from the center of the layers, indicating that superimposed on the bending stresses are more slowly varying stresses from intergrain interactions and other inhomogeneities. The maximum shear stress in the lamellae was computed from the difference in the refractive index of the fast and slow rays, and was found to be equal to or greater than 2.5×10^7 dynes per sq cm (25 bars) which is to be compared with the elastic limit of AgCl crystals, 6.9 bars. This stress corresponds to a radius of curvature equal to or less than 28 cm for the lamellae of 0.07 mm thickness that were studied. In terms of edge dislocations the bending represents positive dislocations in each slip plane throughout a grain (or an excess of positive over negative). As a rough estimate, for every 10,000 dislocations that pass over a slip plane, about 600 become lodged on the plane (or an excess of positives over negatives of 600).

Pratt has made a detailed study of plastic deformation in rock salt using refined photoelastic and optical methods[2] and has correlated the active slip systems with strain hardening curves (p. 352).[3]

X-ray Studies of Fatigue. A reliable means of forestalling breakage of machines and structures from fatigue under repeated stresses would be of immense importance to engineers and metallurgists. For many years there has been a search for some nondestructive test that would reveal the extent of damage caused by repeated stresses and thus predict whether or not the stresses will lead to fracture.

The publications of Gough and Wood[4] imply that progressive damage can be identified by X-ray diffraction patterns. Gough concludes that patterns will remain unchanged during stressing—or will change only at the first application of the load and will not alter their character after this—if stresses are within the *safe* range, whereas patterns will change

[1] G. I. Taylor and C. F. Elam, *Proc. Roy. Soc. (London)*, vol. A112, p. 337, 1926.

[2] W. M. Lomer and P. L. Pratt, *J. Inst. Metals*, vol. 80, p. 409, 1951–52 (Schlieren photography).

[3] P. L. Pratt, private communication, to be published.

[4] H. J. Gough and W. A. Wood, A New Attack upon the Problem of Fatigue of Metals, Using X-ray Methods of Precision, *Proc. Roy. Soc. (London)*, vol. A154, pp. 510–539, 1936; summarized in lecture to Royal Aeronautical Society, Apr. 20, 1936, by Gough and Wood, and in *Metal Progress*, vol. 30, p. 91, July, 1936.

progressively if stresses are employed that are unsafe and that will eventually cause fracture. Some experimenters have drawn similar conclusions[1] while others find no such correlation.[2]

Results of tests conducted in cooperation with the Fatigue Committee of the ASTM[3] indicated that changes in X-ray diffraction patterns reveal cold work from fatigue, not damage. Cold work may occur in the safe range of stress as well as in the unsafe and may, in fact, be beneficial; so a

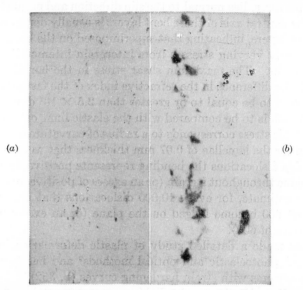

(a)   (b)

Fig. 11. Spot sharpness in 2S-O aluminum after specimen had withstood 505,000,000 cycles in fatigue stressing. Made with camera of Fig. 7. (a) Unstressed area, (b) area stressed at 4000 psi (which is below the endurance limit).

test that reveals cold work obviously does not afford a direct diagnosis of ultimate failure from fatigue. The point is illustrated for 2S-O aluminum by Fig. 11, where spots that are sharp in the unstressed material (Fig. 11a) are seen to be extensively blurred by 505 million cycles in the safe range of stresses (Fig. 11b).

Gough has concluded that unsafe stressing can be detected by noticing whether diffraction spots continue to change as stressing continues. This cannot be accepted as a safe principle, for too many experiments indicate that cold work in the safe range may continue for millions of cycles.

[1] E. B. Martin, Arch. Eisenhüttenw., vol. 10, p. 415, 1937. F. Wever and H. Möller, Naturwissenschaften, vol. 25, p. 449, 1937.

[2] C. S. Barrett, Metals & Alloys, vol. 8, p. 13, January, 1937; Metal Progress, vol. 32, p. 677, 1937; Trans. ASM, vol. 25, p. 1115, 1937. J. A. Kies and G. W. Quick, NACA Rept. 659, 1939.

[3] C. S. Barrett, Metals & Alloys, vol. 8, p. 13, January, 1937.

Kommers, for example, has reported[1] experiments in which cold work at stresses below the endurance limit must have continued for 15 million cycles or more, since there was an increase in the endurance limit throughout this period. A number of investigators have studied also the temperature of fatigue specimens during stressing and have found heating, which is evidence for plastic flow; this is very marked at the beginning of the stressing and continues in lesser degree for many thousands of cycles. X-ray experiments of Wever and Möller indicate that flow may occur irregularly, with a sudden local deformation appearing after some millions of cycles of stressing during which flow is negligible. Spencer and Marshall[2] find that in 17S-T aluminum there is rarely any change in the sharpness of diffracted spots until the very last stages of fatigue; in fact, they usually find blurring of spots only in specimens that have already been broken, where the distortion could have occurred at the time of breaking. Their results, therefore, seem not at variance with the conclusions of Kies and Quick[3] and of the author[4] that the progress of fatigue damage does not correlate with blurring of spots.

Apparently the amount of blurring in X-ray patterns cannot serve to indicate whether a specimen is being stressed above or below the fatigue limit. For some metals and for some types of stressing there is very little alteration of the pattern caused by stressing below the endurance limit, even with the most prolonged tests, and yet other specimens will show drastic changes. Nor is the amount of plastic flow necessarily uniform over the surface of the metal; those spots where cracks are eventually to occur are doubtless the most highly deformed spots on the surface and probably yield diffraction patterns unlike those from neighboring areas where there is less flow. At the present time, no conditions have been found for which X-ray tests or any other nondestructive test[5] has proved a reliable predictor of fatigue failure.

[1] J. B. Kommers, *ASTM, Proc.*, vol. 30, pt. 2, p. 368, 1930.

[2] R. G. Spencer and J. W. Marshall, *J. Applied Phys.*, vol. 12, p. 191, 1941.

[3] J. A. Kies and G. W. Quick, NACA Rept. 659, 1939.

[4] C. S. Barrett, *Trans.* ASM, vol. 25, p. 1115, 1937; *Metals & Alloys*, vol. 8, p. 13, January, 1937; *Metal Progress*, vol. 32, p. 677, 1937.

[5] "Prevention of the Failure of Metals under Repeated Stress," Battelle Memorial Institute Staff, Wiley, New York, 1941.

CHAPTER XVIII

PREFERRED ORIENTATIONS RESULTING FROM COLD WORK

When a polycrystalline metal is plastically deformed, the lattice orientation in individual grains is altered toward a preferred orientation in which certain lattice directions are aligned with the principal directions of flow in the metal. The progress of reorientation is gradual; it is usually noticed on X-ray films only after the cross section of the metal has been reduced by a third or a half but is not completed until the metal has received reductions of 90 per cent or more. The nature of the preferred orientation, or "deformation texture," that is finally reached and the manner in which it is reached are characteristic of the metal and of the nature of the flow (the magnitude of the three principal strains).

Much attention has been given to the subject because of its relation to the properties of commercial products. A fine-grained metal in which the grains are oriented at random will possess identical properties in all directions (provided that there are no elongated inclusions, segregations, or boundaries), but a metal with a preferred orientation of grains will have directional properties, "anisotropy," which may be troublesome, as, for example, in the deep drawing of sheet material. Orientations that are generated by the forming process are not returned to a random state by recovery, recrystallization and grain growth in subsequent annealing, as a rule, but are altered to new orientations in the final annealing textures, which are treated in the following chapter. It is usually necessary to maintain careful control of both rolling and annealing operations in order to produce a sheet that flows uniformly in all directions during subsequent deep drawing. Preferred orientations are also of prime importance in the manufacture of steel for electrical instruments, for magnetic anisotropy may be very desirable in some applications and a serious disadvantage in others. Anisotropy is discussed in Chap. XXI.

The first part of this chapter summarizes the deformation textures produced by wire drawing, swaging, extrusion, and compression—*i.e.*, by uniaxial strains—and discusses the theories that have been advanced to account for them. The second part deals with the textures produced by rolling and related forming processes.

The texture of a wire is frequently described as a "fiber texture" because it resembles the arrangement in natural fibrous materials. In the ideal case it consists simply of orientations having a definite crystallographic direction parallel to the wire axis. The texture is symmetrical around the wire axis, which is known as the "fiber axis." Deviations from an ideal texture are common and may have the nature of (1) a scatter about the ideal position or a random orientation superimposed upon the ideal texture; (2) a "double fiber texture," in which two different crystal directions are found in the axial position; and (3) a structure in which surface layers are disturbed by friction or other external factors.

Textures of Polycrystalline Wires. In *face-centered cubic* (f.c.c.) *metals* the wire texture is usually a double fiber texture with [111] and [100] parallel to the axis; *i.e.*, the crystallites have either [111] or [100] parallel to the axis of the wire and have random orientations around the axis. The percentages of crystals in these two positions differ from metal to

TABLE XIX

Metal	Percentage of crystals	
	With [100] parallel to the wire axis	With [111] parallel to the wire axis
Aluminum..............	0	100
Copper................	40	60
Gold..................	50	50
Silver................	75	25

metal, as shown by the measurements of Schmid and Wassermann,[1] summarized in Table XIX. Lead resembles aluminum, with a single [111] texture,[2] while nickel has a double texture resembling copper.[3] Brass containing more than 10 per cent zinc resembles silver, as does also bronze containing 5 per cent tin, and copper containing 30 per cent silver.[4] Hibbard concluded that the [100] component in wires of copper, aluminum, silver, gold, nickel, lead, and alloys of copper containing 2 per cent aluminum, 8 per cent zinc, or 30 per cent nickel, is an intermediate texture that disappears when the reduction is extreme.[5] The [100] component of severely drawn aluminum[5] and copper[6] may also be due to recrystallization, since this occurs at room temperature when purity is high enough.

[1] E. Schmid and G. Wassermann, *Z. Physik*, vol. 42, p. 779, 1927.

[2] W. Hofmann, *Z. Metallkunde*, vol. 29, p. 266, 1937.

[3] M. Ettisch, M. Polanyi, and K. Weissenberg, *Z. Physik*, vol. 7, p. 181, 1921; *Z. physik. Chem.*, vol. A99, p. 332, 1921.

[4] G. v. Göler and G. Sachs, *Z. Physik*, vol. 41, pp. 873, 889, 1927.

[5] W. R. Hibbard, *Trans. AIME*, vol. 185, p. 598, 1949; *J. Inst. Metals*, vol. 77, p. 581, 1950.

[6] W. A. Backofen, *J. Metals*, vol. 3, p. 250, 1951.

Body-centered cubic (b.c.c.) *metals* have a simple [110] texture.   This was discovered for iron by Ettish, Polanyi, and Weissenberg[1] and has been confirmed many times.   There appear to be no minor components in this texture, and it is not altered by elements in solid solution, such as vanadium and silicon.[2]   Tungsten, molybdenum, and beta-brass also are known to have a simple [110] texture.[3]

Hexagonal metals have wire textures that are less easily interpreted. Magnesium wire was first thought to have all directions in the basal plane parallel to the wire axis (owing to a scatter from the ideal orientation).[4] However, later work on drawn and on extruded Dowmetal (magnesium alloyed with aluminum, manganese, and zinc) indicates that only one set of directions in the basal plane has this position,[5] *viz.*, the direction [210], in wire that has been formed at low temperatures.[6]   At a working temperature of 450°C the fiber axis shifts to [110].   The temperature at which the slip mechanism changes to (101) planes and [110] close-packed directions is 225°C and does not correlate with this change in texture or explain it.   Morell and Hanawalt suggest that duplex slip in [110] directions seems required to explain the low-temperature texture, while single slip suffices to explain the high-temperature texture.   Zinc wires have the hexagonal axis about 70° from the wire axis with uniform distribution about the wire axis.   This texture is obtained only after severe drawing; smaller reductions give a texture in which the hexagonal axis lies along the wire.   Zirconium has a texture like magnesium, with the [210] direction in the basal plane parallel to the wire axis and with close-packed rows of atoms 30° to the axis.[7]

Twinning is responsible for producing those hexagonal textures in which the basal plane is not parallel to the wire axis.   Studies of single crystals

[1] M. Ettisch, M. Polanyi, and K. Weissenberg, *Z. Physik*, vol. 7, p. 181, 1921; *Z. physik. Chem.*, vol. A99, p. 332, 1921.

[2] C. S. Barrett and L. H. Levenson, *Trans. AIME*, vol. 135, p. 327, 1939.

[3] M. Ettisch, M. Polanyi, and K. Weissenberg, *Z. Physik*, vol. 7, p. 181, 1921; *Z. physik. Chem.*, vol. A99, p. 332, 1921.   H. C. Burger, *Physik. Z.*, vol. 23, p. 14, 1922.   Z. Jeffries, *Trans. AIME*, vol. 70, p. 303, 1924.   H. B. DeVore and W. P. Davey, *Phys. Rev.*, vol. 31, p. 160, 1928.   W. G. Burgers, *Z. Physik*, vol. 58, p. 11, 1929.   T. Fujiwara and Y. Seiki, *Hiroshima J. Sci.*, vol. 6, p. 307, 1936 (*cf. Met. Abstracts*, vol. 3, p. 664, 1936).   T. Fujiwara, *Proc. World Eng. Congr., Tokyo*, vol. 36, pt. 4, p. 171, 1931.   H. C. Burger, *Physica*, vol. 1, p. 214, 1921.   G. v. Vargha and G. Wassermann, *Z. Metallkunde*, vol. 25, p. 310, 1933.

[4] E. Schmid and G. Wassermann, *Naturwissenschaften*, vol. 17, p. 312, 1929.

[5] L. G. Morell and J. D. Hanawalt, *J. Applied Phys.*, vol. 3, p. 161, 1932.

[6] This direction is expressed in the three-indices system and is equivalent to [10$\bar{1}$0] in the four-indices notation.   The indices mean a diagonal axis of type II, a direction midway between two close-packed rows of atoms in the basal plane.   The close-packed rows are directions of the form [110] = [100] = [2$\bar{1}\bar{1}$0].

[7] W. G. Burgers, J. D. Fast, and F. M. Jacobs, *Z. Metallkunde*, vol. 29, p. 410, 1937.

have shown that twinning becomes frequent, particularly in zinc, when the basal plane rotates into a position nearly parallel to the wire axis, and as a result the basal plane is suddenly reoriented to a position far removed from the original (a shift of 85°55′ in zinc).

Extruded rods usually have the same textures as drawn wires. This is true of magnesium[1] and cubic metals[2] but is not true of zinc. Extruded rods of alloyed zinc (10% Al, 2.0% Cu, 0.03% Mg) have a texture with the basal plane parallel to the axis of extrusion; extruded pure zinc has basal planes in both the parallel and perpendicular positions.[3] Drawing

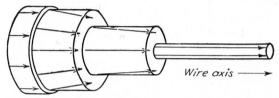

Wire axis ⟶

FIG. 1. Zonal texture of drawn wires of cubic metals. Arrows show directions of fiber axes. (*Schmid and Wassermann.*)

through a die, after extrusion, alters this texture by twinning and rotation until the normal drawing texture is obtained, with reductions of 50 per cent or more. Beryllium extruded at 1000°C has a [210] fiber texture.[4]

Wires formed by *rolling* and by *swaging* have the same textures at their centers as those formed by drawing through a die.[5] The *outer layers,* however, with almost any type of forming operation, contain orientations not found in the center.[6] The scatter about the mean orientation is greatest in the outer layers and decreases as successive layers are etched away. The metal at the center of a thin wire has a larger scatter than that at the center of a thick one. Schmid and Wassermann have shown that in hard-drawn copper wire the fiber axis is inclined to the axis of the wire in these outer layers in the manner indicated by the arrows in Fig. 1.

[1] L. G. Morrell and J. D. Hanawalt, *J. Applied Phys.*, vol. 3, p. 161, 1932. E. Schiebold and G. Siebel, *Z. Physik*, vol. 69, p. 458, 1931.

[2] W. Hofmann, *Naturwissenschaften*, vol. 24, p. 507, 1936; *Z. Metallkunde*, vol. 29, p. 266, 1937. G. Wassermann, *Z. Metallkunde*, vol. 30, Vorträge der Hauptverslg., p. 53, 1938.

[3] F. Wolbank, *Z. Metallkunde*, vol. 31, p. 249, 1939.

[4] A. R. Kaufman, P. Gordon, and D. W. Lillie, *Trans. ASM*, vol. 42, p. 785, 1950.

[5] J. T. Norton and R. E. Hiller, *Trans. AIME*, vol. 99, p. 190, 1932. G. v. Vargha and G. Wassermann, *Z. Metallkunde*, vol. 25, p. 310, 1933. J. Thewlis, *Phil. Mag.*, vol. 10, p. 953, 1930. C. S. Barrett and L. H. Levenson, *Trans. AIME*, vol. 135, p. 327, 1939.

[6] E. Schmid and G. Wassermann, *Z. Metallkunde*, vol. 19, p. 325, 1927; *Z. Physik*, vol. 42, p. 779, 1927. R. W. Drier and C. T. Eddy, *Trans. AIME*, vol. 89, p. 140, 1930. W. A. Wood, *Phil. Mag.*, vol. 11, p. 610, 1931. G. Greenwood, *Z. Krist.*, vol. 78, p. 242, 1931; vol. 72, p. 309, 1929.

The directions of the arrows in the different concentric zones of this figure indicate the directions of the fiber axes of the crystallites (the [111] and [100] directions in copper, for instance). The angle of inclination reaches 8 to 10° in some cubic metals. The length of the arrows indicates the sharpness of the orientation in each zone. Their conical arrangement has led some to use the term "conical fiber texture." This zonal structure originates in the conical (or irregular) flow of metal in the forming process and is therefore altered to some extent by variables in the forming process such as unidirectional vs. forward-and-backward drawing, die design, drawing vs. rolling, etc.[1]

With hexagonal metals, also, there is a zonal structure. Magnesium and zirconium wires, for instance, have the hexagonal axis 90° from the wire axis only in the core; in the outer zones this angle is about 75°.[2]

Textures of Eutectic Wires. When the two phases of a binary eutectic are both deformed about equally by the wire-drawing operation, each phase takes up the texture it would exhibit in a single-phase wire. This is the case in Ag-Cu (72 per cent Ag) and Cd-Zn (83 per cent Cd).[3] On the other hand, if one phase is practically undeformed during drawing it disturbs the flow in the other and distorts the texture, or it may even produce a random one, as in Al-Si alloys (12 per cent silicon).[4]

Compression Textures. *Face-centered cubic metals* after uniaxial compression have a fiber texture that is most simply described as [110] texture, *i.e.*, a face diagonal is parallel to the axis of compression and normal to the plane of compression.[5] However, this description is only a first approximation to a rather complex orientation; in the case of aluminum, half the crystallites are more than 10° from this orientation, regardless of the amount of compression.[6] Although there is a marked concentration near this [110] orientation, all possible orientations are found except those having [111] within about 20° of the compression axis. Crystallites in

[1] E. Schmid and G. Wassermann, *Z. Metallkunde*, vol. 19, p. 325, 1927. T. Fujiwara, *Mem. Coll. Sci., Kyoto Imp. Univ.*, vol. A15, p. 35, 1932. G. Wassermann, "Texturen metallischer Werkstoffe," Springer, Berlin, 1939; *Z. Metallkunde*, vol. 30, Vorträge der Hauptverslg., p. 53, 1938.

[2] E. Schmid and G. Wassermann, *Naturwissenschaften*, vol. 17, p. 312, 1929. W. G. Burgers and F. M. Jacobs, *Metallwirtschaft*, vol. 14, p. 285, 1935. E. Schiebold and G. Siebel, *Z. Physik*, vol. 69, p. 458, 1931.

[3] G. Wassermann, "Texturen metallischer Werkstoffe," p. 71, Springer, Berlin, 1939.

[4] E. Schmid and G. Wassermann, *Z. tech. Physik*, vol. 9, p. 106, 1928.

[5] A. Ono, *Mem. Coll. Eng. Kyushu Imp. Univ.*, vol. 3, p. 195, 1925. G. Sachs and E. Schiebold, *Z. Ver. deut. Ing.*, vol. 69, pp. 1557, 1601, 1925; *Naturwissenschaften*, vol. 13, p. 964, 1925. F. Wever, *Z. tech. Physik*, vol. 8, p. 404, 1927. G. I. Taylor, *Trans. Faraday Soc.*, vol. 24, p. 121, 1928. W. G. Burgers and P. C. Louwerse, *Z. Physik*, vol. 67, p. 605, 1931.

[6] C. S. Barrett and L. H. Levenson, *Trans. AIME*, vol. 137, p. 112, 1940.

any one of these secondary orientations are less numerous than those near the [110] position, and only a very small number are found with [100] within 15° of the compression axis. The range of orientations found can be presented best on a unit triangle of a standard stereographic projection, as in Fig. 2. Each point on this plot shows the orientation of the compression axis in an area about 1 mm in diameter on an inner surface of a compression block. The orientations were determined by an optical goniometer with a compression of 84 per cent. The distribution determined by X-rays after "compression rolling"—rolling with many passes, each pass in a different direction—is shown in Fig. 3 and illustrates again

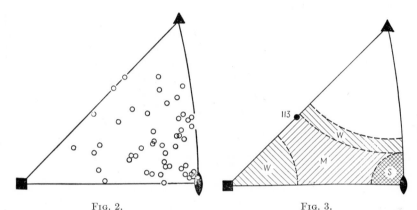

FIG. 2.   FIG. 3.

FIG. 2. Orientations on inner faces of aluminum blocks after 84 per cent compression. Optical determination; the orientations of the compression axis of randomly chosen areas, about 1 mm in diameter, are indicated by small circles in the standard stereographic projection triangle bounded by the directions ■ [001], ▲ [111], and ▮ [011]. Note absence around [100] and [111] and wide, unsymmetrical scatter around [110].

FIG. 3. Orientations in aluminum compressed 98 per cent by compression rolling. Shaded areas on the projection indicate concentrations of orientations, deduced from X-ray line intensities (S, strong; M, medium; W, weak). Copper and nickel give similar plots.

the absence of orientations around [111], the near absence around [100], the concentration around [110], and the spread from [110] to [311]. It is concluded that the wide scatter would exist with any amount of reduction, for it was found after 99.9 per cent reduction nearly as in Fig. 3.

The compression textures of nickel and copper are almost identical with the texture shown in Fig. 3, according to experiments by E. L. Layland and the author,[1] but the texture of 70–30 brass is different, as shown in Fig. 4. No crystallites of alpha-brass have [100] directions near the axis of compression, while a fair number have [111] in this region; the concentration around the [110] position is still predominant, and the range from [110] to [311] still persists.[2]

[1] E. L. Layland, unpublished senior thesis at Carnegie Institute of Technology, 1941.

[2] Unpublished results by the author.

The suggestion has been made that the spread away from [110] is due to impure compression stresses produced by friction at the compression surfaces, and that the ideal texture is [110], as in single f.c.c. crystals.[1]

Body-centered cubic metals have not been extensively investigated for compression textures. Iron has a double fiber texture, with [111] and [100] parallel to the axis of compression. The weaker [100] component of this texture was not observed by some experimenters, but is now well established (see Fig. 5, in which the spot at the top center is caused by

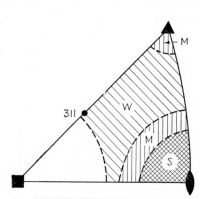

Fig. 4. Orientations in 70–30 brass compressed 97 per cent by compression rolling (X-ray results).

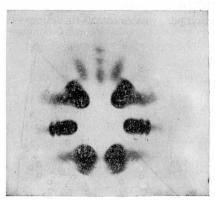

Fig. 5. Diffraction pattern for iron after compression. X-ray beam directed at 14° to compressed sheet to show reflection from (100) planes lying in compression plane, which give spot at top center. Other prominent spots are from [111] texture.

this component).[2] Experiments of J. J. Heger and the author[3] show that an Fe-Si alloy containing 4.6 per cent silicon also has the double texture.

The *hexagonal metal* magnesium has a compression texture with the hexagonal axis parallel to the axis of compression.[4] The magnesium alloy Dowmetal has the same orientation after forging, although modifications can be produced.[5]

Theories of Tension and Compression Textures. It is not possible to account for the textures of polycrystalline metals by assuming that each grain rotates in the way a single crystal does. Not merely one or two, but several, sets of slip planes are active in each grain, because the grains

[1] W. H. Hibbard and M. K. Yen, *Trans. AIME*, vol. 175, p. 126, 1948.

[2] A. Ono, *Mem. Coll. Eng. Kyushu Imp. Univ.*, vol. 3, p. 267, 1925. C. S. Barrett, *Trans. AIME*, vol. 135, p. 296, 1939.

[3] J. J. Heger, unpublished senior thesis, Carnegie Institute of Technology, 1941.

[4] S. Tsuboi, *Mem. Coll. Sci. Kyoto Imp. Univ.*, vol. A11, p. 375, 1928.

[5] L. G. Morrell and J. D. Hanawalt, *J. Applied Phys.*, vol. 3, p. 161, 1932. J. T. Norton, "Symposium on Radiography and X-ray Diffraction," p. 302, American Society for Testing Materials, Philadelphia, Pa., 1936.

are required to fit together without voids after the deformation. The more successful theories of deformation textures have differed chiefly in the number of slip systems that are assumed to operate. Boas and Schmid[1] proposed that the three most highly stressed slip systems are active and the deformation texture is composed of orientations which are stable under the action of slip of this kind. That is, the rotations due to slip on these systems cancel one another when the stable position is reached. Boas and Schmid were able in this way to account for both the [100] and the [111] components of the tension texture and for the [110] compression texture of f.c.c. metals.

When applied to b.c.c. metals Boas and Schmid's theory predicts a [111] compression texture when (110) planes are the only slip planes, and a double texture, [111] + [100], when additional slip planes of the type (112) are assumed. The same double texture would be expected on the basis of this theory if the slip systems are [110] + [112] + [123].* The tension texture is predicted to be [110]. The theory is thus in satisfactory agreement with the principal textures that are observed but does not agree with some of the minor textures. For example, the compression texture of an Fe-Si alloy (4.6 per cent silicon), in which slip is found to be only on (110) planes, has [111] + [100] textures while only [111] is predicted.[2] Face-centered cubic metals have many crystallites in minor orientations not accounted for by the theory. Pickus and Mathewson[3] suggested that three or more slip systems operate leading to end positions in which the functioning slip directions are symmetrically disposed about the direction of flow so that the lattice rotations cancel one another and the resolved shear stresses are equal on each plane. The probability of occurrence of each of the end positions is assumed to be proportional to the cosine of the angle between the direction of flow and the active slip directions—a factor suggested in order to take account of the component of the movement on slip planes that is effective in producing the required flow. It has been suggested that a minimum of two slip systems contributes to the dynamic equilibrium of deformation textures,[4] that all systems do,[5] and that an indefinite number do,[6] but theories along these lines have not been fully developed.

Hibbard and Yen[7] pointed out that the stable end position for a single f.c.c. crystal in tensile strain, the [112] position, could not be expected to

[1] W. Boas and E. Schmid, Z. tech. Physik, vol. 12, p. 71, 1931.

* C. S. Barrett, Trans. AIME. vol. 135, p. 296, 1939.

[2] J. J. Heger, unpublished senior thesis, Carnegie Institute of Technology, 1941.

[3] M. R. Pickus and C. H. Mathewson, J. Inst. Metals, vol. 5, p. 555, 1938.

[4] F. Wever, Trans. AIME, vol. 93, p. 51, 1931.

[5] M. Polanyi, Z. Physik, vol. 17, p. 42, 1923.

[6] C. S. Barrett, Trans. AIME, vol. 135, p. 296, 1939.

[7] W. R. Hibbard and M. K. Yen, Trans. AIME, vol. 175, p. 126, 1948.

be stable in drawn wires because it provides only two slip directions in "favorable orientation for flow" (*i.e.*, less than 45° to the wire axis so that the component of flow in the desired direction is greater than that in directions normal to this). These two operating slip directions, which lie in a plane containing the wire axis, would yield a wire of elliptical rather than circular cross section; but the orientation that is stable in poly-crystalline wires, [111], provides *three* favorably oriented slip directions, and is thus better suited to yield a wire of circular cross section. With b.c.c. metals three favorably situated active slip directions are not available in any stable end orientation, so the [110] orientation, which provides only two, must be used. This accounts for the fact that the poly-crystalline texture agrees with the single-crystal tension texture in the b.c.c. metals. In compression, this theory requires end orientations in which the active slip directions are more than 45° to the axis of compression; these are, for f.c.c. metals, [110], which is stable and [100] which is metastable; for b.c.c. metals, [111] and [100]; for hexagonal metals [0001]. These are in agreement with the main components of the observed textures.

Another modification of Pickus and Mathewson's theory has been proposed by Calnan and Clews,[1] based on qualitative geometrical considerations somewhat different from Hibbard and Yen's but with about equally good results in accounting for the observed textures of f.c.c. metals; emphasis is placed on rotation from single-slip to duplex-slip orientations and toward multiple-slip positions, where it is postulated that adjustments at grain boundaries become easier and rotational stability is reached.

G. I. Taylor has worked out a theory of deformation textures that has a more rigorous basis than any previous one.[2] To permit any desired change of shape—such as will let grains fit together after deformation and will produce the same change of shape in the grains as in the aggregate as a whole—there must be at least five slip systems operating.[3] The "principle of least work" governs the choice of systems that must operate. This principle states that the *minimum* number will function which can produce the required change in shape. This number is five, except for special orientations. Furthermore, that group of five will be chosen for which the total work of deformation will be less than for any other group. Taylor computed the work that would be required on every group of five slip systems that could be chosen from the 12 possible systems in aluminum. There are 792 groups to be computed or ruled out by

[1] E. A. Calnan and C. J. B. Clews, *Phil. Mag.*, Ser. 7, vol. 41, p. 1085, 1950.
[2] G. I. Taylor, *J. Inst. Metals*, vol. 62, p. 307, 1938; "Stephen Timoshenko 60th Anniversary Volume," p. 218, Macmillan, New York, 1938.
[3] R. v. Mises, *Z. angew. Math. Mech.*, vol. 8, p. 161, 1928.

symmetry considerations of one kind or another, and Taylor considered all of these for each of 44 different orientations of aluminum single crystals. Having computed what groups of systems would operate at each orientation, he predicted in what direction the lattice would rotate. Some ambiguity arose when two groups gave the same minimum values of total work; a grain having an orientation in which this occurs will have a tendency to rotate in two or more directions. Taylor remarked that in this case the direction of rotation can be a result of any combination of the two groups and thus can be any direction within a considerable range.

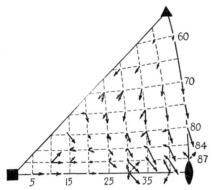

FIG. 6. Taylor's calculated rotations of crystal axes in grains of a face-centered cubic polycrystalline aggregate during compression of 2.37 per cent.

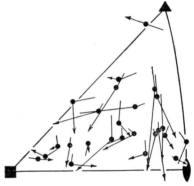

FIG. 7. Observed rotations of crystal axes in grains of aluminum during compression. Arrows connect initial orientations with those after 11 per cent (dots) and 31 per cent (arrowheads) compression.

Taylor's computed rotations for grains of f.c.c. metals during compression are plotted in Fig. 6.[1] The rotation of the axis of compression is indicated by vectors originating at the orientation considered and extending in the direction of the calculated rotation. The length of the arrows corresponds to the rotation that should accompany a compression of 2.37 per cent. Double arrows indicate equally favored sets of five slip systems; any direction that lies between them could equally well occur. The predicted rotations of Taylor have been tested[2] in individual grains of aluminum with an optical goniometer; the results are plotted in Fig. 7. In this figure the tails of the arrows are the initial orientations, the dots on the arrows are the orientations after 11 per cent compression, and the heads of the arrows those after 31 per cent compression. When Figs. 6 and 7 are compared, it is found that about half the grains rotate as predicted by the theory, about a third do not, and the rest are uncertain.

[1] This figure is derived from the published chart that applies to tension, which is reproduced in Fig. 9.

[2] C. S. Barrett and L. H. Levenson, *Trans. AIME*, vol. 137, p. 112, 1940.

It is possible to explain the discrepancies between Figs. 6 and 7 by considering that there are nonuniform constraints on all sides of each grain affecting its strain and resulting in an irregular strain throughout the material. That this occurs cannot be questioned, for it is the origin of the "orange-peel" surface sometimes encountered in deep-drawing operations, and it can readily be seen if a pair of polycrystalline blocks are placed together and compressed. After deformation the inner surfaces are roughened (Fig. 8), clearly showing that each grain deforms in a manner influenced by the flow of its neighbors and not in the simple

homogeneous manner that can be computed from the change of shape of the blocks. Consequently the rotation in an individual grain is not solely a function of the orientation of the grain. The theoretical predictions, on the other hand, were based on the assumption that every grain changes its shape exactly as does the whole. If one considers Fig. 6 as merely indicating the general trends of lattice

FIG. 8. Polycrystalline blocks of aluminum with coarse grains compressed 22 per cent. Rumpled surfaces show inhomogeneity of the deformation.

rotations, it is seen that the trends are downward and to the right, in qualitative agreement with the observed rotations. This accounts for the observed compression texture, [110]. Furthermore, if one notes the regions in which the direction of rotation is uncertain, it will be seen that these correspond to the lower intensity regions of the pole figure (Fig. 3).

The corresponding plot for tensional deformation is reproduced in Fig. 9. The arrows here are the reverse of those for the compression case, and their trend predicts a tension texture with [111] and [100] components, in agreement with experimental data.

Unfortunately, Taylor's mathematical solution of deformation textures is highly complex and unwieldy. To apply it to iron, which has slip on 48 slip systems, it would be necessary to consider all ways of choosing 5 from the 48, and there are no less than 1,712,304 ways of doing this. Even if considerations of symmetry and geometry should reduce the number of calculations that must be made to less than one-thirtieth of this number, as the f.c.c. problem, the problem is still prohibitive in its rigorous form.[1] Neither Taylor's theory nor the ones that preceded it

---

[1] A vector plot can be made of the resolved shear stresses on each system and of the rotation direction that each would cause if acting alone (C. S. Barrett, *Trans. AIME*, vol. 135, p. 296, 1939), but this does not assist in applying the principle of least work.

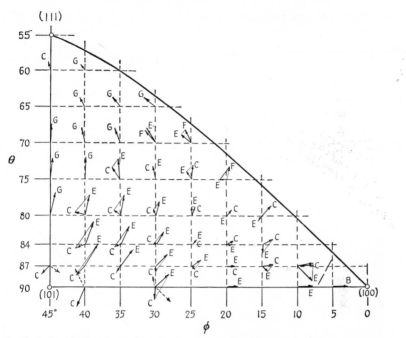

FIG. 9. Taylor's calculated rotations for face-centered cubic polycrystalline grains during elongation of 2.37 per cent. θ and ϕ are angles of the specimen axes from [010] and [100], respectively.

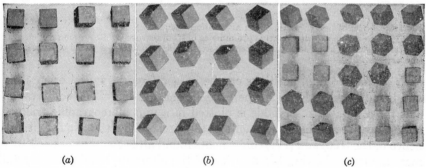

FIG. 10. Models of orientations assumed by grains of iron after compression, viewed from a point on the axis of compression. (a) [100] texture, (b) [111] texture, (c) deformation bands, [100] and [111].

predicted deformation bands and the role they play in deformation textures. (Deformation bands are treated on p. 372.)

Deformation Bands in the Compression of Iron. A micrographic and X-ray study of the structure of iron after compression has shown how the individual grains contribute to the preferred orientations of the aggregate.[1]

[1] C. S. Barrett. *Trans. AIME*, vol. 135, p. 296, 1939.

The rotation of a grain is conditioned by its original orientation as follows: If it initially has [100] nearly parallel to the axis of compression, it will seek the [100] position and retain it. If it initially has [111] near the axis of compression, it will seek and retain the [111] position. But if the initial orientation is removed from either of these two stable positions, the grain will subdivide into deformation bands and alternate bands will rotate to the [111] and [100] positions.

These three types of behavior are illustrated by models of compressed grains in which the orientations of unit cells are represented by blocks, Fig. 10. The structure of the aggregate, similarly illustrated in Fig. 11, is merely the sum of grains of all types. The contribution of a grain to

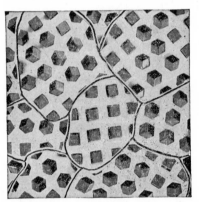 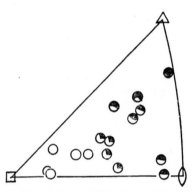

Fig. 11.   Fig. 12.

Fig. 11. Model of polycrystalline iron after compression.
Fig. 12. Projection showing relative prominence of [100] texture (white segments of circles) and [111] texture (black segments) after compression, as a function of initial orientation of iron crystal.

each of the two final positions can be judged from its initial orientation and is indicated in Fig. 12, where the initial position of the compression axis for a number of crystals is plotted in a unit stereographic triangle and the white and black segments of the circles show the relative prominence of the [100] and [111] components found after compression. X-ray measurements showing the rotation of the alternate bands in a crystal are plotted in Fig. 13, where the circular regions indicate the positions of the compression axis after various compressive deformations up to 72 per cent reduction in thickness, at which point the final texture was reached.[1]

Deformation Bands in the Compression of Aluminum. Individual grains of aluminum appear to undergo a more haphazard distortion during compression than do grains of iron.[2] Typical grains contain a spread in

[1] C. S. Barrett, *Trans. AIME*, vol. 135, p. 296, 1939.
[2] C. S. Barrett and L. H. Levenson, *Trans. AIME*, vol. 137, p. 112, 1940.

orientation as high as 10° after a 10 per cent reduction in thickness.   This is increased to a maximum of about 30° after 30 per cent reduction and a maximum of about 50° after 60 per cent reduction.   The spread in orienta-

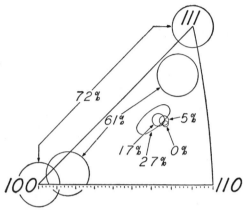

Fig. 13. Rotation of a crystal of iron during successive stages of compression up to 72 per cent.

tion is usually much greater than the average rotation of the material in the grain and is of a random nature that follows no simple rules; grains of identical orientation rotate and spread in different directions, presumably

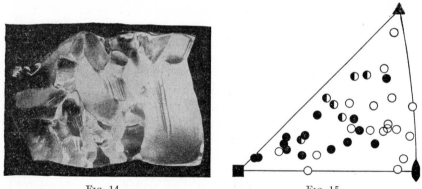

Fig. 14.   Fig. 15.

Fig. 14. Large-grained aluminum compressed 44 per cent, etched to reveal deformation bands and inhomogeneous orientations.   ×1.

Fig. 15. Dependence of banding tendency, during compression, on initial orientation of grains of aluminum.   (●) Grains forming bands; (○) no bands; (◐) uncertain, irregular orientations.

owing to perturbations in the direction of flow caused by neighboring grains.[1]   As will be noted in Fig. 14, deformation bands are especially prominent in grains of certain orientations.   The orientation dependence of the banding tendency is plotted in Fig. 15, where filled and partly filled

[1] C. S. Barrett and L. H. Levenson, *Trans. AIME*, vol. 137, p. 112, 1940.

circles indicate the initial orientations of grains which subsequently formed bands or irregularities in orientation and open circles indicate the initial orientations of those which did not. Frequently the boundaries of the bands are initially along cube planes, but with further deformation they become curved.

The compression texture of aluminum is not a set of stable orientations retained by crystallites when once reached by them; instead, it is a large range of orientations within which the fragments are constantly moving during deformation. It seems to represent merely a statistical equilibrium between a tendency to rotate away from [111] and [100] directions toward [110] and an opposing tendency toward randomness.

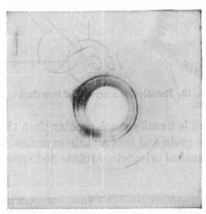

FIG. 16. Transverse section of elongated iron crystal showing curved deformation bands.

FIG. 17. Diffraction pattern of a crystal similar to Fig. 16. X-ray beam parallel to axis of elongation.

Deformation Bands in the Elongation of Iron. During drawing, swaging, or elongating in tension individual grains of iron also take up increasingly wide ranges of orientation.[1] The spread is usually greatest in the azimuthal direction around the wire. Deformation bands form on crystallographic planes of the form [100] and [111] in the early stages of deformation, and the subsequent curving of these bands, their interpenetration, and the lattice rotation within them contribute to the scatter in orientation and sometimes produce a complete [110] fiber texture in a single grain. Figure 16 is a photomicrograph of a single crystal deformed to simulate the deformation of a grain in an aggregate during elongation. It exhibits marked bands. Figure 17 is the X-ray pattern for such a crystal, with the X-ray beam parallel to the axis of elongation, showing a large range of orientations around the axis. Wire-forming processes force the deformation bands to swing into positions more and more closely parallel to the axis of the wire as the length of the wire increases and its

[1] C. S. Barrett and L. H. Levenson, *Trans. AIME*, vol. 135, p. 327, 1939.

diameter decreases. Such a structure may be represented by the model photographed in Fig. 18.

Textures produced in wires by recrystallization after cold drawing are discussed in the following chapter, together with other recrystallization textures.

ROLLING TEXTURES

It was recognized by the early X-ray investigators of cold-rolled metal that preferred orientations must be specified in terms not only of the crystallographic directions parallel to the direction of rolling but also of the crystallographic planes parallel to the plane of the rolled sheet.[1] The orientations found in greatest frequency can be readily described by choosing one or two ideal orientations, but the details of the scatter about these ideal orientations can be specified only by listing a considerable number of less prominent orientations somewhat arbitrarily chosen. A less artificial description is possible by constructing a map of the orientation distribution—a pole figure (*cf.* Chap. IX). It has seemed advisable, there-

Fig. 18. Model of deformation band in a crystal of iron drawn into a wire.

fore, to present much of the data of this chapter in the form of pole figures.

Face-centered Cubic Rolling Textures. The principal orientation for all cold-rolled f.c.c. metals is usually described as one in which a plane of the form {110} is parallel to the rolling plane and a direction of the form <112> is parallel to the rolling direction, which may be written (110)‖R.P. [$\bar{1}$12]‖R.D. or simply (110)[$\bar{1}$12]. Metals having this principal texture are Cu,* Al,† Ni,‡ Pt,§ Au,‖ and Ag,¶ as well as face-centered

---

[1] H. Mark and K. Weissenberg, *Z. Physik*, vol. 14, p. 328, 1923; vol. 16, p. 314, 1923.

* G. Tammann, *J. Inst. Metals*, vol. 44, p. 29, 1930. E. Schmid and F. Staffelbach, *Schweiz. Arch. angew. Wiss. Tech.*, vol. 1, p. 221, 1935. W. Iweronowa and G. Schdanow, *Tech. Phys. U.S.S.R.*, vol. 1, p. 64, 1934.

† E. A. Owen and G. D. Preston, *Proc. Phys. Soc. (London)*, vol. 38, p. 132, 1925. G. v. Vargha and G. Wassermann, *Metallwirtschaft*, vol. 12, p. 511, 1933.

‡ E. Schmid and F. Staffelbach, *Schweiz. Arch. angew. Wiss. Tech.*, vol. 1, p. 221, 1935. S. T. Konobejewski, *Z. Physik*, vol. 39, p. 415, 1926.

§ S. Tanaka, *Mem. Coll. Sci. Kyoto Imp. Univ.* (A), vol. 8, p. 319, 1925; vol. 9, p. 197, 1925.

‖ G. Tammann, *J. Inst. Metals*, vol. 44, p. 29, 1930.

¶ F. v. Göler and G. Sachs, *Z. Physik*, vol. 41, p. 873, 1927; vol. 56, p. 477, 1929.

alloys of Cu-Zn,* Cu-Sn,† Au-Ag,† Fe-Ni,‡ Cu-Ni (40 per cent nickel, constantan),† and dilute lead alloys (*e.g.*, 0.26 per cent calcium).§ The only exception seems to be rolled lead,‖ which probably recrystallizes during rolling and thus is not cold-rolled.

To describe the other orientations also present in many of these metals the indices $(112)[11\bar{1}]$ are generally used;[1] so the rolled textures of aluminum, copper, gold, nickel, and the f.c.c. alloys of the Fe-Ni system can be listed as $(110)[\bar{1}12]$ plus $(112)[11\bar{1}]$. The second of these two orientations is weak in silver† and is absent in alpha-brass containing 5 per cent or more of zinc according to some investigators[2] but is present according to others.[3]

In addition to the two principal orientations listed above, traces of the orientation $(100)[001]$ have been found in Fe-Ni (35.6 per cent nickel),[1] in 70–30 brass,[4] and in copper;[2] weak orientations of the type $(110)[001]$ have been noted in copper,[2] as well as an orientation near $(124)[53\bar{3}]$ or $(236)[53\bar{3}]$. The indices $(135)[53\bar{3}]$ have also been used for aluminum, copper, gold, and nickel,[5] and the indices $(135)[21\bar{1}]$ for copper.[6] It must be pointed out that different observers will list different ideal orientations for textures that are fundamentally the same. This is the principal argument in favor of the use of pole figures to describe the experimental data. Quantitative pole figures determined by modern Geiger-counter methods have led Hu and Beck[7] to conclude that the texture near the center of rolled-aluminum sheet is best described by an ideal orientation near $(123)[1\bar{2}1]$; this orientation and the pole-figure evidence for it is plotted in Figs. 19 and 20. Very similar but qualitative rather than quantitative pole figures have been obtained by Göler and Sachs.[1] If a

* F. v. Göler and G. Sachs, *Z. Physik*, vol. 41, p. 873 ,1927; vol. 56, p. 477, 1929. W. Iweronowa and G. Schdanow, *Tech. Phys. U.S.S.R.*, vol. 1, p. 64, 1934. A. Bass and R. Glocker, *Z. Metallkunde*, vol. 20, p. 179, 1928. R. M. Brick, *Trans. AIME*, vol. 137, p. 193, 1940.

† F. v. Göler and G. Sachs, *Z. Physik*, vol. 41, p. 873, 1927; vol. 56, p. 477, 1929.

‡ G. Sachs and J. Spretnak, *Metals Technol.*, *Tech. Pub.* 1143, January, 1940. W. G. Burgers and J. L. Snoek, *Z. Metallkunde*, vol. 27, p. 158, 1935.

§ H. Hirst, *J. Inst. Metals*, vol. 66, p. 39, 1940.

‖ W. Hoffmann, *Z. Metallkunde*, vol. 29, p. 266, 1937.

[1] G. Sachs and J. Spretnak, *Metals Technol.*, *Tech. Pub.* 1143, January, 1940.

[2] W. Iweronowa and G. Schdanow, *Tech. Phys. U.S.S.R.*, vol. 1, p. 64, 1934.

[3] O. Dahl and F. Pawlek, *Z. Metallkunde*, vol. 28, p. 266, 1936. F. Pawlek, *Z. Metallkunde*, vol. 27, p. 160, 1935. R. M. Brick and M. A. Williamson, *Trans. AIME*, vol. 143, p. 84, 1941.

[4] R. M. Brick and M. A. Williamson, *Trans. AIME*, vol. 143, p. 84, 1941.

[5] O. Dahl and F. Pawlek, *Z. Metallkunde*, vol. 28, p. 266, 1936. F. Pawlek, *Z. Metallkunde*, vol. 27, p. 160, 1935.

[6] C. S. Barrett and F. W. Steadman, *Trans. AIME*, vol. 147, p. 57, 1942.

[7] H. Hu and P. A. Beck, *Trans. AIME*, vol. 188, p. 1214, 1950.

sheet is rolled in one direction only, the pole figure is not symmetrical about the transverse direction (see Fig. 21).[2] (Figs. 19 through 27 are all Geiger-counter plots.)

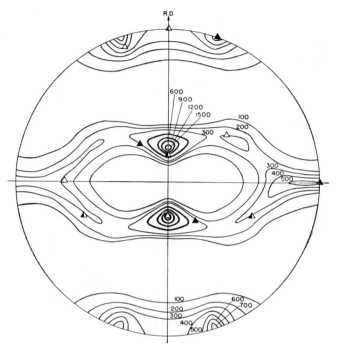

R.D.

600
900
1200
1500
100
200
300

300
400
500

100
200
300
600
700

400
500

Fig. 19. (111) pole figure for the "inside texture" of 95 per cent rolled 2S aluminum strip reversed end to end between passes. Rolled strip thickness 0.024 in., specimen 0.004 in. thick from center portion of strip. The positions of (111) poles for ideal orientation near (123)[1$\bar{2}$1] are indicated by △. The (110)[1$\bar{1}$2] and (112)[11$\bar{1}$] orientations, previously proposed in the literature, are indicated by ▲ and △, respectively. Intensities in this plot and similar ones following were determined by Geiger counter; they are indicated in arbitrary units. (*Hu, Sperry, and Beck.*)

There are small but possibly significant differences between the pole figures for rolled aluminum and for rolled copper (Figs. 22 and 23, for the center of the rolled sheet, and Fig. 24 for the material at the surface). There are marked differences between these textures and the texture of

[1] F. v. Göler and G. Sachs, *Z. Physik*, vol. 41, p. 873, 1927; vol. 56, p. 477, 1929. (Reproductions of these and other qualitative pole figures appeared in the first edition of this book.)

[2] H. Hu, P. R. Sperry, and P. A. Beck, *Trans. AIME, J. Metals*, vol. 4, p. 76, 1952. The (100) [011] surface texture reported by Vargha and Wassermann was confirmed in Al samples reversed between passes, but with Cu and 70–30 brass the surface and inside textures are the same in samples reversed between passes. Unidirectional rolling of brass gave a surface texture that resembled the symmetrical "inside texture" tilted 5° about the transverse direction.

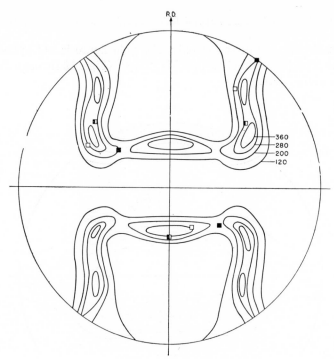

FIG. 20. (200) pole figure for the rolling texture of 2S aluminum strip obtained from the same specimen used for Fig. 19; □ near (123) [1$\bar{2}$1], ■ (110) [1$\bar{1}$2], ◪ (112) [11$\bar{1}$]. (*Hu, Sperry, and Beck.*)

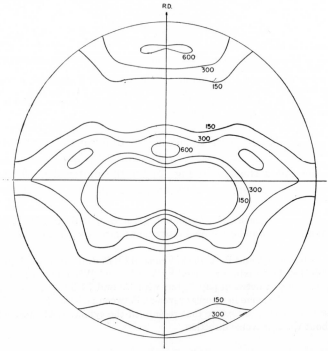

FIG. 21. (111) pole figure for the "surface texture" of 95 per cent rolled 2S aluminum strip (rolled in one direction without reversing strip end for end between passes). Strip 0.024 in. thick, specimen 0.004 in. thick from surface of strip. (*Hu, Sperry, and Beck.*)

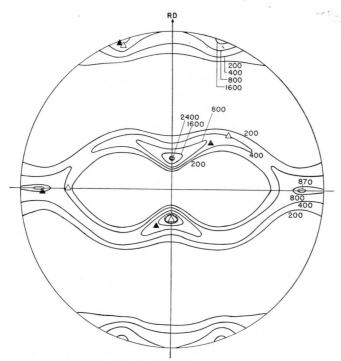

FIG. 22. (111) pole figure for the "inside texture" of 96 per cent rolled strip of tough pitch copper. Specimen 0.002 in. thick, from center portion of 0.020-in.-thick rolled strip; △ near (123) [1$\bar{2}$1], ▲ near (146) [21$\bar{1}$]. (*Hu, Sperry, and Beck.*)

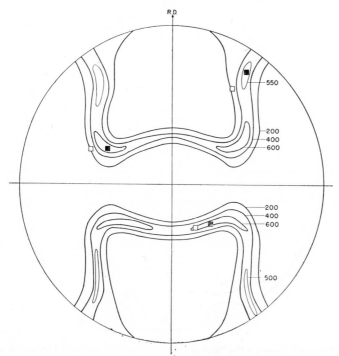

FIG. 23. (200) pole figure for the rolling texture of tough pitch copper strip, from the same specimen as in Fig. 22; □ near (123) [12$\bar{1}$], ■ near (146) [21$\bar{1}$]. (*Hu, Sperry, and Beck.*)

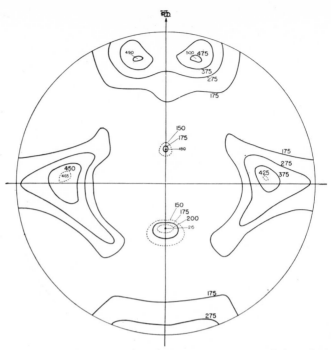

Fig. 24. (111) pole figure for the "surface texture" of 96 per cent rolled tough pitch copper strip (rolled in one direction, without reversing strip end for end between passes). Strip thickness 0.020 in., specimen 0.002 in. thick, from surface of strip. (*Hu, Sperry, and Beck.*)

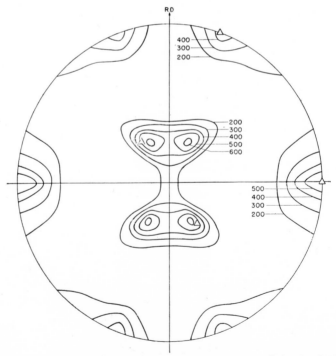

Fig. 25. (111) pole figure for the "inside texture" of 95 per cent rolled strip of commercial 70–30 brass. Specimen 0.002 in. thick, from center portion of 0.024-in.-thick rolled strip; △ (110) [1Ī2]. (*Hu, Sperry, and Beck.*)

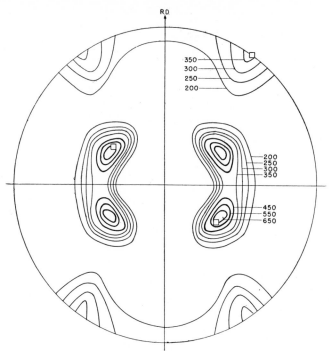

Fig. 26. (200) pole figure for the rolling texture of commercial 70–30 brass strip. Same specimen used for Fig. 25; □ (110) [1$\bar{1}$2]. (*Hu, Sperry, and Beck*.)

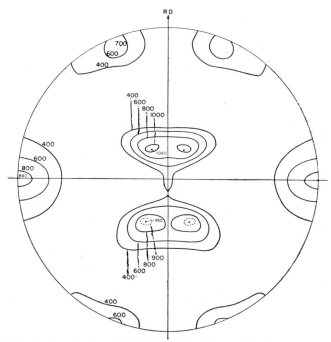

Fig. 27. (111) pole figure for the "surface texture" of 95 per cent rolled strip of commercial 70–30 brass (rolled in one direction without reversing strip end for end between passes). Strip thickness 0.024 in., specimen 0.002 in. thick, from surface of strip. (*Hu, Sperry, and Beck*.)

rolled brass, shown in Figs. 25, 26, and 27. Earlier plots will be found in the papers of Iweronowa and Schdanow,[1] Schmid and Staffelbach,[2] Brick,[3] Brick, Martin, and Angier,[4] and Hibbard.[5] The surface texture of aluminum sheet has also been studied by Vargha and Wassermann, who chose (100)[011] as the mean orientation in the outer layers.[6] When several sheets of metal are rolled together, the inhomogeneity in texture is different for the outer and inner sheets of the pack.[7] The texture of rolled lead containing calcium resembles the texture of copper, and appears to be somewhat different from the texture of lead containing 2 per cent antimony.[8]

Brick concludes that a considerable part of the metal in rolled brass has (110) in the rolling plane and a spread of orientation from [113] to [117] in the rolling direction. From an analysis of rolled single crystals it appears that this entire spread from [113] to [117], together with "complementary orientations" symmetrical with these in the planes of symmetry of the rolling process, can be generated in a single brass crystal; identical results have been obtained with a copper crystal[9] having the initial orientation (110)[001]. Large ranges of orientation are, in fact, generated in most copper crystals during rolling,[10] and so it is probable that most of the orientations of the polycrystalline rolled sheet are not truly stable—with the exception of (110)[$\bar{1}$12], which remains a pseudo-single crystal even after 97.6 per cent reduction.[9]

The presence of the β phase in 62–38 brass makes no detectable difference in the texture of the α phase, but merely takes up its typical b.c.c. texture independently of the α phase. The background intensity, corresponding to unoriented crystallites, increases with the percentage of zinc.[11]

A degree of correlation exists between rolling textures and the simple elongation and compression textures, as if the rolling process could be considered as the superposition of elongation in the rolling direction and compression normal to the rolling plane.[12] While the fundamental

[1] W. Iweronowa and G. Schdanow, *Tech. Phys. U.S.S.R.*, vol. 1, p. 64, 1934.

[2] E. Schmid and F. Staffelbach, *Schweiz. Arch. angew. Wiss. Tech.*, vol. 1, p. 221, 1935.

[3] R. M. Brick, *Trans. AIME*, vol. 137, p. 193, 1940.

[4] R. M. Brick, D. L. Martin, and R. P. Angier, *Trans. ASM*, vol. 31, p. 671, 1943.

[5] W. R. Hibbard, *Trans. AIME*, vol. 188, p. 122, 1950. The texture of brass is found to differ from that of copper if the brass contains more than 5 per cent zinc, and the differences persist even after reductions in thickness of 99.993 per cent.

[6] G. v. Vargha and G. Wassermann, *Metallwirtschaft*, vol. 12, p. 511, 1933.

[7] S. Konobejewski, *Z. Physik*, vol. 43, p. 741, 1927.

[8] W. Hoffmann, *Z. Metallkunde*, vol. 29, p. 266, 1937.

[9] C. S. Barrett and F. W. Steadman, *Trans. AIME*, vol. 147, p. 57, 1942.

[10] H C. Vacher, *J. Research Natl. Bur. Standards*, vol. 26, p. 385, 1941.

[11] W. Iweronowa and G. Schdanow, *Tech. Phys. U.S.S.R.*, vol. 1, p. 64, 1934.

[12] F. Wever, *Trans. AIME*, vol. 93, p. 51. 1931.

significance of this correlation may be problematical, it affords an interesting basis for comparing textures of f.c.c. materials. Thus the wire textures of silver and brass should resemble each other and differ from that of aluminum, which has no crystallites with [100] in the wire axis. This is in agreement with the observations on rolled textures.

Deformation Bands in Rolled Face-centered Cubic Metals. The optical goniometer shows the role of deformation bands in developing the rolling texture.[1] After high reductions each band has a mean orientation within the more intense regions of the polycrystalline pole figure. In many instances, the bands within a single grain are oriented symmetrically with respect to the rolling and normal directions of the sheet (*i.e.*, their orientations are mirror images of each other in the plane of the sheet or in the rolling direction–normal direction plane). Thus the development of "complementary" orientations in the sheet frequently occurs within individual grains as well as in the aggregate as a whole.

In photomicrographs of sections normal to the transverse direction, it has been noted that the deformation bands in the early stages of rolling lie at various angles to the surface and as rolling progresses are flattened into thin lamellae parallel to the surface, as a consequence of the elongation and thinning of the grains.

The microstructure of rolled copper and brass is complex, and doubtless it would be an oversimplification to say that all the markings are deformation bands of some simple type. However, Brick[2] notes that pronounced strain markings accompany the development of complementary orientations in a single crystal of brass. It is known also that macroscopic deformation bands in large-grained copper are often of complementary orientations.[3] X-ray experiments indicate that deformation bands, not deformation twins, constitute the principal mechanism of fragmentation by which complementary orientations are produced in the grains of cubic metals.[4]

Body-centered Cubic Rolling Textures. The numerous determinations of the texture of cold-rolled iron and steel have been in satisfactory agreement as to the principal features of the texture (with the exception of a few conclusions that apparently have been based on insufficient data). The texture is chiefly one in which [110] directions of the grains lie along the direction of rolling—with a deviation of a few degrees—and (001)

[1] C. S. Barrett and F. W. Steadman, *Trans. AIME*, vol. 147, p. 57, 1942.

[2] R. M. Brick, *Trans. AIME*, vol. 137, p. 193, 1940.

[3] C. S. Barrett and F. W. Steadman, *Metals Technol.*, vol. 9, *Tech. Pub.* 1430, February, 1942. H. C. Vacher, *J. Research Natl. Bur. Standards*, vol. 26, p. 385, 1941.

[4] C. S. Barrett and F. W. Steadman, *Metals Technol.*, *Tech. Pub.* 1430, February, 1942.

planes lie in the plane of the rolled sheet, with a deviation from this position chiefly about the rolling direction as an axis.[1] Orientations are found that are rotated about the rolling direction, [110], various amounts up to 45 or 55° each way from the ideal (001) position[2]—usually about 50° in mild steel.[3] The range of this deviation is a function of the percentage of total reduction.[4] Post[5] reported that it decreases with increasing reduction, but apparently he studied only the surface material, which Gensamer and Mehl[6] found to be somewhat differently oriented from the material in the inside of the sheet. McLachlan and Davey[7] found that the deviation also decreases with increasing percentage of total reduction for the material in the interior of the sheet and is independent of the reduction per pass.

The deviation about the cross direction as an axis (the direction in the plane of rolling 90° to the rolling direction) varies[8] under different conditions from about 20 to 6°, decreases with increasing percentage reduction,[4] and in the surface layers decreases with increasing roll diameter.[5] Exact comparison among the results of different observers is meaningless, for the crystallites decrease in number with increasing deviation from the ideal orientation,[9] and the limit that is observed depends greatly upon the X-ray technique, e.g., length of exposure, use of white or characteristic

[1] Z. Jeffries, *Trans. AIME*, vol. 70, p. 303, 1924. S. T. Konobejewski, *Z. Physik*, vol. 39, p. 415, 1926. F. Wever, *Mitt. Kaiser-Wilhelm-Inst. Eisenforsch., Düsseldorf*, vol. 5, p. 69, 1924; *Z. Physik*, vol. 28, p. 69, 1924; *Trans. AIME*, vol. 93, p. 51, 1931. G. Kurdjumow and G. Sachs, *Z. Physik*, vol. 62, p. 592, 1930. M. Gensamer and R. F. Mehl, *Trans. AIME*, vol. 120, p. 277, 1936. C. B. Post, *Trans. ASM*, vol. 24, p. 679, 1936. R. M. Bozorth, *Phys. Rev.*, vol. 50, p. 1076, 1936.

[2] F. Wever, *Mitt. Kaiser-Wilhelm-Inst. Eisenforsch., Düsseldorf*, vol. 5, p. 69, 1924; *Z. Physik*, vol. 28, p. 69, 1924; *Trans. AIME*, vol. 93, p. 51, 1931. G. Kurdjumow and G. Sachs, *Z. Physik*, vol. 62, p. 592, 1930. R. M. Bozorth, *Phys. Rev.*, vol. 50, p. 1076, 1936.

[3] G. Kurdjumow and G. Sachs, *Z. Physik*, vol. 62, p. 592, 1930. M. Gensamer and R. F. Mehl, *Trans. AIME*, vol. 120, p. 277, 1936. C. B. Post, *Trans. ASM*, vol. 24, p. 679, 1936.

[4] C. B. Post, *Trans. ASM*, vol. 24, p. 679, 1936. D. L. McLachlan and W. P. Davey, *Trans. ASM*, vol. 25, p. 1084, 1937.

[5] C. B. Post, *Trans. ASM*, vol. 24, p. 679, 1936.

[6] M. Gensamer and R. F. Mehl, *Trans. AIME*, vol. 120, p. 277, 1936.

[7] D. L. McLachlan and W. P. Davey, *Trans. ASM*, vol. 25, p. 1084, 1937.

[8] F. Wever, *Mitt. Kaiser-Wilhelm-Inst. Eisenforsch., Düsseldorf*, vol. 5, p. 69, 1924; *Z. Physik*, vol. 28, p. 69, 1924; *Trans. AIME*, vol. 93, p. 51, 1931. G. Kurdzumow and G. Sachs, *Z. Physik*, vol. 62, p. 592, 1930. M. Gensamer and R. F. Mehl, *Trans. AIME*, vol. 120, p. 277, 1936. C. B. Post, *Trans. ASM*, vol. 24, p. 679, 1936. R. M. Bozorth, *Phys. Rev.*, vol. 50, p. 1076, 1936. D. L. McLachlan and W. P. Davey, *Trans. ASM*, vol. 25, p. 1084, 1937.

[9] D. L. McLachlan and W. P. Davey, *Trans. ASM*, vol. 25, p. 1084, 1937. R. M. Bozorth, *Trans. ASM*, vol. 23, p. 1107, 1935.

radiation, reflection of the beam from the surface or transmission through the sheet, and grain size of the material.

Typical pole figures for rolled iron are reproduced in Fig. 28, after Kurdjumow and Sachs.[1] The reduction was 98.5 per cent from an initial

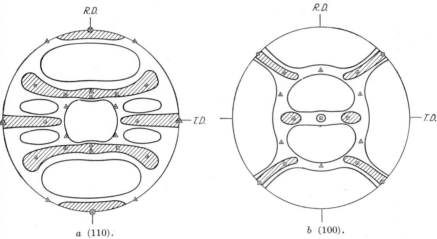

a (110).   *b* (100).

FIG. 28. Pole figures for iron reduced 98.5 per cent by cold rolling. Ideal orientations indicated as follows: □ (100)[011], Ō (112)[1$\bar{1}$0], △ (111)[11$\bar{2}$]. (*Kurdjumow and Sachs.*)

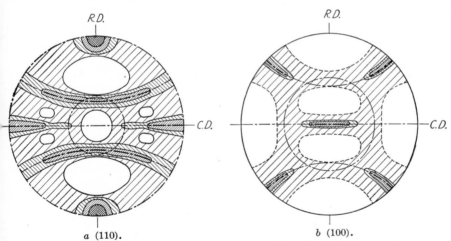

a (110).   *b* (100).

FIG. 29. Pole figures for iron-silicon alloy (4.6% Si) cold-rolled 95 per cent.

thickness before cold rolling of about 0.8 mm. Certain of the less prominent orientations were described by Kurdjumow and Sachs with the ideal orientations (112)[1$\bar{1}$0] and (111)[11$\bar{2}$], which are indicated in Fig. 28. Gensamer and Mehl[2] obtained a pole figure in mild steel (0.05 per cent

[1] G. Kurdjumow and G. Sachs, *Z. Physik*, vol. 62, p. 592, 1930.
[2] M. Gensamer and R. F. Mehl, *Trans. AIME*, vol. 120, p. 277, 1936.

carbon) rolled 99 per cent that was slightly sharper than that of Fig. 28 but was otherwise similar.

Pole figures for ferrite containing 4.6 per cent silicon are practically identical with those for pure iron, as will be seen from Fig. 29, and the same is true of an alloy with a lower silicon content.[1] Nickel in solid solution in ferrite, judging by experiments of McLachlan and Davey,[2] seems to decrease merely the intensity of those orientations having (111) in the plane of the sheet (the orientations of the compression texture); the principal orientations, however, are similar to those in iron.

A more complete understanding of the rolling texture was obtained from a study of single crystals deformed to simulate the deformation of individual grains of an aggregate.[3] Depending on the initial orientation of both the normal and the rolling directions, certain crystals maintained a reasonably sharp single orientation during rolling; others rotated into two or more such orientations, and some fragmented into a texture that resembled the polycrystalline texture. Rotation of crystals and fragments occurred such that the final orientations of the crystals were within the shaded areas of the polycrystalline pole figure, which, of course, must represent the sum of the end positions sought by the individual grains.

In Fig. 30, which is a typical pole figure for (100) planes of ferrite, the rolling texture can be interpreted as the sum of the ideal positions A to F.[4] A model illustrating each of these orientations is shown in Fig. 31. The single-crystal studies show that these ideal positions have no special significance since the intermediate positions are equally numerous after rolling. It seems better, therefore, to say that there are two continuous sets of end positions: (1) a set including the orientations A, B, C, and D, having the [110] direction parallel to the rolling direction and the (001) plane at any angle up to 45 or 55° from the rolling plane; and (2) a set including the orientations E and F, having the (111) plane in the plane of the sheet and all possible positions of the rolling direction in this plane. The spread in orientation of a crystal that rotates into the first set is chiefly a spread about the rolling direction as an axis, while the spread for the second set is chiefly about the normal to the rolling plane.

The principal orientations in cold-rolled *molybdenum* are similar to those in iron, centering in the position (100)[011]. Jeffries[5] showed that the [011] directions deviated some 10° and the (100) about 13° from the ideal position, and Fujiwara[6] found a similar spread. Patterns made by

[1] C. S. Barrett, G. Ansel, and R. F. Mehl, *Trans. AIME*, vol. 125, p. 516, 1937.

[2] D. L. McLachlan and W. P. Davey, *Trans. ASM*, vol. 25, p. 1084, 1937.

[3] C. S. Barrett and L. H. Levenson, *Trans. AIME*, vol. 145, p. 281, 1941.

[4] C. S. Barrett, G. Ansel, and R. F. Mehl, *Trans. AIME*, vol. 125, p. 516, 1937.

[5] Z. Jeffries, *Trans. AIME*, vol. 70, p. 303, 1924.

[6] T. Fujiwara, *Proc. World Eng. Congr. Tokyo*, 1929, vol. 36, p. 179, 1931.

Ransley and Rooksby[1] on molybdenum reduced 88 per cent by straight rolling show a spread about the rolling direction as an axis that is of the same order as the spread with iron.

Semchyshen[2] found that the pole figure for vacuum-arc cast molybdenum containing 0.03 per cent carbon, straight rolled cold to a reduction of 93 per cent, is very nearly the same as for iron and iron-silicon discussed above. The (112)[1$\bar{1}$0] component is somewhat more prominent than in Fig. 28, and the (100)[011] is less so. Custers and Riemersma[3] also found that pole figures for molybdenum resembled those for iron.

Theories of the Rolling Textures. The flow of metal during rolling is such as to lengthen the rolled

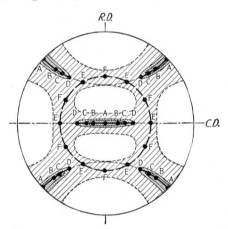

Fig. 30.

Fig. 31.

Fig. 30. (100) pole figure for rolled iron with various ideal orientations shown as follows: *A*, (100)[011]; *B*, ($\bar{1}$15)[110]; *C*, (113)[$\bar{1}$10]; *D*, (112)[1$\bar{1}$0]; *E*, ($\bar{1}$11)[110]; *F*, (111)[11$\bar{2}$]. Heavy full lines represent a continuous set containing *A* to *D*. Dashed circle is a second continuous set containing *E* and *F*.

Fig. 31. Model illustrating various ideal orientations stable in rolled iron. Reader is looking at rolling plane, with rolling direction vertical. Orientations are lettered to correspond to Fig. 30.

sheet at the expense of its thickness, leaving the width unchanged. If the sheet were appreciably widened, the flow would be equivalent to a superposition of elongation in the direction of rolling and compression in the direction normal to the sheet.[4] But actually there

[1] C. E. Ransley and H. P. Rooksby, *J. Inst. Metals*, vol. 62, p. 205, 1938.

[2] M. Semchyshen and G. A. Timmons, *Trans. AIME, J. Metals*, vol. 4, p. 279, 1952.

[3] J. F. H. Custers and J. C. Riemersma, *Physica*, vol. 12, p. 195, 1946.

[4] F. Wever, *Mitt. Kaiser-Wilhelm-Inst. Eisenforsch.*, *Düsseldorf*, vol. 5, p. 69, 1924; *Z. Physik*, vol. 28, p. 69, 1924; *Trans. AIME*, vol. 93, p. 51, 1931.

are only two end positions consistent with the requirements of both tension and compression, *viz.*, A and E of Fig. 31.

The three "ideal" orientations used by Kurdjumow and Sachs to describe the texture, (100)[011], (112)[1$\bar{1}$0], and (111)[11$\bar{2}$], have been found to be end orientations of single crystals, but the rest of the pole figure is not adequately explained as a spread about these three orientations alone, for there are, in fact, two continuous sets.

No theory has been worked out to date that will predict these end positions of the rolling texture on rigorous grounds. The complexity of the slip mechanism in iron makes Taylor's method[1] extremely laborious; it has not yet been applied to any rolling texture. Boas and Schmid extended their theory of tension and compression textures (page 449) to rolling textures by assuming that only those slip systems operate in rolling which lead to a thinning of the sheet. This excludes any slip system having a slip direction in the rolling plane or a slip plane perpendicular to the rolling plane. With these excluded, the three most highly stressed slip systems should rotate the grains of f.c.c. metals into the texture (110)[$\bar{1}$12]. This is the principal ideal texture of most face-centered cubic metals.

The theory advanced by Pickus and Mathewson (page 449) when applied to cold-rolled f.c.c. metals gives the following list of stable orientations in the order of decreasing frequency of their occurrence, with the most prominent first: (110)[$\bar{1}$12], (100)[001], (110)[001], (112)[11$\bar{1}$], (010)[101], (101)[10$\bar{1}$]. The list is in satisfying agreement with the ideal textures that have been listed by various experimenters. Hibbard and Yen rearranged the list on the basis that textures with [110] or [001] in the rolling direction should be metastable, since operating slip directions would not lie within 45° of the rolling direction for these. Their list retains (110)[$\bar{1}$12] as the most stable, because for this orientation the active slip directions are normal to the cross direction—and no cross-direction flow occurs in idealized rolling. Their second stable position is (112)[11$\bar{1}$], and the remaining orientations in the list are regarded as metastable. Calnan and Clews[2] made stereographic plots of the contours of equal resolved shear stress in crystals and on the basis of several assumptions that reduce the labor of calculation they attempted to account for rotation into the observed stable orientations of tension, compression, and rolling.

Gensamer and Mehl[3] found that the surface layers of a sheet of mild steel reduced 85 per cent by cold rolling had a texture somewhat modified

[1] G. I. Taylor, *J. Inst. Metals*, vol. 62, p. 307, 1938; "Stephen Timoshenko, 60th Anniversary Volume," p. 218, Macmillan, New York, 1938.

[2] E. A. Calnan and C. J. B. Clews, *Phil. Mag.*, vol. 41, p. 1085, 1950; vol. 42, pp. 616, 919, 1951.

[3] M. Gensamer and R. F. Mehl, *Trans. AIME*, vol. 135, p. 327, 1939.

from the interior texture. Possibly this surface texture arises because of shearing of the outer layers over the inner ones.

Variables Affecting the Texture of Steel. Preferred orientations develop gradually when a sheet is given increasing reductions. When X-ray patterns are made with the beam perpendicular to the sheet the preferred orientation maxima on Debye rings first appear at reductions in the neighborhood of 30 to 60 per cent. The first traces can be detected more easily with fine-grained sheets and by the use of an integrating camera that shifts the specimen under the beam during the exposure. The texture can be detected at earlier stages if the reflection circle is made to pass through the most intense maxima of the pole figure. Sisson[1] noted the beginnings of the texture with 10 to 30 per cent reductions when the beam was directed along the transverse direction of the sheet (normal to the rolling direction and parallel to the plane of the sheet). Goss[2] gives 5 to 15 per cent for this figure with commercial mild steel, but the effect of his small reduction may have been only to smear out the individual spots so as to render visible a texture present before rolling—a device that has been used as a substitute for an integrating camera.[3] Since more crystallites have their (110) planes normal to the rolling direction than in any other position, it follows that the most sensitive way to pick up faint orientations is to reflect from these. This may be done by directing the X-ray beam at an angle θ to the sheet normal and along the plane containing the normal and the rolling direction, where θ, the Bragg angle for the radiation used, is about 7° for the usual white radiation or 10° for molybdenum $K\alpha$ radiation. This position puts the reflection circle through the rolling direction and yields the type of pattern shown in Fig. 32. Slightly better sensitivity should be obtained with the beam parallel to the plane of the sheet and θ from the transverse direction, although this is less convenient.

Sisson studied the effect of several variables on the texture of rolled steel and concluded that the nature and degree of preferred orientation are independent of roll diameter (at least from $1\frac{1}{2}$ to 24 in.), reduction per pass (tested from 10 to 80 per cent), and rolling speed (tested at 70 and 800 ft per min). Unidirectional rolling did not differ from reversed passes through the rolls. The application of tension to the strip as it passes through the rolls is without effect on the establishment or final degree of preferred orientation[4] (unless perhaps it lowers the relative

[1] W. A. Sisson, *Metals & Alloys*, vol. 4, p. 193, 1933.

[2] N. P. Goss, *Metals & Alloys*, vol. 7, p. 131, 1936; *Trans. ASM*, vol. 23, p. 511, 1935.

[3] G. Sachs and J. Spretnak, *Metals Technol.*, *Tech. Pub.* 1143, January, 1940.

[4] C. B. Post, *Trans. ASM*, vol. 24, p. 679, 1936. A. Hayes and R. S. Burns, *Trans. ASM*, vol. 25, p. 129, 1937. J. K. Wood, Jr., *Trans. ASM*, vol. 39, p. 725, 1947.

amount of unoriented background material[1]), but smaller roll diameters give greater ranges of scattering about the transverse direction, according to Post.[1] Drawing sheets through a rectangular die gives textures equivalent to rolling a sheet the same amount[2] and again emphasizes the general principle that the direction of flow of the metal is the controlling factor in producing textures, rather than the details of the forming process.

The effect of increasing carbon content on the texture of steel is to increase the amount of randomness.[3] This arises from the fact that

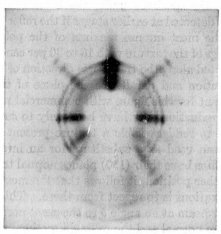

FIG. 32. Pattern for rolled steel with intense spot (top center) from (110) planes normal to rolling direction (beam 80° from rolling direction, 10° from normal direction).

cementite is harder than ferrite. Because it deforms less, it forces the plastic ferrite to flow in irregular directions.

The degree to which preferred orientation has developed serves as a rough measure of the amount of reduction that has been given a strip, provided that this has been considerable. (Sisson remarks that the lengths of the arcs are related to the amount of reduction.[4]) This does not apply to reductions of some 15 per cent or less, but in this range it is possible to distinguish between different amounts of cold work by noting to what extent the individual diffraction spots are blurred and by judging how clearly one can see the Debye rings. Commercial steel sheet of ordinary grain size changes progressively from a spotty pattern into a ring pattern with reductions between 5 and 30 per cent,[5] the exact appearance at any

[1] C. B. Post, *Trans. ASM*, vol. 24, p. 679, 1936.

[2] J. T. Norton and R. E. Hiller, *Trans. AIME*, vol. 99, p. 190, 1932. W. M. Baldwin, Jr., *Trans. ASM*, vol. 39, p. 737, 1947 (copper strip).

[3] George L. Clark, "Applied X-rays," pp. 532, 577, McGraw-Hill, New York, 1940.

[4] W. A. Sisson, *Metals & Alloys*, vol. 4, p. 193, 1933.

[5] George L. Clark, "Applied X-rays," p. 574, McGraw-Hill, New York, 1940.

stage depending on the initial grain size, specimen thickness, and camera design. Some blurring can be seen after the small amounts of cold work involved in roller leveling.

Close-packed Hexagonal Rolling Textures. Rolling should tend to rotate the slip plane of close-packed hexagonal (c.p.h.) metals into the plane of the rolled sheet, and in accord with this tendency the predominating texture is one in which the basal plane, which is the slip plane, lies in or near the rolling plane, although modifications are found, as discussed

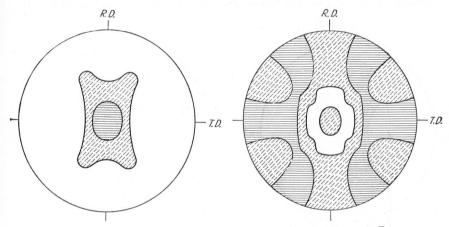

a, Basal plane, (0001).   *b,* Pyramidal planes, (10$\bar{1}$1).
Fig. 33. Pole figures for magnesium foil cold-rolled 97.5 per cent. (*Caglioti and Sachs.*)

below. This simple texture is most pronounced in metals with an axial ratio near that for the close packing of spheres ($c/a = 1.633$), as in magnesium,[1] zirconium,[2] and hexagonal cobalt,[3] with $c/a = 1.624$, 1.589, and 1.624, respectively. Schmid and Wassermann[4] found nearly equal scattering in all directions from this position with magnesium, but Caglioti and Sachs,[5] as well as Bakarian,[6] found some directionality to the scatter, as indicated in Fig. 33*a*. The central shaded areas contain about 98 per cent of the total material.[6] There is a tendency for the [100] direction to align with the rolling direction, as might be expected from the fact that this is the slip direction. This effect is to be seen in Fig. 33*b*,

[1] E. Schmid and G. Wassermann, *Metallwirtschift,* vol. 9, p. 698, 1930. E. Schiebold and G. Siebel, *Z. Physik,* vol. 69, p. 458, 1931. V. Caglioti and G. Sachs, *Metallwirtschaft,* vol. 11, p. 1, 1932. J. C. McDonald, *Phys. Rev.,* vol. 52, p 886, 1937. P. W. Bakarian, *Metals. Technol., Tech. Pub.* 1355, August, 1941.

[2] W. G. Burgers and F. M. Jacobs, *Metallwirtschaft,* vol. 14, p. 285, 1935.

[3] G. Wassermann, *Metallwirtschaft,* vol. 11, p. 61, 1932.

[4] E. Schmid and G. Wassermann, *Metallwirtschaft,* vol. 9, p. 698, 1930.

[5] V. Caglioti and G. Sachs, *Metallwirtschaft,* vol. 11, p. 1, 1932.

[6] P. W. Bakarian, *Metals Technol., Tech. Pub.* 1355, August, 1941.

which is the pole figure for the pyramidal faces, but since a relatively small scatter will destroy this directionality in the basal plane it is not always found.   Burgers and Jacobs's pole figures for zirconium are similar to these in most respects, but the principal deviation from the mean position is toward the transverse direction, rather than toward the rolling direction as in magnesium.

Zinc and cadmium (with axial ratios $c/a = 1.856$ and 1.885, respectively) have rolling textures in which there is little material having the basal plane in the plane of the sheet.   The hexagonal axis is found most

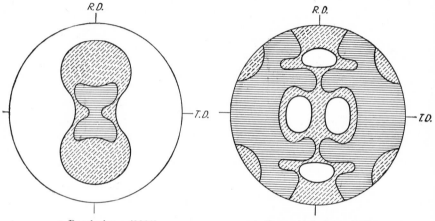

a, Basal plane, (0001).   b, Pyramidal plane, (10ī1).
Fɪɢ. 34. Pole figure for rolled zinc.   (Caglioti and Sachs.)

frequently inclined 20 to 25° toward the rolling direction,[1] as shown in Fig. 34 for rolled zinc.

Another modification of this type of texture was found by Fuller and Edmunds[2] in a zinc alloy containing 1 per cent copper and 0.01 per cent magnesium, Fig. 35.   (In this pole figure the rolling direction appears at the center of the plot rather than the top.)   A zinc alloy containing 10 per cent aluminum and 0.3 per cent copper gave similar results.[3]   The orientations in the region A are developed by slip rotation; the region between A and ND, into which slip should also rotate crystals, is unpopulated.   This is attributed to the action of twinning, which would carry the crystals out of this region into the equatorial zone between B and TD.   Twinning into the area B of this zone is believed to be most frequent because this gives a reorientation conforming to the external change in

[1] V. Caglioti and G. Sachs, Metallwirtschaft, vol. 11, p. 1, 1932.   M. A. Valouch, Metallwirtschaft, vol. 11, p. 165, 1932.

[2] M. L. Fuller and G. Edmunds, Trans. AIME, vol. 111, p. 146, 1934.

[3] E. Schmid, Z. Metallkunde, vol. 31, p. 125, 1939.   F. Wolbank, Z. Metallkunde, vol. 31, p. 249, 1939.

dimensions of the strip during rolling. There can be no question that twinning is common during the rolling of zinc,[1] and the explanation of both the wire texture and the rolling texture on this basis is adequate; the dimensional changes are such as to tend to relieve the applied stresses. In extruded rods of zinc the axis of pressure is longitudinal and the effect of twinning would be to oppose this flow; accordingly, twinning is said to be absent.[2] Owing to the different axial ratio, twinning on (102) in magnesium leads to a lengthening in the direction of the hexagonal axis

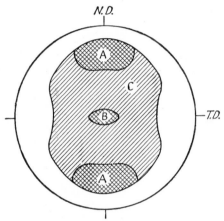

FIG. 35. Pole figure for basal plane of a zinc alloy (1 % Cu, 0.01 % Mg). Rolling direction at center of plot. (*Fuller and Edmunds.*)

of the parent crystal. It would therefore oppose the flow in rolling and wire drawing and is not observed after these operations. However, it can be induced in sheets of rolled magnesium when the sheets are bent.[3] Detectable twinning occurs with bending to a radius of $25t$ where t is the sheet thickness and complete twinning in the surface layer on the compression side occurs with bending to $6t$; complete twinning of the entire sheet occurs with a 7 per cent compression in any direction lying in the plane of the sheet,[4] unless the deformation is done slowly at temperatures above 300°C, a condition that suppresses twinning.

There is a difference between the surface and interior textures of cold-rolled magnesium, according to Hargreaves.[5] The basal planes are parallel to the surface near the surface, but in the interior the c axis lies in

[1] C. H. Mathewson and A. J. Phillips, *Trans. AIME*, vol. 74, p. 143, 1927; vol. 78, p. 445, 1928.

[2] G. Wassermann, "Texturen metallischer Werkstoffe," Springer, Berlin, 1939.

[3] J. D. Hanawalt, paper presented before the ASTM meeting in Detroit, Mich., June, 1935.

[4] C. S. Barrett and C. T. Haller, *Trans. AIME*, vol. 171, p. 246, 1947.

[5] A. Hargreaves, *J. Inst. Metals*, vol. 71, p. 73, 1945 (data on Electron AM503).

the N.D.-R.D. plane about 15° each side of N.D.; [11$\bar{2}$0] is parallel to R.D. in the surface, but has a random orientation around N.D. in the interior. When the surface texture has a small spread in orientation it is detrimental to the ductility of the sheet in bend tests.[1] Bending properties can be improved by altering the surface layers.[1] This may be done by (1) etching; (2) bending the sheet to about 15t radius, straightening, bending in the opposite direction, straightening, and annealing; (3) shot peening and annealing; or (4) hot rolling with large reductions per

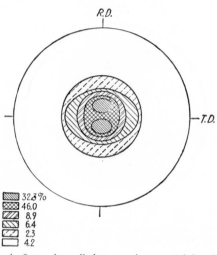

Fig. 36. Basal-plane pole figure for rolled magnesium containing 0.20 per cent calcium. Legend at left gives percentage of grains having orientations in the various shaded regions. (*Bakarian.*)

pass and adequate lubrication. It should be noted that the surface orientation puts the basal plane in a position that would be stable during the flow that would shear surface layers over the interior during rolling, so the shearing flow at the surface may be responsible for it.

The presence of calcium may be responsible, in the interior of the sheet, for the 15° tilting of the basal planes in the pole figure of rolled magnesium.[2] The addition of 0.20 per cent calcium to 99.98 per cent magnesium breaks the central area into two maxima, Fig. 36. A commercial alloy of 2.0 per cent manganese and 0.15 per cent calcium has a similar pole figure. The true cause of this double maximum will not be known until the effect of composition on twinning planes and slip planes is determined.

Rolling variables also alter the texture of rolled zinc and its alloys.

[1] R. L. Dietrich, *Trans. AIME*, vol. 185, p. 621, 1949.
[2] P. W. Bakarian, *Trans. AIME*, vol. 147, p. 266, 1942.

There is a marked layer structure,[1] and the surface layers play an important role in determining the bending qualities of the sheet.[2] A typical pole figure of surface material having poor bending properties is shown in Fig. 37 (the rolling direction is at the center). When the texture of Fig. 37 extends to a depth of 0.0005 in. or more, strips cut in any direction in the sheet tend to fracture easily on a bend test; it is believed that this is related to the lack of material oriented so as to have the maximum resolved shear stress on the slip plane. The dashed circles *A* and *B*

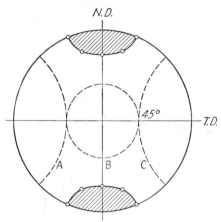

FIG. 37. Basal-plane pole figure for surface orientation of rolled zinc alloy (1 % Cu, 0.01 % Mg). Rolling direction at center of plot. Orientations having maximum shear stress for basal-plane slip are indicated by *A* and *B* for bending in two different directions in the sheet. (*Fuller and Edmunds.*)

in the figure, which represent poles 45° to the axis of tension during bending and thus indicate planes of high shear stress, lie in low-density areas of the pole figure.

Cold-rolled beryllium $(c/a = 1.57)$ has a pole figure resembling magnesium $(c/a = 1.62)$ in that the mean orientation is $(0001)[10\bar{1}0]$, Fig. 38.[3] But there is a scatter from this mean position toward the cross direction (unlike magnesium in which the scatter is toward the rolling direction). Rolling beryllium at 350°C and at 800°C yields essentially the same texture. The rolling texture of zirconium $(c/a = 1.59)$ is also similar.[4] Titanium $(c/a = 1.58)$ has a cold-rolling texture resembling beryllium in that the scatter of the central maximum of the (0001) pole figure is toward

---

[1] E. Schmid and G. Wassermann, *Z. Metallkunde*, vol. 23, p. 87, 1931. G. Edmunds and M. L. Fuller, *Trans. AIME*, vol. 99, p. 175, 1932.

[2] G. Edmunds and M. L. Fuller, *Trans. AIME*, vol. 99, p. 175, 1932.

[3] A. Smigelskas and C. S. Barrett, *Trans. AIME*, vol. 185, p. 145, 1949.

[4] W. G. Burgers and F. M. Jacobs, *Metallwirtschaft*, vol. 14, p. 285, 1935. Confirmed by R. K. McGeary and B. Lustman, *J. Metals*, vol. 3, p. 994, 1951. Surface and interior textures are similar.

the cross direction, but in titanium the scatter extends all the way to the cross direction, with maxima at the positions 30° from the normal direction, 60° from the cross direction.[1] This double texture begins to develop at about 75 per cent reduction in thickness and becomes more pronounced as reduction increases.

Cross Rolling. Important practical results are obtained by rolling a sheet in two directions 90° to each other, and various patents are concerned with the process. It will be remembered that b.c.c. metals have a rolling texture, after straight rolling, in which the cube plane is parallel

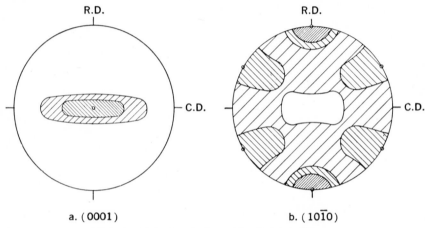

a. (0001) b. (10$\bar{1}$0)

Fig. 38. Pole figures for cold-rolled beryllium.

to the surface and the face diagonal is in the direction of rolling, (100)[011], with [01$\bar{1}$] in the cross direction, and that the scattering is almost entirely about the rolling direction. This scatter is remarkably reduced by rolling in the cross direction, leaving the orientation (100)[011] as the only important component of the texture.[2] The transverse direction in the sheet thus becomes similar to the longitudinal direction. The relative range of scatter around each of the two rolling directions (which are each [110] directions) is governed by the relative reductions by each kind of rolling. When only one change of rolling direction is used, the one used last has a somewhat greater influence on the texture if the percentage is more than three-fourths that of the first rolling, in which case the predominating range of scatter has the second rolling direction as the axis of scatter.[3]

[1] H. T. Clark, *Trans. AIME*, vol. 188, p. 1154, 1950.

[2] C. J. Smithells and C. E. Ransley, *J. Inst. Metals*, vol. 60, p. 172, 1937. C. E. Ransley and H. P. Rooksby, *J. Inst. Metals*, vol. 62, p. 205, 1938. G. Wassermann, *Z. Metallkunde*, vol. 30, Sonderheft Vorträge Hauptverslg., p. 53, 1938.

[3] G. Wassermann, *Z. Metallkunde*, vol. 30, Sonderheft Vorträge Hauptverslg., p. 53, 1938.

The highly preferred orientation produced by cross rolling molybdenum sheet causes marked brittleness along the cube planes, which stand 45° to the rolling direction.[1]

Custers and Riemersma have reported that cross-rolled molybdenum has, in addition to the (100)[011] texture, a second component having (111) parallel to the rolling plane and rotational symmetry around the normal to the rolling plane.[2]   This has been confirmed by Semchyshen and Timmons.[3]

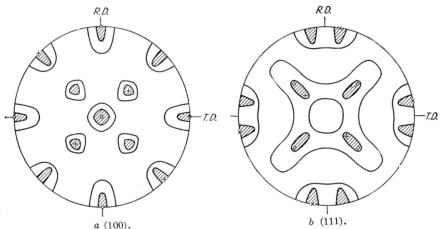

a (100).   b (111).

FIG. 39. Pole figure for cross-rolled face-centered cubic iron-nickel alloy.   (*Wassermann.*)

With f.c.c. metals, cross rolling is sometimes used commercially to reduce the directional dependence of the mechanical properties. Von Göler and Sachs[4] found the texture of cross-rolled copper more complex than the sum of two straight-rolling textures. Wassermann[5] obtained the texture of Fig. 39 by cross rolling face-centered cubic Fe-Ni sheet. The orientations in this texture are (*a*) (110) parallel to the sheet and [1̄12] 10° from each rolling direction, as indicated by crosses in the figure, and (*b*) (100)[001], indicated by small circles. The amount of strain hardening is less than with equal reductions in straight rolling, the recrystallization temperature is lower, and both deformation and recrys-

[1] C. E. Ransley and H. P. Rooksby, *J. Inst. Metals*, vol. 62, p. 205, 1938.

[2] J. H. F. Custers and J. C. Riemersma, *Physica*, vol. 12, p. 195, 1946.

[3] M. Semchyshen and G. A. Timmons, *J. Metals*, vol. 4, p. 279, 1952.   The "rotational symmetry" mentioned in the paper obviously applies only to the (111) component; the (100) [011] component has a scatter of only about 8° in all directions from the ideal position.

[4] F. v. Göler and G. Sachs, *Z. Physik*, vol. 41, p. 889, 1927.

[5] G. Wassermann, "Texturen metallischer Werkstoffe," Springer, Berlin, 1939.

tallization textures are different from those encountered during straight rolling.[1]

Hexagonal zirconium has a cross-rolling texture with (0001) parallel to the rolling plane and with [10$\bar{1}$0] and [11$\bar{2}$0] parallel to the rolling directions, respectively; the effect of the cross rolling is to remove the tilt of the c axis toward the cross direction, a tilt that is marked in the straight rolling texture.[2]

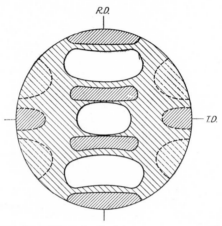

Fig. 40. (110) pole figure for mild steel rolled 85 per cent at 780°C. Maxima in dotted areas uncertain. (*Gensamer and Vukmanic.*)

Hot Rolling. Hot-rolled steel is not free from preferred orientations;[3] in some cases, the texture is nearly the same as in cold-rolled steel. An example is seen in Fig. 40, the (110) pole figure for low-carbon steel reduced 85 per cent by rolling at 780°C.[4] Since the texture is unlike the recrystallization texture for steel, it is probable that recrystallization did not occur to any considerable extent, unless a different recrystallization texture occurs under these conditions. Rolling the same material near 910°C produces a more nearly random texture; here the transformation from γ to α also contributes to randomness.

Textures in c.p.h. metals also are less sharply defined after hot rolling than after cold rolling.[5]

[1] R. M. Brick and M. A. Williamson, *Trans. AIME*, vol. 143, p. 84, 1941.

[2] R. K. McGeary and B. Lustman, *J. Metals*, vol. 3, p. 994, 1951.

[3] K. J. Sixtus, *Physics*, vol. 6, p. 105, 1935.   N. P. Goss, *Trans. ASM*, vol. 24, p. 967, 1936; *Metals & Alloys*, vol. 7, p. 131, 1936.   M. Gensamer and P. A. Vukmanic, *Trans. AIME*, vol. 125, p. 507, 1937.   J. K. Stanley, *Trans. AIME*, vol. 158, p. 354, 1944.

[4] M. Gensamer and P. A. Vukmanic, *Trans. AIME*, vol. 125, p. 507, 1937.

[5] A. Smigelskas and C. S. Barrett, *Trans. AIME*, vol. 185, p. 145, 1949 (Be). R. K. McGeary and B. Lustman, *J. Metals*, vol. 3, p. 994, 1951 (Zr).

Torsion Textures. Relatively little study has been devoted to textures developed by torsional deformation. The principal strains in a twisted rod or tube have been analyzed by Nadai[1] and by Hill.[2] The principal normal strains at the beginning of straining lie 45° to the axis of the bar, but they rotate with continued torsion until they finally reach a position in which the maximum tensile elongation is transverse to the axis of the bar and the maximum compressive strain is longitudinal. Applying the principle that textures are determined by the principal strains, this would imply[2] that the symmetry axis of the texture developed by torsion should

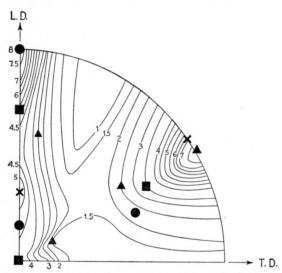

Fig. 41. Backofen's (111) pole figure for oxygen-free high-conductivity copper twisted to a shear strain of 6.75, for material at the surface, with longitudinal (L.D.) and tangential (T.D.) directions as indicated. Ideal orientations as follows: ● (112)[11$\bar{1}$]; ■ (11$\bar{1}$)[112]; ✕ (110)[001]; ▲ (112)[1$\bar{3}$1]. Intensities indicated by numbers along contour lines.

coincide with the direction of maximum tensile strain and therefore should rotate as the torsional strain increases. Recent pole figures of copper after various amounts of torsional strain, however, do not confirm this theory. The pole figures for a series of shear strains from 0.70 to 6.75 were identical in type, and showed no evidence of rotation.[3] One of the series, determined by Geiger-counter measurements, is shown in Fig. 41. The same type of pole figure was also obtained when a torsional shear strain of 5.25 was followed by an equal strain in the reverse direction, *i.e.*, complete untwisting. To explain this, Backofen points to the fact that the planes of maximum shear stress do not rotate during twisting and untwisting; therefore a grain with a slip direction in the plane of maximum

[1] A. L. Nadai, *Proc. Inst. Mech. Engrs. (London) Applied Mech.*, vol. 157, p. 121, 1948.

[2] R. Hill, *Proc. Roy. Soc. (London)*, vol. A193, p. 281, 1948.

[3] W. A. Backofen, *Trans. AIME*, vol. 188, p. 1454, 1950.

shear stress need not rotate.   There is such a plane normal to the longitudinal axis, and slip directions, [110], do lie in this plane for the ideal orientations (112)[11$\bar{1}$], (11$\bar{1}$)[112], (110) [001] and (112)[1$\bar{3}$1] indicated in Fig. 41.   (In these orientations the planes are tangential and the directions are longitudinal.)   The first of these three orientations, in fact, has slip directions tangential to the specimen and normal to the rod axis. Earlier determinations of torsion textures[1] did not provide an adequate test of theories, but did establish that there is a [111] component in the torsion texture of aluminum and copper, and [110] plus [121] components in alpha-iron, parallel to the longitudinal axis.

Cold-drawn Tubes.   Norton and Hiller[2] showed that in the cold reduction of seamless steel tubing the texture is determined by the relative reductions of wall thickness and circumference—thus again by the magnitude of the principal strains.   When only the wall thickness is reduced, the structure is identical with that of a rolled sheet, while when the wall thickness and circumference are reduced equally the texture is that of a wire.   Other variables in the commercial drawing operation are without effect on the principal orientations of the tubes.   For similar experiments on brass tubing see page 489.

Textures in Deep Drawing.   Textures in deep-drawn articles can be predicted from the nature of the flow of metal, which can be specified in terms of the magnitude of the three principal strains.   Hermann and Sachs[3] found this to be the case in drawn-brass cups, where a pole-figure analysis showed that the texture varied from point to point in accordance with the varying nature of the deformation.   At the center of the bottom of the cup the texture was identical with an ordinary compression texture and was caused by the thinning of the sheet and the radial flow outward in all directions, just as in a compression test.   At the upper rim of the cup, on the other hand, there was a compression texture with the compression axis tangential.   This texture was caused by the shortening of the circumference and the thickening of the sheet at the rim during the drawing operation.   The compression texture persisted throughout the upper part of the side wall, but in the lower portions it was superimposed on a tension texture having the tension axis vertical (parallel to the axis of the cup).

An analysis of the plastic flow and orientations in a steel water pail[4] disclosed different conditions of strain and, of course, different textures

[1] A. Ono, *Mem. Coll. Eng. Kyushu Imp. Univ.*, vol. 2, pp. 241, 261, 1922.   G. Sachs and E. Schiebold, *Z. Ver. deut. Ing.*, vol. 9, pp. 1557, 1601, 1925; *Naturwissenschaften*, vol. 13, p. 964, 1925.   N. P. Goss, "The Working of Metals," p. 1009, American Society for Metals Symposium, 1937.

[2] J. T. Norton and R. E. Hiller, *Trans. AIME*, vol. 99, p. 190, 1932.

[3] L. Hermann and G. Sachs. *Metallwirtschaft*, vol. 13, p. 745, 1934.

[4] Unpublished research by H. C. Arnold and the author.

for the b.c.c. ferrite, but the same underlying correlation between the nature of the flow and the textures was found. Wall thicknesses were changed only a few per cent by the draw. At the rim of the pail the circumference was reduced and the steel was elongated vertically along the

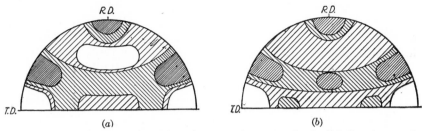

FIG. 42. (110) pole figures for a deep-drawn steel water pail. Radial direction on the original blank is at R.D.; tangential at T.D. (*a*) Rim of the pail; deformation corresponds to 45 per cent reduction by cold rolling. (*b*) Middle of wall; deformation corresponds to 30 per cent reduction by cold rolling.

wall of the pail (radially on the original blank) so that each element of volume was deformed as it would be in rolling a sheet, provided that one assumed the rolling direction to be radial in the blank and the rolling plane to be perpendicular to the plane of the blank. The deformation at the rim corresponded to a reduction of about 45 per cent in rolling; at the middle of the wall the flow was similar and corresponded to about 30 per cent reduction by rolling. Textures at these two points are shown in Fig. 42 and are, as expected, not very different from a rolling texture that has been rotated so that the transverse direction of the sheet is brought to the center

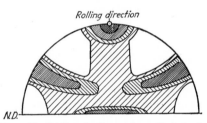

FIG. 43. (110) pole figure for rolled steel, rotated 90° about the rolling direction for comparison with Fig. 42.

of the projection, as in Fig. 43. It seems to be true generally in deep drawing that textures develop at smaller deformations than in rolling, perhaps because the flow is more homogeneous within the sheet.

Textures from Machining and Polishing. The outermost layers of a steel block have a characteristic preferred orientation after machining in a shaper. A pole figure showing this has been plotted by Renninger[1] using data from back-reflection patterns. Polishing is also able to orient material near the surface. Lees,[2] using electron diffraction, found a very thin random layer at the surface of polished copper and gold and under this a layer in which the (110) planes were approximately parallel to the

---

[1] M. Renninger, *Metallwirtschaft*, vol. 13, p. 889, 1934.

[2] C. S. Lees, *Trans. Faraday Soc.*, vol. 31, p. 1102, 1935.

surface. The thickness of the oriented layer was of the order of 150 to 500 A in copper, depending on the method of polishing, and was several thousand angstroms in gold.

Summary. The predominant texture in *cold-drawn wires* of f.c.c. metals is a double fiber texture with [111] and [100] parallel to the wire axis; b.c.c. metals have a simple [110] fiber texture; hexagonal magnesium and zirconium have a [210] fiber texture, but zinc has a texture in which the hexagonal axis is about 70° from the axis of the wire.

The principal orientations after *compression* are [110] for f.c.c., [111] plus [100] for b.c.c., and [001] for hexagonal metals.

Rolling textures require pole figures for a full description. Principal "ideal" textures are as follows:

F.c.c., (110)[$\bar{1}$12] + (112)[11$\bar{1}$]; near (123)[1$\bar{2}$1].

B.c.c., (100)[011].

C.p.h., (001)[100], modified in some instances by twinning.

Other kinds of deformation, as in tube drawing and deep drawing, produce orientations that depend upon the magnitude of the three principal strains during flow. Smearing of the surface of a metal during forming operations is responsible for producing orientations on the surface that differ from those in the interior.

It is thought that all textures of cubic metals can be accounted for on the basis of lattice rotation resulting from crystal slip, but the computation of what planes will slip is very difficult and has been attempted rigorously in only one instance. Simpler methods of computing these rotations have been employed with some success. Textures of the hexagonal metals are produced not only by rotation from slip but also by twinning, when twinning does not oppose the enforced change in dimensions.

Rotation of the lattice in grains of many metals is not a homogeneous rotation within each grain but is accompanied by the generation of deformation bands and less regular types of distortion so that some grains spread into the entire polycrystalline texture and only occasional ones have a small scatter in orientation.

CHAPTER XIX

PREFERRED ORIENTATIONS AFTER ANNEALING

The textures developed in deformed metals by annealing have been studied extensively not only because of their influence on the directionality of properties in the finished products (discussed in Chap. XXI), but also because of their scientific interest. Yet progress in understanding the fundamental principles controlling the textures has been slow. This has been due in part to the inadequacy of the early data, which has encouraged misconceptions, and also to the many variables that influence the final textures: alloy composition and purity, degree and type of deformation preceding annealing, grain sizes at various stages in the working and annealing schedule, annealing temperatures and times, and textures before and after cold deformation. But perhaps a greater handicap has been the lack of sufficient research on fundamental questions related to the subject, such as the relative energies and mobilities of grain boundaries between grains of various relative orientations, and the relative frequency of nucleation of grains in different orientations. The late 1940's brought a rapid acceleration of fundamental research of the kind needed for an understanding of the formation of the textures.

In the following sections the experimental data on annealing textures are reviewed, and in the final sections the current theories are discussed. In viewing the early work it should be kept in mind that observers often failed to realize that an annealing texture may result not only from recrystallization but also from recovery without recrystallization, and also from grain growth subsequent to recrystallization. Grain growth may be either "continuous" ("normal") with the grain-size distribution remaining substantially unchanged, or it may be the result of excessive growth of a very limited number of the grains while the rest remain approximately unchanged until devoured by the large ones. The latter type of grain growth has been called "discontinuous," "abnormal," and "exaggerated"; the process has also been called "coarsening," "germination," and "secondary recrystallization."[1]   It was often assumed by early observers

---

[1] This type of growth becomes possible only when continuous growth is impeded; from the researches of Beck, of Burke, and of Dunn and others it is now clear that the presence of particles of a dispersed phase impedes continuous growth, and that the presence of a strongly developed texture may do so. The large grains continue to devour the small ones because the boundaries of the large grains contain many grain junctions, and as the dihedral angles at each junction approximate 120° there must

that, when deformation and recrystallization textures agree, each new grain has an orientation identical with the principal orientation of the strained grain in which it grows. This, however, is not necessarily true, for the deformation texture may include various orientations, and grains of some orientations may devour grains of others without substantially altering the texture (particularly in fiber textures.)[1]

Recrystallized Face-centered Cubic Fiber Textures. Textures in *aluminum wires* after recrystallization have been found as follows:

1. No alteration of the deformation texture, which is [111], with recrystallization below 500°C.[2]

2. Increasing randomness with recrystallization above about 500°C,[3] particularly with wires of lower purity.[4]

3. A new texture, [112], in 99.95 per cent aluminum recrystallized at 600°C.[5]

4. A sharpening of the deformation texture in 99.95 per cent wire recrystallized at 600°C[6] (perhaps merely a less pronounced zonal effect in the smaller diameter wire).

5. Retention and sharpening of the [111] component (in wire that had been drawn 99.7 per cent) at 500°C, and conversion to [210] after coarsening at 630°C.[7]

In *copper wires*, in which the deformation texture is usually [111] + [100], various results have been reported:

1. No change in texture with recrystallization at or below 1000°C.[8]

2. A new texture, [112], after recrystallization at 1000°C.[8]

3. Retention of old texture in oxygen-free high-conductivity copper (99.996 per cent) recrystallized at 300 and 500°C; retention of [111] component, with [100] component uncertain or absent, at 1000°C.[9]

---

necessarily be strong curvature in the segments between the junctions. Movement of these curved boundary segments toward their centers of curvature results in continued growth of the large grains.

[1] C. S. Barrett, *Trans. AIME*, vol. 137, p. 128, 1940. P. A. Beck and H. Hu, *Trans. AIME*, vol. 188, p. 1215, 1950.

[2] E. Schmid and G. Wassermann, *Z. tech. Physik*, vol. 9, p. 106, 1928. G. Greenwood, *Z. Krist*, vol. 80, p. 481, 1931. G. Sachs and E. Schiebold, *Z. Metallkunde*, vol. 17, p. 400, 1925. F. v. Göler and G. Sachs, *Z. Metallkunde*, vol. 19, p. 90, 1927. Unpublished experiments in the author's laboratory.

[3] G. Sachs and E. Schiebold, *Z. Metallkunde*, vol. 17, p. 400, 1925.

[4] E. Schmid and G. Wassermann, *Z. tech. Physik*, vol. 9, p. 106, 1928. F. v. Göler and G. Sachs, *Z. Metallkunde*, vol. 19, p. 90, 1927.

[5] E. Schmid and G. Wassermann, *Z. Physik*, vol. 40, p. 451, 1926.

[6] E. Schmid and G. Wassermann, *Z. tech. Physik*, vol. 9, p. 106, 1928.

[7] W. G. Burgers and J. Sandee, *Physica*, vol. 9, p. 996, 1942.

[8] E. Schmid and G. Wassermann, *Z. Physik*, vol. 40, p. 451, 1926.

[9] Unpublished experiments in the author's laboratory.

4. Incompletely identified change in texture with recrystallization near 800°C.[1]

5. Increase of the [100] and random components at the expense of the [111] components with annealing at 130°C (varied in degree by change in silver content and amount of reduction),[2] and with annealing OFHC copper at 300 to 450°C.[3]

Retention of the [111] deformation texture after annealing at about 425 to 450°C was found in wires of copper alloyed with 2 to 7.7 per cent

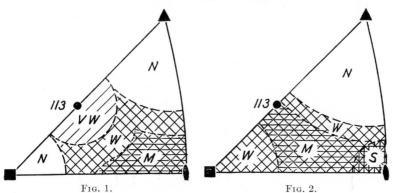

Fig. 1.   Fig. 2.

Fig. 1. Orientations in aluminum compression-rolled 98 per cent. Orientations of compression axis indicated by shading within a standard stereographic-projection triangle. Concentrations of orientations, deduced from intensities of X-ray lines, are labeled strong, medium, weak, very weak, or none (S, M, W, VW, N).

Fig. 2. Orientations after recrystallization at 400°C in specimen of Fig. 1. X-ray determination; only minor differences exist between deformation and recrystallization textures.

aluminum, or 5 to 10 per cent zinc;[4] nearly random textures were found[4] with lower alloy contents and in a copper-nickel alloy of 30.7 per cent nickel, these being compositions with [111] + [100] deformation textures. Retention of [111] + [100] has also been found in copper–30 per cent zinc after 360°C annealing.[5]   In wires of *lead* containing 2 per cent antimony the deformation texture, [111], is retained upon recrystallization at room temperature.[6]   In wires of an *Fe-Ni alloy* (53 atomic per cent iron) a [100] texture resulted from annealing at 1100°C.[7]

Compression specimens of *aluminum* retain their deformation texture upon recrystallization at 400 to 440°C[8] and at 600°C.[9]   Pole figures show-

[1] G. Tammann and H. Meyer, *Z. Metallkunde*, vol. 18, p. 176, 1926.

[2] G. S. Farnum and H. O'Neil, *J. Inst. Metals*, vol. 55, p. 201, 1934.

[3] W. A. Backofen, *J. Metals*, vol. 3, p. 251, March, 1951.

[4] W. R. Hibbard and M. K. Yen, *Trans. AIME*, vol. 175, p. 126, 1948.

[5] Unpublished experiments in the author's laboratory. One wonders whether [100] might not be a growth texture and [111] a retained texture.

[6] W. Hoffman, *Z. Metallkunde*, vol. 29, p. 266, 1937.

[7] W. G. Burgers and F. M. Jacobs, *Metallwirtschaft*, vol. 15, p. 1063, 1936.

[8] C. S. Barrett, *Trans. AIME*, vol. 137, p. 128, 1940.

[9] W. G. Burgers and P. C. Louwerse, *Z. Physik*, vol. 67, p. 605, 1931.

ing the distribution of the axis of compression before and after recrystallization are shown in Figs. 1 and 2 for 99.97 per cent aluminum compressed 98 per cent by compression rolling.[1]   Although the texture of the aggregate is almost unchanged, individual areas alter their orientation.   This

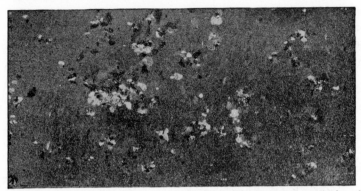

Fɪɢ. 3. Partly recrystallized aluminum grain showing new orientations; etched to develop cubic etch pits.   ×6.

can be seen by partly recrystallizing large grains and etching to bring out the difference between the new grains and the strained matrix, as in Fig. 3. Figure 4 shows the orientation history of a crystal that started as a single crystal at the orientation marked by a cross. It was deformed with the production of deformation bands having orientations marked with open circles and finally was recrystallized into still other orientations, which are indicated with black circles tied to the deformation orientations of the corresponding areas. The recrystallized grains were not oriented as *twins* of the deformed crystal, but could be considered as rotated from the deformed crystal around a common [111] axis. Beck and Hu[2] confirmed this reorientation in a crystal of aluminum that was compressed between repeatedly greased plates. An approximate [110] orientation was reached in compression, without deformation bands, and recrystallization gave a sharply defined texture which corresponded

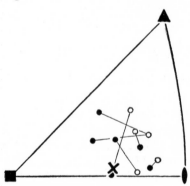

Fɪɢ. 4. Orientations of individual areas of an aluminum crystal before and after recrystallization. Initial orientation shown by a cross, deformed areas by open circles, and recrystallized areas by black circles. Every area altered its orientation.

[1] C. S. Barrett, *Trans. AIME*, vol. 137, p. 128, 1940.
[2] P. A. Beck and H. Hu, *Trans. AIME*, vol. 185, p. 627, 1949.

to a rotation of 47° around a [111] axis that was normal to the compression axis. A similar experiment by Burgers and Louwerse[1] can be interpreted, in a similar way, as [111] rotation, although the original interpretation was a [112] rotation.

Bowles and Boas found that compression rolling followed by recrystallization and grain coarsening ("secondary recrystallization") produces a [111] texture in aluminum and a [110] texture in silver.[2]

Brass and Copper Tubing. Drawn brass tubing, with approximately equal reductions of diameter and wall thickness (29 per cent zinc), has a [111] plus a weaker [100] drawing texture and an annealing texture that is a slightly randomized version of this, according to Hibbard.[3] Pole-figure studies by Wilson[4] of phosphorus-deoxidized copper tubes showed that rolled tubes have [111] + [100] textures, but that there is a tendency for the [011] direction to be radial in the [100] fiber texture, the radial direction being a compression direction in the tube rolling. Sinking the tube tends to bring [011] to the tangential position, which is then the direction of maximum compression. Annealing at 400°C gives a weak texture, and at 575°C gives a weakened deformation texture with increased randomness around the [111] fiber axis; annealing at 650°C gives a new pole figure with principal maxima corresponding to $(111)[11\bar{2}]$ and $(110)[\bar{1}12]$, (the planes mentioned being tangential and the directions longitudinal). Subsequent sinking yields $(110)[001]$ + $(112)[11\bar{1}]$, which is retained when a final anneal is given at 650°C.

Recrystallized Body-centered Cubic Fiber Textures. Wires of *tungsten* and *molybdenum* retain their deformation texture, [110], after recrystallization, at least when recrystallized at low temperatures;[5] a [100] texture has also been reported in molybdenum[6] and in *Fe-Ni* (53 atomic per cent nickel).[7] *Iron* wires (hydrogen-purified low-carbon mild steel) as well as wires of ferrite containing 1.95 per cent vanadium or 1.95 per cent silicon retain their texture upon recrystallization at 580 and 800°C.[8] Steel wires behave in a similar fashion.[9]

Iron wires that have been swaged or rolled to an approximately square cross section have textures no different from round drawn wires either before or after recrystallization;[8] so presumably the symmetry of flow of

[1] W. A. Burgers and P. C. Louwerse, *Z. Physik*, vol. 67, p. 605, 1931.

[2] J. S. Bowles and W. Boas, *J. Inst. Metals*, vol. 74, p. 501, 1948.

[3] W. R. Hibbard, *Trans. AIME*, vol. 175, p. 52, 1948.

[4] F. H. Wilson, *Trans. AIME*, vol. 175, p. 59, 1948.

[5] Z. Jeffries, *Trans. AIME*, vol. 70, p. 303, 1924.   T. Fujiwara, *Proc. World Eng. Congr., Tokyo*, 1929, pt. 4, vol. 36, p. 171, 1931.

[6] T. Fujiwara, *Proc. World Eng. Congr., Tokyo*, 1929, pt. 4, vol. 36, p. 171, 1931.

[7] W. G. Burgers and F. M. Jacobs, *Metallwirtschaft*, vol. 15, p. 1063, 1936.

[8] Unpublished experiments in the author's laboratory.

[9] N. P. Goss, *Trans. Am. Soc. Steel Treating*, vol. 16, p. 405, 1929.

the metal and not the manner of deformation governs recrystallization textures, just as it does deformation textures.

Compression specimens of iron (hydrogen-purified mild steel, also Armco iron) retain the major component, [111], but appear to lose the minor component, [100], upon recrystallization at 580 and 850°C.[1]

Face-centered Cubic Rolling Recrystallization Textures. Glocker made the first extended study of recrystallization textures when he studied rolled silver. The deformation texture, which could be described as one in which a (110) plane is parallel to the rolling plane, and a [$\bar{1}$12] direction is parallel to the rolling direction, *i.e.*, (110)[$\bar{1}$12], went over to the texture (113)[$\bar{2}\bar{1}$1] upon annealing at low temperatures but became random when annealed above 800°C.[2] The (113)[$\bar{2}\bar{1}$1] texture is obtained not only with silver but also with brass (33 to 39% Zn), bronze (5% Sn), 99% Ag–1% Zn, and Au-Ag alloys with more than 70% Ag.[3] It also occurs in Cu-Be and Cu-Al alloys[4] (admixed with a (100)[001] texture in 99% Cu–1% Al). In brass the same indices, (113)[$\bar{2}\bar{1}$1], have often been used to describe the texture,[5] although few have contended that these particular indices are of special significance.

Quantitative pole figures, with intensity contours, for commercial brass containing 30 per cent zinc are reproduced in Fig. 5. (The rolling texture corresponding to these is seen in Fig. 25 page 462.) The indices (225)[73$\bar{4}$] adequately describe the texture, as Hu and Beck point out, and are somewhat better than the older indices (113)[$\bar{2}\bar{1}$1]. One of the symmetrical, equivalent variants of (225)[73$\bar{4}$] is indicated in Fig. 5a by the open triangles, and in Fig. 5b by the open squares. As indicated in Fig. 6, this texture can be derived from the ideal orientation of the rolling texture, (110)[1$\bar{1}$2], by rotations of 30° each way about an axis (+) very near the (111) poles of both deformation and annealing ideal orientations.[6]

Wilson and Brick's[7] extensive pole-figure study of rolled 70–30 brass showed that the deformation texture, (110)[1$\bar{1}$2], recrystallizes at a low temperature (400°C) to a texture like Fig. 5, but the texture changes back

[1] Unpublished experiments in the author's laboratory.

[2] R. Glocker, *Z. Physik*, vol. 31, p. 386, 1925. R. Glocker and E. Kaupp, *Z. Metallkunde*, vol. 16, p. 377, 1924. R. Glocker, E. Kaupp, and H. Widmann, *Z. Metallkunde*, vol. 17, p. 353, 1925. H. Widmann, *Z. Physik*, vol. 45, p. 200, 1927.

[3] F. v. Göler and G. Sachs, *Z. Physik*, vol. 56, p. 485, 1929.

[4] O. Dahl and F. Pawlek, *Z. Metallkunde*, vol. 28, p. 266, 1936.

[5] A. Bass and R. Glocker, *Z. Metallkunde*, vol. 20, p. 179, 1928. R. M. Brick, *Trans. AIME*, vol. 137, p. 193, 1940. R. M. Brick and M. A. Williamson, *Trans. AIME*, vol. 143, p. 84, 1941.

[6] P. A. Beck and H. Hu, *Trans. AIME, J. Metals*, vol. 4, p. 83, 1952. M. Cook and T. L. Richards, *J. Inst. Metals*, vol. 69, p. 351, 1943.

[7] F. H. Wilson and R. M. Brick, *Trans. AIME*, vol. 161, p. 173, 1945. (Includes 38 pole figures; see Chap. XXI for discussion of anisotropy in the sheet.)

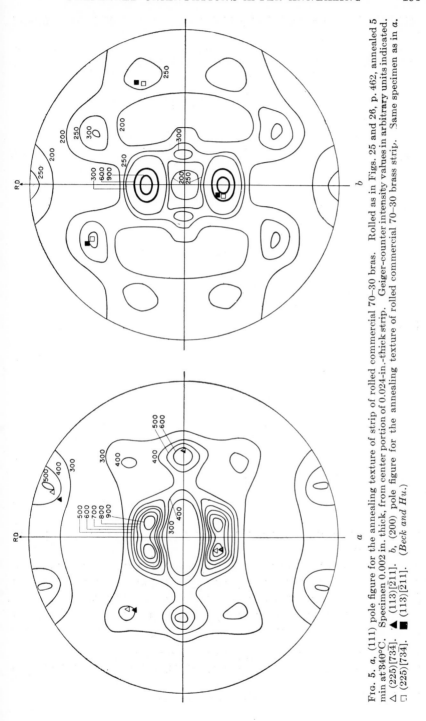

FIG. 5. *a*, (111) pole figure for the annealing texture of strip of rolled commercial 70–30 bras. Rolled as in Figs. 25 and 26, p. 462, annealed 5 min at 340°C. Specimen 0.002 in. thick, from center portion of 0.024-in.-thick strip. Geiger-counter intensity values in arbitrary units indicated. *b*, (200) pole figure for the annealing texture of rolled commercial 70–30 brass strip. Same specimen as in *a*. △ (225)[734]. ▲ (225)[734]. ◆ (113)[2̄11]. ◼ (113)[2̄11]. (*Beck and Hu.*)

to (110)[1$\bar{1}$2] when annealed at a high temperature (600 to 700°C), and this occurs also in silver.[1]

Coheur and Lejeune[2] find the annealing texture of 99.5 per cent aluminum sheet to be (236)[335] + (100)[001] + (110)[1$\bar{1}$0] after annealing at 235 to 300°C, with (236)[335], and later also (110)[1$\bar{1}$0] disappearing in favor of (100)[001] during annealing at 500°C; traces of some of the recrys-

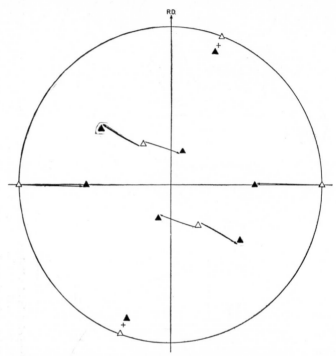

Fig. 6. (111) pole figure showing the orientation relationship between the rolling texture and the annealing texture of commercial 70–30 brass. △ (110)[1$\bar{1}$2] rolling texture. ▲ (225)[73$\bar{4}$] annealing texture. Arrows indicate rotations of 30° around +, which is at intermediate position between the approximately coinciding (111) poles of the two ideal orientations. (*Beck and Hu.*)

tallization orientations existed in the deformation texture prior to recrystallization.

Beck and Hu, using a Geiger counter, found that the maxima in a precision pole figure of 2S aluminum strip annealed at 300°C (Fig. 7) could be described as a retention of the rolling texture, which is not very far from (123)[1$\bar{2}$1], plus the cube texture (100)[001].[3] They point out that a [111] direction of each of the four symmetrical components of the rolling

[1] F. D. Rossi and B. H. Alexander, *J. Metals*, vol. 188, p. 1217, 1950.

[2] P. Coheur and J. M. Lejeune, *Rev. mét.*, vol. 46, p. 439, 1949 (includes 50 pole figures).

[3] P. A. Beck and H. Hu, *Trans. AIME*, vol. 188, p. 1215, 1950.

texture and of the cube texture nearly coincide.   Microscopic observation showed that polygonization plays a part in retaining the deformation texture, as does also the growth of grains with the orientation of one component into strained material of another component (in an adjacent deformation band) related to the first by a rotation of about 38° around a common [111] axis.   Favorable conditions then permit the development of the

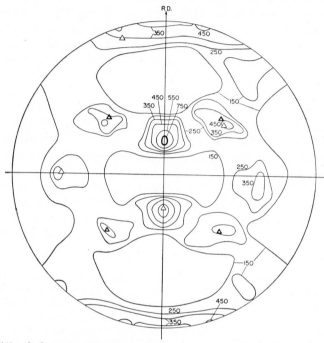

FIG. 7. (111) pole figure for the annealing texture of 2S aluminum strip.   Rolling as above, annealed 5 min at 300°C.   Specimen 0.004 in. thick, from center portion of 0.024-in.-thick strip.   △ near (123)[1̄2̄1].   ▲ (100)[001].   (*Beck and Hu.*)

cube texture by grain growth, as will be discussed later.   Rolled single crystals reoriented in ways also interpreted as [111] rotations of 30 to 50°, one with well-clustered orientations near 40° rotation, another with much scatter in the amount of rotation.[1]   After grain growth in a recrystallized (100)[001] texture of copper the large grains are also rotated roughly 30° around [111] from the cube position, according to Bowles and Boas,[2] and in 50 per cent Ni-Fe, according to Rathenau and Custers.[3] Coarsening in recrystallized pure aluminum[1] of single orientation texture

[1] P. A. Beck and H. Hu, *Trans. AIME*, vol. 185, p. 627, 1949; *J. Metals*, vol. 4, p. 83, 1952.

[2] J. S. Bowles and W. Boas, *J. Inst. Metals*, vol. 74, p. 501, 1948.

[3] G. W. Rathenau and J. F. H. Custers, *Philips Research Repts.*, vol. 4, p. 241, 1949.

(obtained by recrystallizing a deformed single crystal) also leads to [111] rotation of about 40°.

The Cube Texture. The most striking recrystallization texture known is the famous "cube texture," (100)[001], which can be produced in many f.c.c. metals and alloys under certain conditions. In this texture the precision with which the cube axes are aligned with the rolling direction, the transverse direction, and the normal direction of the sheet is remarkable, as will be seen from Fig. 8. It is naturally of commercial importance, since it produces marked anisotropy in the physical properties, and it is a scientific curiosity of the first order. It is readily recognized even without X-rays, by the uniform sheen, resembling a single crystal, that is seen after etching, or by an analysis of the direction of twin bands in the grains.

The cube texture has been obtained only in certain f.c.c. metals and alloys: Cu,[*] Fe-Ni alloys containing 30 to 100 per cent nickel,[†] Au,[‡] Al,[§] Cu-Zn containing up to 1 per cent zinc,[1] Cu-Al with 0.2 per cent aluminum,[1] Cu-Cd with 0.1 per cent cadmium,[1] Cu containing 0.1 per cent oxygen,[1] Ni, Ni-Mn with 1 per cent manganese,[2] and some ternary alloys of Fe, Ni, and Cu.[3] A well-developed deformation texture must be obtained before recrystallization will give the cube texture; this requires 80 to 95 per cent reduction. Baldwin[4] shows the relation between the percentage of reduction and the percentage of cubically aligned grains as in Fig. 9 for a strip that had been previously hot-rolled. Figure 10 illustrates the same relation for strips in which the cube texture had pre-

[*] W. Köster, Z. Metallkunde, vol. 18, p. 112, 1926. G. Tammann and H. Meyer, Z. Metallkunde, vol. 18, p. 176, 1926. G. Sachs, Z. Ver. deut. Ing., vol. 70, p. 1634, 1926. F. v. Göler, and G. Sachs, Z. Physik, vol. 41, p. 889, 1927. R. Glocker and H. Widmann, Z. Metallkunde, vol. 19, p. 41, 1927. H. Widmann, Z. Physik, vol. 45, p. 200, 1927. W. Fahrenhorst, K. Matthaes, and E. Schmid, Z. Ver. deut. Ing., vol. 76, p. 797, 1932. O. Dahl and F. Pawlek, Z. Metallkunde, vol. 28, p. 266, 1936. M. Cook and T. L. Richards, J. Inst. Metals, vol. 66, p. 1, 1940. W. H. Baldwin, Metals Technol., Tech. Pub. 1455, April, 1942.

[†] O. Dahl and F. Pawlek, Z. Metallkunde, vol. 28, pp. 266, 230, 1936. F. Pawlek, Z. Metallkunde, vol. 27, p. 160, 1935. O. Dahl and F. Pawlek, Z. Physik, vol. 94, p. 504, 1935. W. G. Burgers and J. L. Snoek, Z. Metallkunde, vol. 27, p. 158, 1935. G. Sachs and J. Spretnak, Trans. AIME, vol. 140, p. 359, 1940. H. G. Müller, Z. Metallkunde, vol. 31, p. 322, 1939. G. Wassermann, Z. Metallkunde, vol. 28, p. 262, 1936. J. F. H. Custers, Physica, vol. 13, p. 97, 1947.

[‡] F. v. Göler and G. Sachs, Z. Physik, vol. 56, p. 485, 1929.

[§] E. Schmid and G. Wassermann, Metallwirtschaft, vol. 10, p. 409, 1931.

[1] O. Dahl and F. Pawlek, Z. Metallkunde, vol. 28, p. 266, 1936.

[2] O. Dahl and F. Pawlek, Z. Physik, vol. 94, p. 504, 1935. F. v. Göler and G. Sachs, Z. Physik, vol. 56, p. 485, 1929.

[3] W. G. Burgers and J. L. Snoek, Z. Metallkunde, vol. 27, p. 158, 1935. H. G. Müller, Z. Metallkunde, vol. 31, p. 322, 1939.

[4] W. H. Baldwin, Metals Technol., Tech. Pub. 1455, April, 1942; Trans. AIME, vol. 166, p. 591, 1946.

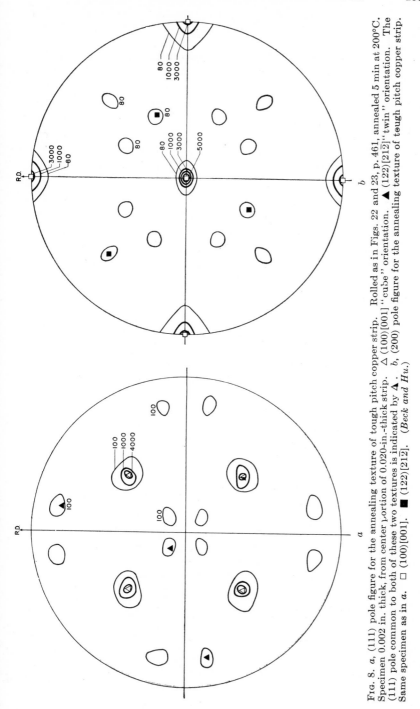

Fig. 8. *a*, (111) pole figure for the annealing texture of tough pitch copper strip. Rolled as in Figs. 22 and 23, p. 461, annealed 5 min at 200°C. Specimen 0.002 in. thick, from center portion of 0.020-in.-thick strip. △ (100)[001] "cube" orientation. ▲ (122)[2Ī2] "twin" orientation. The (111) pole common to both of these two textures is indicated by ▲. *b*, (200) pole figure for the annealing texture of tough pitch copper strip. Same specimen as in *a*. □ (100)[001]. ■ (122)[212]. (*Beck and Hu*.)

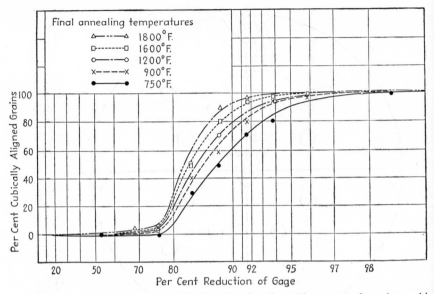

Fig. 9. Variation of percentage of cubically aligned grains with amount of previous cold rolling. Starting material is hot-rolled copper (99.96% Cu), 0.512-in. gauge. (*Baldwin.*)

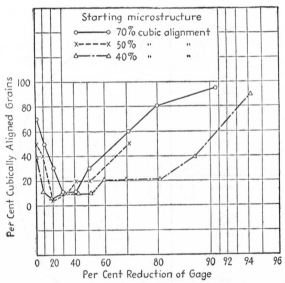

Fig. 10. Percentage of cubically aligned grains after annealing versus cold reduction before annealing for copper having initially different percentages of grains in cubic alignment. Ready-to-finish anneal, 1200°F; final anneal, 1200°F. (*Baldwin.*)

viously been developed. From the numerous studies of this texture it is clear that the following factors are effective in reducing and eliminating directionality caused by the presence of this texture:

1. Small cold reduction (roughly 50 per cent or less) with intermediate anneals.
2. Large penultimate grain size.[1]
3. A final anneal at a low temperature.
4. Minor additions of certain alloying elements[2] (discussed below).

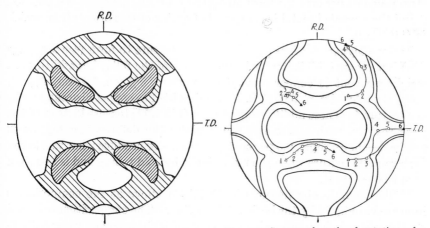

FIG. 11. Octahedral pole figure for copper, initially having a complete cube texture, after 53.5 per cent reduction. (*Baldwin.*)

FIG. 12. Suggested path of rotation of a cubically aligned grain during cold rolling, superimposed upon outline of final texture; (111) pole figure. (*Baldwin.*)

Extensive studies have been made of the effect of mill variables on the textures and grain sizes produced in copper and its alloys.[3] These are discussed further in Chap. XXI.

The transition from the cube texture to the ordinary deformation texture during rolling is worthy of study. A copper strip containing a fully developed cube texture acquired the texture of Fig. 11 after 53.5 per cent reduction by cold rolling and acquired the normal rolling texture after 91 per cent reduction.[4] Upon the final rolling texture, indicated in Fig. 12 by the outlined areas, is superimposed a set of paths along which Baldwin suggests that the individual poles have migrated from position 1 to posi-

[1] M. Cook and T. L. Richards, *J. Inst. Metals*, vol. 70, p. 159, 1944.

[2] H. Widmann, *Z. Physik*, vol. 45, p. 200, 1927.

[3] O. Dahl and F. Pawlek, *Z. Metallkunde*, vol. 28, p. 266, 1936. W. H. Baldwin, *Trans. AIME*, vol. 166, p. 591, 1946. T. S. Howald, *Trans. AIME*, vol. 175, p. 137, 1948.

[4] W. H. Baldwin, *Metals Technol.*, *Tech. Pub.* 1455, April, 1942; *Trans. AIME*, vol. 166, p. 591, 1946.

tion 6.[1] (The path was drawn by Baldwin in accord with Boas and Schmid's theory of rotation during deformation by compression.[2]) It is interesting that when strips such as these are again annealed the resulting orientations appear to fall at points along these paths. For example, after the cube texture has been rolled 22 per cent, recrystallization produces grains with an orientation between positions 3 and 4 on this path, as if those particles which have rotated to the most advanced positions along the path serve as recrystallization nuclei. Similarly, in the same strip rolled 91 per cent the most advanced rotations have reached position 6 and the annealed metal is composed of grains of this orientation, which is (110)[$\bar{1}$12].

Many *alloying additions* permit the cube texture to form (see list, page 494) but others inhibit it;[3] for instance, any of the following additions in weight per cent to copper prevent the texture: 5% Zn, 1% Sn, 4% Al, 0.5% Be, 0.5% Cd, or 0.05% P. Arsenic added to copper also suppresses the texture.[4] These additions produce a (113)[$\bar{2}$11] texture instead of the cube texture, with a few exceptions where the deformation texture is retained—for example, 0.5 per cent cadmium—or produce what was taken for a random texture when the reduction is by cold rolling and is less than about 90 per cent.

Müller[5] found cube textures in Fe-Ni-Cu alloys at the compositions indicated in Fig. 13 by the horizontal shading. The compositions covered by the vertical shading retained the rolling texture during recrystallization, and the region of overlap could be made to produce either texture with proper control of temperature.

Kronberg and Wilson[6] found that the large grains that grow in cube-texture copper sheet during coarsening ("secondary recrystallization") are related to the cubically aligned grains by rotations around [111] of 22° one way or 38° the other way, together with some that are rotated 19° either way around [100]. These grow spontaneously if the cubically aligned copper contains twins. After light deformation of twin-free cubically aligned copper, recrystallized grains with [111] rotations of 30° and [100] rotations of 15° were observed. Lightly rolled twin-free

---

[1] A single crystal of copper, initially in the (100)[001] position, when rolled 98.1 per cent also spread into a nearly complete polycrystalline texture in which the most intense regions were complementary (135)[21$\bar{1}$] positions, which were not far from position 6 of this figure. (C. S. Barrett and F. W. Steadman, *Metals Technol, Tech. Pub.* 1430, February, 1942.)

[2] W. Boas and E. Schmid, *Z. tech. Physik*, vol. 12, p. 71, 1931. See discussion on p. 449.

[3] O. Dahl and F. Pawlek, *Z. Metallkunde*, vol. 28, p. 266, 1936.

[4] F. v. Göler and G. Sachs, *Z. Physik*, vol. 56, p. 485, 1929.

[5] H. G. Müller, *Z. Metallkunde*, vol. 31, p. 322, 1939.

[6] M. L. Kronberg and F. H. Wilson, *Trans. AIME*, vol. 185, p. 501, 1949.

cubically aligned aluminum yielded large grains with [111] rotations of 38°. Rotations somewhat similar to these (perhaps identical) were found in coarsening experiments on copper by Bowles and Boas,[1] though a different relationship was found by Dahl and Pawlek,[2] who concluded that their final texture, (210)[001], corresponded to approximately 30° rotation around [100], and by Cook and Richards[3] who obtained a coarsening texture similar to the rolling texture of copper.[4]

Brick, Martin, and Angier[5] have studied the deformation and recrystallization textures in a series of copper alloys and have proposed two generalizations applying to alloys that have been given high reductions and low-temperature anneals: (1) The *recrystallization texture* of copper is changed by smaller additions of alloying elements than the additions required to change the *deformation texture*. (2) Solute elements that have the more marked *solution-hardening effect* on copper seem to generate the more *complex recrystallization textures* —those more closely approximating a random distribution of orientations.

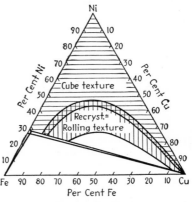

Fig. 13. Recrystallization textures in Fe-Ni-Cu alloys. (*Müller.*)

The results of this study show that in the Cu-Zn system the rolling texture changes from the copper to the brass type at about 5 atomic per cent zinc, with a transition type appearing near 1 per cent zinc. In alloys of copper with Mn, Al, As, Sb, Si, Mg, Sn, and Cu-Ni-Zn ("nickel silver") the texture changes similarly to the rolling texture of brass; but in the systems Cu-Ni and Cu-Co only the copper rolling texture was observed. Upon recrystallization at temperatures between 425 and 550°C the recrystallization textures were found to have many variations. Complex textures approximating near randomness were induced by additions of 0.3 atomic per cent Sb, 1.2 atomic per cent Sn, 1.5 atomic per cent Mg, and 4.2 and 5.4 atomic per cent Ni. These elements (with the exception

[1] J. S. Bowles and W. Boas, *J. Inst. Metals*, vol. 75, p. 449, 1948.

[2] O. Dahl and F. Pawlek, *Z. Metallkunde*, vol. 28, p. 266, 1936.

[3] M. Cook and T. L. Richards, *J. Inst. Metals*, vol. 66, p. 1, 1940.

[4] For other recrystallization studies of lightly deformed crystals see E. Schmid and H. Thomas, *Z. Metallkunde*, vol. 41, p. 45, 1950; N. K. Chen, reported in *Trans. AIME*, vol. 188, p. 1055, 1950; W. G. Burgers, "Handbuch der Metallphysik," vol. 3, pt. 2, Edwards Brothers, Ann Arbor, Mich., 1944; R. W. Cahn, Doctorate Thesis, Cambridge University, 1949 (aluminum grains, only a slight recrystallization texture); P. A. Beck, P. R. Sperry, and H. Hu, *J. Applied Phys.*, vol. 21, p. 420, 1950.

[5] R. M. Brick, D. L. Martin, and R. P. Angier, *Trans. ASM*, vol. 31, p. 671, 1943.

of nickel) are the ones that differ most markedly from copper in atomic radii and in the solution hardening effect in copper.[1] The nickel alloys, which had deformation textures like copper, took up a brasslike annealing

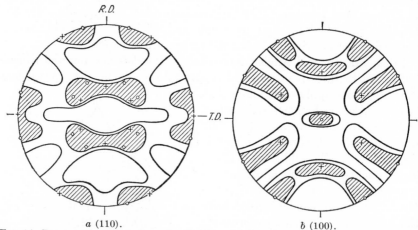

a (110).   b (100).

FIG. 14. Recrystallization texture of rolled iron. (○) position near (100)[011], (+)(111) [11$\bar{2}$] position. (*Kurdjumow and Sachs.*)

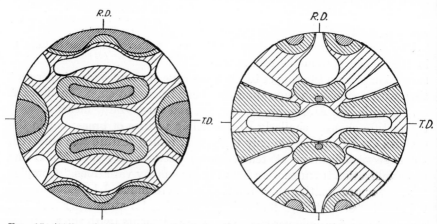

FIG. 15. (110) pole figure for mild-steel sheet recrystallized at 580°C. (*Gensamer and Lustman.*)

FIG. 16. (110) pole figure for silicon-steel sheet (Fe–4.61% Si) recrystallized at 590°C (originally cold-rolled 95 per cent).

texture at about 5 atomic per cent. Other alloys also exhibited a change in the recrystallization texture at lower compositions than the change in deformation texture, *viz.*, the alloys containing Zn, Mn, and Al.

Body-centered Cubic Rolling Recrystallization Textures. The important texture in recrystallized iron and steel was first fully analyzed by

[1] The curve of relative hardening is given on p. 357.

Kurdjumow and Sachs.[1]   Their pole figures are reproduced in Fig. 14.
The principal orientations were identified as follows: (1) rolling plane
(100), rolling direction 15° from [011]; (2) rolling plane (111), rolling
direction [112]; and (3) rolling plane (112), rolling direction 15° from [110].
A comparison of other results with these is given in Table XX.   Pole

TABLE XX.   BODY-CENTERED CUBIC RECRYSTALLIZATION TEXTURES

Material	Recrystallization temperature, degrees centigrade	Recrystallization texture		Investigator	Method
		Rolling plane	Rolling direction		
Iron..............	Above 600	(100)	~15° from [011]	Glocker[3]	X-ray
Electrolytic iron and mild steel.	550 to 840	(100)	~15° from [011]		
		(111)	[11$\bar{2}$]	Kurdjumow	X-ray, pole
		(112)	~15° from [1$\bar{1}$0]	and Sachs[1]	figure
Mild steel.........	650	Similar to ref. 1		Gensamer and	X-ray, pole
	580	Slightly different from ref. 1		Lustman[2]	figure
Fe + 3.05% Si....	1100*	(100)	[001]	Sixtus[4]	Optical (etch pits)
		(110)	[001]		
Fe + 3.50% Si....	1093*	(110)	[001]	Bozorth[5]	X-ray
Fe + 2.07% Si....	580	Similar to ref. 1		Barrett, Ansel,	X-ray, pole
Fe + 4.61% Si....	590	Similar to ref. 1		and Mehl[6]	figure
Fe + 4.61% Si....	860	Slightly different from			
Fe + 4.61% Si....	1093	refs. 1 and 2			
Fe + 3.1% Si.....	~1100*	(110)	[001]	Burwell[7]	X-ray, pole figure
Mo..............	1320	(100)	[011]	Semchyshen[8]	X-ray, pole figure

* With intermediate anneal (see N. P. Goss, *Trans. ASM*, vol. 23, p. 511, 1935; U.S. Patent 1,965,559.
[1] G. Kurdjumow and G. Sachs, *Z. Physik*, vol. 62, p. 592, 1930.
[2] M. Gensamer and B. Lustman, *Trans. AIME*, vol. 125, p. 501, 1937.
[3] R. Glocker, "Materialprüfung mit Röntgenstrahlen," p. 338, Springer, Berlin, 1927.
[4] K. J. Sixtus, *Physics*, vol. 6, p. 105, 1935.
[5] R. M. Bozorth, *Trans. ASM*, vol. 23, p. 1107, 1935.
[6] C. S. Barrett, G. Ansel, and R. F. Mehl, *Trans. AIME*, vol. 125, p. 516, 1937.
[7] J. T. Burwell, *Trans. AIME*, vol. 140, p. 353, 1940.
[8] Private communication.   Pole figure like that of cold-rolled Mo.

figures for mild steel recrystallized at 580°C[2] and for an Fe-Si alloy[3] are
also shown (Figs. 15 and 16).   The general features are similar; the
recrystallization texture resembles the deformation texture rotated 15°
in each direction around the sheet normal.   The appearance of a diffrac-

[1] G. Kurdjumow and G. Sachs, *Z. Physik*, vol. 62, p. 592, 1930.
[2] M. Gensamer and B. Lustman, *Trans. AIME*, vol. 125, p. 501, 1937.
[3] C. S. Barrett, G. Ansel, and R. F. Mehl, *Trans. AIME*, vol. 125, p. 516, 1937.

tion pattern made with the beam perpendicular to a sheet having this texture is shown in Fig. 17.

Recrystallization textures are sensitive to the schedule of rolling and intermediate annealing. The control of all such variables in the manufacture of steel sheet is of great importance, and much attention is devoted to the problem in plant laboratories. Published research represents but a fraction of the total knowledge of the subject. Goss,[1] using cycles of cold reduction followed by recrystallization, has produced a (110)[001] texture, which possesses high permeability in the rolling direction.[2] Frey and

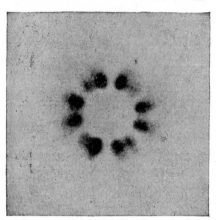

FIG. 17. Pattern for recrystallized steel sheet, beam normal to the sheet (same sample as for Fig. 16).

Bitter[3] find that each cycle of cold reduction followed by recrystallization serves to increase the percentage of crystals having the (110)[001] position and to decrease the percentage having the (100)[011] position. A marked improvement in silicon steel for transformer cores has been made in recent years by improving the magnetic permeability in the rolling direction through control of orientation.[4]

When steel is heated into the austenite range, the transformation to austenite and the reverse transformation to ferrite produce a random or nearly random texture, because of the multiplicity of orientations that results from a single orientation in the preceding phase.

Cross rolling decreases the scatter in orientation about the rolling direction in the deformation texture of steel and other b.c.c. metals (see page 478). Use is made of this fact to produce desirable orientations in commercial sheet by a method due to Bitter.[5] By careful annealing following controlled rolling in both the longitudinal and transverse directions the deformation texture is maintained, giving a sheet in which the cube plane is parallel to the rolling plane and the [110] directions are parallel to each rolling direction. The direction of easiest magnetization, [100], is then at 45° to the rolling direction.

[1] N. P. Goss, *Trans. ASM*, vol. 23, p. 511, 1935; U.S. Patent 1,965,559.

[2] R. M. Bozorth, *Trans. ASM*, vol. 23, p. 1107, 1935. J. T. Burwell, *Trans. AIME*, vol. 140, p. 353, 1940.

[3] A. A. Frey and F. Bitter, U.S. Patent 2,112,084.

[4] Other U.S. Patents dealing with this subject are 2,287,466 and 2,158,065.

[5] F. Bitter, U.S. Patent 2,046,717.

Cross-rolled molybdenum retains the (100)[011] component during recrystallization at 1315°C, but loses some of the (111) component.[1]

Close-packed Hexagonal Rolling Recrystallization Textures. Hexagonal metals seem to retain their rolling texture upon recrystallization. Straumann[2] found this with zinc and with Zn-Cd and Zn-Cu alloys, which showed uniform scattering of the hexagonal axis around the sheet normal, while Caglioti and Sachs[3] found the same with zinc and magnesium.

Titanium, which has a rolling texture with the *c* axis scattering toward the transverse direction and clustering at 30° from the normal, recrystallizes with the same texture (Fig. 18) except that material with the *c* axis near the normal appears to have disappeared during annealing.[4]

Beryllium remains unchanged in texture during recrystallization. The texture produced by rolling at 800 and 350°C also closely resembles the cold-rolling texture.[5]

Zirconium changes from the rolling texture (McGeary and Lustman, p. 477) to one with the same basal plane positions but with [11$\bar{2}$0] parallel to RD; and after cross rolling, also, the [10$\bar{1}$0] direction in the parent becomes the [11$\bar{2}$0] in the recrystallized sheet, leaving the basal plane parallel to the sheet.

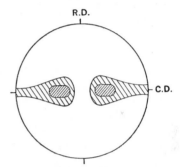

Fig. 18. Basal plane pole figure for titanium annealed at 500°C after 98.4 per cent reduction by cold rolling. (*Clark.*)

Theories of Recrystallization Textures. Burgers and Louwerse[6] proposed that recrystallization textures were determined by nuclei in the deformed material that had the orientation of the recrystallized metal. Oriented nucleation theories encounter the objection that there are likely to be sufficient nuclei in any orientation whatever to provide the number that are needed to determine a texture.[7]

It was proposed[7] that a theory of recrystallization textures might better be based on the principle that certain orientations grow into the deformation texture material more rapidly than others, the shifting of atoms from the strained matrix to the new grain proceeding slowly when the new grain has about the orientation of the matrix, and fastest when it differs from the matrix in a certain way—roughly a rotation of 45° around [111].

[1] M. Semchyshen and G. A. Timmons, *J. Metals*, vol. 4, p. 279, 1952.

[2] R. Straumann, *Helv. Phys. Acta*, vol. 3, p. 463, 1930.

[3] V. Caglioti and G. Sachs, *Metallwirtschaft*, vol. 11, p. 1, 1932.

[4] H. T. Clark, Jr., *Trans. AIME*, vol. 188, p. 1154, 1950.

[5] A. Smigelskas and C. S. Barrett, *Trans. AIME*, vol. 185, p. 145, 1949.

[6] W. G. Burgers and P. C. Louwerse, *Z. Physik*, vol. 67, p. 605, 1931.

[7] C. S. Barrett, *Trans. AIME*, vol. 137, p. 128, 1940.

Beck and coworkers have adopted this point of view and have found experimental evidence in support of this as distinguished from the oriented nucleation hypothesis.[1] Many of the final grains found in recrystallized lightly rolled cube-textured copper have orientations differing from those of the deformed metal by 30° rotations around [111] and some, also, by 15° rotations around [100].[2] Rotations of 38° ± 4° seem prominent in aluminum and in single crystals of copper,[2] though other rotations in the range 30 to 45° have been proposed.[1] (Kronberg and Wilson have also suggested that 30° rotations around [0001] occur in the recrystallization of sheets of hexagonal metals.) It is these orientations, then, that are proposed as the favored ones in the orientation-dependent growth-rate theory.[3]

It may be concluded, then, that one important principle governing recrystallization texture formation is orientation-dependent growth velocity, and that the textures in recrystallized aluminum strip, in deformed and receystallized single crystals of aluminum and copper, and in some other metals and alloys can be accounted for chiefly by this principle. However, there can be no doubt that supplementary principles must also be assumed; otherwise it is impossible to account for the fact that when deformation and recrystallization textures are related by [111] rotations, only one or two, not all eight such rotations, are involved. Beck suggests[4] that this may be ascribed to a lack of full symmetry in the deformed crystals or possibly to an orientation distribution in the nuclei, a distribution favoring one or two and eliminating the rest even though it has considerable scatter. Texture theory must also recognize that the retention of deformation texture, when it occurs in whole or in part, requires a different explanation. From the researches of Dunn on silicon iron and of Crussard on "recrystallization in situ," and from many other studies on recovery and "polygonization" it is clear that grain-boundary migration may occur (even lengthening of a boundary) without the nucleation of newly oriented grains, and that strained grains may "polygonize" into strain-free states with but slight change in orientation. It is also certain that recrystallization sometimes occurs with a change in orientation of each new grain of such a type that the deformation texture is retained as a whole or as one component of the texture. This occurs in

---

[1] P. A. Beck, P. R. Sperry, and H. Hu, *J. Applied Phys.*, vol. 21, p. 420, 1950. P. A. Beck and H. Hu, *Trans. AIME*, vol. 185, p. 627, 1949; vol. 188, p. 1057, 1950; *J. Metals*, vol. 188, p. 1215, October, 1950.

[2] M. L. Kronberg and F. H. Wilson, *Trans. AIME*, vol. 185, p. 501, 1949.

[3] There seems to be adequate evidence that orientation relationships of near identity or of twinning create boundaries of very *low* mobility, both in recrystallization process and in the grain-growth process discussed in the following section.

[4] P. A. Beck, *Trans. AIME*, vol. 191, p. 475, 1951.

aluminum wires and compressed disks[1] and in rolled aluminum.[2]   In the latter case, it was found that the new grains seen in one set of deformation bands had the orientation of the strained metal of another set of deformation bands.   It has also been suggested[3] that polygonization supplies the strain-free nuclei of orientations suited to rapid growth.   Polygonization itself seems to be at a rate dependent upon orientation.[4]

The physical basis for the orientation dependence of boundary mobility is at present a matter of speculation.   Surely the orientation dependence of boundary energy is not a suitable basis.   Beck and coworkers have suggested[5] that the required basis lies in the rate of self-diffusion along the boundary, but data are not at hand to test this point of view.[6]

Kronberg and Wilson,[7] in discussing grain growth, have plotted the positions of atoms in grains that meet at one of the favored boundaries, and find that a portion of the atoms do not have to shift position at all as the boundary moves past them; the rest have to merely shift slightly in coordinated ring movements, as in Fig. 19.   The magnitude of the shifts is of the order of one-third interatomic distance, and the coordination is such that there would be cooperation rather than interference between individual atoms that shift.

The Kronberg-Wilson plots, though originally discussed from the standpoint of oriented-nucleation theory, are an attractive starting point for speculation in oriented growth theory.   Perhaps the activation energy for the atom shifts indicated by these plots is very low, as might be imagined from the small magnitude and coordinated nature of the shifts.   Perhaps the shifts, when they have occurred within a ring on, say, a (111) plane, easily spread over the plane like an expanding partial-dislocation ring, driven by either strain energy in the cold-worked metal, or grain-boundary tension or both.   Perhaps the importance of these boundaries lies in the fact that displacement of the boundaries is by cooperative atom movements that have no component of *macroscopic* distortion, provided that

[1] C. S. Barrett, *Trans. AIME*, vol. 137, p. 128, 1940.

[2] P. A. Beck and H. Hu, *J. Metals*, vol. 188, p. 1215, October, 1950.

[3] R. W. Cahn, *Proc. Phys. Soc. (London)*, vol. 63, p. 323, 1950.   P. A. Beck, *J. Applied Phys.*, vol. 20, p. 633, 1949.

[4] W. G. Burgers, Y. H. Liu, and T. J. Tiedema, *Proc. Koninkl. Nederland. Akad. Wetenschap.*, vol. B54, p. 459, 1951.   Tiedema, in his doctorate thesis, opposes the oriented growth theory of annealing textures.

[5] P. A. Beck, P. R. Sperry, and H. Hu, *J. Applied Phys.*, vol. 21, p. 420, 1950.

[6] Slow diffusion has been reported for coherent twin boundaries and boundaries between near-identically oriented grains, and fast diffusion along ordinary boundaries: P. J. Fensham, *Australian J. Sci. Research*, vol. A3, p. 105, 1950; R. S. Barnes, *Nature*, vol. 166, p. 1032, 1950; but there is no evidence available regarding exceptionally high rates at specific orientations, and no proof that diffusion *along* the boundary is the controlling factor.

[7] M. L. Kronberg and F. H. Wilson, *Trans. AIME*, vol. 185, p. 501, 1949.

the orientation relationship across the boundary is ideal, thus resembling movements in martensite formation but without martensitic lattice strains (*cf.* Chap. XXII).

Grain-boundary tension may be the driving force, not only in grain growth,[1] but also in recrystallization,[2] where the boundaries are sub-boundaries, arrays of dislocations, or even individual dislocations. This tension can cause a boundary to migrate only if it becomes a curved sur-

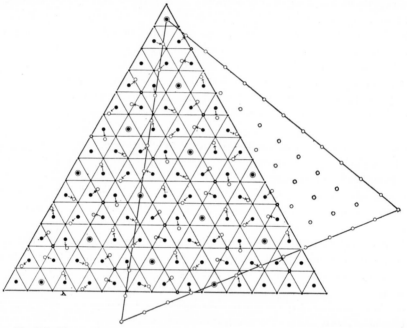

FIG. 19. Coincidence plot showing positions of atoms on f.c.c. (111) plane before and after a 22° rotation (or a 38° opposite rotation). Dots represent one layer; filled circles the adjacent layer; open circles, the latter after rotation; coincidences indicated by concentric circles. (*Kronberg and Wilson.*)

face. The Kronberg-Wilson shifts are not inconsistent with this requirement, for the boundary of the shifted region can be curved without introducing misfits such as would characterize a high-energy boundary.

Decker and Harker[3] have proposed an explanation of the texture of annealed silicon ferrite sheet—the texture of desirable magnetic properties, (110)[001]—on the basis of the varying tendencies for grains of different initial orientation to recrystallize after cold rolling. Grains with an initial orientation less than 5° from (110)[001] were found to be distorted severely by the rolling, so that no back-reflection Laue pattern could be

[1] Cyril S. Smith, *Trans. AIME*, vol. 175, p. 15, 1948.

[2] Cyril S. Smith, private communication.

[3] B. F. Decker and D. Harker, *J. Applied Phys.*, vol. 22, p. 900, 1951.

seen, yet pole figures showed that their average orientation remained essentially unchanged. These recrystallized in a subsequent anneal at 800°C. On the other hand, grains far from this initial orientation— except (110)[$\overline{1}$10]—showed only slight asterism after rolling, rotated by slip principally on parallel planes, without severe internal distortions, and did not recrystallize. The texture is thus accounted for by stating that symmetrically oriented grains, in which slip occurs simultaneously on intersecting slip systems, acquire large amounts of strain energy during rolling, and recrystallize before the others. This recrystallization occurs without major changes in orientation; thus the (110)[001] texture is retained, and less symmetrically oriented grains are devoured by the recrystallized grains.

As Dunn[1] points out, however, the production of highly oriented (110)[001] texture in silicon iron sheet involves not only recrystallization —which results in few grains with (110) in the plane of the sheet—but also much grain growth. The problem is one of selective grain growth in a sheet having a certain recrystallization texture and a critical amount of cold rolling.

Theories of Growth Textures. Textures that develop during the growth of grains in recrystallized metals must be caused by the preferential growth of grains having certain orientations relative to their neighbors.[2] That growth rates are orientation-dependent is well established by experiment.[3] Several experiments on aluminum, copper, and an iron-nickel alloy indicate that high boundary mobility is associated with boundaries where there is a rotation of 30 to 40° around [111].[4] While some evidence exists for other orientation relationships of similar mobility—particularly rotation around [100],[5,6]—the [111] rotation has been used most frequently in theories of growth textures. Kronberg and Wilson[5] have postulated that oriented nucleation accounts for the prevalence of the favored orientations after growth, though they agree that most experiments can

[1] C. G. Dunn, in "Cold Working of Metals," p. 113, American Society for Metals, Cleveland, Ohio, 1949.

[2] A. E. van Arkel, *Rev. mét.*, vol. 33, p. 197, 1936. W. G. Burgers, *Proc. Konink. Nederland. Akad. Wetenschap.*, vol. 50, p. 723, 1947.

[3] C. G. Dunn in "Cold Working of Metals," American Society for Metals, Cleveland, Ohio, 1949. P. A. Beck and H. Hu, *Trans. AIME*, vol. 185, p. 627, 1949. J. E. Burke in "Atom Movements," American Society for Metals, Cleveland, Ohio, 1951.

[4] J. S. Bowles and W. Boas, *J. Inst. Metals*, vol. 74, p. 501, 1948. M. L. Kronberg and F. H. Wilson, *Trans. AIME*, vol. 185, p. 501, 1949; vol. 188, p. 1055, 1950. G. W. Rathenau and J. F. H. Custers, *Philips Research Repts.*, vol. 4, p. 241, 1949. P. A. Beck and H. Hu, *Trans. AIME*, vol. 185, p. 627, 1949.

[5] M. L. Kronberg and F. H. Wilson, *Trans. AIME*, vol. 185, p. 501, 1949; vol. 188, p. 1055, 1950.

[6] J. S. Bowles, *Trans. AIME*, vol. 188, p. 1054, 1950.

be interpreted by either oriented-growth or oriented-nucleation theories. They have pointed out that atom shifts of a cooperative nature and of one-third atom diameter or less could serve to shift the boundary when the relationship at the boundary is a rotation of either 22° one way or 38° the opposite way around [111], or 19° around [100].

Beck[1] has proposed a theory for the cube texture that is based entirely upon oriented growth. The deformation texture of rolled sheet that is capable of being converted to the cube texture may be treated as four symmetrical ideal orientations near (123)[1$\bar{2}$1]. This texture is partially retained by a recovery process and by a process in which one of these four components grows into another of the four, rotated about 40° around [111] from the first. The cube texture also appears upon recrystallization, for this is also a [111] rotation of 40° from each of the four components. It is proposed that, upon further annealing, the cube texture grains grow more than any others because they are in favorable orientation to every one of the four components. Reasoning that the growth of grains in the (100)[001] orientation is fastest relative to others when they are in contact with all four components, Beck accounts qualitatively for the fact that the cube texture develops earlier in the annealing process when there is greater opportunity for contact with all four components. This occurs when the average thickness of the rolled grains and deformation bands is smaller (when the penultimate grain size is smaller or the reductions are higher), or when opportunity for growth is greater (higher annealing temperatures). He ascribes the lack of cube textures in some alloys (e.g., 70–30 brass, silver) to a change in the deformation texture such that these relations no longer hold. In 70–30 brass and silver he accounts for the recrystallization texture by a [111] rotation of 30° from the deformation texture, and the growth texture, which matches the deformation texture, by a 30° [111] rotation back to the original deformation texture, rather than by the more common assumption that traces of the deformation texture serve as nuclei for this growth texture. Kronberg and Wilson also called attention to this rotation and rotation-back relationship (using 38° rotations in their discussion).

Summary. Some recrystallization textures resemble the deformation textures from which they grew, some are entirely different, and some are random. The control of preferred orientations is accomplished by control of hot-working, cold-working, and annealing schedules; metal purity; alloy composition; and amount of cross rolling. Commercial products having a well-developed orientation of a desirable type (as in transformer cores of high permeability in the rolling direction) or having a highly com-

[1] P. A. Beck, *J. Metals*, vol. 3, p. 474, 1951. P. A. Beck and H. Hu, *J. Metals*, vol. 4, p. 83, 1952.

plex, near-random texture (as in sheet of deep-drawing quality) are usually developed by cut-and-try methods.

A well-developed deformation texture is usually a prerequisite to a sharp recrystallization texture. Recrystallization textures of copper alloys are more sensitive to change by the addition of alloying elements than are deformation textures, and the alloying elements having the greatest solution-hardening effects on copper seem to generate the most nearly random recrystallization textures.

The sharply developed cube texture, (100)[001], which is common to many f.c.c. metals and alloys after rolling and recrystallization, becomes most pronounced with heavy cold reductions and high annealing temperatures. Many alloying additions prevent it; for example, any of the following additions, in weight per cent, to copper, 5% Zn, 1% Sn, 4% Al, 0.5% Be, 0.5% Cd, 0.05% P.

Iron, steel, and alloyed ferrites have complex recrystallization textures in which the principal orientation is one having (100) in the rolling plane and [011] 15° from the rolling direction. By employing various cycles of cold reduction and intermediate annealing, sometimes with cross rolling, it has been found possible to develop pronounced textures of the types (100)[001], (110)[001], and (100)[011].

Current theories make use of the principle that rates of grain-boundary migration are dependent upon orientations at the boundary; preferentially oriented nuclei may also be involved, and recovery without reorientation occurs in some instances.

CHAPTER XX

ORIENTATIONS IN CASTINGS AND IN DEPOSITED FILMS

Metal castings frequently contain long columnar grains which extend from the surface inward in the direction of the greatest temperature gradient during freezing. The columnar structure is illustrated by a photograph of a copper ingot reproduced in Fig. 1. The long axis of the columnar grains tends to be an important crystal direction; *i.e.*, prominent crystal planes tend to be aligned parallel to the mold wall. The preferred orientations near the surface of a casting thus resemble the type of orientations found in a metal after compression, in that a crystal direction

FIG. 1. Columnar grains in cast copper.

of low indices stands perpendicular to the surface and other crystal axes are oriented at random around this axis.

In electrodeposited films there is also a tendency for a texture, but the tendency is frequently overcome by conditions in the plating bath and in the underlying surface. Sometimes the orientations in the underlying metal are inherited in the deposit. Films deposited by sputtering during an electric discharge in a vacuum may be amorphous or crystalline, and when crystalline they also have a preferred orientation of the fiber-texture type unless conditions are such that they inherit an orientation from the material on which they are deposited.

Freezing, and the Textures in Cast Metals. As solidification proceeds inward from nuclei at the mold wall, some grains grow more rapidly than

510

others.[1] Under some conditions these may block the growth of their slower growing neighbors and form a zone of columnar grains which may extend to the center of the casting, as in Fig. 1, or may ultimately give way to solidification of equiaxed grains. The outer skin, the columnar zone, and the inner zone of equiaxed grains, when these layers exist, have different textures; the textures in the skin and the columnar zone are summarized in Table XXI. The central zone of equiaxed grains has a

TABLE XXI. TEXTURES OF CAST METALS

Structure	Metal	Directions [*uvw*], or planes (*hkl*) normal to cold surface
B.c.c.	Fe-Si (4.3% Si)	[100]
	β-Brass	[100]
F.c.c.	Al	
	Cu	
	Ag	[100]
	Au	
	Pb	
	α-Brass	
C.p.h.*	Cd(*c/a* ⩰ 1.885)	Columnar grains, (001)
		Columnar grains, [210]; chilled surface, [001]
	Zn(*c/a* = 1.856)	Columnar grains, (001)
		Columnar grains, [210]; chilled surface, [001]
	Mg(*c/a* = 1.624)	Columnar grains, [100]
		Columnar grains with (205)‖surface
Rhombohedral	Bi	[111]
Tetragonal	β-Sn	[110]

* Three-indices system; equivalent indices in four-indices systems are as follows: (001) = (0001) = basal plane; [100] = [$2\bar{1}\bar{1}0$] = digonal axis of type I = close-packed row of atoms in basal plane; [100] normal to the surface = ($\bar{2}$10) parallel to surface; [210] normal to surface = (100) parallel to surface.

random texture, and the equiaxed crystals at a chilled surface are random in orientation in some cases. The chilled surfaces of aluminum and of α + β brass die castings, for example, are random in texture.[2] Yet in zinc and cadmium the outer skin seems to have (001) parallel to the surface and frequently, according to Edmunds, there is an intermediate layer between this and the columnar zone, which has (101) parallel to the surface. The crystallographic directions along which growth is at a maximum rate in body-centered and face-centered cubic metals are the cube axes; so these are found pointing in the direction of growth, normal to the

[1] W. Boas and E. Schmid, *Z. Physik*, vol. 54, p. 16, 1929.   A. G. Hoyem and E. P. T. Tyndall, *Phys. Rev.*, vol. 33, p. 81, 1929.   S. Tsuboi, *Mem. Coll. Sci. Kyoto Imp. Univ.*, vol. A12, p. 223, 1929.   R. Gross and H. Möller, *Z. Physik*, vol. 19, p. 375, 1923.

[2] G. Edmunds, *Trans. AIME*, vol. 161, p. 114, 1945.

mold wall.[1] Northcott and Thomas showed that the striations seen on cross sections of such ingots (at least with copper alloys) are the intersections of {100} faces with the polished surface.[2] According to Edmunds,[3] if the natural faces that tend to develop are the planes of maximum atomic density, {111} in face-centered cubic (f.c.c.) metals, {110} in body-centered cubic (b.c.c.), and (001) + {110} in close-packed hexagonal (c.p.h.), the maximum growth velocity should be in the direction of maximum dimension of the solid formed by these bounding surfaces. This would predict [100] for cubic crystals, since this is the maximum dimension for both octahedra and dodecahedra, and a direction dependent upon c/a for c.p.h., as observed in the data[1,3] listed in Table XXI.

In alloys of copper, Northcott[4] found the length of columnar grains to increase with decreasing temperature range between liquidus and solidus. With pure metals, which freeze at constant temperature, the grains may be wholly columnar. A temperature gradient normal to the mold wall favors long columnar grains, and the presence of an additional gradient parallel to the wall favors equiaxed grains.[5] Northcott concludes that the *ratio* of these gradients rather than their absolute magnitude determines the tendency toward columnar or toward equiaxed freezing of grains. Freezing does not always occur by the thickening of a frozen skin, but may occur simultaneously throughout the entire pasty mass, as Ruddle finds, for example, in an alloy of aluminum–4 per cent copper.[6] Chalmers and his coworkers find that the contour of the liquid-solid interface in pure tin depends upon the degree of supercooling at the growing interface,[7] and may be either smooth, cellular, or dendritic.

The growth of dendrites may be understood as the result of the tendency for freezing to develop idiomorphic forms. At the corners of the growing idiomorphic crystals there is a relatively larger volume of liquid to draw upon than at the centers of the faces and as a consequence the concentration gradient in the liquid near idiomorph corners should be more favorable to growth than the gradient at the centers of faces. Thermal gradients and heat-transfer characteristics are also involved. The preferential growth of a corner of the first crystal to freeze does not continue indefinitely, however, so as to produce a long rod. After extending a distance out into the surrounding liquid, a rod thickens and forms a second

---

[1] E. Schmid, *Z. Metallkunde*, vol. 20, p. 373, 1928. F. C. Nix and E. Schmid, *Z. Metallkunde*, vol. 21, p. 291, 1929.

[2] L. Northcott and D. E. Thomas, *J. Inst. Metals*, vol. 65, p. 205, 1939.

[3] G. Edmunds, *Trans. AIME*, vol. 143, p. 183, 1941.

[4] L. Northcott, *J. Inst. Metals*, vol. 65, p. 173, 1939.

[5] L. Northcott, *J. Inst. Metals*, vol. 72, p. 283, 1946.

[6] R. W. Ruddle, *J. Inst. Metals*, vol. 77, p. 1, 1950.

[7] B. Chalmers, private communication.

idiomorphic crystal like the first. This process continues, resulting in a string of crystals connected at their corners, the string forming the trunk of the treelike dendrite.[1] Each crystal along the string has corners that are potential sites for secondary arms—the branches of the tree. These proceed to grow if they are sufficiently removed from the shielding influence of those that had formed previously, and these in turn may develop similarly, with tertiary arms appearing. This view of the freezing process suggests that the spacing of dendrite arms should depend, among other variables, upon the rates of material and heat diffusion and the latent heat. For different alloys of a given alloy system, Alexander and Rhines[2] find a fairly good correlation between the spacings of dendrite arms and the ratio of heat of fusion to the thermal diffusivity. They also find that the spacings in a given alloy are approximately inversely proportional to the rate of crystal growth. A dendrite grows with similar orientation throughout, though the imperfections of growth may cause deviations in orientation up to several degrees.

The textures in two *binary eutectics* have been studied.[3] In Zn-Cd (17 per cent zinc) each of the two phases has the texture it has when alone, but in Al-Si (13 per cent silicon) only the predominating phase is oriented. This phase (aluminum-rich) has its usual texture, with [100] as fiber axis, while the minor phase is randomly oriented.

Orientations in Electrodeposits. The nature of the orientation in electrodeposited metal is of considerable technical importance and has been the object of much investigation with the microscope and with X-ray and electron diffraction. The subject is complex, for the deposit is affected by the nature of the electrolyte, its hydrogen-ion concentration, the presence of addition agents, the temperature, the current density, the nature and condition of the base metal, stirring, rubbing, etc. There are also changes in texture as the deposited layer thickens, some of which have been ascribed directly to the thickness and others to changing conditions of temperature or concentration in the electrolyte.

Under some plating conditions the orientation of the base metal is copied by the deposit.[4] In fact, microscopic investigation of a cross section through deposit and base metal shows that the grains in the deposit are frequently continuations of the grains in the base metal.[5]

[1] This sequence was observed in the crystallization of nonmetallic substances by A. Papapetrou, *Z. Krist.*, vol. 92, p. 89, 1935.

[2] B. H. Alexander and F. N. Rhines, *Trans. AIME*, vol. 188, p. 1267, 1950.

[3] F. C. Nix and E. Schmid, *Z. Metallkunde*, vol. 21, p. 286, 1929.

[4] W. A. Wood, *Proc. Phys. Soc. (London)*, vol. 43, p. 138, 1931. W. Cochrane, *Proc. Phys. Soc. (London)*, vol. 48, p. 723, 1936. G. P. Thomson, *Proc. Roy. Soc. (London)*, vol. A133, p. 1, 1931.

[5] A. K. Huntington, *Trans. Faraday Soc.*, vol. 1, p. 324, 1905. A. K. Graham, *Trans. Am. Electrochem. Soc.*, vol. 44, p. 427, 1923. A. W. Hothersall, *Trans. Faraday*

The conditions most favorable to the continuation of base-metal grains into the electrodeposit are the following: clean, freshly etched surfaces, small current densities, electrolytes without colloidal additions, and similarity in structure between base metal and deposit. When both metals are cubic, continuation is found only if the base metal has a parameter approximately equal to that of the deposit (2.4 per cent smaller to 12.5 per cent greater).[1] Exceptions to these rules have been observed, however. It is possible to have continuation when the two metals have different structures, presumably because of related atomic patterns at the interface, as in Widmanstätten structures. It is also possible to have continuation across a thin interposed layer of a second substance,[2] (perhaps through connecting pores or through orientations imparted to the layer). The continuity may occur only for certain grains of the base metal, as in rapidly applied industrial deposits, or it may be observed for all grains, for example, when the base metal itself is an electrodeposit.

The influence of the base metal does not extend very far into the deposited metal, and the outer layers are free to take up their characteristic orientation. Under some conditions the underlying layers are randomly oriented and succeeding layers become progressively more sharply oriented for some distance.[3] Current density and electrolyte composition may be such that the entire deposit is random,[4] or varying degrees of orientation can be produced.[5] Not only the degree of orientation but even the nature of the texture can be altered by the plating conditions.[6] In every case where a deposit is free to assume its own texture the orientations are such that a crystal axis stands perpendicular to the surface or parallel to the direction of current flow, and there is rotational symmetry around this axis. Thus the deposit has a fiber texture (or a double fiber texture) resembling the texture of a wire, the thickness direction of the deposit corresponding to the axial direction in the wire.

A brief summary of orientations that have been observed, assembled for the most part by Wassermann,[7] is given in Table XXII.

Soc., vol. 31, p. 1242, 1935. W. Blum and H. S. Rawdon, *Trans. Am. Electrochem. Soc.*, vol. 44, p. 305, 1923. G. Tammann and M. Straumanis, *Z. anorg. allgem. Chem.*, vol. 175, p. 131, 1928.

[1] A. W. Hothersall, *Trans. Faraday Soc.*, vol. 31, p. 1242, 1935. Nonparallel but well-oriented deposits of iron on gold are accounted for by matching at the interface: G. I. Finch and C. H. Sun, *Trans. Faraday Soc.*, vol. 32, p. 852, 1936.

[2] A. M. Portevin and M. Cymboliste, *Trans. Faraday Soc.*, vol. 31, p. 1211, 1935.

[3] W. G. Burgers, *Philips Tech. Rev.*, vol. 1, p. 95, 1936.

[4] R. Glocker and E. Kaupp, *Z. Physik*, vol. 24, p. 121, 1924.

[5] W. A. Wood, *Phil. Mag.*, vol. 20, p. 964, 1935.

[6] R. Glocker and E. Kaupp, *Z. Physik*, vol. 24, p. 121, 1924. R. Bozorth, *Phys. Rev.*, vol. 26, p. 390, 1925.

[7] G. Wassermann, "Texturen metallischer Werkstoffe," Springer, Berlin, 1939.

Chromium deposited from chromic acid solutions may be either as the body-centered cubic metal, as a hydride of hexagonal structure (a = 2.27, c = 4.42 A), or as a hydride of face-centered cubic structure (a = 3.84 A).[1] The composition and temperature of the plating solution and the pH at the cathode govern the form that is deposited; aging at room temperature a few hours decomposes the face-centered cubic, and annealing at 150°C

TABLE XXII. TEXTURES IN ELECTRODEPOSITS

Metal	Fiber textures	Observers
Nickel	[100]; [100] + [110]; [112]; [111]	1, 5, 8, 9, 10, 11, 18
Copper	[110]; [100]	1, 6, 7
Silver	[111] + [100]; [111]; [110]	1, 2, 3, 4, 5
Lead	[112]	12
Gold	[110]	5
Iron	[111]; [112]	1, 5, 9, 11
Cobalt	[110]	5
Chromium	[100] + [111] (f.c.c.); [0001] (hexagonal)	1, 13, 14
Tin	[111]; [001]	5, 16
Cadmium	[11$\bar{2}$2]	17
Bismuth	[211]; [100]	5, 15
Zinc	0001; $\perp$ (10$\bar{1}$1) or (10$\bar{1}$2)	18

[1] R. Glocker and E. Kaupp, *Z. Physik*, vol. 24, p. 121, 1924.

[2] S. Tsuboi, *Mem. Coll. Sci. Kyoto Imp. Univ.*, vol. A11, p. 271, 1928.

[3] G. R. Levi and M. Tabet, *Atti accad. nazl. Lincei*, vol. 18 (6), p. 463, 1934.

[4] H. Hirata and H. Komatsubara, *Mem. Coll. Sci. Kyoto Imp. Univ.*, vol. A10, p. 95, 1926.

[5] G. I. Finch, A. G. Quarrell, and H. Wilman, *Trans. Faraday Soc.*, vol. 31, p. 1051, 1935.

[6] W. Köster, *Z. Metallkunde*, vol. 18, p. 219, 1926.

[7] H. Hirata and Y. Tanaka, *Mem. Coll. Sci. Kyoto Imp. Univ.*, vol. A15, p. 9, 1932.

[8] G. L. Clark and P. K. Frölich, *Z. Elektrochem.*, vol. 31, p. 655, 1925.

[9] R. Bozorth, *Phys. Rev.*, vol. 26, p. 390, 1925.

[10] W. G. Burgers and W. Elenbaas, *Naturwissenschaften*, vol. 21, p. 465, 1933.

[11] W. Elenbaas, *Z. Physik* vol. 76, p. 829, 1932.

[12] P. K. Frölich, G. L. Clark, and R. A. Aborn, *Z. Elektrochem.*, vol. 32, p. 295, 1926.

[13] W. Arkharow, *J. Tech. Phys.*, *U.S.S.R.*, vol. 6, p. 1777, 1936 (*Metal Abstracts*, vol. 3, p. 665, 1936).

[14] W. A. Wood, *Phil. Mag.*, vol. 24, p. 772, 1937.

[15] H. Hirata, *Mem. Coll. Sci. Kyoto Imp. Univ.*, vol. A11, p. 429, 1928.

[16] H. Hirata and Y. Tanaka, *Mem. Coll. Sci. Kyoto Imp. Univ.*, vol. A17, p. 143, 1934.

[17] A. Rubio and J. Garcia de la Cueva, *Anales soc. españ. fis. y quim.*, vol. 33, p. 521, 1935.

[18] G. Edmunds, private communication.

decomposes the hexagonal hydride to body-centered cubic, with the hydrogen in the interstices of the hydride structures being evolved or being occluded in the plate, and with shrinkage of the plate that may lead to cracking. Snavely concludes that the face-centered cubic structure is a zinc blende type of structure with 50 atomic per cent H, possibly changing continuously to the fluorite type as H increases from 50 to 67 atomic per cent, and that the hexagonal is a wurtzite type of structure with any

[1] C. A. Snavely, *Electrochem. Soc. Preprint* 92–35, 1947; *Trans. Electrochem. Soc.*, vol. 92, p. 537, 1947.

formula between CrH and Cr$_2$H.   From the relationship between these structures, one would expect stacking faults to be common, and the fact that mixtures of the hydrides have been reported is in accord with this.

Even in electrodeposited copper there is metallographic evidence that mistakes in stacking are common, for repeated twinning can be seen in some deposits, as in Fig. 2, and each twin boundary represents a mistake in the stacking of (111) planes—but not an alteration of the (111) texture, since the planes are parallel to the surface throughout.

Fig. 2. Twins formed during electrodeposition of copper.   Cross section through deposit and base (at bottom).   ×50.   (*J. B. Hess.*)

An increase in the degree of preferred orientation has been correlated, by some investigators, with the brightness of electrodeposits of nickel,[1] chromium,[2] zinc,[3,4] and cadmium.[4]   But other investigators have found that in bright deposits of nickel the orientation may be of any degree of fibering or may be random.[5]   Hard chromium plate on an electrolytically polished steel plate was found to be more highly oriented than on a

[1] W. A. Wood, *Phil. Mag.*, vol. 20, p. 964, 1935.

[2] W. Hume-Rothery and M. R. Wyllie, *Proc. Roy. Soc. (London)*, vol. A181, p. 331, 1943.   W. A. Wood, *Trans. Faraday Soc.*, vol. 31, p. 1248, 1935.

[3] A. Rubio, *Anales soc. españ. fis. y quím.*, vol. 36, p. 76, 1940.   G. F. Kosolapov and B. Mett, *J. Tech. Phys. U.S.S.R.*, vol. 9, p. 1421, 1939.

[4] L. S. Patanik, *Trans. Faraday Soc.*, vol. 32, p. 939, 1936.

[5] A. W. Hothersall and G. E. Gardam, *J. Electrodepositors' Tech. Soc.*, vol. 15, p. 127, 1939.   W. Smith, J. H. Keeler, and H. J. Read, *Plating*, vol. 36, p. 355, 1949.

mechanically polished plate, and to have a different lattice constant and different cracking tendencies.[1]

Evaporated and Sputtered Metal Films. Thin layers of metals condensed from the vapor phase or deposited by cathodic sputtering have received extensive study by electron diffraction as well as by X-rays. They are of practical interest; for example, evaporated films are widely used in the manufacture of household articles and toys; evaporated films of aluminum make durable coatings for mirrors;[2] evaporated films of metals of the eighth group form catalysts of high intrinsic activity.[3] Electron-diffraction studies[3,4] show that deposits on noncrystalline substrates are usually random in orientation when very thin, provided that vaporization is carried out in a high vacuum; there is a tendency for a weak fiber texture to develop as a film thickens (unless the substrate is maintained at liquid air temperature). On the other hand, vaporization in a gas promotes the formation of sharply defined textures, which Beek[3] states are [110] fiber textures with f.c.c. metals and [111] with b.c.c. iron.[5]

Metals evaporated on amorphous, vitreous, or polished base material are likely to be oriented randomly if the base is at a low temperature and to be oriented in some fiber texture if the base is hot. In many cases, the low-temperature deposit is almost amorphous and gives very diffuse diffraction rings.[6] The presence of gas in the deposit may have much to do with the structure,[7] and the crystal lattice of sputtered films also seems to be definitely affected by the nature of the gas.[8]

[1] P. A. Jacquet and A. R. Weill, *Chrome Dur.*, 1949, pp. 4–19.

[2] J. Strong, *Astrophys. J.*, vol. 83, p. 401, 1936.

[3] O. Beek, *Rev. Modern Phys.*, vol. 17, p. 61, 1945.

[4] L. H. Germer, *Phys. Rev.*, vol. 56, p. 58, 1939. Orientation and catalytic activity in sputtered metal films were studied by G. I. Finch, C. A. Murison, N. Stuart, and G. P. Thomson, *Proc. Roy. Soc. (London)*, vol. A141, p. 414, 1933; G. I. Finch and A. W. Ikin, *Proc. Roy. Soc. (London)*, vol. A145, p. 551, 1934.

[5] Catalytic activity appears to be strongly affected by the degree of orientation (which may also be correlated with porosity or submicroscopic roughness in the deposit) and is related to atom matching between hydrogen atoms of a hydrocarbon with atoms on the surface of the metal catalyst; activity thus varies with the lattice constant of the metal.

[6] F. Kirchner, *Z. Physik*, vol. 76, p. 576, 1932 (Sb, Se, Ag, Tl, Au, Bi). J. A. Prins, *Nature*, vol. 131, p. 760, 1933. T. Fukuroi, *Sci. Papers Inst. Phys. Chem. Research (Tokyo)*, vol. 32, p. 196, 1937 (Cd, Zn). L. R. Ingersoll and S. S. de Vinney, *Phys. Rev.*, vol. 26, p. 86, 1925 (Ni). L. R. Ingersoll and J. D. Hanawalt, *Phys. Rev.*, vol. 34, p. 972, 1929 (Ni). M. Gen, J. Zelmanoff, and A. Schalnikoff, *Physik. Z. Sowjetunion*, vol. 4, p. 826, 1933 (Fe, Cd, Hg, Ni). G. Hass, *Naturwissenschaften*, vol. 25, p. 232, 1937; *Ann. Physik*, vol. 31, p. 245, 1938 (Sb, Ag). L. H. Germer, *Phys. Rev.*, vol. 56, p. 58, 1939 (Au, Pd, Cu, Al, Mg).

[7] G. P. Thomson and W. Cochrane, "Theory and Practice of Electron Diffraction," p. 164, Macmillan, New York, 1939.

[8] S. Ogawa, *Sci. Repts., Tôhoku Imp. Univ.*, vol. 26, p. 93, 1937. L. R. Ingersoll

When a deposited metal takes up a preferred orientation at the time of deposition or upon subsequent annealing, the texture is usually a fiber texture with the fiber axis normal to the surface. That is, there is a tendency for a certain crystallographic plane to lie parallel to the surface of the base material. There may be two such orientations coexisting, however, and they may form a double fiber texture. Exceptions have been noted when a stream of metal strikes a condensing surface obliquely. There is then a fiber texture with the fiber axis inclined both to the stream of metal and to the condensing surface.[1]

A summary of the fiber textures that have been observed with different temperatures of deposition and of annealing is given in Table XXIII.[2] For a discussion of the conditions governing the choice of the different possible orientations the references cited in the table should be consulted.

Dixit[1] has observed three different orientations when an aluminum deposit 10^{-5} or 10^{-6} cm thick is heated to various temperatures and has proposed that the transition $[111] \rightarrow [100] \rightarrow [110]$ with increasing temperature is because the surface atoms behave as a two-dimensional gas. His theory is that with increasing temperature the area on the surface required for each atom increases and that this increase governs the crystal plane that can lie on the surface.

Levinstein[3] found that metals with high melting point produce continuous films of small unoriented microcrystals, while metals with low melting point cluster into larger, oriented crystallites. Varying the velocity of the impinging atoms produces no effect with metals having monatomic vapor, but alters the grain size of deposited antimony (the vapor of which contains molecules as well as atoms).

Films Deposited on Single Crystals. Orientations in films deposited on single crystals are affected not only by the conditions mentioned above, but also by the atomic arrangement in the supporting crystal. The force fields around the atoms in the base material may be sufficient to produce a single orientation instead of a fiber texture, although at room temperature random deposits usually prevail. Gold, silver, nickel, and platinum deposited on the cleavage face (100) of rock salt take up the orientation

and J. D. Hanawalt, *Phys. Rev.*, vol. 34, p. 972, 1929. L. R. Ingersoll, *Phys. Rev.*, vol. 33, p. 1094, 1929. W. Bussen and F. Gross, *Z. Physik*, vol. 86, p. 135, 1933; vol. 87, p. 778, 1934.

[1] K. R. Dixit, *Phil. Mag.*, vol. 16, p. 1049, 1933. M. Kubo and S. Miyake, *J. Phys. Soc. Japan*, vol. 2, p. 15, 1947; vol. 3, p. 114, 1948. S. Konobeevsky and M. Umansky, *J. Phys. U.S.R.R.*, vol. 10, p. 388, 1946.

[2] G. Wassermann, "Texturen metallischer Werkstoffe," Springer, Berlin, 1939.

[3] H. Levinstein, *J. Applied Phys.*, vol. 20, p. 306, 1949.

of the underlying crystal[1] or an orientation related thereto[2] when the temperature is above a certain critical value. The body-centered cubic metals iron and chromium deposit with more than one orientation; some crystals in the layer take up the orientation of the rock salt and others

TABLE XXIII. TEXTURES IN EVAPORATED AND SPUTTERED FILMS

Metal deposited	Texture	Technique	References
F.c.c.:			
Ag	[111]; [100]; [110]	Evaporated	1, 2
Al	[111]; [100]; [110]	Evaporated	1, 3, 4, 18
Au	[110]; [111]	Evaporated	3, 5, 6, 7
Pt	[100]; [111]	Sputtered	5, 9
Pd, Cu, Ni	[111]	Evaporated	8, 9
B.c.c.:			
Fe	[111]	Evaporated	9
Mo	[110]	Evaporated	10
Hexagonal:			
Cd, Zn	[0001]	Evaporated	5, 11, 12, 13
Rhombohedral:			
Bi	[111]; [110]	Evaporated	14, 15, 16, 17

[1] K. R. Dixit, *Phil. Mag.*, vol. 16, p. 1049, 1933.
[2] H. Mark and R. Wierl, *Z. Physik*, vol. 60, p. 741, 1930.
[3] L. Brück, *Ann. Physik*, vol. 26, p. 233, 1936.
[4] R. Beeching, *Phil. Mag.*, vol. 22, p. 928, 1936.
[5] G. I. Finch, A. G. Quarrell, and H. Wilman, *Trans. Faraday Soc.*, vol. 31, p. 1051, 1935.
[6] E. N. da C. Andrade, *Trans. Faraday Soc.*, vol. 31, p. 1137, 1935.
[7] S. R. Swamy, *Proc. Phys. Soc. (London)*, vol. 46, p. 739, 1934.
[8] O. Rüdiger, *Ann. Physik*, vol. 30, p. 505, 1937.
[9] S. Dembínska, *Z. Physik*, vol. 54, p. 46, 1929.
[10] I. R. Landau, *Metals & Alloys*, vol. 9, pp. 73, 100, 1938.
[11] M. Volmer, *Z. Physik*, vol. 5, p. 31, 1921.
[12] E. A. Owen and E. W. Roberts, *Phil. Mag.*, vol. 22, p. 290, 1936.
[13] M. Straumanis, *Z. Physik. Chem.*, vol. B13, p. 316, 1931.
[14] F. Kirchner, *Z. Physik*, vol. 76, p. 576, 1932.
[15] C. T. Lane, *Phys. Rev.*, vol. 48, p. 193, 1935.
[16] F. Gross, *Z. Physik*, vol. 64, p. 520, 1930.
[17] W. Büssem, F. Gross, and K. Herrmann, *Z. Physik*, vol. 64, p. 537, 1930.
[18] L. H. Germer, *Phys. Rev.*, vol. 56, p. 58, 1939.

have (110) parallel to the cube face and [110] parallel to the cube edge of the rock salt.

Gold, silver, and platinum on cleavage faces of calcite, mica, and quartz take up orientations that depend on the temperature and on the support-

[1] H. Lassen, *Physik. Z.*, vol. 35, p. 172, 1934. H. Lassen and L. Brück, *Ann. Physik*, vol. 22, p. 65, 1935. L. Brück, *Ann. Physik*, vol. 26, p. 233, 1935.
[2] G. Menzer, *Z. Krist*, vol. 99, p. 410, 1938. L. Royer, *Ann. Physik*, vol. 23, p. 16, 1935.

ing crystal[1]. Presumably the factors governing orientations are closely related to those governing Widmanstätten structures, but the basic principles are sometimes complicated by the presence of twinning in the deposit.[2]

Rhodin[3] found that thick deposits of aluminum on clean cleavage surfaces of ionic substrates take up orientations that appear to be related, at the interface, to the geometry of the atomic distribution in the substrate surface: aluminum (100) planes lie on (100) cleavage faces of alkali halides, aluminum (111) planes tend to predominate on cleavage faces of hexagonal symmetry, and (110) planes on (110) cleavages of NaCl and on cleaved mica. Films deposited at 300 to 500°C do not alter in orientation on annealing at 600°C, although Dixit found orientation changes on annealing 400 A films.[4]

Using electron diffraction, Schulz has studied the growth of very thin films of alkali halides on cleaved crystals of other alkali halides.[5] Oriented overgrowths are formed in all cases, even when the mismatch is as great as that of CsI ($a = 7.66$ A) on LiF ($a = 4.02$ A). When the mismatch in lattice constants is greater than 20 per cent the molecules of the condensing vapor migrate distances of the order of 1000 A or less into individual similarly oriented crystallites which grow to a 100 to 200 A size, with their crystal axes parallel to those of the substrate. Further growth causes the deposit first to take up a [100] fiber texture, then ultimately a random texture. When the mismatch is less than 20 per cent a uniform layer is produced up to a thickness of about 15 A, and further thickening then is by the growth of separate crystals.

[1] O. Rüdiger, Ann. Physik, vol. 30, p. 505, 1937.

[2] F. Kirchner and H. Cramer, Ann. Physik, vol. 33, p. 138, 1938. G. Menzer, Naturwissenschaften, vol. 26, p. 385, 1938.

[3] T. N. Rhodin, Trans. AIME, vol. 185, p. 371, 1949.

[4] R. Dixit, Phil. Mag., vol. 16, p. 1049, 1933.

[5] L. G. Schulz, Acta Cryst., vol. 5, p. 130, 1952.

CHAPTER XXI

ANISOTROPY

The practical importance of preferred orientations lies in the variation in properties with direction in commercial material, especially in rolled sheet. Directionality is usually undesirable in a product and is generally kept under strict control in the mills. Sheet used in deep drawing, for instance, must flow uniformly in all directions if a scalloped rim is to be avoided.

Anisotropy is responsible not only for this "earing" of deep-drawn objects, but also for uneven thinning, puckering and splitting of the walls. Directionality in forgings may lead to insufficient ductility in some directions. Directionality in sheet steel for electrical uses may lead to undesirable electrical characteristics in one apparatus, but in another it may be exploited to give high permeability in an important direction (for example, parallel to the magnetic flux in a transformer core).

Owing to the interaction of each grain with the neighboring grains and with grain boundaries and imperfections, it is seldom possible to compute the anisotropy of a polycrystalline aggregate directly from the anisotropic properties of single crystals. Accordingly, the earlier sections of this chapter are devoted to the polycrystalline properties, which are of more general interest, and single crystal data are deferred to the later sections.

Directionality in the Strength Properties. Directional properties in polycrystalline metals may arise from preferred orientations or from other causes, such as elongated inclusions, blowholes, cavities, segregation, nonmetallic inclusions, strings and layers of small grains, and the elongated shape of the grains themselves. Anisotropy caused by the preferred orientation of crystals is sometimes called "crystallographic fibering," and it is this with which we are chiefly concerned here, rather than with the so-called "mechanical fibering" from other causes. The properties of forgings in different directions depend more on mechanical than on crystallographic fibering[1] although in forgings of magnesium the reverse is true.[2] In many cases the causes are combined.

Face-centered cubic metals in the cold-rolled state are not highly anisotropic, but the tensile strength in the cross direction definitely exceeds

---

[1] G. Sachs and K. R. Van Horn, "Practical Metallurgy," American Society for Metals, Cleveland, Ohio, 1940.

[2] W. Schmidt, *Z. Metallkunde*, vol. 25, p. 229, 1933.

that in the longitudinal direction for copper and brass,* nickel,† aluminum,‡ silver,§ Fe-Ni,|| and bronze¶ after severe cold rolling. High tensile and yield strengths and low ductility (elongation, reduction in area, ability to withstand bending) are usually found in the same directions. Anisotropy increases with the degree of reduction by rolling,** as would be expected from the progressive development of rolling textures, but the anisotropy seldom amounts to as much as 10 per cent in yield strength or tensile strength. Reduction of area in transverse specimens may be as low as half that in longitudinal specimens in brass and bronze.¶ Bend tests and notch-bend tests of all types are anisotropic,[1] owing to both crystallographic and mechanical fibering.[2] Test strips cut along the cross direction are least able to withstand bending, and the bending number increases as the rolling direction is approached in aluminum, copper, brass, and bronze.¶ Annealed sheets can be produced with varying degrees of anisotropy. An example of the degree of directionality encountered in brass is shown in Fig. 1, which gives the results of tensile tests on 65-35 brass strip that has had various annealing treatments.

* W. B. Price and P. Davidson, *Trans. Am. Inst. Metals*, vol. 10, p. 133, 1916. F. Körber and P. Wieland, *Mitt. Kaiser-Wilhelm-Inst. Eisenforsch., Düsseldorf*, vol. 3, p. 57, 1921. F. Körber and H. Hoff, *Mitt. Kaiser-Wilhelm-Inst. Eisenforsch., Düsseldorf*, vol. 10, p. 175, 1928. E. Schmid and G. Wassermann, *Metallwirtschaft*, vol. 10, p. 409, 1931. A. Phillips and C. H. Samans, *Trans. AIME*, vol. 104, p. 171, 1933. A. Phillips and E. S. Bunn, *Trans. AIME*, vol. 93, p. 353, 1931. F. v. Göler and G. Sachs, *Z. Physik*, vol. 56, p. 495, 1929. H. Unckel, *Z. Metallkunde*, vol. 31, p. 104, 1939. O. Bauer, F. v. Göler, and G. Sachs. *Z. Metallkunde*, vol. 20, p. 202, 1928. F. v. Göler and G. Sachs, *Z. Physik*, vol. 56, p. 495, 1929. M. Cook, *J. Inst. Metals*, vol. 60, p. 159, 1937; *Metal Ind. (London)*, vol. 50, pp. 337, 405, 1937.

† F. Körber and H. Hoff, *Mitt. Kaiser-Wilhelm-Inst. Eisenforsch., Düsseldorf*, vol. 10, p. 175, 1928.

‡ F. Körber and H. Hoff, *Mitt. Kaiser-Wilhelm-Inst. Eisenforsch., Düsseldorf*, vol. 10, p. 175, 1928. H. Unckel, *Z. Metallkunde*, vol. 31, p. 104, 1939.

§ E. Schmid and G. Wassermann, *Metallwirtschaft*, vol. 10, p. 409, 1931. F. v. Göler and G. Sachs, *Z. Physik*, vol. 56, p. 495, 1929. E. Raub, *Z. Metallkunde*, vol. 27, p. 77, 1935.

|| O. Dahl and F. Pawlek, *Z. Metallkunde*, vol. 28, p. 230, 1936.

¶ H. Unckel, *Z. Metallkunde*, vol. 31, p. 104, 1939.

** F. Körber and H. Hoff, *Mitt. Kaiser-Wilhelm-Inst. Eisenforsch., Düssendorf*, vol. 10, p. 175, 1928. A Phillips and E. S. Bunn, *Trans. AIME*, vol. 93, p. 353, 1931. H. Unckel, *Z. Metallkunde*, vol. 31, p. 104, 1939.

[1] G. Tammann and H. H. Meyer, *Z. Metallkunde*, vol. 18, p. 176, 1926; vol. 19, p. 82, 1927. H. Unckel, *Z. Metallkunde*, vol. 31, p. 104, 1939. W. A. Straw, M. D. Helfrick, and C. R. Fischrupp, *Trans. AIME*, vol. 93, p. 317, 1931. F. Körber and P. Wieland, *Mitt. Kaiser-Wilhelm-Inst. Eisenforsch., Düsseldorf*, vol. 3, p. 57, 1921. H. Röhrig and K. Schönherr, *Z. Metallkunde*, vol. 29, p. 337, 1937. E. Mohr, *Metallwirtschaft*, vol. 18, p. 405, 1939.

[2] G. Sachs and K. R. Van Horn, "Practical Metallurgy," American Society for Metals, Cleveland, Ohio, 1940.

Palmer and Smith[1] draw the following conclusions from many investigations of this type on brass.

1. If brass is fully recrystallized, *the higher the final annealing temperature*, the greater, invariably, is the directionality in the sheet, as revealed by the height of ears that form in drawing cups.

2. *The lower the temperature of the anneal before the last rolling*, the greater, invariably, is the degree of final directionality.

3. *The lower the temperature of earlier anneals* ("running-down" or "process" anneals), the greater the final directionality, unless very high reductions are used between anneals.

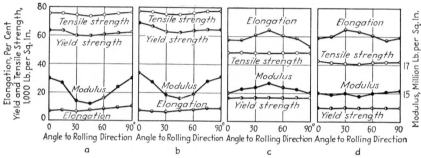

FIG. 1. Directionality of physical properties in 65–35 brass strip. Normal reductions (four to six B. & S. numbers) and normal anneals (about 600°C), followed by final treatments: (a) hard rolled; (b) annealed 2 hours at 200°C; (c) annealed at 500°C (produced no ears); (d) annealed at 700°C (no ears). (*Palmer and Smith.*)

4. The degree of directionality is not significantly affected by the type or speed of the rolling mill, reduction per pass, lubrication of the strip during rolling, size and orientation of grains in the casting, or impurities in the 65–35 brass (provided that they do not exceed 0.5% Pb, 0.05% Fe, 0.1% Si, 1% Mn, 1% Ni, 1% Al, 0.5% Cd, or small amounts of Li or Na added for deoxidation).

Burghoff and Bohlen[2] conclude that the directionality of 68–32 brass strip increases as follows:

1. As the penultimate reduction by rolling increases.
2. As the final reduction increases.
3. As the penultimate annealing temperature decreases.
4. As the final annealing temperature increases.

Sheets may be produced that form cups with four ears 45° to the rolling direction or six ears at 0 and 60° positions, depending upon the mill variables. Pole figures for samples giving four and six ears, respectively, are reproduced in Figs. 2a and 2b (the black triangles indicate the symmetrical positions (110) [$\bar{1}12$] which appeared to be somewhat more

[1] E. W. Palmer and C. S. Smith, *Trans. AIME*, vol. 147, p. 164, 1942.

[2] H. L. Burghoff and E. C. Bohlen, *Trans. AIME*, vol. 147, p. 144, 1942.

applicable than the usual (113) [$\overline{2}11$] positions). Four dense areas will be noted near the outside on one pole figure, six on the other; these correlate with the tendency to produce four and six ears, respectively. It will be seen further that, since the (111) planes are slip planes in this material, these (111) pole figures give directly the distribution of available slip planes and, to a first approximation, the distribution of slip systems. It would be expected that slip would be facilitated when a stress is applied to the sheet in directions that would cause the greatest resolved shear stress on the greatest number of grains. In Fig. 2a, this will be seen to

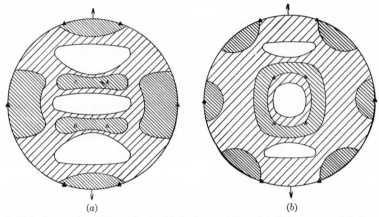

(a)   (b)

Fig. 2. Pole figures for (111) poles in 68–32 brass strip. (a) Forms cups with four ears (rolled 84 per cent, annealed 425°C; rolled 50 per cent, annealed 650°C). (b) Forms cups with six ears) rolled 50 per cent annealed 565°C; rolled 85 per cent annealed 650°C). (*Burghoff and Bohlen.*)

correspond to directions 45° to the rolling direction, for then the concentrations in the rolling direction (at the top) and in the transverse direction (at the side) will lie 45° to the axis of tension and will receive large shear stress components. There is reason to expect, therefore, the observed behavior: in the drawing of a cup with symmetrical dies the metal would flow more easily in directions 45° to the rolling direction and produce ears at these positions. A similar argument applies—though less convincingly —to Fig. 2b.

Wilson and Brick[1] reasoned along similar lines to explain the cupping behavior of copper and 70–30 brass. They found some correlation between the directions in which ears form and the directions in which rates of work hardening are low in brass, but the same correlation was not found in copper. However, both copper and brass develop ears at the azimuthal positions on the cups where the circumferential compressive stresses act in a [100] direction in the grains, and this is a direction, they

[1] F. H. Wilson and R. M. Brick, *Trans. AIME*, vol. 161, p. 173, 1945.

point out, that develops maximum resolved shear stress on the four sets of {111} planes.

When recrystallization produces a *cube texture*, (100)[001], the directionality of physical properties is extreme, as will be seen from the typical curves in Fig. 3 for copper.[1] There is a marked minimum in ductility at 0 and 90° positions and a peak at 45°. It is readily understandable that earing in the cup test is sensitive to the percentage of the grains that have this texture. Baldwin finds, in fact, a linear relation between ear height

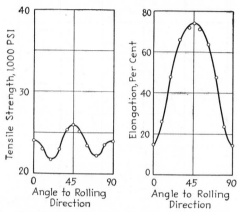

FIG. 3. Directionality of tensile properties of copper strip having cube texture. (*Baldwin.*)

and this percentage. Ears occur at 0 and 90° to the rolling direction in sheets having 30 per cent or more of the grains in cubic alignment, whereas in the absence of this cube texture ears in face-centered cubic metals are usually at 45° to the rolling direction.[2]

Among *body-centered cubic metals*, cold-rolled iron has its highest tensile values in the transverse direction of the sheet.[3] Anisotropy in cold-rolled

[1] W. M. Baldwin, *Metals Technol.*, *Tech. Pub.* 1455, April, 1942; *Trans. AIME*, vol. 166, p. 591, 1946.

[2] K. Kaiser, *Z. Metallkunde*, vol. 19, p. 435, 1927. W. H. Bassett and J. C. Bradley, *Trans. AIME*, vol. 104, p. 181, 1933. Arthur Phillips and C. H. Samans, *Trans. AIME*, vol. 104, p. 171, 1933. Arthur Phillips and G. Edmunds, *ASTM, Proc.*, vol. 29, pt. II, p. 438, 1929. E. Raub, *Z. Metallkunde*, vol. 27, p. 77, 1935; *Mitt. Forsch-Inst. Probieramts Edelmetalle*, vol. 10, p. 53, 1936. M. Cook, *J. Inst. Metals*, vol. 60, p. 159, 1937; *Metal Ind. (London)*, vol. 50, p. 337, 1937. J. D. Jevons, *J. Inst. Metals*, vol. 60, p. 174, 1937. M. Cook and T. L. Richards, *J. Inst. Metals*, vol. 69, p. 201, 1943. Control of the cube texture is also treated in Chap. XXI, p. 494, of the present book.

[3] J. Winlock and G. L. Kelley, *Trans. Am. Soc. Steel Treating*, vol. 12, p. 635, 1927. F. Körber and H. Hoff, *Mitt. Kaiser-Wilhelm-Inst. Eisenforsch., Düsseldorf*, vol. 10, p. 175, 1928. Arthur Phillips and H. H. Dunkle, *Trans. ASM*, vol. 23, p. 398, 1935. C. A. Edwards, D. L. Phillips, and C. R. Pipe, *J. Iron Steel Inst.*, vol. 133, p. 95, 1936.

low-carbon steel after annealing at various temperatures is illustrated in Fig. 4.[1]

Ears on cups drawn from annealed sheet steel may be found at the 45° positions when the degree of reduction is low (about 40 per cent) or at 0 and 90° to the rolling direction with higher reductions;[2] they increase in height with the amount of rolling. Control of furnace practice, of hot-

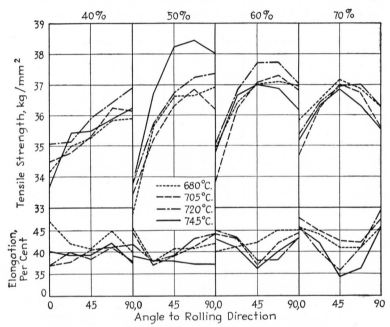

FIG. 4. Directionality of tensile strength and elongation in annealed steel sheet with various reductions and annealing temperatures. (*Phillips and Dunkle.*)

and cold-rolling schedules and of finishing and annealing temperatures in the modern mills yields a product that is effectively isotropic.

Anisotropy in *hot-rolled structural steel plate* is small[3] (carbon steel from 0.17 to 0.25% C, low-alloy steels containing up to 0.36% Si, 1.84% Ni, 1.14% Cu, 0.80% Cr). The elastic constants are isotropic ($E = 29.54 \times 10^6$ psi, $\nu = 0.297$, $G = 11.39 \times 10^6$ psi), but ductility and strength vary with direction of testing. Average values for elongation in 2 in. for a series of carbon steels are 40.2 and 36.0 per cent for

[1] Arthur Phillips and H. H. Dunkle, *Trans. ASM.*, vol. 23, p. 398, 1935.

[2] Arthur Phillips and H. H. Dunkle, *Trans. ASM*, vol. 23, p. 398, 1935. O. Dahl and J. Pfaffenberger, *Z. Physik*, vol. 71, p. 93, 1931.

[3] B. Johnston and F. Opila, *Trans. ASTM*, vol. 41, p. 552, 1941.

longitudinal and transverse directions, respectively; the corresponding values for average true stress at fracture are 117,600 and 110,500 psi.[1]

Straight-rolled *molybdenum* has a minimum strength in bending when test strips are cut along the transverse direction of the sheet, but the minimum shifts to the 45° position if the sheet is made by cross rolling and is annealed without recrystallization.[2] The cross-rolled sheet is extremely brittle, with cleavage along the cube planes that lie 45° from the rolling direction and normal to the sheet—the texture is (100)[011]. Similar brittleness has been observed in *tungsten foil* recrystallized at a high temperature.[3] It is never wise to assume, however, that a sharp texture is the fundamental cause of brittleness with metals such as these, for other causes may exist which may be quite independent of texture.

Hexagonal metals with their distinctive and limited manner of crystallographic slip show a marked influence of texture on directionality of properties. The tensile strength and yield strength of rolled *zinc* is lower in the rolling direction than in the cross direction,[4] whereas the measures of ductility vary conversely. Bending properties are strongly influenced by the texture of surface layers (see page 476),[5] and these can be altered by mill practice. Directionality is not greatly altered by purity or rolling temperature,[6] but when the degree of working alters the nature of the preferred orientation there are marked alterations in the properties and their directionality which may be understood when the textures are compared with the properties of single crystals.[7]

Textures, directionality of physical properties, and formability are strongly correlated in the case of *magnesium* and its alloys.[8] It is possible

[1] *True stress* is the load divided by the area of the cross section at the necked-down section; *tensile strength* is the maximum load sustained by the specimen divided by the original area of the cross section.

[2] C. E. Ransley and H. P. Rooksby, *J. Inst. Metals*, vol. 62, p. 205, 1938. C. J. Smithells, *J. Inst. Metals*, vol. 60, p. 172, 1937.

[3] W. G. Burgers and J. J. A. Ploos van Amstel, *Physica*, vol. 3, p. 1064, 1936.

[4] E. Schmid and G. Wassermann, *Z. Metallkunde*, vol. 23, p. 87, 1931. H. Sieglerschmidt, *Z. Metallkunde*, vol. 24, p. 55, 1932. C. H. Mathewson, C. S. Trewin, and W. H. Finkeldey, *Trans. AIME*, vol. 64, p. 305, 1920. H. F. Moore, *Univ. Illinois Bull. Eng. Expt. Sta.*, vol. 9, no. 52, 1911. O. Bauer, J. Weerts, and F. Beck, *Metallwirtschaft*, vol. 12, p. 615, 1933. G. Sachs, *Z. Metallkunde*, vol. 17, p. 187, 1925.

[5] G. Edmunds and M. L. Fuller, *Trans. AIME*, vol. 99, p. 175, 1932.

[6] O. Bauer, J. Weerts, and F. Beck, *Metallwirtschaft*, vol. 12, p. 615, 1933. W. Guertler, F. Kleweta, W. Claus, and E. Rickertsen, *Z. Metallkunde*, vol. 27, p. 1, 1935. G. Wassermann, "Texturen metallischer Werkstoffe," Springer, Berlin, 1939.

[7] E. Schmid, *Z. Metallkunde*, vol. 31, p. 125, 1929; *Metallwirtschaft*, vol. 18, p. 524, 1939. F. Wolbank, *Z. Metallkunde*, vol. 31, p. 249, 1939.

[8] "Symposium on Radiography and X-ray Diffraction," American Society for Testing Materials, Philadelphia, 1936. W. Schmidt, *Z. Metallkunde*, vol. 25, p. 229, 1933.

to plan forming processes so that maximum yield and tensile strengths can be had in the direction of the maximum service stress or to increase greatly the elongation both in the cross direction and in the rolling direction by bending a sheet back and forth in straightening rolls, thus causing twinning and producing new possibilities for slip. Magnesium-alloy rods formed by cold drawing or cold extrusion (below 300°C) possess a unique form of anisotropy: the yield strength in compression is only about half that in tension. This results from the fact that compression produces twinning, whereas tension does not. The effect is less in fine-grained alloys, which twin less readily. An extensive discussion of directionality in magnesium and its alloys will be found in Beck's "Technology of Magnesium and Its Alloys."[1]

Miscellaneous Tests for Anisotropy. In addition to yield strength, tensile strength, elongation, reduction in area, elastic moduli, bend and notch-bend tests, and the formation of ears on drawn cups, there are other tests that have been used occasionally to reveal anisotropy.

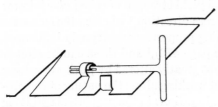

FIG. 5. Tear test for anisotropy in sheet metal. (*Jevons.*)

A *tear test* proposed by Brownsdon[2] and Jevons[3] is one of the simplest. Slots about 1 cm wide are cut at different directions in a sheet, and by the use of a slotted key as shown in Fig. 5 strips are torn from the sheet in the way one opens a can of sardines. For reasons that are not understood, the relative lengths of the strips in different directions in the sheet seem to be indicative of the anisotropy.

Cupping tests frequently indicate directionality by the appearance of the metal around the deformed dome or cup and by the direction of splitting.[4] The Erickson cup test applied to copper, for example, results in characteristic breaks 0 and 90° to the direction of rolling if the specimen contains high percentages (60 to 100 per cent) of grains aligned in the cube texture.[5] The breaks are at the positions where the true stress at fracture is a minimum.

The *vibrations in plates* form patterns of great variety, which can be

[1] A. Beck, "The Technology of Magnesium and Its Alloys," F. A. Hughes & Co. Ltd., London, 1940.

[2] H. W. Brownsdon, *J. Inst. Metals*, vol. 60, p. 178, 1937.

[3] J. D. Jevons, *J. Inst. Metals*, vol. 60, p. 174, 1937; *Metal Ind.* (*London*), vol. 48, p. 607, 1936.

[4] J. D. Jevons, *J. Inst. Metals*, vol. 60, p. 174, 1937; *Metal Ind.* (*London*), vol. 48, p. 607, 1936. C. H. Marshall, *ASTM, Proc.*, vol. 37, pt. 1, p. 518, 1937. J. D. Jevons, *Metal Ind.* (*London*), vol. 50, p. 405, 1937.

[5] W. M. Baldwin, *Metals Technol.*, *Tech. Pub.* 1455, April, 1942.

seen if sand is scattered on the plate. If a plate is clamped at the center and stroked with a bow at the edge, the sand arranges itself along the nodal lines, forming Cladni figures. Tammann and his coworkers found that on round disks these figures, *Klangfiguren,* were sensitive to preferred orientations in the metal, and they correlated the figures for round disks with the rolling and annealing treatment.[1] No attempts were made to correlate them with X-ray determinations of the textures, with measurements of internal stresses (which were also thought to be a factor),

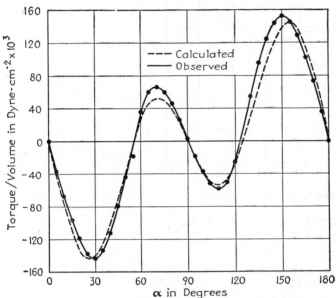

Fig. 6. Magnetic-torque curve for a single crystal of silicon ferrite, with (110) in the plane of the disk. Field is parallel to [001] at the azimuthal position $\alpha = 0$. (*Williams.*)

or with direct measurements of the elastic constants; they were simply studied as a sensitive qualitative indication of internal changes.

Magnetic-torque measurements can be used to reveal anisotropy in ferromagnetic materials. In a torque magnetometer a disk-shaped sample is suspended on a wire in a magnetic field.[2] Pointers are attached to the wire to indicate the angular position of the specimen and the torque exerted by the disk in twisting the supporting wire. The torque per unit volume is plotted against the azimuthal position of the disk, as shown in Fig. 6. Both single crystals and polycrystalline disks can be studied by

[1] E. Schröder and G. Tammann, Z. *Metallkunde,* vol. 16, p. 201, 1924. G. Tammann and W. Riedelsberger, Z. *Metallkunde,* vol. 18, p. 105, 1926.

[2] H. J. Williams, *Rev. Sci. Instruments,* vol. 8, p. 56, 1937.

instruments of this general type.[1]   These instruments have been used commercially to investigate and control manufacturing processes for producing steel for electrical purposes, since the torque curve is sensitive to changes caused by rolling and annealing procedures.[2]

Torque is exerted whenever the direction of the magnetic field does not coincide with a direction of easy magnetization in the material.   A single crystal of iron is saturated most easily when the magnetization is along a [100] direction; the ease of magnetization is intermediate along [110] and

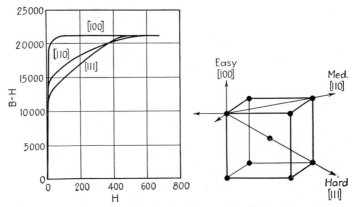

FIG. 7. Ease of magnetization in the three principal directions of iron.

least along [111], as indicated in Fig. 7.[3]   From equations giving the energy of the disk when magnetized in different directions the torque can be computed for all positions of a single crystal with any crystal plane in the plane of the disk.[4]   The empirical torque curve for polycrystalline material may then be compared with the curves computed for orientations that are assumed to be present in the disk.

As a means of determining unknown textures this method has serious disadvantages, for there seems to be no possibility of deriving rigorously the complete texture from an observed curve.   Any texture or texture

[1] O. Dahl and J. Pfaffenberger, Z. Physik, vol. 71, p. 93, 1931.   N. S. Akulov and N. Bruckatov, Ann. Physik, (5), vol. 15, p. 741, 1932.   R. M. Bozorth, Phys. Rev., vol. 50, p. 1076, 1936.   L. P. Tarasov and F. Bitter, Phys. Rev., vol. 52, p. 353, 1937.

[2] H. J. Williams, Rev. Sci. Instruments, vol. 8, p. 56, 1937.   N. P. Goss, Trans. ASM, vol. 23, p. 511, 1935.   K. J. Sixtus, Physics, vol. 6, p. 105, 1935.   L. P. Tarasov, Trans. AIME, vol. 135, p. 353, 1939.

[3] Intensity of magnetization is $I = (B - H)/4\pi$, where H is the field strength and B is the magnetic induction.

[4] N. S. Akulov and N. Bruckatov, Ann. Physik, vol. 15, p. 741, 1932.   R. M. Bozorth, Phys. Rev., vol. 50, p. 1076, 1936.   L. P. Tarasov and F. Bitter, Phys. Rev., vol. 52, p. 353, 1937.   R. M. Bozorth and H. J. Williams, Phys. Rev., vol. 59, p. 827, 1941.

component that is random around the normal to the disk gives no variation in torque, and the same is usually true for any material having (111) in the plane of the disk. However, simple textures, such as the cube texture, are readily recognized by comparison with observed or computed single-crystal curves, and reasonable agreement has been obtained by calculating torque curves from X-ray pole-figure data in highly cold rolled silicon steel and in cube-textured iron-nickel alloy.[1] When textures are less pronounced, as after smaller cold reductions, hot rolling, or recrystallization, there is less certainty in the interpretation. Nevertheless, the high sensitivity of torque curves and related methods of test to slight anisotropy and to variations in rolling and annealing schedules has made it of value in industrial laboratories.

Anisotropy of Elastic Properties of Crystals. Single crystals are generally anisotropic, and the formulas relating stress to strain must take account of the variation in "stiffness" of a crystal in different directions; many more constants of proportionality are required than for isotropic materials.[2] The relations between stress and strain are defined by the generalized Hooke's law, which is applicable to any homogeneous body, crystalline or not,

$$\left.\begin{array}{l}
\epsilon_x = s_{11}\sigma_x + s_{12}\sigma_y + s_{13}\sigma_z + s_{14}\tau_{yz} + s_{15}\tau_{zx} + s_{16}\tau_{xy} \\
\epsilon_y = s_{21}\sigma_x + s_{22}\sigma_y + s_{23}\sigma_z + s_{24}\tau_{yz} + s_{25}\tau_{zx} + s_{26}\tau_{xy} \\
\epsilon_z = s_{31}\sigma_x + s_{32}\sigma_y + s_{33}\sigma_z + s_{34}\tau_{yz} + s_{35}\tau_{zx} + s_{36}\tau_{xy} \\
\gamma_{yz} = s_{41}\sigma_x + s_{42}\sigma_y + s_{43}\sigma_z + s_{44}\tau_{yz} + s_{45}\tau_{zx} + s_{46}\tau_{xy} \\
\gamma_{zx} = s_{51}\sigma_x + s_{52}\sigma_y + s_{53}\sigma_z + s_{54}\tau_{yz} + s_{55}\tau_{zx} + s_{56}\tau_{xy} \\
\gamma_{xy} = s_{61}\sigma_x + s_{62}\sigma_y + s_{63}\sigma_z + s_{64}\tau_{yz} + s_{65}\tau_{zx} + s_{66}\tau_{xy}
\end{array}\right\} \quad (1)$$

and a corresponding set of relations

$$\left.\begin{array}{l}
\sigma_x = c_{11}\epsilon_x + c_{12}\epsilon_y + c_{13}\epsilon_z + c_{14}\gamma_{yz} + c_{15}\gamma_{zx} + c_{16}\gamma_{xy} \\
\sigma_y = c_{21}\epsilon_x + c_{22}\epsilon_y + c_{23}\epsilon_z + c_{24}\gamma_{yz} + c_{25}\gamma_{zx} + c_{26}\gamma_{xy} \\
\sigma_z = c_{31}\epsilon_x + c_{32}\epsilon_y + c_{33}\epsilon_z + c_{34}\gamma_{yz} + c_{35}\gamma_{zx} + c_{36}\gamma_{xy} \\
\tau_{yz} = c_{41}\epsilon_x + c_{42}\epsilon_y + c_{43}\epsilon_z + c_{44}\gamma_{yz} + c_{45}\gamma_{zx} + c_{46}\gamma_{xy} \\
\tau_{zx} = c_{51}\epsilon_x + c_{52}\epsilon_y + c_{53}\epsilon_z + c_{54}\gamma_{yz} + c_{55}\gamma_{zx} + c_{56}\gamma_{xy} \\
\tau_{xy} = c_{61}\epsilon_x + c_{62}\epsilon_y + c_{63}\epsilon_z + c_{64}\gamma_{yz} + c_{65}\gamma_{zx} + c_{66}\gamma_{xy}
\end{array}\right\} \quad (2)$$

where the symbols σ and τ represent normal and shear stresses and ϵ and γ elongation and shear strains, respectively. In these equations the elastic constants s_{ij} and c_{ij} differ for each crystal and must be determined experimentally. Many of the coefficients are equal,[3] the number of

[1] R. M. Bozorth, *Phys. Rev.*, vol. 50, p. 1076, 1936. L. P. Tarasov, *Trans. AIME*, vol. 135, p. 353, 1939. H. W. Conradt, O. Dahl, and K. J. Sixtus, *Z. Metallkunde*, vol. 32, p. 231, 1940.

[2] For the isotropic case, see p. 317.

[3] A. E. H. Love, "The Mathematical Theory of Elasticity," Cambridge, London, 1927. W. A. Wooster, "A Textbook on Crystal Physics," Cambridge, London, 1938.

independent constants decreasing as the symmetry of the crystal increases. In triclinic crystals, 21 are independent; in hexagonal crystals, 5; in cubic crystals, only 3. For example, in the cubic system the coefficients for Eqs. (1) are

$$
\begin{pmatrix}
s_{11} & s_{12} & s_{12} & 0 & 0 & 0 \\
s_{12} & s_{11} & s_{12} & 0 & 0 & 0 \\
s_{12} & s_{12} & s_{11} & 0 & 0 & 0 \\
0 & 0 & 0 & s_{44} & 0 & 0 \\
0 & 0 & 0 & 0 & s_{44} & 0 \\
0 & 0 & 0 & 0 & 0 & s_{44}
\end{pmatrix}
\tag{3}
$$

When these are known, the strains along all axes of a cubic crystal can be computed from the stresses. Additional relations among the coefficients—the Cauchy-Poisson relations—should hold if all the forces in a crystal were acting between atom centers,[1] but measurements show that these relations rarely exist (i.e., the early theories are inadequate). Recent theories are able to account remarkably well, usually to within 2 or 3 per cent,[2] for the measured values of the elastic constants in some metals.

If a cylindrical crystal of a cubic metal is prepared with an orientation such that the direction cosines of the axis of the cylinder with respect to the crystal axes are α, β, and γ, then

$$
\left.
\begin{aligned}
\frac{1}{E} &= s_{11} - 2\left[(s_{11} - s_{12}) - \frac{1}{2}s_{44}\right](\alpha^2\beta^2 + \beta^2\gamma^2 + \gamma^2\alpha^2) \\
\frac{1}{G} &= s_{44} + 4\left[(s_{11} - s_{12}) - \frac{1}{2}s_{44}\right](\alpha^2\beta^2 + \beta^2\gamma^2 + \gamma^2\alpha^2)
\end{aligned}
\right\}
\tag{4}
$$

For a hexagonal crystal, with γ the direction cosine of the specimen axis with respect to the hexagonal axis of the crystal,

$$
\left.
\begin{aligned}
\frac{1}{E} &= s_{11}(1 - \gamma^2)^2 + s_{33}\gamma^4 + (2s_{13} + s_{44})\gamma^2(1 - \gamma^2) \\
\frac{1}{G} &= s_{44} + \left[(s_{11} - s_{12}) - \frac{1}{2}s_{44}\right](1 - \gamma^2) \\
&\quad + 2(s_{11} + s_{33} - 2s_{13} - s_{44})\gamma^2(1 - \gamma^2)
\end{aligned}
\right\}
\tag{5}
$$

The same arrangement of coefficients holds for an isotropic body, except that there are only two independent coefficients, since $s_{44} = 2(s_{11} - s_{12})$ and $c_{44} = \frac{1}{2}(c_{11} - c_{12})$. The equations in scheme (3) are then identical

---

[1] Max Born, Atomtheorie des festen Zustandes, "Encyklopädie der mathematischen Wissenschaften," vol. V, pt. 3, 1926. P. P. Ewald, T. Pöschl, and L. Prandtl, "The Physics of Solids and Fluids," Blackie, Glasgow, 1936. F. Seitz, "The Modern Theory of Solids," McGraw-Hill, New York, 1940.

[2] F. Seitz, "The Modern Theory of Solids," McGraw-Hill, New York, 1940.

Table XXIV. Maximum and Minimum Values of Elastic Moduli in Single Crystals[1]

Metal	E_{max} kg./ mm.^{2}	Direction	E_{min} kg./ mm.^{2}	Direction	G_{max} kg./ mm.^{2}	Direction	G_{min} kg./ mm.^{2}	Direction
Aluminum	7,700	[111]	6,400	[100]	2,900	[100]	2,500	[111]
Copper	19,400	[111]	6,800	[100]	7,700	[100]	3,100	[111]
Silver	11,700	[111]	4,400	[100]	4,450	[100]	1,970	[111]
Gold	11,400	[111]	4,200	[100]	4,100	[100]	1,800	[111]
α-Iron	29,000	[111]	13,500	[100]	11,800	[100]	6,100	[111]
Tungsten	40,000	[111]	40,000	[100]	15,500	[100]	15,500	[111]
Magnesium	5,140	0°*	4,370	53.3°*	1,840	44.5°*	1,710	90°*
Zinc	12,630	70.2°	3,560	0°	4,970	90°	2,780	41.8°
Cadmium	8,300	90°	2,880	0°	2,510	90°	1,840	30°
β-Tin	8,640	[001]	2,680	[110]	1,820	45.7°†	1,060	[100]

* Angle to the hexagonal axis.
† In the plane (11$\bar{2}$0) at 45.7° to the hexgonal axis.
[1] E. Schmid and W. Boas, "Kristallplastizität," Springer, Berlin, 1935.

with the equations between the principal stresses and strains previously given for an isotropic medium (page 319) where

$$E = \frac{1}{s_{11}} \qquad G = \frac{1}{s_{44}} \qquad \nu = -\frac{s_{12}}{s_{11}} = \frac{E}{2G} - 1 \qquad (6)$$

Measured values of the elastic constants are summarized in Tables XXIV and XXV.[1]

Elastic Moduli in Aggregates. The directional dependence of the elastic moduli in polycrystalline metal is dependent upon the orientations in the specimen and can be semiquantitatively predicted from the anisotropy of single crystals. The maximum value of Young's modulus, E, in face-centered cubic crystals is along the [111] direction, and the minimum is along [100], the former about three times the latter in most face-centered cubic metals (aluminum is an exception and is nearly isotropic). In a direction α, β, and $\gamma°$ from the cube axes, respectively, the value is given by[2]

$$\frac{1}{E} = \frac{1}{E_{100}} - 3\left(\frac{1}{E_{100}} - \frac{1}{E_{111}}\right)(\cos^2 \alpha \cos^2 \beta + \cos^2 \beta \cos^2 \gamma + \cos^2 \gamma \cos^2 \alpha)$$

When a double fiber texture is present or when a pole figure can be repre-

[1] For method of measurement using frequency of vibration of specimens, see W. F. Brown, *Phys. Rev.*, vol. 57, p. 558, 1940; vol. 58, p. 998, 1940. See also W. A. Good, *Phys. Rev.*, vol. 60, p. 605, 1941. For the ultrasonic pulsing method see H. B. Huntington, *Phys. Rev.*, vol. 72, p. 321, 1947; W. G. Cady, "Piezoelectricity," McGraw-Hill, New York, 1946.
[2] J. Weerts. *Z. Metallkunde*, vol. 25, p. 101, 1933.

TABLE XXV. ELASTIC DATA FOR METALS AND ALLOYS AT ROOM TEMPERATURE*
(s_{ij} in 10^{-12} sq cm per dyne. c_{ij} in 10^{12} dyne per sq cm)

Crystal	s_{11}	s_{12}	s_{44}	c_{11}	c_{12}	c_{44}
Face-centered cubic:						
Al	1.59	− 0.58	3.52	1.08	0.622	0.284
Cu	1.49	− 0.625	1.33	1.70	1.23	0.753
Ag	2.32	− 0.993	2.29	1.20	0.897	0.436
Au	2.33	− 1.07	2.38	1.86	1.57	0.420
Pb	9.30	− 4.26	6.94	0.483	0.409	0.144
Body-centered cubic:						
Fe	0.757	− 0.282	0.862	2.37	1.41	1.16
Na ($-63°$C)	53.5	−23.2	20.37	0.0555	0.0425	0.0491
K($-185°$C)	82.3	−37	38.0	0.0459	0.0372	0.0263
W	0.257	− 0.073	0.660	5.01	1.98	1.51
Alloys:						
Cu$_3$Au	1.34	− 0.565	1.51			
72 Cu-28 Zn	1.94	− 0.84	1.39			
CuZn	3.88	− 1.52	0.578			
5 Cu 95 Al	1.5	− 0.69	3.7			
75 Ag 25 Au	2.07	− 0.891	2.052			
50 Ag 50 Au	1.97	− 0.852	1.966			
25 Ag 75 Au	2.05	− 0.909	2.063			

	s_{11}	s_{33}	s_{44}	s_{12}	s_{13}
Cd	1.29	3.69	6.40	−0.15	−0.9`
Mg	2.21	1.97	6.03	−0.77	−0.4`
Zn	0.823	2.64	2.50	+0.034	−0.6`

	s_{11}	s_{33}	s_{44}	s_{12}	s_{13}	s_{14}	s_6
Lower symmetry metals:							
(Rhombohedral) Sb	1.77	3.38	4.10	− 0.38	−0.85	− 0.80	
(Rhombohedral) Bi	2.69	2.87	10.48	− 1.40	−0.62	+ 1.60	
(Hexagonal) Te	4.87	2.34	5.81	− 0.69	−1.38	?	
(Rhombohedral) Hg ($-190°$C)	1.54	4.5	15.1	−11.9	−2.1	−10.0	
(Tetragonal) Sn	1.85	1.18	5.70	− 0.99	−0.25		13.5

* Values chosen from lists by R. F. S. Hearmon, *Rev. Modern Phys.*, vol. 18, p. 409, 1946; and C. Zener, "Elasticity and Anelasticity of Metals," University of Chicago Press, Chicago, 1948. Some later values by D. Lazarus (*Phys. Rev.*, vol. 74, p. 1726, 1948) from ultrasonic pulsing are, in 10^{12} dynes per sq cm: beta-brass, $c_{11} = 1.279$, $c_{12} = 1.091$, $c_{44} = 0.822$; Al, $c_{11} = 1.056$, $c_{12} = 0.639$, $c_{44} = 0.2853$; Cu, $c_{11} = 1.710$, $c_{12} = 1.239$, $c_{44} = 0.756$.

sented by two or more ideal orientations, it has been assumed that the quantity $(1/E)$ for each orientation is additive and is weighted according to the amount of material in each orientation. Using this additivity principle, Weerts has computed $(1/E)$ for rolled and for recrystallized copper sheet, with results agreeing satisfactorily with measured values, as shown in the polar plot of E in Fig. 8. The textures for these computations were assumed to be $(110)[\bar{1}12]$ and $(112)[11\bar{1}]$ in equal amounts for the rolled sheet and $(100)[001]$ for the recrystallized material.

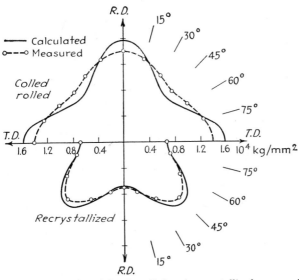

Fig. 8. Polar plot of Young's modulus in rolled and recrystallized copper sheet. Upper curves for rolled, lower for recrystallized. (*Weerts.*)

The large variation in elastic modulus of wires with annealing must arise from alterations in texture, since the elastic constants are almost unaffected by cold work and recovery. An example is the drop in E from 18,000,000 to 13,400,000 psi when hard-drawn copper wire is annealed.[1] This is attributable to varying amounts of material in the two positions of the wire texture, [111] and [100], with annealing.[2]

The anisotropy of E in rolled iron has been computed[3] for an ideal texture composed of equal amounts of $(100)[011]$ and $(112)[1\bar{1}0]$ material with results that deviate in some directions as much as 40 per cent from

[1] A. J. Phillips and A. A. Smith, *ASTM, Proc.*, vol. 36, pt. 2, p. 263, 1936.

[2] With $E_{111} = 27,600,000$ and $E_{100} = 9,690,000$, the principle of additivity of $(1/E)$ would indicate that 73 per cent of the cold-drawn wire was in the [111] position and 27 per cent in the [100] position, whereas after recrystallization this is altered to 43 per cent [111] and 57 per cent [100], assuming for simplicity that there is no randomly oriented material in either sample.

[3] E. Goens and E. Schmid, *Naturwissenschaften.* vol. 19, p. 520, 1931.

the measured values. Bruggeman[1] has made a more elaborate computation, using a closer representation of the actual pole figure. His results are within 10 per cent of the measured values but are somewhat dependent upon assumed shapes of lamellar grains (the tangential deformation component and the normal stress component are assumed to be continuous across grain boundaries). Bruggeman[2] also has made computations of moduli for textures of many different metals, with fair agreement; random orientations have also been computed[3] using different methods of averaging, with and without considerations of grain-boundary conditions.

For hexagonal metals, anisotropy can be related to texture quite simply,[4] for properties vary only with angular distance from the hexagonal axis. The frequency with which the axis occurs at a given angle to the observation direction can be read from the pole figure. This frequency is used as the weight of the corresponding property value in the averaging process. Calculated values for an extruded zinc alloy (10% Al, 2%, Cu, 0.03% Mg) were $E = 11{,}200$ kg per sq mm and expansion coefficient $= 19 \times 10^{-6}$; the observed values were 10,750 and 21.4×10^{-6}, respectively. For wire cold-drawn 80 per cent the calculated values were $E = 11{,}200$ and expansion coefficient $= 23 \times 10^{-6}$, while the observed values were 10,100 and 22.3×10^{-6}.

Anisotropy of Physical Properties in Crystals. Specific electrical resistance does not vary with direction in crystals of the cubic metals, but with crystals of lower symmetry it is anisotropic. The law of variation in hexagonal, rhombohedral, and tetragonal crystals depends on the angle, ϕ, between the direction of measurement and the principal axis of the crystal (the hexagonal, trigonal, or tetragonal axis) according to the relation

$$\rho = \rho_\perp + (\rho_\| - \rho_\perp) \cos^2 \phi \qquad (7)$$

where $\rho_\|$ and $\rho_\perp$ are the resistances parallel and perpendicular to the principal axis. The resistance has rotational symmetry around the principal axis.

The same orientation dependence is obtained for other properties:[5] the specific resistance to heat flow; the coefficient of thermal expansion; the thermoelectric force (the emf against a comparison metal, say copper,

---

[1] D. A. G. Bruggeman, *Naturwissenschaften*, vol. 19, p. 814, 1931; *Z. Physik*, vol. 92, p. 561, 1934.

[2] D. A. G. Bruggeman, *Z. Physik*, vol. 92, p. 561, 1934.

[3] D. A. G. Bruggeman, *Z. Physik*, vol. 92, p. 561, 1934. A. Huber and E. Schmid, *Helv. Chim. Acta*, vol. 7, p. 620, 1934. W. Boas and E. Schmid, *Helv. Chim. Acta*, vol. 7, p. 628, 1934.

[4] W. Boas, *Helv. Phys. Acta*, vol. 7, p. 878, 1934. E. Schmid, *Z. Metallkunde*, vol. 30, Vorträge der Hauptverslg., p. 5, 1938. F. Wolbank, *Z. Metallkunde*, vol. 31, p. 249, 1939.

[5] E. Schmid and W. Boas, "Kristallplastizität," Springer, Berlin, 1935.

with a 1° temperature difference); the constant in the Thomson effect (the quantity of heat generated in a unit length of wire having a temperature gradient of 1° per cm and carrying a unit current of electricity); and the magnetic susceptibility (intensity of magnetization divided by the field strength). Each of these properties is isotropic for cubic crystals.

Representative values for some of these properties near room temperature in noncubic metals are given in Table XXVI. Other anisotropic properties include linear compressibility, temperature coefficient of

TABLE XXVI. ANISOTROPY OF PROPERTIES OF SINGLE CRYSTALS PARALLEL AND PERPENDICULAR TO THE PRINCIPAL AXIS[1]

Metal	Specific electrical resistance, 10^{-6} ohm-cm.		Thermal expansion $\times 10^{-6}$			Thermoelectric force* $\times 10^{-6}$ volt/ °C.	
	$\parallel$	$\perp$	Temperature range, °C.	$\parallel$	$\perp$	$\parallel$	$\perp$
Magnesium....	3.85	4.55	Near 20	26.4	25.6	1.87	1.66
Zinc..........	6.06	5.83	20–100	63.9	14.1	1.32	− 0.50
Cadmium......	8.36	6.87	20–100	52.6	21.4	1.60	− 1.74
Mercury.......			−188–79	47.0	37.5	−17.9†	−15.1
Bismuth.......	138	109	Near 20	14.0	10.4		
Antimony......	35.6	42.6	Near 20	15.6	8.0		
Tellurium......	56000	154000	Near 20	−1.6	27.2		
β-Tin..........	14.3	9.9	Near 20	30.5	15.5		

* Comparison metal is copper. Minus sign indicates current flowing toward the copper at the cold junction.

† Measured against constantan.

[1] Data selected from the tabulation in E. Schmid and W. Boas, "Kristallplastizität," Springer, Berlin, 1935.

thermal expansion, temperature coefficient of electrical conductivity, magnetic permeability, rates of diffusion and self-diffusion, and rates of chemical reactions such as oxidation and etching, etc.[1] All these properties are altered when a metal is cold-worked. Electrode potential, thermal expansion, compressibility, coercive force, and electrical resistance are *increased* (the last usually about 2 per cent, but 18 per cent in molybdenum and 50 per cent in tungsten); the temperature coefficients of electrical resistance, thermal conductivity, and maximum permeability are *decreased* when polycrystalline metal is cold-worked. Some of these changes may be due to changes in the physical properties of the individual grains, and some may be due to changes in texture or to the two causes combined.

[1] A more extensive review and tabulation of anisotropic properties is given by W. Boas and J. T. Mackenzie in "Progress in Metal Physics," vol. II, Interscience Publishers, New York. 1950.

CHAPTER XXII

AGE HARDENING AND TRANSFORMATIONS

The hardening of alloys by aging is of great industrial importance and unusual scientific interest. The changes of physical properties, which are exceedingly varied and complex, are worthy of much study and have been the subject of so many investigations it would not be possible adequately to summarize them here. The present discussion is limited to the more striking *crystallographic* features of the subject.[1]

Merica, Waltenberg, and Scott[2] were the first to point out that for an alloy to age-harden it must have a decreasing solubility with decreasing temperature, so that when the alloy is given a solution heat-treatment and then a quench it will be supersaturated with respect to one or more dissolved elements. Subsequent aging at a lower temperature is associated with changes in the supersaturated alloy.

Theories of Age Hardening. Age hardening was first believed to be due to the keying of slip planes by particles that precipitated from the supersaturated matrix.[3] Many complexities were later discovered that made it necessary to modify this theory.

A major obstacle to the simple theory arose when various observers were unable to see any precipitate in Al-Cu alloys or in duralumin when aged to the maximum hardness at low temperatures. A number of theories were then proposed which associated the hardening with a pre-precipitation process—some variety of association of solute atoms on the lattice of the matrix.

The fact that yield strength increases before there is any evidence of a change in the lattice parameter of the matrix, as indicated in Fig. 1 for Al-Cu (5.17 per cent Cu),[4] was thought by some to prove the existence of pre-precipitation hardening, since precipitation would be expected to remove dissolved atoms from solid solution and thereby alter the parame-

---

[1] The reader is referred to the following reviews for extensive bibliographies and summaries wider in scope: "Symposium on the Age-hardening of Metals," American Society for Metals, Cleveland, Ohio, 1940. W. L. Fink, *J. Applied Phys.*, vol. 13, p. 75, 1942. A. H. Geisler, in "Phase Transformations in Solids," Wiley, New York, 1951. G. C. Smith, in "Progress in Metal Physics," vol. I, Interscience Publishers, New York, 1949.

[2] P. D. Merica, R. G. Waltenberg, and H. Scott, *Trans. AIME*, vol. 64, p. 41, 1920.

[3] Z. Jeffries and R. S. Archer, "The Science of Metals," p. 390, McGraw-Hill, New York, 1924.

[4] W. L. Fink and D. W. Smith, *Trans. AIME*, vol. 122, p. 284, 1936.

ter of the matrix.[1] But Fink and Smith[2] as well as others have shown that the delayed parameter change can have a very different interpretation. Precipitation in many instances occurs much more rapidly in certain restricted areas than in others, and may be well advanced in narrow bands before the bulk of the matrix is altered.[3] Slip bands and grain boundaries are favored regions for rapid precipitation in some alloys, as will be seen from Figs. 2 and 3. In the regions of rapid precipitation the lattice parameter may alter to that of the depleted matrix (the upper

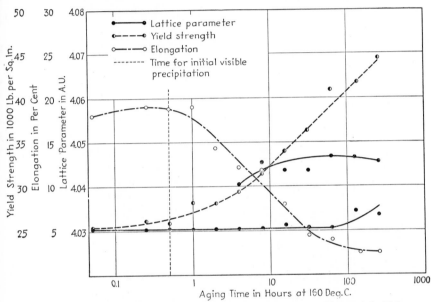

Fig. 1. Aging curves for Al-Cu (5.17 % Cu) aged at 160°C. (*Fink and Smith.*)

branch of the parameter curve in Fig. 1) before the diffraction lines from other regions register any parameter change. Many examples can be listed in which there is a *uniform* distribution of particles throughout the grains, and in these alloys the lattice constant of the matrix changes continuously during aging; other alloys show intermediate and mixed types. Thus, X-ray investigations and investigations of physical properties during aging must be accompanied by careful metallographic observations if

[1] E. Schmid and C. Wassermann, *Metallwirtschaft*, vol. 7, p. 1329, 1928. F. v. Göler and G. Sachs, *Z. Metallkunde*, vol. 22, p. 141, 1930.

[2] W. L. Fink and D. W. Smith, *Trans. AIME*, vol. 122, p. 284, 1936.

[3] An example of this is found in the alloys of beryllium in copper: A. G. Guy, C. S. Barrett, and R. F. Mehl, *Trans. AIME*, vol. 175, p. 216, 1948. The amount of the material that undergoes the grain boundary reaction, forming the dark recrystallized bands of Fig. 3, is sensitive to the presence of cobalt and to the temperature from which the sample is quenched: P. A. Beck, *J. Applied Phys.*, vol. 20, p. 666, 1949.

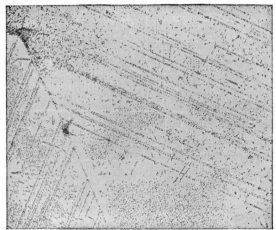

FIG. 2. Microstructure of Al-Cu (5.17% Cu) aged 4 hours at 200°C. Precipitation is concentrated along slip planes and along grain boundary (at lower left). ×500. (*Fink and Smith.*)

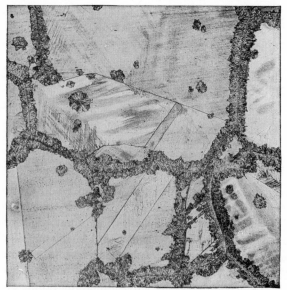

FIG. 3. Microstructure of Cu-Be alloy (1.97% Be, 0.03% Fe, no Ni) showing band of rapid precipitation at grain boundaries. Quenched from 820°C, aged 2 hours at 325°C. ×75. (*C. S. Smith.*)

the changes are to be understood. As research continues to reveal unsuspected complexities in the aging process of various alloys, it has become evident that a sequence of events that occurs in one alloy does not necessarily hold in another; there is evidence, also, that some alloys go through different stages during low-temperature and high-temperature aging.

The simplest mechanism involves merely the precipitation of a stable phase dispersed uniformly throughout a matrix, probably at points where supersaturation is the greatest. A more complicated mechanism has been found in various alloys in which a metastable phase first precipitates and later gives way to a stable one. Still more distinguishable steps have been detected by means of streaks on X-ray diffraction patterns that have been interpreted as evidence of stringlets of atoms which grow into thin platelets and then into small three-dimensional particles of the metastable precipitate (in Al-Mg-Si and in Al-Ag alloys).[1]

A different sequence seems to occur in Al-Cu alloys when aged at low temperatures, where Cu atoms segregate on planes of the Al matrix and build up a superlattice, then form a metastable precipitate with a new structure (θ') and finally change to a stable precipitate of different structure (θ).[2] In the same alloy, slow cooling seemed to generate only the stable phase. Still another sequence has been observed in Al-Ag, where spherical regions rich in Ag atoms have an ordered superlattice arrangement before any new precipitate structure appears.[2]

Each of these various stages doubtless has its own specific effect on physical and mechanical properties, either through the simple effect of a dispersed phase, or through an interaction with the matrix. The most important contribution to hardening is believed to be made when a metastable phase is coherent with the matrix in a way that produces severe coherency strains.[3] Strains arising merely from the difference in specific volume between matrix and precipitate are probably minor causes of hardening compared with those arising from coherency. The release of coherency strains, which brings softening (overaging), may be accomplished by the passage of dislocations over the interface between precipitate and matrix, or may involve more far-reaching changes. In some alloys it is accomplished by a noncoherent boundary sweeping across a grain. The matrix ahead of the moving boundary is strained and the matrix behind it is strain-free, recrystallized, and overaged (the dark bands in Fig. 3 are the recrystallized matrix). The driving force for this mechanism is the strain energy resulting from the coherency strains that are believed to cause the hardening. Diffusion at the moving boundary must be rapid, for the plates of equilibrium precipitate behind the moving boundary are not where they were before the boundary reached them.[4]

[1] A. H. Geisler and J. K. Hill, *Acta Cryst.*, vol. 1, p. 238, 1948.

[2] A. Guinier, *J. phys. radium*, Ser. 8, vol. 3, p. 124, 1942; *Acta Cryst.*, vol. 5, p. 121, 1952. See also p. 553 of this book.

[3] R. F. Mehl and L. K. Jetter, "Symposium on the Age-hardening of Metals," American Society for Metals, Cleveland, Ohio, 1940. J. S. Bowles and C. S. Barrett, "Progress in Metal Physics," vol. 3, Interscience Publishers, New York, 1952.

[4] Cyril S. Smith, *Trans. AIME*, vol. 175, p. 15, 1948.

The stresses around a coherent particle have not been measured, and their distribution is on such a fine scale that direct observation of them would be extremely difficult. Some investigators have proposed that the stresses arise from a biaxial tension or compression of a thin plate of precipitate, the principal stresses lying in the plane of the precipitate and having a magnitude sufficient to make the precipitate match the matrix.[1] There is a possibility, however, that some precipitates form by atom movements that include a component of homogeneous shear, and that there is coherence between the precipitate and the matrix such that the matrix is sheared along with the precipitate, just as occurs in the formation of a martensite crystal.[2] The strains and residual stresses in the matrix caused by such martensitic nucleation, discussed in the sections concerned with martensite, would be different from those caused by biaxial tension or compression of a thin plate. Their magnitude should be adequate to account for the severe matrix distortions, registered by X-ray reflections,[3] that must be a major cause of hardening, and that even cause recrystallization of some alloys during aging.

The beautifully regular markings on a polished and etched surface of an iron-nickel meteorite were first discovered by Widmanstätten early in the nineteenth century. It was nearly a century later that Osmond and Cortaud explained their origin, the precipitation of a new phase along certain crystallographic planes of the existing matrix crystal. It is a surprising fact that the study of meteorites has occupied an important place in the development of physical metallurgy. The petrographer Sorby, who is recognized as the father of the metallurgical microscope, initiated metallography when he looked at steels under the microscope in a search for figures similar to the figures in meteorites. Osmond, Cortaud, and Roozeboom, inspired by an interest in meteorites, published the first phase diagram—one for the Fe-Ni system. Neumann bands were first found in meteorites and were eventually shown to be twins generated when the meteorites struck the earth. The study of meteorites has been continued to this day.

Networks of parallel lamellae similar to the meteoric structure have now been observed in artificially prepared Fe-Ni alloys (Fig. 4) and in a great number of other alloys and have come to be known as Widmanstätten structures. They are to be expected whenever a solid solution, homogeneous at one temperature, is made to become supersaturated at

[1] C. S. Barrett, A. H. Geisler, and R. F. Mehl, *Trans. AIME*, vol. 143, p. 134, 1941. A. H. Geisler and J. K. Hill, *Acta Cryst.*, vol. 1, p. 238, 1948. F. R. N. Nabarro, *Proc. Phys. Soc. (London)*, vol. 52, p. 90, 1940.

[2] J. S. Bowles and C. S. Barrett, "Progress in Metal Physics," vol. III, Interscience Publishers, New York, 1952.

[3] C. S. Barrett, *Trans. AIME*, vol. 161, p. 15, 1945.

another temperature.   In the majority of cases the precipitating crystals
are thin plates forming on matrix planes of low indices, as shown in Figs.
4 and 5; occasionally, they form on planes of high indices or on irrational
planes, and in some instances they form needles, geometrical shapes,

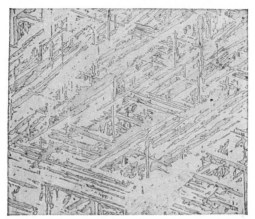

Fig. 4. Widmanstätten pattern produced by slowly cooling an Fe-Ni alloy (27% Ni).
×50.   (*Derge and Kommel.*)

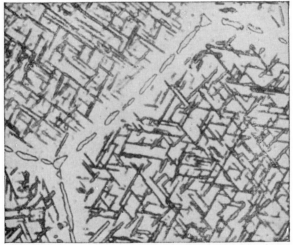

Fig. 5. Widmanstätten pattern in Al-Ag (20.2% Ag) aged 25 hours at 387°C.   Precipitation is γ' and γ in the form of plates on (111) planes of matrix.   ×2000.

rosettes, or irregular particles instead of plates.   The orientation of the
precipitate lattice is definitely related to the orientation of the matrix
lattice.   Because the crystallography of these structures and the orientation relationships involved are fundamental to the theory of age hardening, there has been continued interest in Widmanstätten figures.   A
tabulation of the results of research in this field is given on page 548.

Lattice Relationships in Widmanstätten Structures. Young[1] first showed by X-rays that the lamellae of meteorites were single crystals of definite orientation. The high-temperature face-centered cubic (f.c.c.) phase, γ, of the Fe-Ni alloy (roughly 8 per cent nickel) precipitates body-centered cubic (b.c.c.) α crystals as plates along the octahedral planes of the γ matrix. Within the α plates the (110) planes are parallel to the plane of union with the matrix. There is close similarity between the atomic array on the (110) plane in the plate and the (111) plane of the matrix, to which it is joined. One of the first Widmanstätten structures of microscopic dimensions to receive a thorough analysis is found in Al-Ag

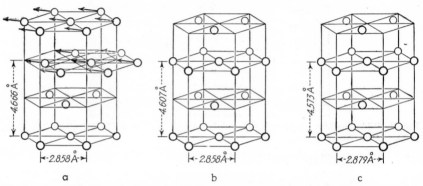

a   b   c

FIG. 6. Crystal lattice of phases in Al-Ag alloys. a, matrix, δ (face-centered cubic); b, transition phase γ' (close-packed hexagonal): c, equilibrium precipitate, γ (close-packed hexagonal).

alloys (Fig. 5).[2] It was found that in the Al-Ag system each plate of the precipitate, which is close-packed hexagonal (c.p.h.), forms along an octahedral plane of the f.c.c. matrix; the basal plane of the precipitate lies parallel to the octahedral plane of the matrix. Furthermore, the closest packed rows of atoms in matrix and precipitate are parallel. The two planes that face each other across the interface between plate and matrix are both close-packed atom layers identical in pattern and almost identical in dimensions; the planes lying behind them are likewise similar. Merely the *sequence* of the layers undergoes a major alteration during precipitation. It was therefore concluded that precipitation takes place when certain close-packed layers of the matrix shift over one another so as to abandon the face-centered sequence of these layers, $ABCABC$ . . . , and acquire the c.p.h. sequence $ABAB$ . . . , in which every third layer, instead of every fourth, is above the first.

Further details of this process can be presented with the aid of Fig. 6.[3]

[1] J. Young, *Proc. Roy. Soc. (London)*, vol. A112, p. 630, 1926.

[2] R. F. Mehl and C. S. Barrett, *Trans. AIME*, vol. 93, p. 78, 1931.

[3] C. S. Barrett and A. H. Geisler, *J. Applied Phys.*, vol. 11, p. 733, 1940. C. S. Barrett, A. H. Geisler, and R. F. Mehl, *Trans. AIME*, vol. 143, p. 134, 1941.

The matrix structure (f.c.c. δ) is indicated in Fig. 6a with (111) as the base plane of the sketch. Figure 6b shows the transition structure that forms first during precipitation as the result of movements suggested by the arrows in Fig. 6a. This transitional structure (γ′) is c.p.h. The atom spacings in the horizontal layers do not change during the δ to γ′ transition, though the vertical spacing decreases 1.4 per cent. The basal plane of the new lattice maintains complete registry with the (111) plane of the matrix and continues to do so until the plate has grown to a thickness of many hundreds of angstroms. Finally, the stresses tending to tear the particle from registry become intolerable, and the transition to the stable structure of Fig. 6c occurs. The stable phase γ differs from the transition phase only in its dimensions a and c.

It has been suggested that the transition phase is merely a stressed form of the stable phase, the stresses arising from the coherency between precipitate and matrix.[1]

Assuming that biaxial stresses in the precipitate strain it into registry with the matrix in examples of this type, Mott and Nabarro[2] computed the thickness to which the precipitate would grow before the strain energy arising from the forced coherency would equal the latent heat of melting a monatomic layer of metal at the surface of the particle, in this way arriving at the order of magnitude of the thickness at which the precipitate would break away from coherency. For silver precipitating from a copper-rich solid solution, this theory predicts that breaking away will occur when the particle is only two atoms thick and is incapable of giving sharp X-ray reflections. Applying the theory to Al-Ag alloys, breaking away is predicted when the particle reaches about 320 atom layers (730 A), which is in accord with the fact that sharp Debye rings can be obtained from the coherent phase before it breaks away to become the stable phase. It should be pointed out that assumptions that might be invalid were made in these estimates of stresses and breakaway thicknesses. It was assumed, for example, that the coherent phase and the equilibrium phase would have the same lattice dimensions in the unstrained state, which would be true only if the compositions were identical. It was also assumed implicitly that no shearing movements were involved of the sort that would arise if martensitic nucleation occurred. And it was assumed that a high energy barrier must be surmounted in the breakaway process.

It would be desirable to be able to tell from the lattice orientation rela-

---

[1] If γ′ is considered as elastically strained γ, it has been estimated that the stresses required are about 100,000 psi, compressional, in all directions parallel to the basal plane of the precipitate, and approximately zero along the c axis.

[2] N. F. Mott and F. R. N. Nabarro, *Proc. Phys. Soc. (London)*, vol. 52, p. 86, 1940. F. R. N. Nabarro, *Proc. Phys. Soc. (London)*, vol. 52, p. 90, 1940; *Proc. Roy. Soc. (London)*, vol. A175, p. 519, 1940.

tionships whether or not the nuclei in precipitation processes form by shearing or shearlike atom movements of a martensitic type. This can rarely be done, however, for the orientations resulting from martensitic transformations are sometimes the same as those produced by the nucleation and growth process; similarity in orientation relationships, for a given change of structure, does not necessarily mean similarity in the mode of nucleation.

Plane of Precipitation. Upon what crystallographic plane of the matrix will a plate of precipitate form? A review of some of the published data on various systems (Table XXVII, page 548) shows immediately that a plate will not necessarily grow on the plane of greatest atomic density, nor even on a plane containing one of the closest packed rows of atoms, nor on the cleavage, slip, or twinning planes. The plane chosen is the result of an interaction between matrix and precipitate structures, but thus far it has not been possible to state a crystallographic rule that applies to all systems. A rule that applies to most alloys is that the atomic planes facing each other across the matrix-precipitate interface have very similar atom patterns and atom spacings. This may be a manifestation of a more fundamental rule that the energy required to produce the interface must be a minimum. It appears that this energy requirement will be met when the new crystal forms in such a way as to be as nearly as possible a continuation of the old; hence, one would expect planes at the interface that fit together with a minimum of mismatch.

A factor that may be determinative in some alloys is the activation energy that is required to shear or otherwise distort a matrix lattice so as to generate the new crystal within it. Some attempts have been made to estimate this factor quantitatively,[1] but the computations have been made with such simplified models that the conclusions are of uncertain validity. The computations concerned the choice of the plane of precipitation in Ag-rich and Cu-rich Cu-Ag alloys, where at both ends of the system, which is simple eutectic, a precipitate of f.c.c. structure forms in a f.c.c. matrix, the precipitate having an orientation the same as that of the matrix.[2]

Clearly, any theory of orientation relationships and habit planes must rest on a thorough knowledge of all metastable states that may precede the stable precipitate, detailed knowledge of orientation and habit, and knowledge of whether nucleation is by a martensitic process or a thermally

---

[1] R. Smoluchowski, *Physica*, vol. 15, p. 175, 1949. C. S. Barrett, discussion to paper by A. H. Geisler, in "Phase Transformations in Solids," Wiley, New York, 1951.

[2] There is some uncertainty in the habit plane for the Cu-rich alloys; an early conclusion that it was {100} has been followed by a suggestion that it is {111}, just as in the Ag-rich alloys. See A. H. Geisler, in "Phase Transformations in Solids," Wiley, New York, 1951.

activated equilibrium process. One factor that must influence the habit plane of a precipitate, and its lattice orientation as well, is the energy of the interface between matrix and precipitate.[1] It is clear that there is a strong dependence of interfacial energy on the orientations at a boundary, as Smith has pointed out.[2] Calculations of Read and Shockley[3] show that in single-phase samples, near certain orientations where a minimum interface energy exists, there is a rapid change of energy with change in some (or probably all) of the five variables that specify the orientation of the interface in the two adjoining crystals, and experimental determinations of Dunn and coworkers[4] and of Aust and Chalmers[5] confirm this rapid change. For boundaries that have reached thermal equilibrium and for nuclei that must either grow or dissolve, this orientation dependence must be an important factor. It would not be correct to assume, however, that the orientation dependence of boundaries between different phases is identical with that between grains of the same phase.

Shape of Precipitated Particles. The external shape of precipitated crystals is platelike with a few exceptions, such as the α needles that can be made to form in the β phase of Cu-Zn alloys[6] by suitable heat-treatment. Platelets and equiaxed polyhedra can also be formed in these alloys without altering the lattice orientation of the new crystals with respect to the old. It appears that external habit can be sensitive to conditions during growth somewhat as it is in the growth of crystals from liquid solution. It has been argued that if the original nucleus is platelike in shape the concentration gradients around the particle will tend to maintain this shape.[7] The orientation dependence of the interface energy, mentioned above, may be a more decisive factor when spheroidization of precipitate particles is not rapid compared with the rate of diffusion of the solute.

A theoretical approach to the problem of shape has been made by Mott and Nabarro[8] by calculating the strain energy that will be developed when precipitate particles of various shapes form in a matrix. They have

[1] R. F. Mehl and L. K. Jetter, "Symposium on Age-hardening of Metals," American Society for Metals, Cleveland, Ohio, 1940.

[2] Cyril S. Smith, *Trans. AIME*, vol. 175, p. 15, 1948.

[3] W. T. Read and W. Shockley, *Phys. Rev.*, vol. 78, p. 275, 1950.

[4] C. G. Dunn and F. Lionetti, *Trans. AIME*, vol. 185, p. 125, 1949. C. G. Dunn, F. W. Daniels, and M. J. Bolton, *Trans. AIME*, vol. 188, p. 368, 1950.

[5] K. T. Aust and B. Chalmers, *Proc. Roy. Soc. (London)*, vol. A201, p. 210, 1950.

[6] R. F. Mehl and O. T. Marzke, *Trans. AIME*, vol. 93, p. 123, 1931. J. Weerts, *Z. Metallkuhde*, vol. 24, p. 265, 1932. O. T. Marzke, *Trans. AIME*, vol. 104, p. 64, 1933.

[7] R. F. Mehl and C. S. Barrett, *Trans. AIME*, vol. 93, p. 78, 1931.

[8] N. F. Mott and F. R. N. Nabarro, *Proc. Phys. Soc. (London)*, vol. 52, p. 86, 1940. F. R. N. Nabarro, *Proc. Phys. Soc. (London)*, vol. 52, p. 90, 1940; *Proc. Roy. Soc. (London)*, vol. A175, p. 519, 1940.

TABLE XXVII. CRYSTALLOGRAPHIC RELATIONSHIPS IN METALS AND ALLOYS*

System	Type of change	Parent phase		New phase		Crystallographic relations (Parent phase described first)	Reference
		Name	Lattice	Name	Lattice		
Fe	Transformation	γ-Fe	F.c.c.	α-Fe	B.c.c.	(111)γ∥(110)α, [110]γ∥[111]α	28
Fe-Ni (meteoric)	Transformation	Taenite or γ-Fe solid solution	F.c.c.	Kamacite or α-Fe solid solution	B.c.c.	(111)γ∥(110)α, [111]α rotated 2 to 4° from [011]γ, about [111]γ	43, 44
						(100)γ∥(100)α, (011)γ∥(010)α	4
						(111)γ∥(110)α, [110]γ∥[111]α	26
Fe-Ni (28-34% Ni)	Transformation	γ-Fe solid solution	F.c.c.	α-Fe solid solution	B.c.c.	(111)γ∥(110)α, [211]γ∥[110]α	30, 39
						(111)γ∥(110)α, [110]γ∥[111]α when transformed above room temperature	26
Fe-C	Precipitation (slowly cooled)	Austenite(γ) 0.4% C	F.c.c.	Ferrite (proeutectoid)	B.c.c.	(111)γ∥(110)α, [110]γ∥[111]α	23
	Precipitation	Austenite(γ) 1.30% C	F.c.c.	Fe₃C(cementite)	Orthorhombic	Plates which are not ∥(111)γ; (001)Fe₃C∥to plane of plate	23
	Eutectoid decomposition	Austenite(γ) 0.80% C	F.c.c.	Ferrite in pearlite	B.c.c.	(110)γ∥(112)α, [112]γ∥[110]α or possibly (321)γ∥(331)α, [331]γ∥[321]α	29, 35
				Ferrite in bainite	B.c.c.	See text, p. 572	
				Ferrite in 350 and 450° bainite	B.c.c.	(111)γ∥(110)α, [211]γ∥[110]α	35
				Ferrite in 250° bainite		(111)γ∥(110)α, [110]γ∥[111]α	35

	Superlattice transformation	Random α solid solution	F.c.c.	Ordered β solid solution	B.c.c.		
Cu-Pd	Superlattice reaction	α solid solution	F.c.c.	Ordered β solid solution	B.c.c.	$(001)\alpha\|(113)\beta$, $[311]\alpha\|[100]\beta$	13
Cu-Zn	Peritectic reaction	α solid solution	F.c.c.	β solid solution	B.c.c.	$(111)\alpha\|(110)\beta$, $(1\bar{1}0)\alpha\|(001)\beta$; $(111)\alpha\|(110)\beta$, $(1\bar{1}0)\alpha\|(11\bar{1})\beta$; $(100)\alpha\|(100)\beta$, $(010)\alpha\|(01\bar{1})\beta$	14
Pb-Sb	Precipitation	Pb solid solution	F.c.c.	Sb solid solution	Rhombohedral	(111)Pb$\|(001)$Sb, $[110]$Pb$\|[100]$Sb	7
Tl	Transformation Martensitic?	α-Tl	F.c.c.	β-Tl	C.p.h.	$(111)\|(0001)$, $[110]\|[11\bar{2}0]$	6
Al-Ag	Precipitation	Al solid solution	F.c.c.	γ phase (Ag₂Al)	C.p.h.	$(111)\|(0001)$, $[110]\|[11\bar{2}0]$	22
				γ' phase (transitional)	C.p.h.	$(111)\|(0001)$, $[110]\|[11\bar{2}0]$	2
Cu-Ag	Precipitation	Ag solid solution / Cu solid solution	F.c.c. / F.c.c.	Cu solid solution / Ag solid solution	F.c.c. / F.c.c.	Plates on {100}, all directions ∥ / Plates on {111} or {100}, all directions ∥	3, 15
Al-Cu	Precipitation	Al solid solution	F.c.c.	θ (CuAl₂)	Tetragonal	Plates on (100)Al $(100)\|(100)$, $[120]\|[011]$?	25
				θ' (transitional)	Tetragonal	(100)Al$\|(001)\theta'$, $[110]$Al$\|[010]\theta'$	32, 40
Cu-Ni-Co Cu-Ni-Fe	Precipitation	α solid solution	F.c.c.	Co(Fe)-rich precipitate	F.c.c.	Plates on {100}; lattice orientation same as matrix	11
Cu-Co	Precipitation	α solid solution	F.c.c.		F.c.c.	Plates on {100}; lattice orientation same as matrix	12
Al-Mg-Si	Precipitation	α solid solution	F.c.c.	Mg₂Si	Cubic	Plates on {100}	25, 20
Al-Mg	Precipitation	α solid solution	F.c.c.	β phase	Hexagonal	Plates first on {100} later probably on {120}	8, 10
Al-Zn	Precipitation	α solid solution	F.c.c.	Nearly pure Zn	C.p.h.	Plates on {111} $(111)\|(0001)$, $[110]\|[11\bar{2}0]$	10

* Directions lie in plane of matching, unless noted otherwise. Martensitic transformations are covered in Table XXVIII.

TABLE XXVII. CRYSTALLOGRAPHIC RELATIONSHIPS IN METALS AND ALLOYS.*—(Continued)

System	Type of change	Parent phase		New phase		Crystallographic relations (Parent phase described first)	Reference
		Name	Lattice	Name	Lattice		
Cu-Be	Precipitation	α solid solution	F.c.c.	γ (CsCl type)	Cubic	Guinier-Preston zones on {100}, later γ with [100]α‖[100]γ, [011]α‖[010]γ Habit undetermined	16, 17
Cu-Si	Precipitation	α solid solution	F.c.c.	κ phase	C.p.h.	Plates on {111} (111)‖(0001), [110]‖[1120]	33, 1
Cu-Zn	Diffusion layer	α solid solution	F.c.c.	β phase	B.c.c.	Near (111)$_{f.c.c.}$‖(110)$_{b.c.c.}$, [110]$_{f.c.c.}$‖[111]$_{b.c.c.}$	42
		γ phase	Cubic	β phase	B.c.c.	Axes β‖γ	27
Au-Cu	Superlattice transformation	α solid solution	F.c.c.	AuCu	F.c. tetragonal	(100)‖(100), [010]‖[010]	31, 5
Cu-Zn	Precipitation	β phase	B.c.c.	α solid solution	F.c.c.	(110)β‖(111)α, [111]β‖[110]α Variable habit; plates; needles ‖[556]β	41, 36, 21
Cu-Sn	Precipitation	β phase	B.c.c.	α solid solution	F.c.c.	(110)β‖(111)α, [111]β‖[110]α	34
Cu-Sn	Eutectoid decomposition	β phase	B.c.c.	α solid solution	F.c.c.	(110)β‖(111)α, [111]β‖[110]α	19
Ag-Zn	Precipitation	β phase	B.c.c.	α solid solution	F.c.c.	(110)β‖(111)α, [111]β‖[110]α	34
Fe-N	Precipitation	α solid solution	B.c.c.	Fe4N	F.c.c.	(210)α‖(112)	24
Cu-Al	Eutectoid decomposition	β phase	B.c.c.	α solid solution	F.c.c.	(110)β‖(100)α	37
Cu-Zn	Precipitation	β phase	B.c.c.	γ phase	γ cubic	(100)β‖(100)γ, [010]β‖[010]γ	41

System	Reaction	Parent phase	Structure	Product phase	Structure	Orientation relationship	Ref.
Cu-Sn	Eutectoid decomposition	β phase	B.c.c.	γ' intermediate phase	Hex, ~γ	$(100)\beta\|(100)\gamma$, $[010]\beta\|[010]\gamma$	18, 19
						Nearly like β to γ	18, 19
Cu-Al	Eutectoid decomposition	β phase	B.c.c.	γ phase	γ cubic	$(100)\beta\|(100)\gamma$, $[010]\beta\|[010]\gamma$	38
Ag-Zn	Transformation	β phase	B.c.c.	ε phase	C.p.h.	$(111)\|(0001)$, $(110)\|(10\bar{1}0)$	41
						Nearly like β→γ in Cu-Sn	19
Ag-Zn	Precipitation	β phase	B.c.c.	γ phase	γ cubic	$(100)\beta\|(100)\gamma$, $[010]\beta\|[010]\gamma$	41
Fe-P	Precipitation	α solid solution	B.c.c.	Fe_3P	B.c. tetragonal	Plates$\|$(21 1 4)α	23
Zn-Cu	Precipitation	ε phase (Zn)	C.p.h.	η phase	C.p.h.	$(10\bar{1}4)\epsilon\|(10\bar{1}4)\eta$, $[11\bar{2}0]\epsilon\|[11\bar{2}0]\eta$	9
Mg-Sn	Precipitation	Mg solid solution	C.p.h.	Mg_2Sn	Cubic (CaF₂ type)	$(00\cdot1)Mg\|(111)$, $[10\cdot0]\|[110]$; $(00\cdot1)Mg\|(110)$, $[10\cdot0]\|[110]$; $(00\cdot1)Mg\|(111)$, $[11\cdot0]\|[110]$	7

References

[1] C. S. Barrett, Trans. AIME, vol. 188, p. 123, 1950.

[2] C. S. Barrett, A. H. Geisler, and R. F. Mehl, Trans. AIME, vol. 143, p. 134, 1941.

[3] C. S. Barrett, H. F. Kaiser, and R. F. Mehl, Trans. AIME, vol. 117, p. 39, 1935 (Cu-Ag).

[4] O. B. Bøggild, Saertryk af Meddelser am Grønland, vol. 74, p. 1, 1927.

[5] U. Dehlinger and L. Graf, Z. Physik, vol. 64, p. 359, 1930.

[6] U. Dehlinger, E. Osswald, and H. Bumm, Z. Metallkunde, vol. 25, p. 62, 1933.

[7] G. Derge, A. R. Kommel, and R. F. Mehl, Trans. AIME, vol. 124, p. 367, 1937 (Mg-Sn).

[8] W. L. Fink and D. W. Smith, Trans. AIME, vol. 124, p. 162, 1937.

[9] M. L. Fuller and J. L. Rodda, Trans. AIME, vol. 104, p. 116, 1933 (Cu-Zn).

[10] A. H. Geisler, C. S. Barrett, and R. F. Mehl, Trans. AIME, vol. 152, p. 201, 1943.

[11] A. H. Geisler and J. B. Newkirk, Trans. AIME, vol. 180, p. 101, 1949.

[12] R. B. Gordon and M. Cohen, "Age Hardening of Metals," p. 161, American Society for Metals, Cleveland, Ohio, 1940.

[13] L. Graf, Physik. Z., vol. 14, p. 489, 1935.

[14] A. R. Greninger, Trans. AIME, vol. 124, p. 379, 1937.

[15] A. H. Geisler, in "Phase Transformations in Solids," Wiley, New York, 1951.

(Footnotes continued on p. 552.)

[16] A. Guinier and P. Jacquet, *Compt. rend.*, vol. 217 (1), p. 22, 1943; *Rêv. mét.*, vol. 41, p. 1, 1944.

[17] A. H. Guy, C. S. Barrett, and R. F. Mehl, *Trans. AIME*, vol. 175, p. 216, 1948.

[18] J. Isaitschew and G. Kurdjumow, *Metallwirtschaft*, vol. 11, p. 554, 1932.

[19] J. Isaitschew and G. Kurdjumow, *Physik. Z. Sowjetunion*, vol. 5, pp. 6, 22, 1934.

[20] F. Keller and A. H. Geisler, *Trans. AIME*, vol. 156, p. 82, 1944.

[21] O. T. Marzke, *Trans. AIME*, vol. 104, p. 64, 1933.

[22] R. F. Mehl and C. S. Barrett, *Trans. AIME*, vol. 93, p. 78, 1931 (Al-Ag, Cu-Si).

[23] R. F. Mehl, C. S. Barrett, and D. W. Smith, *Trans. AIME*, vol. 105, p. 215, 1933.

[24] R. F. Mehl, C. S. Barrett, and H. S. Jerabek, *Trans. AIME*, vol. 113, p. 211, 1934 (Fe-N, Fe-P).

[25] R. F. Mehl, C. S. Barrett, and F. N. Rhines, *Trans. AIME*, vol. 99, p. 203, 1932 (Al-Cu, Al-Mg2Si).

[26] R. F. Mehl and G. Derge, *Trans. AIME*, vol. 125, p. 482, 1937.

[27] R. F. Mehl and O. T. Marzke, *Trans. AIME*, vol. 93, p. 123, 1931 (Cu-Zn, Cu-Al).

[28] R. F. Mehl and D. W. Smith, *Trans. AIME*, vol. 113, p. 203, 1934 (Fe-C).

[29] R. F. Mehl and D. W. Smith, *Trans. AIME*, vol. 116, p. 330, 1935.

[30] Z. Nishiyama, *Sci. Repts., Tôhoku Imp. Univ.*, vol. 23, p. 637, 1934.

[31] K. Oshima and G. Sachs, *Z. Physik*, vol. 63, p. 210, 1930.

[32] G. D. Preston, *Phil. Mag.*, vol. 26, p. 855, 1938.

[33] Cyril S. Smith, *Trans. AIME*, vol. 137, p. 313, 1940.

[34] D. W. Smith, *Trans. AIME*, vol. 104, p. 48, 1933.

[35] G. V. Smith and R. F. Mehl, *Trans. AIME*, vol. 150, p. 211, 1942.

[36] M. Straumanis and G. Weerts, *Z. Physik*, vol. 78, p. 1, 1932.

[37] G. Wassermann, *Metallwirtschaft*, vol. 13, p. 133, 1934.

[38] G. Wassermann, *Z. Metallkunde*, vol. 26, p. 256, 1934.

[39] G. Wassermann, *Mitt. Kaiser-Wilhelm-Inst. Eisenforsch., Düsseldorf*, vol. 17, p. 149, 1935.

[40] G. Wassermann and J. Weerts, *Metallwirtschaft*, vol. 14, p. 605, 1935.

[41] J. Weerts, *Z. Metallkunde*, vol. 24, p. 265, 1932.

[42] Shueling Woo, C. S. Barrett, and R. F. Mehl, *Trans. AIME*, vol. 156, p. 100, 1944.

[43] J. Young, *Proc. Roy. Soc. (London)*, vol. A112, p. 630, 1926.

[44] J. Young, *Phil. Trans. Roy. Soc. (London)*, vol. A238, p. 393, 1939.

shown that the least strain energy is associated with particles having the form of a thin plate. This holds even after a particle has broken away from its registry with the matrix and in spite of the opposing tendency for the particle to become more spherical so as to minimize the surface energy. Since the tendency to spheroidization decreases with larger particles, the resulting form should be flatter the larger the particle.

Diffraction in the Early Stages of Aging. X-ray diffraction has recently furnished much information on the changes occurring in the early stages of the precipitation process during age hardening. The existence of transitional states, which precede the stable ones, was proved for the systems Al-Cu,[1] Al-Ag,[2] and many others. Before transition structures become fully developed, however, X-ray diffraction effects can be obtained from regions where the precipitation process is beginning. This was discovered in Al-Cu alloys by Guinier and his coworkers[3] and independently by Preston,[4] who found streaks on Laue photographs such as would be caused by two-dimensional gratings located on {100} planes of the aluminum matrix. Guinier and Preston concluded that these platelets are clusters of copper atoms in the solid solution; others have reasoned that they are thin platelets of the transition phase (θ'), richer in copper than the matrix.[5] The dimensions of the platelets can be determined from the length and width of the diffraction streaks and average a few atomic layers in thickness by a few hundreds of angstroms in diameter; the dimensions increase as aging is continued and eventually reach a value that gives three-dimensional diffraction. At a later stage the lattice transforms to the stable phase (θ).

Similar streaks in X-ray photographs now have been observed and studied in detail in other age-hardening alloys. In aluminum-rich aluminum-silver alloys Geisler and Hill[6] found evidence of a stage that

[1] G. Wassermann and J. Weerts, *Metallwirtschaft*, vol. 14, p. 605, 1935. W. L. Fink and D. W. Smith, *Trans. AIME*, vol. 122, p. 284, 1936; vol. 137, p. 95, 1940. G. D. Preston, *Proc. Roy. Soc. (London)*, vol. A167, p. 526, 1938; *Phil. Mag.*, vol. 26, p. 855, 1938.

[2] C. S. Barrett, A. H. Geisler, and R. F. Mehl, *Trans. AIME*, vol. 143, p. 134, 1941.

[3] A. Guinier, *Compt. rend.*, vol. 204, p. 1115, 1937; vol. 206, p. 1641, 1938; *Nature*, vol. 142, p. 669, 1938. J. Calvet, P. Jacquet, and A. Guinier, *J. Inst. Metals*, vol. 6, p. 177, 1939.

[4] G. D. Preston, *Nature*, vol. 142, p. 570, 1938; *Phil. Mag.*, vol. 26, p. 855, 1938; *Proc. Roy. Soc. (London)*, vol. A167, p. 526, 1938; *Proc. Phys. Soc. (London)*, vol. 52, p. 77, 1940. The platelets producing these diffraction effects have sometimes been called "Guinier-Preston zones" and "Guinier-Preston aggregates," after their discoverers.

[5] R. F. Mehl and L. K. Jetter, "Symposium on the Age-hardening of Metals," American Society for Metals, Cleveland, Ohio, 1940. C. S. Barrett, A. H. Geisler, and R. F. Mehl, *Trans. AIME*, vol. 143, p. 134, 1941. A. H. Geisler, Dissertation, Carnegie Institute of Technology, Pittsburgh, Pa., 1942.

[6] A. H. Geisler and J. K. Hill, *Acta Cryst.*, vol. 1, p. 238, 1948.

precedes even the platelet stage, during aging at room temperature. This stage produces the diffraction streaks shown in Fig. 7a, which correspond to planes in reciprocal space, and which are interpreted as diffraction from a one-dimensional grating in the form of a "stringlet" of precipitate. The proposed stringlets lie along the close-packed rows, <110>, of the matrix, and are estimated to have dimensions roughly 10 by 20 by 100 A. As aging continues, the diffraction effects change, as illustrated in Fig. 7b. The reciprocal lattice at this stage contains rods, which may be accounted for by two-dimensional gratings consisting of

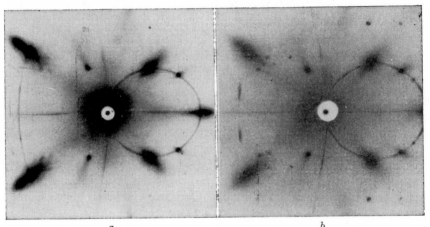

a   *b*

FIG. 7. Laue photographs of "stringlet" and "platelet" stages of aged Al-Mg-Si alloy. Cu radiation incident 20° from [100], 90° from [001], which is vertical on the page. (a) Stringlet stage; ellipses correspond to planes in reciprocal space. (b) Platelet stage; arcs correspond to rods in reciprocal space. For changes caused by addition of Cu see H. Lambot, *Rev. mét.*, vol. 47, p. 709, 1950. (*Geisler and Hill.*)

"platelets" on the close-packed planes of the matrix. At a later stage, the rods coalesce into spots, as if the platelets thickened into three-dimensional crystals. Thus Geisler and Hill propose that stringlets widen into thin platelets and that these ultimately thicken, thereby accounting for the geometrical features of the diffraction patterns.

It is not easy to choose among a number of different causes for unusual diffraction effects in aging experiments. There may be clustering within the matrix of solute atoms, and the clusters may possess various types of order or semiorder and have various shapes. There may be small particles of a structure differing from the matrix, of various shapes, and with various types of superstructures. There may be distortion gradients in the matrix around a particle that yield unusual effects.[1] And there may be stacking faults in one or both phases.

[1] Some interesting streaks that bridge between diffraction spots have been observed by F. Laves (*J. Geol.*, vol. 58, p. 548, 1950); he attributes the streaks to distortion

Guinier (see page 553) and his coworkers rely heavily on a comparison of the vicinity of reciprocal-lattice point 000 with others, since size effects due to precipitates, superlattices, or enriched zones should be the same around 000 as around all other points, whereas effects due to stacking disorders and various distortions should not be found around 000. Stringlet and platelet effects in Al-Ag are ascribed not to particles of precipitate but to superlattice domains and to stacking disorders. The sequence in Al-Cu is interpreted as first an enrichment of some (100) planes, then progressive sorting of these into a superlattice, θ'', with hardness increasing meanwhile, then the growth of metastable θ' during overaging, and finally the appearance of stable θ.

In alloys of aluminum and magnesium it is unlikely that the clustering of Mg atoms would yield the strong streaks that are observed because the scattering powers of Al and Mg atoms are nearly equal, so it has been concluded that the streaks are due to an alteration in the structure involving new atomic sites and not merely a shifting of atoms to certain of the existing sites. In the system Al-Mg$_2$Si also Geisler and Hill[1] conclude that new atom sites are involved, since the streaks correspond to reciprocal lattice rods that do not pass through the reciprocal lattice points of the matrix. (In this system the platelet stage is preceded by a stringlet stage analogous to that in Al-Ag except that the direction of the stringlets is along $<100>$.)

There are striking examples of unusual diffraction effects in certain ternary alloys. A phase in the Fe-Ni-Al system that has the CsCl type structure for Ni and Al atoms, with Fe atoms replacing these at random, may be made to precipitate a disordered body-centered cubic phase richer in iron, the matrix becoming poorer in iron but retaining its order. Bradley and Taylor[2] found that when the precipitate and matrix phases were present in about equal amounts they took the form of lamellae parallel to {100} planes of the matrix and were coherent on these planes. There appeared to be a wave pattern of varying iron content, with a wavelength of the order of a micron after annealing 16 days at 850°C. Similarly in the alloy Cu$_4$FeNi$_3$ a wavelike precipitation was found by Daniel and Lipson.[3] At high temperatures this alloy consists of a face-centered cubic structure, which transforms at lower temperatures into

---

associated with the transformation of thin lamellae of monoclinic orthoclase into a triclinic modification without breaking coherence with the parent phase.

[1] A. H. Geisler and J. K. Hill, *Acta Cryst.*, vol. 1, p. 238, 1948.

[2] A. J. Bradley and A. Taylor, "Physics in Industry—Magnetism," Institute of Physics, 1938; A. Taylor, "X-ray Metallography," Wiley, New York, 1945.

[3] V. Daniel and H. Lipson, *Proc. Roy. Soc. (London)*, vol. A181, p. 368, 1943; vol. A182, p. 378, 1944. The analysis of these patterns is covered in R. W. James, "Optical Principles of the Diffraction of X-rays," G. Bell, London, 1948, and A. J. C. Wilson, "X-ray Optics," Methuen, London, 1949.

copper-rich and copper-poor phases, both face-centered cubic, of different parameter. Before precipitation is complete the alloy passes through a stage in which the diffraction lines become flanked by slightly diffuse side bands. Daniel and Lipson account for these by assuming that there is a sinusoidal variation in lattice spacing of (100) planes with a wavelength in the range 100 to 5000 A, increasing with annealing time.[1] This stage is followed by a stage in which two metastable tetragonal phases coexist. These have *a* dimensions that are equal to those of the matrix and *c/a* ratios greater and less than unity, respectively, and are coherent with

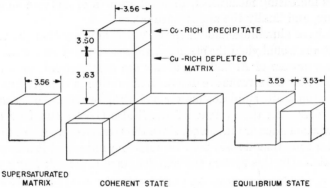

SUPERSATURATED MATRIX   COHERENT STATE   EQUILIBRIUM STATE

FIG. 8. Lattice dimensions and orientations in precipitation from a Cu-Ni-Co. The tetragonally of the early-stage precipitate and depleted matrix is ascribed to the coherency between precipitate and matrix. (*Geisler and Hill.*)

the matrix on their basal planes. Annealing finally causes the equilibrium cubic phases to appear.

Hargreaves,[2] in a further study, concludes that the diffraction effects can best be interpreted as the result of the tetragonal phases which exist in lamellar form and retain complete coherence with the matrix. The apparent movement of the side bands relative to the main lines is explained by Hargreaves as being due to superposition of various orders of the side bands rather than an increase in wavelength of the modulated structure. This stage of complete coherence is followed by the stage of coherence on basal planes only and then by complete loss of coherence.

Geisler and Newkirk[3] found an analagous situation in the Cu-Ni-Co system where the equilibrium precipitate and the depleted matrix are both face-centered in structure but have lattice parameters smaller and

[1] Daniel and Lipson conclude that the predominant factor in producing the side bands is the *spacing variation* rather than the accompanying scattering factor variation due to segregation. The intensities of the side bands relative to the main lines vary with the order of diffraction, whereas if *scattering factor* were the cause the side bands would have been of equal intensity in the different orders.

[2] M. E. Hargreaves, *Acta Cryst.*, vol. 2, p. 259, 1949; *Acta Cryst.*, vol. 4, p. 301, 1951.

[3] A. H. Geisler and J. B. Newkirk, *Trans. AIME*, vol. 180, p. 101, 1949.

larger, respectively, than the parent phase.   The coherence that exists in the early phases of precipitation, and that accounts for the presence of tetragonal metastable phases, is indicated by the sketches in Fig. 8.   The side bands in this alloy are like those in the other ternary alloys mentioned.

Phase Transformations in Metals.   The numerous polymorphic transformations among the elements are not confined to a limited portion of the periodic table or to one or two crystal-structure types; a full understanding of them will not be had from a simple theory.   And since the difference between the free energies of the polymorphic forms is small, theoretical estimations of the energies must be very exact before they can account for the relative stability of the phases at different temperatures and pressures.   Advances in the field have been made predominantly by experiment.

The manner of stacking close-packed layers to form the face-centered cubic and the close-packed hexagonal structures results in very similar environments for the atoms—in fact, with similarly spaced layers, both the 12 nearest neighbors and the 6 second nearest neighbors remain at the same distance from a given atom, and only third nearest and more remote ones alter their distances.   It is not surprising, then, to find examples of changes from one of these structures to the other among metals.   This occurs in calcium, scandium, and lanthanum, which are hexagonal at high temperatures and cubic at low, and cobalt, which has the reverse relationship.

Iron, titanium, zirconium, thallium, lithium, and perhaps sodium transform from a body-centered cubic structure to a close-packed structure that is stable at lower temperatures.   The body-centered cubic structure is mechanically less stable, and provides opportunity for greater amplitudes in the thermal vibrations of the atoms than the close-packed structures; it therefore would be expected to have larger entropy, S, in the equation $F = U - TS$, where F is the free energy, U is the internal energy, and T is the temperature.   It is thought that, because the entropy term is larger for the body-centered structure, this form becomes more stable with respect to the close-packed form as the temperature is raised.[1] Not only temperature, but pressure, and pressure combined with plastic flow can induce phase transformations in metals, as the extensive experiments of Bridgman have shown.   High pressures always cause transformation to a higher density modification.   An interesting example is cerium, which transforms to a phase of 16 per cent greater density under

[1] C. Zener, "Elasticity and Anelasticity of Metals," University of Chicago Press, Chicago, 1948.   This reasoning, in fact, led to the search for the lithium transformation.   The body-centered cubic form of iron is also stable *below* the range of stability of the face-centered cubic; divergent suggestions have been made as to the reason for this, and theoretical opinion cannot be said to have crystallized as yet.

pressure, without changing from its face-centered cubic structure;[1] the same change can be made to take place at low temperatures.[2]

Crystal Structures in Steels. Before taking up a discussion of the crystallography of transformations it is well to review the various phases encountered in steels and their crystal structures, for these have been intimately associated with each advance in our knowledge of transforma-

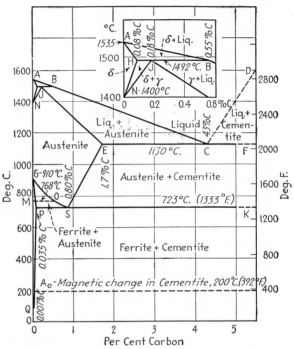

FIG. 9. The iron-cementite diagram. Recent values place E at 2.0 per cent weight per cent carbon, P at 0.025, A_0 at 210°C; and in the iron-graphite diagram, E at 1.98, S at 0.69 and 738°C. (*Data are from "Metals Handbook," American Society for Metals, Cleveland,* 1948.)

tions in the solid state and have always been of tremendous importance in industrial metallurgy.

The *constitution diagram* of Fe-C alloys, Fig. 9, concerns equilibria between iron and cementite (Fe_3C), and ignores the fact that cementite is metastable and decomposes, given sufficient annealing, into iron plus graphite; it also ignores the phases that are formed only by quenching, or by quenching and tempering.

Austenite, an interstitial solid solution of carbon in face-centered cubic (γ) iron, has carbon atoms in interstitial positions at the center of the

[1] A. W. Lawson and Ting-Yuan Tang, *Phys. Rev.*, vol. 76, p. 301, 1949 (see p. 220).

[2] A. P. Schuck and J. H. Sturdivant, *J. Chem. Phys.*, vol. 18, p. 145, 1950.

f.c.c. unit cell of iron atoms (at $\frac{1}{2}\frac{1}{2}\frac{1}{2}$) and also at the mid-points of the cell edges ($\frac{1}{2}00$, $0\frac{1}{2}0$, $00\frac{1}{2}$). These interstices, which are structurally equivalent and are the largest interstices in the lattice, provide more positions than can be filled by carbon atoms even in saturated austenite, (2.0 per cent C). That these largest interstices are the ones actually occupied was indicated by the intensities of X-ray diffraction lines, in precision intensity determinations by Petch.[1]

Ferrite, the solid solution of carbon in body-centered cubic (α) iron, has a maximum solubility of 0.025 per cent C at the eutectoid temperature (723°C). The fact that ferrite dissolves far less carbon than does austenite is accounted for by the smaller size of the interstices in ferrite (see page 223). The interstices at $00\frac{1}{2}$ and equivalent ones are occupied.

Cementite, Fe_3C, has an orthorhombic unit cell containing 12 Fe and 4 C atoms. Lipson and Petch's values[2] for the lattice constants are $a = 4.5235$, $b = 5.0888$, $c = 6.7431$ (when converted to A). The carbon atoms are interstitially located in a nearly close-packed structure of iron atoms, with the coordination shown in Fig. 10, six iron atoms surrounding each carbon atom.[3] The lattice constants are not always the same, but vary with the temperature at which the cementite is brought to equilibrium with austenite. The phase is ferromagnetic below 210°C. In cementite the Fe atoms can be replaced by Mn, Cr, Mo, W, and V (see page 247, Chap. XI).

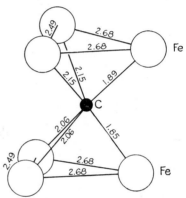

FIG. 10. Interatomic distances in Fe_3C. (*After Goldschmidt.*)

In a steel of composition near the eutectoid (0.80 per cent C) slow cooling produces a lamellar structure of ferrite and cementite known as *pearlite* (Fig. 11). The lamellae become thinner and more close spaced as the cooling rate is increased or when less opportunity is provided for diffusion of carbon.

Martensite is a metastable phase that forms from austenite when a specimen is cooled at a rate exceeding a critical rate (dependent on com-

[1] N. J. Petch, *J. Iron and Steel Inst. (London)*, vol. 145, p. 111, 1942.

[2] H. Lipson and N. J. Petch, *J. Iron Steel Inst. (London)*, vol. 142, p. 95P, 1940; N. J. Petch, *J. Iron Steel Inst. (London)*, vol. 149, p. 143P, 1944. For other determinations see W. Hume-Rothery, G. V. Raynor, and A. T. Little, *J. Iron Steel Inst. (London)*, vol. 145, p. 143, 1942. The space group is V_h^{16}—*Pbnm*.

[3] H. J. Goldschmidt (*J. Iron Steel Inst. (London)*, December, 1948, p. 345) remarks that a sketch similar to Fig. 10 serves also for WC but the lower isosceles triangle must be rotated 180° in its own plane to correspond to Fe_3W_3C or W_2C.

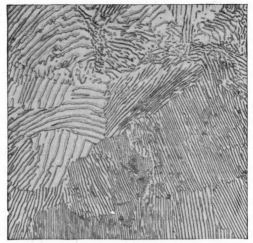

FIG. 11. Pearlite formed in eutectoid simple carbon steel at 705°C. ×1000. (*Vilella.*)

FIG. 12. Martensite in 1.7% C steel quenched from 1150°C. ×1000. (*Greninger.*)

position and metallurgical history) that is sufficient to suppress the formation of pearlite. The martensite crystals are plates arranged on certain planes of the austenite, Fig. 12. Their structure is body-centered tetragonal, with an axial ratio that depends upon composition, Fig. 13.[1]

[1] W. L. Fink and E. D. Campbell, *Trans. Am. Soc. Steel Treating*, vol. 9, p. 717, 1926. N. Seljakow, G. Kurdjumow, and N. Goodtzow, *Z. Physik*, vol. 45, p. 384, 1927. G. Kurdjumow and E. Kaminsky, *Z. Physik*, vol. 53, p. 696, 1929. E. Öhman, *J. Iron Steel Inst. (London)*, vol. 123, p. 445, 1931. G. Hägg, *J. Iron Steel Inst. (London)*, vol. 130, p. 439, 1934.

The curves of *a* and *c* extrapolate linearly to *a* for carbon-free alpha-iron, and while this has been taken by many to indicate that martensite is tetragonal even with concentrations of carbon below 2.5 atomic per cent, this interpretation may be incorrect.[1]

Freshly formed martensite etches slowly and therefore appears white in photomicrographs; upon tempering at temperatures even as low as 100°C, martensite changes to a rapid etching constituent and appears black in photomicrographs. The darkening of the white martensite accompanies the rejection of the carbon from it into a finely divided precipitate and the accompanying change of the tetragonal structure to cubic ferrite.[2] Martensite is almost invariably accompanied by retained austenite. By suitable heat-treatment the first martensite crystals to form may be tempered into the dark etching state, and the remaining austenite may subsequently be transformed into white martensite, giving the contrast shown in Fig. 12.

In the formation of martensite, the atom movements are so coordinated and regular that they produce a change in shape of the transforming region.

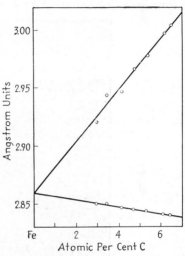

FIG. 13. Variation in lattice constants *a* and *c* of martensite with carbon content of steel. (*Seljakow, Kurdjumow, and Goodtzow.*)

When the crystals lie at the surface of a specimen they produce a visible distortion of the surface, as will be discussed in later sections. Martensite starts to form only when austenite is cooled below a critical temperature M_s that depends on composition, and continues to form only while the temperature continues to fall.[3]

Bainite is the name given to the structure or structures that form on isothermal transformation at temperatures below those for pearlite

---

[1] C. Zener (*Trans. AIME*, vol. 167, p. 550, 1946) concludes on theoretical grounds that tetragonality will disappear when the composition and temperature of a sample puts it above a critical temperature for superlattice ordering, which may be at room temperature for some carbon concentrations between 2.5 atomic per cent C and pure iron.

[2] The first precipitate to form in plain carbon steels may not be Fe_3C, but may be a transition phase which decomposes into Fe_3C with further tempering. There is some evidence that it is Fe_2C or $Fe_{20}C_9$ (see p. 248, Chap. XI).

[3] These statements should be qualified somewhat: M_s is not strictly a sharply defined and exactly reproducible temperature, and observers sometimes find evidence of transformation continuing at constant temperature, usually to a very minor extent.

formation. At reaction temperatures just below those that produce the finest pearlite the characteristic appearance of bainite is that shown in Fig. 14, while at lower temperatures it is as shown in Fig. 15. Freshly formed bainite is dark etching, unlike fresh martensite, and appears to be an aggregate of ferrite and finely divided carbide particles, although it may be that it initially is ferrite supersaturated with carbon.[1] The mechanism of formation may depend on temperature, since the crys-

FIG. 14. Bainite. ×2000. (*Vilella.*)

tallographic features of the product indicate this; its exact nature has had to be inferred from indirect evidence and remains somewhat uncertain.

In alloy steels a constituent with acicular form may appear—near 500°C in the upper bainite range of temperatures—that is known as acicular ferrite,[2] or the "X" constituent.[3] It is prominent in steels rich in elements having strong carbide-forming tendencies, these alloying elements being Cb, Ti, V, W, Mo, Cr, and Mn.

The Crystallography of the Austenite to Martensite Transformation. The extensive research on martensite formation has furnished the data summarized in Table XXVIII. Consideration of these crystallographic data has led to a detailed crystallographic theory for the transformation

[1] E. S. Davenport and E. C. Bain, *Trans. AIME*, vol. 90, p. 117, 1930. J. R. Vilella, G. E. Guellich, and E. C. Bain, *Trans. ASM*, vol. 24, p. 225, 1936. J. M. Robertson, *J. Iron Steel Inst. (London)*, vol. 119, p. 391, 1929 (I). Further references and discussion will be found in C. Zener, *Trans. AIME*, vol. 167, p. 550, 1946; and discussion thereto, and in A. Hultgren, *Trans. ASM*, vol. 39, p. 915, 1947.

[2] A. Hultgren, *Trans. ASM*, vol. 39, p. 915, 1947, and references given therein.

[3] E. S. Davenport, *Trans. ASM*, vol. 27, p. 837, 1939.

and for the atom movements that take place in the process.[1] This is possible because the martensite transformation in steels and analogous transformations in other alloys do not involve interchange in the positions of pairs or rings of neighboring atoms, the displacement of any atom relative to its neighbors being smaller than the atom radius. Therefore, homogeneous distortions of the unit cell produce visible distortions of the surface of a sample.

The first attempt to describe the shifts of atoms during the martensite transformation was made by Bain[2] who proposed that the transformation

Fig. 15. Bainite formed at a lower temperature than that of Fig. 14. (*Vilella.*)

merely involves a compression of the c axis of the austenite unit cell, and an expansion of the a axis. This mechanism could lead to the proper body-centered tetragonal structure and the proper c/a ratio (in fact, austenite may be described as a body-centered tetragonal structure with an axial ratio of $\sqrt{2}$). Bain also proposed that the interstitially dissolved carbon atoms prevent the axial ratio from going completely to unity, a view that is now fully substantiated.

The correspondence between individual atom positions before and after transformation that was suggested by Bain has been retained in all subsequently proposed mechanisms; however, it is now clear that the simple mechanism he proposed does not account for several observed facts.

The next stage in the development of our understanding of the mechanism consisted in determining orientation relationships between the

[1] The crystallography of transformations is reviewed by J. S. Bowles and C. S. Barrett, in "Progress in Metal Physics," vol. III, Interscience Publishers, New York, 1952.

[2] E. C. Bain, *Trans. AIME*, vol. 70, p. 25, 1924.

TABLE XXVIII. CRYSTALLOGRAPHIC RELATIONSHIPS IN MARTENSITE TRANSFORMATIONS

System	Composition	Transformation on cooling	Orientation relationships*	Habit plane in parent phase	Remarks and references
Fe-C	0.0-0.4 % C	F.c.c. → b.c.t.	Presumably as for 1.4 % C	Laths parallel to [110] arranged on the (111) γ planes	(1), (2) This has been referred to as a (111) habit plane but is probably just a further degeneration of the (225) plates into needles
	0.5-1.4 % C	F.c.c. → b.c.t.	$(111)\gamma \| (110)\alpha$ $[1\bar{1}0]\gamma \| [1\bar{1}\bar{1}]\alpha$ This is known as the Kurdjumow-Sachs relationship	(225) With decreasing C % the plates degenerate into laths with axis (110)γ	(1) (2) (3) (4) (5) Orientations by pole figure method
	1.5-1.8 % C	F.c.c. → b.c.t.	Unknown	(259)	(1) Lattice relationships have not been determined in this range. A deviation from the low-carbon relationship is suspected from the difference in habit plane
Fe-Ni	27-34 % Ni	F.c.c. → b.c.c.	$[111]\gamma \| [110]\alpha$ $[\bar{2}11]\gamma \| [\bar{1}10]\alpha$ This is known as the Nishiyama relationship	Approximately (259) but wide scatter	(1) (5) (6) (7) Orientaion determination by pole figure method. The Kurdjumow-Sachs relationship is found above room temperature and Nishiyama below, according to (7)
Fe-Ni-C	1.2 % C 11.5 % Ni	F.c.c. → b.c.t.	$(111)_{f.c.c.} \| (101)_{b.c.c.}$, $[112]_{f.c.c.}$ 2° from $[10\bar{1}]_{b.c.c.}$	Approximately (259)	(1)
	0.8 % C 22 % Ni	F.c.c. → b.c.t.		Approximately (259)	(8) Precision orientation determination
Fe-Mn	1-15 % Mn	F.c.c. → b.c.c.(α')	Unknown	Unknown	(9)
	13-25 % Mn	F.c.c. → c.p. hex (ε)	Unknown	Unknown	(9)
Cu-Zn	40 % Zn	B.c.c. → structure unknown	Unknown	(155) or (166)	(9)
	40 % Zn + 1 % Pb + Sn	B.c.c. → f.c.c.	Unknown	Unknown	(10)
Ci-Sn	25 % Sn	B.c.c. → structure unknown	Unknown	(133)	(10)
Cu-Al	11-13.1 % Al	B.c.c. → β' β' is a distorted c.p.hex. structure with the [001] 2° from normal to the (001) plane. Angle between (100) and (001) differs by 1° from 120°	$(110)4°$ from (0001), $[1\bar{1}1] \| [11\bar{2}0]$	Approximately (133), which is 12° from (110)	(11) (12) (13) (14) Precision orientation determination
	12.9-14.7 % Al	B.c.c. → c.p.hex.	(110)∥(0001),	Approximately (122) 20°	(11) (12) (13) (15) Precision orien-

		The c.p.hex. phase becomes distorted into an orthorhombic lattice with increasing Al%	$[\bar{1}11]\|[11\bar{2}0]$ and (110) 4° from (0001), $[\bar{1}11]\|[11\bar{2}0]$	from (110)	...tation determination
Lithium	"Pure"	B.c.c. → c.p.hex. The hexagonal layers are in faulty stacking sequence	$(110)\|(0001)$ $[\bar{1}11]$ 3° from $[11\bar{2}0]$	(144), which is 10½° from (110) (110)	(16) (17) (18)
Au–Cd	47.5 atomic % Cd	B.c.c. → orthorhombic β'	$(011)\beta'\|(001)\beta'$ $[\bar{1}11]\beta'\|[1\bar{1}0]\beta'$	(133)	(19)
Zirconium	"Pure"	B.c.c. → c.p.hex.	$(110)\|(0001)$ $[\bar{1}11]$ 0 to 2° from $[11\bar{2}0]$	Unknown	(20)
Cobalt	"Pure"	F.c.c. → c.p.hex.	$(111)\|(0001)$ $[1\bar{1}0]\|[11\bar{2}0]$	(111)	(20) (21) (26)
In–Tl	20.75 atomic % Tl	F.c.c. → f.c.t.	F.c.t. axes cluster within 1½° of F.c.c. axes. See Fig. 22	(110)	(22) Analogous transformations probably occur in the systems In–Cd (23), Cu–Mn (24), and Cr–Mn (25)

* The directions lie in the parallel planes.

REFERENCES

1 A. B. Greninger and A. R. Troiano, *Trans. AIME*, vol. 140, p. 307, 1940.
2 R. F. Mehl, C. S. Barrett, and D. W. Smith, *Trans. AIME*, vol. 105, p. 215, 1933.
3 G. V. Smith and R. F. Mehl, *Trans. AIME* vol. 150, p. 211, 1942.
4 G. Kurdjumow and G. Sachs, *Z. Physik*, vol. 64, p. 325, 1930.
5 G. Wassermann, *Mitt. Kaiser-Wilhelm-Inst. Eisenforsch., Düsseldorf*, vol. 17, p. 149, 1935.
6 Z. Nishiyama, *Sci. Repts. Tôhoku Imp. Univ.*, Ser. 1, vol. 23, p. 638, 1934-1935.
7 R. F. Mehl and G. Derge, *Trans. AIME*, vol. 125, p. 482, 1937.
8 A. B. Greninger and A. R. Troiano, *Trans. AIME*, vol. 145, p. 291, 1941; *Trans. AIME*, vol. 185, p. 590, 1949.
9 A. R. Troiano and F. T. McGuire, *Trans. ASM*, vol. 31, p. 340, 1943.
10 A. B. Greninger and V. G. Mooradian, *Trans. AIME*, vol. 128, p. 337, 1938.
11 I. Isartschew, E. Kaminsky, and G. Kurdjumow, discussion of Ref. 10.
12 A. B. Greninger, *Trans. AIME*, vol. 133, p. 204 1939.
13 V. Gawranek, E. Kaminsky, and G. Kurdjumow, *Metallwirtschaft*, vol. 15, p. 370, 1936.
14 G. Wassermann, *Metallwirtschaft*, vol. 8, p. 133, 1934.
15 G. Kurdjumow, discussion of Ref. 12.
16 C. S. Barrett and O. R. Trautz, *Trans. AIME*, vol. 175, p. 579, 1948.
17 C. S. Barrett, in "Phase Transformations in Solids", Wiley, New York, 1951
18 J. S. Bowles, *Trans. AIME*, vol. 191, p. 44, 1951.
19 L. C. Chang and T. A. Read, *Trans. AIME*, vol. 191, p. 47, 1951.
20 W. G. Burgers, *Physica*, vol. 1, p. 561, 1934.
21 A. H. Troiano and J. L. Tokich, *Metals Technol. Tech. Pub.* 2348, April, 1948.
22 J. S. Bowles, C. S. Barrett, and Lester Guttman, *Trans. AIME*, vol. 188, p. 1478, 1950.
23 W. Betteridge, *Proc. Phys. Soc. (London)*, vol. 50, p. 519, 1938. C. Zener, "Elasticity and Anelasticity of Metals," University of Chicago Press, Chicago, 1949.
24 F. T. Worrell, *J. Applied Phys.*, vol. 19, p. 929, 1948.
25 S. J. Carlile, J. W. Christian, and W. Hume-Rothery, *J. Inst. Metals*, vol. 77, p. 169, 1949.
26 J. S. Bowles and C. S. Barrett, in "Progress in Metal Physics," vol. III, Interscience Publishers, New York, 1952.

parent phase and the martensitic phase, not only for the martensite transformation in steels, but also for martensitic transformations in other alloys.   These are summarized in Table XXVIII.

Kurdjumow and Sachs,[1] from their determination of the orientation relationship between austenite and martensite in 1.4 per cent carbon steel (Table XXXVIII), proposed a theory that martensite is formed by the two consecutive shears $(111)_A[\overline{11}2]_A$ and $(1\overline{1}2)_M[\overline{1}11]_M$.   This proposed mechanism is capable of producing a structure that is nearly body-centered cubic, though not exactly so, and predicts the correct orientation relationship, but it fails to account quantitatively for other characteristics, *viz.*, the planes in the austenite on which the thin martensite plates form (the habit plane) and the manner in which a martensite crystal distorts a polished surface when it forms (the relief effects).

Nishiyama[2] observed an orientation relationship for martensite in a 70:30 iron-nickel alloy that differed 5°16′ from the K and S relationship. Nishiyami suggested that the transformation resembled twinning in that a single shear on $(111)_A[\overline{11}2]_A$ was involved.   This shear (of 19°28′) fails to produce the desired structure; in fact it is merely the first shear of the K and S mechanism.   The change of the atom pattern on (111) planes that was accomplished by the second shear in the K and S mechanism, was obtained by "readjustments" in the N mechanism.   This theory, also, fails to account for the habit plane and relief effects.

The next progress came from Greninger and Troiano's work on steel containing 0.8 per cent C and 22 per cent Ni.[3]   They measured the relief effects produced on a polished surface by the transformation and concluded that they were produced by a simple shear on the martensite habit plane, which they found was approximately the (259) plane.   Assuming this to be the case, they made a stereographic analysis of the direction and magnitude of the shear.   They found that when this shear was applied to the austenite lattice it did not produce the martensite lattice.   It did, however, produce from one of the {110} austenite planes a plane identical with the (112) martensite plane; and they found that martensite lattice could then be produced by a second shear on $(112)_M[11\overline{1}]_M$.   Greninger and Troiano therefore proposed a two-stage transformation: the first stage consisting of a homogeneous shear on the habit plane and producing relief effects (Fig. 16), the second stage being a different shear, homogeneous within lamellae so narrow (about 18 atomic planes) that they are invisible, but macroscopically heterogeneous.   The second shear occurs on the martensite twinning elements; this together with the fact that

[1] G. Kurdjumow and G. Sachs, *Z. Physik*, vol. 64, p. 325, 1930.

[2] Z. Nishiyama, *Sci. Repts., Tôkohu Imp. Univ.*, ser. 1, vol. 23, p. 638, 1934–1935.

[3] A. B. Greninger and A. R. Troiano, *Trans. AIME*, vol. 145, p. 291, 1941; vol. 185, p. 590, 1949.

martensite plates sometimes show transverse markings parallel to $\{112\}_M$ planes makes the proposal seem reasonable.

The G-T mechanism accounts for the relief effects, the habit plane (the plane of the first shear), the orientation relationship (to a good approximation), and the change in structure. However, an anisotropic expansion must be assumed in addition to the shears. This amounts to 4.2 per cent in the $[100]_M$ direction. The mechanism also fails to account for the orientation relationship in plain carbon steels containing less than 1.4 per cent C, where the habit plane is $\{225\}_A$.

Jaswon and Wheeler[1] proposed a different interpretation of the habit plane. If an atomic plane in the austenite were to be converted into an atomic plane in martensite and were to serve as the habit plane of the martensite plate, it would involve large-scale plastic distortion of the surrounding austenite unless this conversion left the plane unrotated, *i.e.*, left the direction of its normal unchanged. Thus they identified the

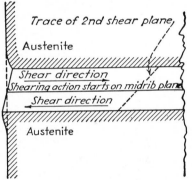

FIG. 16. Shear movements in formation of a martensite crystal according to Greninger and Troiano.

habit plane with one of the crystallographic planes that undergoes no rotation during the transformation. Three such planes were found in their mathematical analysis of the transformation, and one of these lay within 1.5° of $(225)_A$, the observed plane for plain carbon steel of less than 1.5 per cent C, when the orientation relationship was that of *K-S*. Bowles[2] has computed the unrotated plane for other orientation relationships between *K-S* and *N*, which causes the predicted habit plane to vary from $(225)_A$ to $(\bar{1}01)_A$. (All computations were for cubic martensite.)

The Jaswon-Wheeler mechanism is a simple homogeneous distortion. It is not consistent with observed relief effects, as Bowles[3] has pointed out, since rows of atoms within the habit plane according to this theory would be rotated during the transformation, some of them as much as 19°, yet no such rotation is observed metallographically.

Bowles[3] has generalized the *G-T* double-shear theory into a theory based on distortions of a more general type, in which a plane remains undistorted and all atoms move in the same direction. For body-

[1] M. A. Jaswon and J. A. Wheeler, *Acta Cryst.*, vol. 1, p. 216, 1948.

[2] J. S. Bowles and C. S. Barrett in "Progress in Metal Physics," vol. III, Interscience Publishers, New York, 1952).

[3] J. S. Bowles, *Acta Cryst.*, vol. 4, p. 162, 1951.

centered cubic martensite in *K-S* relationship to austenite, the total atom displacement can be accomplished by the distortion $(225)_A[\overline{1}\overline{1}2]_A$ followed by the $(112)_M[11\overline{1}]_M$ distortion, the indices referring to the undistorted planes and the directions of motion, respectively. The displacements are illustrated in Fig. 17. The first distortion which is not a true shear, but is a shear combined with an extension normal to the shear plane, generates

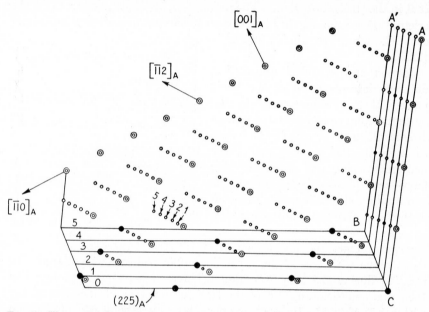

Fig. 17. Illustrating Bowles's theory of atom movements in the formation of a martensite plate. Double circles represent initial positions of atoms in $(1\overline{1}0)_A$ plane of austenite. As the first displacement occurs successively in the $(225)_A$ planes numbered 1 to 5, the austenite above the thickening plate is translated in the $[\overline{1}\overline{1}2]_A$ direction, with atoms taking, successively, positions 1 to 5 in the rows of small circles. (The magnitude of these displacements is exaggerated for clarity.) The distortion of the row of atoms AC into $A'BC$ shows how scratches on a polished surface are bent by the transformation. The second displacement is a shear, the shear plane being normal to the plane of the drawing and containing the row of atoms that were originally $[001]_A$, the shear direction being also normal to the drawing.

the $(112)_M$ plane from the $(110)_A$ plane and produces a structure exactly half-way between two body-centered cubic twins; this intermediate structure can be sheared in either of the two opposite senses with the true shears $(112)_M[11\overline{1}]_M$ or $(112)_M[\overline{1}\overline{1}1]_M$ to produce either of two different martensite orientations. Thus the 24 variants of the *K-S* relationship are obtainable from a mechanism involving a habit plane, (225), which has a multiplicity of only 12. The atom movements of the first and second distortions are in the directions that would produce twinning in austenite and in martensite, respectively.

The Bowles mechanism is consistent with the relief effects that were observed in a plain carbon steel of 1.35 per cent C, provided that the first distortion is assumed to be homogeneous and to determine the shape of the plate, and the second distortion is heterogeneous, as in the *G-T* mechanism, so as to produce no observable change of shape. It is also consistent with the habit plane, (225), that is observed in a plain carbon steel of less than 1.4 per cent C, and also with the observation that the long axes of the martensite needles in low-carbon steel are along $[110]_A$, the only direction that is not rotated either macroscopically or on an

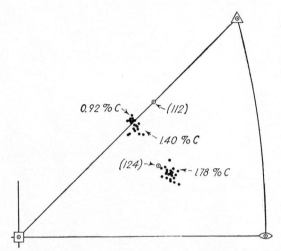

Fig. 18. Variation of martensite habit plane with carbon content of steel shown by stereographic projection of pole of plane. (*Greninger and Troiano.*)

atomic scale by this mechanism. The $[110]_A$ direction is the intersection of the undistorted plane of the first distortion with that of the second distortion.[1] The mechanism requires modification, Bowles concludes, when applied to 1.7 per cent C steels and high-nickel steels, since the orientation relationship in these differs from *K-S* and the habit plane approximates (259) rather than (225), as shown in Fig. 18.

The distortion of a polished surface caused by the martensite transformation is illustrated in Fig. 19, in which the homogeneous shear component of the distortion has caused tilting of the surface and bending of scratches that had been placed on the surface. An important feature of the distortion is that the scratches remain continuous across the austenite-martensite interface.[2] This shows that a high degree of coherence is

[1] Since the close-packed row of atoms [110] is not distorted in this transformation, the atom radius in the martensite is the same as in the austenite. Thus the predicted martensite dimensions are slightly too large and an isotropic contraction must be assumed.

[2] J. S. Bowles, *Acta Cryst.* vol. 4, p. 162, 1951. M. Cohen, E. S. Machlin, and V. G. Paranjpe, *Trans. ASM*, vol. 42A, p. 242, 1950. This feature invalidated a

retained across the interface during the transformation, and this can occur only if the matrix is pulled along during the first distortion.   The resulting inhomogeneous strain in the residual austenite of a partially transformed steel is severe.   The strain extends through substantially all of the austenite, as may be seen with the aid of an interferometer,[1] and must make a major contribution to the hardening.   The displacement of atoms in the austenite can occur during the first distortion of the Bowles

FIG. 19. Martensite crystals in a large grain of partially transformed iron—30 per cent nickel alloy.   Polished and scratched before transformation, to show distortion produced by the transformation.   Unetched.   ×150.

(or the *G-T*) mechanism and can permit coherence throughout this stage. If the martensite plate grows by acquiring successive layers of atoms parallel to the habit plane, as it does in some nonferrous martensitic transformations, each atom in the austenite near the plate receives an added displacement as each layer is added to the plate.   Whether the second distortion is simultaneous with the first or follows it has not been determined; also the relative rate of propagation of the martensite plate parallel to and perpendicular to the habit plane is unknown.   The time of formation of a plate is less than 10^{-4} sec[2] and in many steels is so little

---

tentative suggestion in C. S. Barrett, in "Phase Transformations in Solids," Wiley, New York, 1951.

[1] C. S. Barrett, in "Imperfections in Almost Perfect Crystals," Wiley, New York, 1952.

[2] F. Föster and E. Scheil, *Z. Metallkunde*, vol. 32, p. 165, 1940.

dependent upon the transformation temperature that no appreciable activation energy exists for the growth of the plate.[1]

Theories concerning the origin of the martensite nuclei, their growth, and the thermodynamics of the transformation have been proposed;[2,3,4] it has been suggested[3] that embryos having the structure of martensite have transient existence in the austenite prior to cooling, and that these grow by thermally activated atom transfer. It has also been suggested[4] that a plate grows by shearlike displacement of atoms in a cooperative movement that involves a coherent interface, with the propagation of a strain gradient at a rate dependent upon the elastic constants of the austenite, and with thermal activation playing no part. Although there is much speculation in the theories,[5] it appears certain that strain energy in the residual austenite and energy in the martensite-austenite interface is important, and perhaps also the partitioning of an austenite grain by the plates that form early, so that later plates must be smaller; these factors, perhaps combined with the size distribution of pre-existing embryos and with local variation in composition somehow are responsible for the fact that only with continually increasing undercooling of the austenite can the transformation be made to continue (at least in the usual case). The fact that M_s depends upon grain size, and the fact that lower temperatures must be reached to bring about a given per cent transformation if a specimen is held near M_s for a time ("stabilization"), are accounted for with difficulty in present theories.

Ko and Cottrell[6] have shown, by metallographic and surface contour studies, that *bainite* plates grow in coherence with austenite (distorting the austenite as martensite does) and at a slow rate. They propose that bainite formation is governed by the rate of removal of carbon from the bainite into the surrounding austenite and into the precipitating carbide particles. The fact that bainite grows at temperatures above M_s for martensite is ascribed to the strain energy from density change being less than for martensite, owing to the lower carbon content.

[1] S. A. Kulin and M. Cohen, *Trans. AIME*, vol. 188, p. 1139, 1950. The (259) habit plane is accounted for by a $(259)_A[\overline{1}56]_A$ strain followed by a $(235)_M[11\overline{1}]_M$ strain, and by the strains spreading out as successive waves from the nucleus, spreading more rapidly parallel to the habit plane than normal to it. E. S. Machlin and M. Cohen, *J. Metals*, vol. 3, p. 1019, 1951.

[2] C. Zener, *Trans. AIME*, vol. 167, pp. 513, 550, 1946.

[3] J. C. Fisher, J. H. Hollomon, and D. Turnbull, *Trans. AIME*, vol. 185, p. 691, 1949; *J. Applied Phys.*, vol. 19, p. 775, 1948.

[4] M. Cohen, E. S. Machlin, and V. G. Paranjpe, *Trans. ASM*, vol. 42A, p. 242, 1950.

[5] For reviews see B. Chalmers's volumes on "Progress in Metal Physics," Interscience Publishers, New York. Volume III, 1952, contains a review of some aspects of martensite theory, by J. S. Bowles and C. S. Barrett.

[6] T. Ko and S. A. Cottrell, *J. Iron and Steel Inst.*, vol. 172, p. 307, 1952.

When alloying elements are present that tend to redistribute themselves at a rate slower than the rate of redistribution of carbon, added complexities in the manner of austenite decomposition are introduced, which have been treated by Hultgren[1] and others. Hultgren coined the terms "paraferrite" and "paracementite" for the ferrite and cementite that has reached equilibrium with austenite in regard to carbon concentration but that retains the alloy content it inherited from austenite; after equilibrium partition of the alloying elements has occurred the products are "orthoferrite" and "orthocementite."

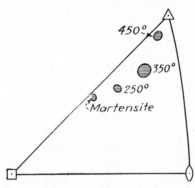

FIG. 20. Stereographic projection of habit planes for martensite and for bainite formed at different temperatures in eutectoid carbon steel. (*Smith and Mehl.*)

Orientations of Other Austenite Decomposition Products.

Orientations in meteorites are not highly precise,[2] though Young[3] found examples that were intermediate between *K-S* and *N* relationships. Mehl and Derge concluded that, in Fe-Ni alloys, transformation at high temperatures produces the *K-S* relationship, while transformation at low temperatures ($-195°C$) produces the *N* relationship, and the products of a $-70°C$ transformation seem to be intermediate.

Smith and Mehl[4] found that bainite in plain carbon steel of eutectoid composition formed at 450 and 350°C has its ferrite in the *N* relationship, but bainite formed at 250°C and martensite displays the *K-S* relationship. The habit plane changes continuously throughout this temperature range, as indicated in Fig. 20.

The orientations of the ferrite in pearlite with respect to the parent austenite show wide scatter, but nevertheless indicate that they are different from the orientations in bainite, martensite, proeutectoid ferrite, and pure iron. Bainite formed at high temperature contains ferrite identical in orientation with ferrite that is formed by proeutectoid precipitation, a relationship which suggests that ferrite nucleates bainite. On the same basis, it may be concluded that ferrite alone does not nucleate the transformation to pearlite. There is reason to believe that, in bainite, ferrite precipitates first, as a supersaturated solid solution which later precipitates cementite.[5]

[1] A. Hultgren, *Trans. ASM*, vol. 39, p. 915, 1947, and references given therein.

[2] R. F. Mehl and G. Derge, *Trans. AIME*, vol. 125, p. 482, 1937.

[3] J. Young, *Trans. Roy. Soc. (London)*, vol. A238, p. 393, 1939.

[4] G. V. Smith and R. F. Mehl, *Trans. AIME*, vol. 150, p. 211, 1942.

[5] E. S. Davenport and E. C. Bain, *Trans. AIME*, vol. 90, p. 117, 1930. G. V. Smith and R. F. Mehl, *Trans. AIME*, vol. 150, p. 211, 1942.

Nonferrous Martensitic Transformations. Phase changes in nonferrous systems may properly be called martensitic if they occur by atom movements so regular that they cause a change of shape of the transforming region. They have also been called "athermal" to distinguish them from nucleation and growth transformations in which atom transfer is clearly thermally activated; and "diffusionless," a name which emphasizes the fact that they occur without composition change in the transforming region.

Several nonferrous alloys change from face-centered cubic to face-centered tetragonal by a martensitic mechanism during cooling. One of

a   *b*

FIG. 21. Microstructure of In-Tl alloy after transformation from cubic to tetragonal with $c/a = 1.03$. (*a*) $\times 75$. (*b*) In polarized light. $\times 250$. The main bands are ascribed to the first shear being alternately $(101)[\bar{1}01]$ and $(101)[10\bar{1}]$; the subbands are ascribed to the second shear being alternately $(001)[01\bar{1}]$ and $(011)[0\bar{1}1]$.

these has been studied in detail by Bowles, Barrett, and Guttman[1]—the transformation that occurs in an alloy of indium—20.75 atomic per cent thallium. The transformation produces an abrupt change of axial ratio from 1.0 to 1.020 at M_s, and this increases gradually to 1.038 at room temperature.[2] Accompanying this is a tilting of crystallographic lamellae that produces the appearance of Fig. 21a on a metallographic surface; etching and proper lighting reveals subbands within the main bands, as shown in Fig. 21b. Analysis shows[1] that both the main bands and subbands are traces of $\{110\}$ planes. This diffusionless transformation is fully accounted for by two consecutive shears on two different $\{110\}$ planes at 60° to each other, the shear directions being $<110>$ directions. The first shear amounts to one-third of the shear that would produce a

[1] J. S. Bowles, C. S. Barrett, and L. Guttman, *Trans. AIME*, vol. 188, p. 1478, 1950.
[2] L. Guttman, *Trans. AIME*, vol. 188, p. 1472, 1950.

twin in the tetragonal crystal on a {101} plane. This shear transforms the parent cubic phase into a structure that can be described as being one-third of the way between two tetragonal {101} twins. The second shear, operating in one sense along a [110] direction, produces the tetragonal structure, and operating in the opposite sense produces its twin. Occurring in one sense, this second shear is equal in magnitude to the first; in the opposite sense, it is twice the magnitude of the first.

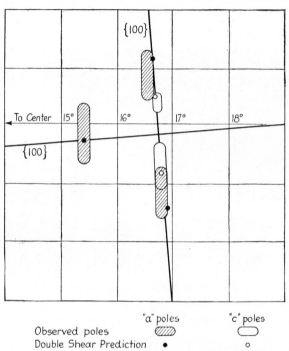

Observed poles
Double Shear Prediction

FIG. 22. Pole figure for cluster of orientations produced by cubic to tetragonal In-Tl transformation in In-20.75% Tl alloy. Cluster surrounds [001] that is not parallel to the main band.

Referring to Fig. 21*b*, the main bands are regions in which the first shear occurs alternately in one sense and in the opposite sense. The subbands within the main bands are traces of the planes on which the second shear occurs. Each set of subbands consists of two twin orientations alternating with each other, the lamellae being so narrow that they are not visible in the relief effects and are seen only after etching.

The evidence for the double-shear mechanism in contrast to other theories was principally its success in predicting with precision the orientation relationship. Although crystallographers had supposed that in similar cubic to tetragonal transformations the axes of the tetragonal structure were always parallel to those of the cubic structure, precision X-ray goniometer measurements showed that this was not so. Figure 22 is a pole figure of the cluster of tetragonal a and c axes surrounding one of the cube axes of a single grain that had transformed into a single set of main bands.[1] There is satisfactory agreement between the measured positions marked out by contours of high reflecting power in the projection and the predictions of the double-shear theory. As cooling continues below M_s, the tetragonality increases by continued shear on the same shear systems.

Similar transformations from cubic to tetragonal occur in other solid solutions, *e.g.*, In-Cd, Cu-Mn, and Cr-Mn; there is every reason to believe that these transformations also occur by the double-shear mechanism.[2] There is considerable similarity, also, to the microstructure of barium-titanate ($BaTiO_3$) after transformation from cubic to tetragonal,[3] and with the cubic-tetragonal transformation accompanying the onset of ordering in the alloys CoPt,[4] FePt,[5] AuCu,[6] and Ni_4W,[7] though the exact degree to which the mechanism of these transformations resembles the In-Tl mechanism is not yet clear.

Guttman found in In-Tl, and Chang and Read found in an alloy of Au-47.5 atomic per cent Cd that undergoes a diffusionless transformation from a CsCl type structure to an orthorhombic structure,[8] that there was first a sudden appearance of a thin plate of the new phase, then a gradual thickening of the plate as temperature falls. The interfaces between the old and new phases move outward from their starting position, remaining parallel to the habit plane, and generating successive lamellae as they move. The atom shifts from the old to the new structure must therefore occur at the moving interface, at least in these alloys.

Martensitic transformations from body-centered cubic to close-packed hexagonal have been found in zirconium,[9] and in lithium and lithium-magnesium alloys.[10] The orientations (see Table XXVIII) are accounted

---

[1] The cluster plotted in this projection surrounds a cube axis that is not parallel to the bands; a different cluster is predicted and found about cube axes that are *parallel* to the main band.

[2] J. S. Bowles, C. S. Barrett, and L. Guttman, *Trans. AIME*, vol. 188, p. 1478, 1950.

[3] B. Matthias and A. von Hippel, *Phys. Rev.*, vol. 73, p. 1378, 1948. P. W. Forsbergh, Jr., *Phys. Rev.*, vol. 76, p. 1187, 1949.

[4] J. B. Newkirk, A. H. Geisler, D. L. Martin, and R. Smoluchowski, *Trans. AIME*, vol. 188, p. 1249, 1950.

[5] H. Lipson, D. Shoenberg, and G. V. Stupart, *J. Inst. Metals*, vol. 67, p. 333, 1941.

[6] D. Harker, *Trans. ASM*, vol. 32, p. 210, 1944. J. L. Haughton and R. J. M. Payne, *J. Inst. Metals*, vol. 46, p. 457, 1931.

[7] E. Epremian and D. Harker, *Trans. AIME*, vol. 185, pp. 267–273, 1949.

[8] L. C. Chang and T. A. Read, *Trans. AIME*, vol. 189, p. 47, 1951.

[9] W. G. Burgers, *Physica*, vol. 1, p. 561, 1934.

[10] C. S. Barrett and O. R. Trautz, *Trans. AIME*, vol. 175, p. 579, 1948.

for to within two to three degrees by Burgers's proposed mechanism of a shear on the system $(112)_{b.c.c.}[11\bar{1}]_{b.c.c.}$, a mechanism suggested by the fact that the pattern of atoms on $(112)_{b.c.c.}$ is the same as the pattern on $(10\bar{1}0)_{c.p.h.}$ into which it is assumed to transform. This mechanism fails, however, to predict the habit plane observed in the lithium transformation, for this is $\{441\}$ rather than the $\{112\}$ that would be anticipated from Burgers's mechanism.[1] In spite of the simplicity of the transformation and its obvious crystalline regularity, a full understanding of the atomic displacements has not been reached.

The simplest, most clearly understood martensitic transformation is from the face-centered cubic to the close-packed hexagonal structure, which occurs in cobalt. Since this may be accomplished by merely changing the stacking sequence of the close-packed $(111)_{f.c.c.}$ planes from the sequence $ABCABC$ . . . to $ABAB$ . . . by sliding pairs of layers over each other, this mechanism is the one to be expected, as was first suggested by Burgers.[2] This mechanism is equivalent to moving half dislocations across every second (111) plane; it successfully accounts for the orientation relationship and the habit plane, (111), that is observed.

Martensitic phases form from the body-centered cubic β phases of the systems Cu-Al, Cu-Sn, and Cu-Zn, with several complexities. According to Kurdjumow,[3] the Cu-Al system yields martensitic β' below 13.1 per cent Al, and γ', with a different structure, above 13.3 per cent Al. The β phase, disordered, can be made to become ordered by annealing above M_s, provided that the Al content exceeds 11 per cent, the ordered phase being designated as β_1. When the diffusionless transformation occurs in the ordered state of either the Cu-Al or Cu-Zn alloys, the new phase also is ordered, which indicates that the transformation mechanism involves a highly regular transfer of atoms across the interface, of the general type discussed in the preceding paragraphs. Kurdjumow concludes that on tempering β' Cu-Al or on coldworking it, a transformation to γ' occurs. In the Cu-Sn system there is a martensitic phase analogous to γ' Cu-Al, and at lower tin contents (below 24.8 per cent Sn) a transformation to a different structure, and in both the Cu-Al and Cu-Sn systems there is a narrow range of compositions in which two phases of martensitic origin appear together. In Cu-Zn Kurdjumow reports only one decomposition product. The M_s temperature decreases in these Cu alloys with increasing Al, Sn, and Zn concentration, but M_s for ordered β_1 Cu-Zn is reported to be raised to room temperature by adding Pb, Sn, and Fe to a total

[1] J. S. Bowles, *Trans. AIME*, vol. 191, p. 44, 1951.

[2] W. G. Burgers, *Physica*, vol. 1, p. 561, 1934.

[3] G. V. Kurdjumow, *J. Tech. Phys. (U.S.S.R.)*, vol. 18, p. 999, 1948 (Translation No. 2300, Henry Brutcher, Altadena, Calif.). See also Table XXVIII.

admixture of about 1 per cent. Other studies and transformation diagrams for Cu-Al alloys have also been published.[1]

Transformations Induced by Strain. Since every martensitic transformation involves a distortion that has a homogeneous component, it would be expected that all could be aided by externally applied stresses. This is found to be the case in general, and perhaps invariably. Plastic strain induces transformation at temperatures well above the martensite start temperature M_s in the systems Fe-Ni,[2] Cu-Zn,[3] Li,[4] Li-Mg,[5] and Au-Cd.[6] In Cu-Al[7] alloys one martensitic phase transforms to another with cold work, and the same occurs in Fe-Mg[8] alloys and in Li-Mg[5] alloys as well as in the common stainless steels (18-8 Cr-Ni). The tendency for plastic strain to produce a transformation diminishes as the temperature is raised above M_s, and above a temperature designated as M_d the strain is no longer effective.[5,9]

In a cold-worked sample M_s is lower than in an annealed sample, presumably because the strain-hardened metal resists the plastic deformation that accompanies martensite formation, and perhaps also because the plates must form in more restricted areas.[5,10]

It appears that cold working *below* M_d acts somewhat in the way thermal agitation does to aid atoms in crossing energy barriers from metastable states into more stable states. Cold work converts one martensitic phase into another in the β' to γ' Cu-Al transformation, according to Kurdjumow. Cold work converts the martensitic phase in Li and Li-Mg alloys, which appear to be highly faulted close-packed hexagonal, into a face-centered cubic phase (probably also faulted). In the Cu-Si system, cold work produces a phase, γ', that has not been seen in thermally

[1] For independent treatments of the β and β_1 Cu-Al transformations see C. S. Smith and W. E. Lindlief, *Trans. AIME*, vol. 104, p. 69, 1933; G. Wassermann, *Metallwirtschaft*, vol. 13, p. 133, 1934; A. B. Greninger, *Trans. AIME*, vol. 133, p. 204, 1939; D. J. Mack, *Trans. AIME*, vol. 175, p. 240, 1948, and the discussions of this. The M_s for β may be much below M_s for β_1 (93 vs. 385°C for Cu-11.9 per cent Al); 300 to 385° tempering transforms β' to $\alpha + \delta$. A bainite-type reaction also occurs: E. P. Klier, *Trans. AIME*, vol. 185, p. 611, 1949.

[2] E. Scheil, *Z. anorg. allgem. Chemie*, vol. 207, p. 21, 1932. A. W. McReynolds, *J. Applied Phys.*, vol. 17, p. 823, 1946.

[3] A. B. Greninger and G. Mooradian, *Trans. AIME*, vol. 128, p. 337, 1938.

[4] C. S. Barrett, *Phys. Rev.*, vol. 72, p. 245, 1947.

[5] C. S. Barrett and O. R. Trautz, *Trans. AIME*, vol. 175, p. 579, 1948.

[6] L. C. Chang and T. A. Read, *Trans. AIME*, vol. 189, p. 47, 1951.

[7] A. B. Greninger, *Trans. AIME*, vol. 133, p. 204, 1939.

[8] A. R. Troiano and F. T. McGuire, *Trans. ASM*, vol. 31, p. 340, 1943.

[9] A. W. McReynolds, *J. Applied Phys.*, vol. 17, p. 823, 1946.

[10] E. Scheil, *Z. anorg. allgem. Chemie*, vol. 207, p. 21, 1932. C. S. Barrett and D. F. Clifton, *Trans. AIME*, vol. 188, p. 1329, 1950.

treated samples, and that is metastable with respect to the equilibrium phase γ,[1] apparently by the shifting of $(111)_{f.c.c.}$ layers of the matrix with respect to each other.   All phases in which stacking faults are produced by plastic deformation may be classed as strain-induced metastable states; the Cu-Si system offers examples, as does also the Ag-Sn and probably also the Ag-Sb systems.[2]

Orientations in Other Reactions.   To the list of reactions in which new phases are generated having their orientations crystallographically related to phases already present must be added *peritectic reactions*, as Greninger has shown,[3] *oxidation reactions*,[4] and alloy layers produced by *diffusion*.[5]

The orienting of *overgrowths* by substrates has been shown to depend upon a sufficient similarity in atomic positions in the matching planes;[6] if the atomic patterns are similar, as in alkali halides, the lattice parameters may differ as much as 25 or 30 per cent without causing the deposited crystal to become randomly oriented.   When the habit of crystals is altered by impurities in the liquids from which they crystallize, it is probable that oriented adsorbed layers of the *impurities* are responsible.[7] Oriented electrodeposits are common; these are treated in Chap. XX.

Orientation relationships are found in all types of transformations. When the two phases are of similar structure and approximately equal lattice dimensions, it can be predicted that the new will have an orientation identical with the old.   When the reaction is at a *surface*, the pattern of atoms in the two interfacial planes will be similar provided that similar planes exist in the phases.   When the reaction generates a new phase *within* the old, there appear to be several factors that can influence the orientation.   The most important among these are probably (1) close matching of atoms at the interface and close similarity in atomic distribution in the neighborhood of the interface, which means that little energy is required to create the interface; and (2) simple shearing proc-

[1] C. S. Barrett, *Trans. AIME*, vol. 188, p. 123, 1950.

[2] C. S. Barrett and Marjorie A. Barrett, *Phys. Rev.* vol. 81, p. 311, 1951.   C. S. Barrett, "Imperfections in Almost Perfect Crystals," Wiley, New York, 1952.

[3] A. B. Greninger, *Trans..AIME*, vol. 124, p. 379, 1937.

[4] Müller and Schwabe, *Z. Elektrochem.*, vol. 37, p. 185, 1931 (Cr_2O_3).   H. C. H. Carpenter and C. F. Elam, *J. Iron Steel Inst.*, vol. 105, p. 83, 1922 (Fe-O).   R. F. Mehl and E. L. McCandless, *Trans. AIME*, vol. 125, p. 531, 1937 (Fe-O).   R. F. Mehl, E. L. McCandless and F. N. Rhines, *Nature*, vol. 134, p. 1009, 1934 (Cu_2O). K. H. Moore, *Ann. Physik*, vol. 33, p. 133, 1938 (Cu_2O).

[5] R. F. Mehl, discussion to A. B. Greninger, *Trans. AIME*, vol. 124, p. 390, 1937 (Cu-Zn).

[6] L. Roger, *Compt. rend.*, vol. 182, p. 326, 1926; vol. 179, p. 2050, 1925.   C. A Sloat and A. W. C. Menzies, *J. Phys. Chem.* vol. 35, p. 2005, 1931.

[7] P. Gaubert, *Compt. rend.*, vol. 143, p. 776, 1906; vol. 167, p. 491, 1918; vol. 180, p. 378, 1925.   C. W. Bunn, *Proc. Roy. Soc. (London)*, vol. A141, p. 567, 1933.

esses that create the new lattice by overcoming a minimum shear resistance or activation energy.

Solid-state Transformations in General. In this chapter the nucleation and growth transformations and the martensitic transformations have been discussed with considerable emphasis upon the fact that only in the former type is the atom transfer at the interface a haphazard process, controlled by diffusion at the interface, and only in the martensitic type does the atom transfer have such regularity that macroscopic distortion of an element of volume occurs when its structure changes. It is instructive to consider transformations from a different standpoint, as Buerger has done,[1] on the basis of the changes in crystal structure that occur, and to look at examples more complex than the simple ones encountered among the metals.

"Displacive transformations" occur when a space network of atoms is systematically distorted without disrupting the atomic linkage of the net; this type includes the martensitic transformations. In this type, the high-temperature form normally has a more open structure, a more symmetrical arrangement of atoms, and a greater amplitude of thermal vibrations and consequently a greater entropy than the low-temperature form into which it "collapses" on cooling. For example, cubic barium titanate collapses into the tetragonal form on cooling with the formation of lamellae having low-energy interfaces and twin (or near twin) orientation relationship to each other.[2] Transformation rates are normally very high.

"Reconstructive transformations"[3] involve disruption of the space network and reconstruction of a new network. The new pattern may have the same coordination as the former in regard to the shortest primary interatomic distances and merely be altered in secondary coordination. This type is more common in compounds of low coordination than in those of high coordination, for the possible alternate arrangements are more numerous with low coordination. Since low coordination is a requirement for the occurrence of a glassy phase,[4] polymorphism is common in substances that can be prepared in a glassy state. SiO_2 is an example; it exists in many polymorphs. The activation energy for reconstructive transformations may be supplied by thermal energy, or in some cases by energy supplied during cold working; if the energy requirement is large the transformation is very sluggish—a compound may retain a

---

[1] M. J. Buerger, in "Phase Transformations in Solids," Wiley, New York, 1951.

[2] "Twinning" from transformations of this type is discussed by M. J. Buerger in *Am. Mineral.*, vol. 30, p. 469, 1945.

[3] This term is also used by R. B. Sosman, Ceramics Conference Proceedings, *Penn. State Coll. Bull.* 14, 1934.

[4] W. H. Zachariasen, *J. Am. Chem. Soc.*, vol. 54, p. 3841, 1932.

metastable phase for geologic ages without changing to its stable phase.[1] In some reconstructive transformations not only the secondary but also the primary coordination is changed, as in $CaCO_3$ when it changes from calcite to aragonite, and even the type of bonds may be changed, as in tin and in the transformation from diamond to graphite. When coordination changes, there is a tendency for the high-temperature phase to be the one of lower coordination, as may be understood if the fewer bonds permit greater freedom of oscillation of the atoms and thus cause this phase to have higher entropy.

[1] A discussion of metastable states is given by M. J. Buerger in *Proc. Natl. Acad. Sci.*, vol. 22, p. 685, 1936.

CHAPTER XXIII

DIFFRACTION OF ELECTRONS, ATOMS, AND NEUTRONS

The use of electrons for diffraction purposes dates from 1927, when Davisson and Germer[1] first showed that it was possible, after De Broglie had predicted that material particles should act as waves. Following the lead of these experimenters in America and G. P. Thomson in England, the field has rapidly developed not only as a branch of physics research but as a practical diffraction method supplementing the X-ray. It is of particular value as a means of investigating extremely thin films and surface layers and has earned a place for itself in many industrial and academic laboratories on this account.

Electron Waves. When a stream of electrons strikes a crystal, it behaves as if it were a train of waves. It is not necessary to insist that the electrons actually consist of waves, but they do proceed in the directions that true waves of a certain wavelength would go. The electron wavelength λ—or, more precisely, the wavelength that accounts for the motion of the electrons—is given by the simple equation

$$\lambda = \frac{h}{mv}$$

where h is Planck's constant and mv is the momentum (mass times velocity) of the electron. The wavelength is therefore inversely proportional to the velocity, which in turn is directly related to the voltage applied to the vacuum tube in which the electron moves. If a potential, V, of a few thousand volts is applied, the kinetic energy of the electron is

$$\frac{1}{2} mv^2 = \frac{eV}{300}$$

where m is the mass of the electron and e is its charge in electrostatic units. From these equations it follows that

$$\lambda = \sqrt{\frac{150}{V}} \quad \text{angstroms*}$$

[1] C. J. Davisson and L. H. Germer, *Phys. Rev.*, vol. 30, p. 705, 1927.

* For values of V above a few thousand volts, this formula requires correction (a 2.5 per cent correction at 50,000 volts) because the mass of the electron varies with its velocity. Relativity theory gives the corrected form, which can be reduced to the

Table XXIX illustrates the range of wavelengths that can be obtained readily in the laboratory.

TABLE XXIX

Voltage	Wavelength, A
150	1.0
10,000	0.1227
30,000	0.0697
50,000	0.0536
70,000	0.0447

Since it is convenient to operate electron-diffraction equipment at potentials between 30,000 and 70,000 volts, it follows that the electrons ordinarily used in diffraction work have a wavelength between one-tenth and one-twentieth of the wavelength of X-rays used for similar work.

A relatively small amount of research is done with slow electrons, (using potentials in the hundreds of volts). Experimental difficulties are greater in this range than in the high-voltage range and the information obtained from the diffraction pattern is less, on the whole. Not only electrons, but all material particles have the property of acting as waves. Diffraction of atoms, molecules, and neutrons is discussed briefly in the last sections of the chapter.

Apparatus. Electron diffraction requires a highly evacuated container in which a collimated stream of electrons (from either a hot filament or a gas-discharge tube) falls on a specimen and then on a photographic plate within the container. The electrons are accelerated by a constant-potential direct-current source. In the camera shown in Fig. 1, electrons from a discharge tube at the top are controlled by passing between trapping plates in which the potential can be varied and through an electromagnet that serves to focus the beam. After diffracting from a specimen on an adjustable specimen holder, the electrons strike a fluorescent screen or a photographic plate. Owing to the short wavelength of the electrons, the diffraction rings are confined to a very narrow range of angles around the primary beam, and the cameras are much larger than X-ray cameras. A distance of 50 cm or more from specimen to plate is common.

Details of construction and operation need not concern us here, for they are adequately treated in books on the subject[1] and in numerous

---

approximate equation

$$\lambda = \frac{h \sqrt{150/eVm_0}}{(1 + eV/1200m_0c^2)}$$

where m_0 is the mass of the electron at rest, h is Planck's constant, and c is the velocity of light (see Appendix VI for values).

[1] "The Structure of Metallic Coatings, Films, and Surfaces," Faraday Society, London (reprinted from *Trans. Faraday Soc.*), 1935. "Theory and Practice of Electron Diffraction," G. P. Thomson and W. Cochrane, Macmillan, London, 1939.

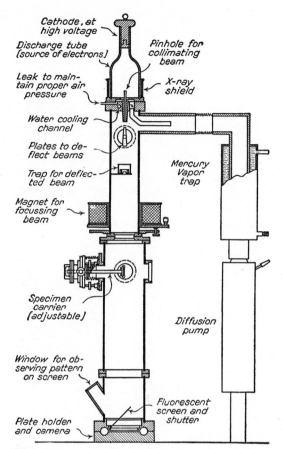

Fig. 1. Electron-diffraction camera with gas discharge to furnish electrons. (*Cambridge Instrument Company.*)

articles.[1]   In constructing an apparatus—many investigators make their own—due attention should be given to means of obtaining a high vacuum

[1] G. I. Finch, A. G. Quarrell, and H. Wilman, *Trans. Faraday Soc.*, vol. 31, p. 1051, 1935.   L. H. Germer, *Rev. Sci. Instruments*, vol. 6, p. 138, 1935.   W. G. Burgers and J. C. Basart, *Physica*, vol. 1, p. 543, 1934.   G. P. Thomson, *Trans. Faraday Soc.*, vol. 31, p. 1049, 1935.   J. R. Tillman, *Phil. Mag.*, vol. 18, p. 656, 1934 (magnetic focusing).   S. B. Hendricks, L. R. Maxwell, V. L. Mosley, and M. E. Jefferson, *J. Chem. Phys.*, vol. 1, p. 549, 1933.   R. Jackson and A. G. Quarrell, *Proc. Phys. Soc. (London)*, vol. 51, p. 237, 1939 (high-temperature specimen holder).   H. J. Yearian and J. D. Howe, *Rev. Sci. Instruments*, vol. 7, p. 26, 1936.   R. Morgan and N. Smith, *Rev. Sci. Instruments*, vol. 6, p. 316, 1935.   R. R. Wilson, *Rev. Sci. Instruments*, vol. 12, p. 91, 1941 (detail of vacuum joint).   E. A. Gulbransen, *J. Applied Phys.*, vol. 16, p. 718, 1945.   G. I. Finch and H. Wilman, *Ergeb. exakt. Naturw.*, vol. 16, p. 353, 1937.   R. G. Picard, P. C. Smith, and J. H. Reisner, *Rev. Sci. Instruments*, vol. 20, p. 601, 1949.

free from contamination by vacuum-pump vapors, adjusting and interchanging of specimens without breaking the vacuum, and changing or removing photographic plates in such a way as to regain the vacuum quickly. A rectified and filtered high-voltage source is essential since a constant voltage is required to maintain a constant wavelength. When a hot filament is used, it should be provided with adjustments to focus the electron beam on the pinhole system. These requirements are met in electron microscopes, which are therefore convertible to diffraction cameras.[1] Since high-voltage electrons strike the metal around the pinhole, there are X-rays emitted that should be absorbed within the apparatus. With a satisfactory beam through the pinholes (10^{-4} to 10^{-5} amp through pinholes 0.1 to 0.2 mm in diameter), the exposure times are much faster than X-ray exposures—a matter of seconds rather than hours. Slow fine-grained plates and films are used. A bar magnet or an electro-

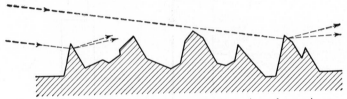

FIG. 2. Diffraction of electrons from projecting points of a specimen.

magnet outside the camera may be used to direct the beam through the pinhole system and onto the specimen.

Specimens. A metallic film so thin as to be translucent or transparent will diffract electrons very strongly; a layer of oxide thin enough to give temper colors likewise produces a good pattern, and in many cases even invisible films can be detected.

It is somewhat difficult to prepare a film so thin that electrons can be transmitted through it, for this requires thicknesses of a few hundred angstroms or less (about a millionth of an inch). Nevertheless, thin *transmission specimens* are prepared in the following ways:

1. Etching a metal foil (usually by floating it on the etching bath).
2. Depositing a substance from the vapor state on a thin cellulose film (or equivalent).
3. Sputtering metal in a gas-discharge tube upon a cellulose film.
4. Precipitating a colloid on a film.
5. Electrodepositing on a substrate which is subsequently etched off.
6. Skimming an oxide layer from molten metal.
7. Oxiding a thin film or etching an oxidized metal so as to leave the oxide layer.

[1] J. Hillier, R. F. Baker, and V. K. Zworykin, *J. Applied Phys.*, vol. **13**, p. 571, 1942.

There is frequently some uncertainty as to whether a film has undergone some change during the process of removal.

Reflection specimens are more readily prepared and more widely applicable to metallurgical problems. A reflection specimen, for best results, should have a surface that is slightly rough on a submicroscopic scale so the electrons can penetrate small projections, as in Fig. 2. The surface must be as clean as the experimenter can make it. A light etch followed by washes in water, alcohol, and benzene serves for metals; oxides are often sufficiently rough when formed on polished surfaces. Electrodeposits and condensed or sputtered films are usually satisfactory without further treatment.

Identification of Polycrystalline Materials. Most applications of electron diffraction involve the identification of reaction products, particularly those formed on metal surfaces. In such studies the patterns are analogous to X-ray powder patterns, consisting of concentric Debye rings that are interpreted just as X-ray patterns are. Typical reflection patterns are reproduced in Fig. 3.

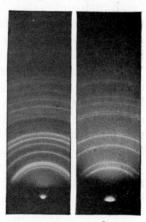

a   b

FIG. 3. Electron diffraction patterns formed by reflection from surface of a specimen. All electron-diffraction patterns reproduced here are direct prints of the original plates, in conformity with the usual practice in papers on the subject, and to distinguish them from the X-ray patterns in this book, which are double printed so as to give diffraction spots that are black. (*a*) Zinc oxide, (*b*) γ Al-Zn. (*Fuller.*)

The patterns provide the same kind of information that X-ray diffraction provides for thicker layers, *viz.*, the identification of the phases in the layer, the crystal structure of the material in the layer—provided this is not masked by anomalies in the diffraction pattern—the approximate grain size in the layer, and the orientations present.

The peculiar advantage of the use of electrons for work with surface layers lies in the fact that they are diffracted strongly by the outermost atoms of the specimen and convey information to the photographic plate concerning these atoms only, whereas X-rays penetrate more deeply and do not register the surface layers unless their thickness is measured in thousands of angstroms.

Identification is carried out by comparison with known materials or by computation of spacings; the card-index system[1] developed for X-rays is applicable here, although some difficulties may be encountered from the lower precision of the spacing measurements and the somewhat altered line intensities.

[1] See p. 152.

Extra Rings. The extraordinary sensitivity of the electron-diffraction camera to thin layers of material can be a considerable nuisance when it comes to carrying out an experiment. It is a standard complaint that almost anything, if given a chance, will collect on the specimen in sufficient quantities to cause trouble. The thinnest invisible deposits of grease, for example, give excellent diffraction patterns, as many investigators have found to their sorrow, and a little mercury deposited from vapor that has worked back into the camera from the vacuum pump will quickly affect the patterns and introduce "extra rings." If a specimen is rubbed lightly with rubber, say during etching, the spectrum of rubber appears. With some metals it is almost impossible to avoid obtaining the spectrum of an oxide film that forms while the specimen is being prepared and loaded into the camera—a few minutes at room temperature will produce a detectable oxide film on copper. One annoying source of extra rings was found to consist of an oriented deposit of $Ni(OH)_2$ dissolved from the surface of the specimen holder, which was a nickel alloy.[1]

Some extra rings from thin deposited films have been identified with an altered crystal structure in the deposit. When aluminum, for example, is deposited on platinum, the first layers of aluminum atoms, according to Finch and Quarrell, are forced into a tetragonal structure with interatomic distances in the basal plane matching those of the platinum with which it is in contact.[2] Similarly, a thin layer of oxide on zinc matches the zinc in its basal plane dimensions, in spite of the fact that the oxide does not normally have a hexagonal structure. Quarrell[3] found, in fact, that all the face-centered metals he examined (Ni, Cu, Pt, Pd, Au, Ag) when evaporated onto cellulose films or deposited electrolytically showed extra rings which he attributed to an abnormal close-packed hexagonal structure, and indexed the innermost ring as 10·0.*

Crystal-structure determination by electron diffraction is much less reliable than by X-rays, not only because of dangers of contamination of the sample, but also because anomalous intensities may be encountered. Anomalous intensities may arise, when rings are broad, from the extremely small size of diffracting crystals;[4] also, with sufficiently imperfect crystals of any size, anomalous intensities may result from a strong first-order

---

[1] L. H. Germer, *Z. Krist*, vol. A100, p. 277, 1938.

[2] G. I. Finch and A. G. Quarrell, *Proc. Roy. Soc. (London)*, vol. A141, p. 398, 1933.

[3] A. G. Quarrell, *Proc. Phys. Soc. (London)*, vol. 49, p. 279, 1937.

* The fact that he observed a weak band extending from this ring out to the f.c.c. 200 ring with these metals and with cobalt suggests that stacking faults are common in all the deposits, but since there are various causes of extra rings and since his findings were not confirmed by L. H. Germer (*Phys. Rev.*, vol. 56, p. 58, 1939) the interpretation of the patterns is somewhat uncertain.

[4] L. H. Germer and A. White, *Phys. Rev.*, vol. 60, p. 447, 1941.

reflection being again reflected in the first order by a portion of the same crystal, the doubly reflected beam having the appearance of a second-order reflection and adding to the intensity of any normal second-order reflection that is present.[1] This is possible with electron diffraction because the diffraction angles are so small that they may be of the same order of magnitude as the range of orientation in the sample (less than 2°). Multiple reflections of various types, in fact, may be observed, leading to diffracted beams that are apparently incompatible with the crystal structure.[2] If a beam reflected by the $h_1k_1l_1$ plane is again reflected by the $h_2k_2l_2$ plane, it appears on the photograph as a reflection having indices $h_1 \pm h_2$, $k_1 \pm k_2$, $l_1 \pm l_2$.

Powder-diffraction patterns with high resolution sometimes reveal fine structure in the lines that would not have been seen in X-ray patterns of the same powders.[3,4,5] Sturkey and Frevel,[4] for instance, found that *hhh* reflections from MgO and CdO smoke particles appeared to be doubled and various other lines were broadened. They suggested that the effect could be accounted for by refraction of the rays at the faces of regularly shaped particles (cubes). Cowley and Rees[5] found examples of 1, 2, 3, and 4 components in various lines, and from a more thorough treatment of the refraction problem showed that cube-shaped particles could give up to six components (a cluster of six spots surrounding a normal spot position, with the normal spot being absent). The deviations for CdO and MgO indicated inner potentials of about 15 volts in these crystals. Powder particles of irregular shape or of varying inner potential will give varying refraction effects such that the lines will be widened from this cause as well as from other causes. The broadening due to refraction will be of the same magnitude as that due to 250 A crystallite size, Cowley and Rees point out, if the inner potential is 15 volts and the accelerating voltage of the electron beam is 50 kv.

A different effect of external shape of particles has been discussed by Laue:[6] reciprocal lattice points are surrounded by intensity regions (identical at each point) with spikes extending out in directions normal to each bounding plane, the spikes extending to a distance inversely proportional to the crystal thickness. This provides a possible explanation

[1] L. H. Germer, *Phys. Rev.*, vol. 61, p. 309, 1942.

[2] H. Raether, *Z. Physik*, vol. 78, p. 527, 1932. G. I. Finch and H. Wilman, *Ergeb. exakt. Naturw.*, vol. 16, p. 353, 1937. L. G. Schulz, *Phys. Rev.*, vol. 78, p. 316, 1950.

[3] J. Hillier and R. F. Baker, *Phys. Rev.*, vol. 68, p. 98, 1945.

[4] L. Sturkey and L. K. Frevel, *Phys. Rev.*, vol. 68, p. 56, 1945; vol. 73, p. 183, 1948.

[5] J. M. Cowley and A. L. G. Rees, *Proc. Phys. Soc. (London)*, vol. 59, p. 287, 1947; *Nature*, vol. 158, p. 550, 1946.

[6] M. von Laue, *Ann. phys.*, vol. 26, p. 55, 1936; vol. 29, p. 311, 1937; "Materiewellen und ihre Interferenzen, "Akademische Verlagsgesellschaft m.b.H., Leipzig, 1944, and Edwards Bros., Inc., Ann Arbor, Mich.

for spikes that extend out from the spots of a highly oriented thin film of silver grown on rock salt.[1]   When the crystallites are very thin plates this effect reduces to a cross-grating pattern, which is discussed in a later section (page 596).   Powdered mica and other layer structures yield a pattern in which there are bands with a sharp limit on their inside edges, corresponding to the $hk0$ diffractions in the case of mica, as expected from extremely thin crystal flakes.[2]

It has also been suggested that extra rings corresponding to submultiples of the normal reflections ("fractional orders") may be obtained with very thin crystals as a result of the subsidiary maxima of the interference function.[3]   (The analogous effect with single crystals and divergent beams has been clearly seen.[4])

Penetration.   The *depth of penetration* of electrons may be estimated by depositing layers of various thicknesses on substrates of a different metal.   Nickel deposited on copper begins to give a recognizable pattern by reflection when the average thickness reaches about 10 A; a 200 A layer diffracts strongly, and a 400 A layer obliterates the effect of the base.[5]   These figures are a function of the roughness of the surface—on some surfaces a monomolecular layer or two or three atomic layers can be detected.   The upper limit is imposed by the inelastic impacts of the electrons, which destroy their ability to cooperate in building the diffraction pattern.   With heavy metals a film must be less than 10^{-6} cm (100 A) if the background scattering from inelastic impacts is to be small, and patterns cannot be expected if films are uniformly thicker than 10^{-5} cm.

Oxide Layers.   There have been many investigations of oxidation with electron diffraction.[6]   The various layers in the oxide scale that forms when iron is heated in air can be dissected and the various surfaces studied separately.   For example, when the film has just increased in thickness through the color stage and has turned black, it consists of hexagonal α-Fe_2O_3 with a pattern illustrated in Fig. 4.   When the scale has grown

[1] G. I. Finch and H. Wilman, *Ergeb. exakt. Naturw.*, vol. 16, p. 353, 1937.

[2] G. I. Finch, A. G. Quarrell, and H. Wilman, *Trans. Faraday Soc.*, vo.. 31, p. 1051, 1935. A. Steinheil, *Z. Physik*, vol. 89, p. 50, 1934. G. I. Finch and H. Wilman, *Proc. Roy. Soc. (London)*, vol. A155, p. 345, 1936; *Trans. Faraday Soc.*, vol. 32, p. 1539, 1936.

[3] A discussion of this is given by G. I. Finch and H. Wilman, *Ergeb. exakt. Naturw.*, vol. 16, p. 353, 1937.

[4] W. Kossel and G. Möllenstedt, *Naturwissenschaften*, vol. 26, p. 660, 1938; *Ann. phys.*, vol. 36, p. 113, 1939. G. Möllenstedt, *Ann. phys.*, vol. 40, p. 39, 1941. H. Raether, *Z. Physik*, vol. 126, p. 185, 1949.

[5] W. Cochrane, *Proc. Phys. Soc. (London)*, vol. 48, p. 723, 1936.

[6] Extensive reviews and bibliographies are given by G. P. Thomson and W. Cochrane, "Theory and Practice of Electron Diffraction," Macmillan, London, 1939; B. Lustman, Dissertation, Carnegie Institute of Technology, Pittsburgh, Pa., 1940.

thick enough to be chipped off, the underside shows the spectrum of Fe_3O_4.* Numerous studies of the oxides of aluminum have shown the value of this method for identifying the various structures, their grain

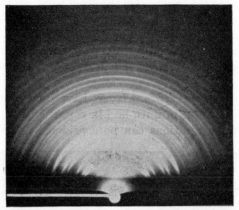

Fig. 4. Surface-reflection pattern of hexagonal α-Fe_2O_3. (*Nelson.*)

size, and their orientation. Similar data have been obtained as a function of temperature and composition for Fe, Co, Ni, and their alloys by Gulbransen and Hickman.[1]

Preferred Orientations. It is usual for the thin deposits to have a preferred orientation of some sort. This is revealed in the patterns by a lack of uniformity in the intensity of each ring on the photographic plate or, in certain cases, by abnormal intensities of certain rings.

The interpretation of the texture patterns is exactly as with X-rays, except that here the angle of incidence is so small one can consider $\theta = 0$ and the reflection circle is a great circle. An oriented electrodeposit of iron is illustrated in the reflection photograph of Fig. 5, and the texture of a specimen

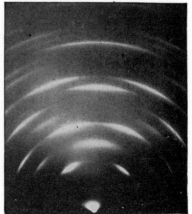

Fig. 5. Reflection pattern showing preferred orientation in electrode-posited iron. (*Finch.*)

of gold leaf is shown by the intensity maxima in the rings of Fig. 6. Germer[2] found the orientations illustrated in Fig. 7 on the surface of

* H. R. Nelson, *J. Applied Phys.*, vol. 9, p. 623, 1938.

[1] E. A. Gulbransen and J. W. Hickman, *Trans. AIME*, vol. 171, pp. 306, 344, 1947; vol. 180, pp. 519, 534, 1949. A summary of the data will be found in E. Gulbransen, *Trans. Electrochem. Soc.*, vol. 91, p. 573, 1947.

[2] L. H. Germer, *Phys. Rev.*, vol. 50, p. 659, 1936.

a galena crystal after filing. When the beam struck the filed surface parallel to the direction of filing, a regular array of spots was produced (Fig. 7b) which is a rotation pattern with the axis of rotation horizontal and perpendicular to the beam. On the other hand, *arcs* are formed when the beam is perpendicular to the direction of filing (Fig. 7c), for the beam is then parallel to the axis of rotation of the crystallites. These spectra represent the etched condition of the filed surface; the unetched surface produces complete Debye rings, as in Fig. 7a, indicating a random orientation.

Similar rotations in the surface layers have been observed in NaCl;[1] and in zinc blende (ZnS), in ZnO, and in copper.[2] Evans and Wilman[2] point out that these rotations can be considered as rotational slip on

FIG. 6. Transmission pattern of gold leaf showing preferred orientation. (*Fuller.*)

important crystal planes that serve as junction planes between fragments, planes that stand normal to the surface, normal to the axis of rotation, and parallel to the direction of abrasion. In ZnS the (110) cleavage plane stands in this position, in ZnO the (11$\bar{2}$0) plane, and in various experiments on copper the rotations were interpreted as rotational slip on (100), (110), and (111).

One source of error in judging preferred orientations by electron diffraction has recently been discovered.[3] Etching a surface to prepare it for the electron microscope actually leaves, on grains of certain orientations, a surface contour exceptionally favorable for diffraction, and these selected grains predominate in forming the pattern. The diffraction pattern therefore represents a *weighted* sampling rather than a *random* sampling under such conditions—and this may be the rule rather than the exception.

Thin Deposits. Films of metal deposited by evaporation in a vacuum have been studied extensively by electron diffraction, for X-ray methods are unsuitable for the thinnest ones. Extensive summaries of the work are available.[4] Deposits on cleavage surfaces of single crystals are com-

---

[1] H. Raether, *Metaux & corrosion*, vol. 22, p. 2, 1947.

[2] D. M. Evans and H. Wilman, *Proc. Phys. Soc. (London)*, vol. 63, p. 298, 1950.

[3] R. P. Johnson and W. R. Grams, *Phys. Rev.*, vol. 62, p. 77, 1942.

[4] F. Kirchner, *Ergeb. exakt. Naturw.*, vol. 11, p. 64, 1932. G. I. Finch and H. Wilman, *Ergeb. exakt. Naturw.*, vol. 16, p. 353, 1937 (in English). G. P. Thomson and

monly found to be oriented ("epitaxy"), with the degree and type of orientation being dependent upon the nature and temperature of the substrate as well as the nature of the deposited metal.[1] Oriented over-

growths of alkali halides on cleaved surfaces of other alkali halides and on mica are advantageously studied by such techniques, and have yielded information on orientation vs. degree of misfit and thickness of the deposit, mechanism of crystal growth, effect of contamination, and polymorphism induced by depositing.[2] Schulz has found, for example, that six salts (CsCl, CsBr, CsI, TlCl, TlBr, and TlI), which normally have the CsCl type of crystal structure, take the NaCl type of structure when grown from the vapor on suitable substrates.[3] Matching of the atom pattern at the interface is a factor in this polymorphism, but close matching is not necessary. Theory has shown that the free energies of the two forms are similar, and it is known that polymorphism can also be induced in some of these compounds by subjecting them to high pressures.

a

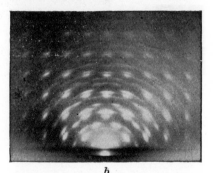

b

c

Fig. 7. Surface-reflection patterns for filed surface of galena crystal. (*a*) Unetched surface, random texture; (*b*) etched, beam parallel to direction of filing; (*c*) etched, beam perpendicular to direction of filing. (*Germer.*)

W. Cochrane, "Theory and Practice of Electron Diffraction," Macmillan, London, 1939. H. Richter, *Physik. Z.*, vol. 44, p. 406, 1943. Orientations are discussed in Chap. XX.

[1] G. P. Thomson, *Proc. Roy. Soc. (London)*, vol. A128, p. 649, 1930. H. Lassen, *Physik. Z.*, vol. 35, p. 172, 1934. H. Lassen and L. Bruck, *Ann. phys.*, vol. 22, p. 65, 1935. L. Bruck, *Ann. phys.*, vol. 26, p. 233, 1936. M. Kubo and S. Miyake, *J. Phys. Soc. (Japan)*, vol. 3, p. 114, 1948.

[2] L. G. Schulz, *Phys. Rev.*, vol. 77, p. 750, 1950; vol. 78, p. 638, 1950; *J. Chem. Phys.*, vol. 18, p. 896, 1950; *J. Applied Phys.*, vol. 9, p. 942, 1950; *Acta Cryst.*, vol. 4, p. 487, 1951.

[3] L. G. Schulz, *Acta Cryst.*, vol. 4, p. 487, 1951.

The *grain size* in a thin-film transmission specimen is indicated by the breadth of the diffraction lines, as with X-rays, though this is recommended only with transmission specimens, not reflection, and for crystallites of about 3 to 100 unit cells in diameter. An electrodeposit of arsenic with exceedingly small crystals gives the pattern reproduced in Fig. 8,[1] in which the line broadening is evident. The usual Scherrer formula for computing crystallite size from line width may be employed; but with electrons this reduces to $b = \lambda/L$ where b is the line width (in radians) at half maximum intensity attributable to crystallite size widening, λ is the wavelength, and L the mean crystal size normal to the beam.[2]

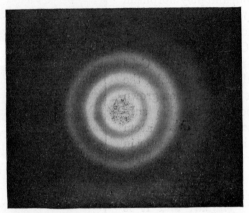

Fig. 8. Transmission pattern for electrodeposited arsenic. Very small crystals, substantially amorphous. (*Finch, Quarrell, and Wilman.*)

For particles so small that diffraction lines overlap, it is possible to judge crystal size by comparison with computed curves of intensity vs. angle; Germer and White plotted these by using the theoretical formula for the intensity of coherent scattering from gas molecules.[3] Curves for clusters of atoms in face-centered cubic array containing 13 atoms or less did not show the 111 ring as resolved from the 200, or 220 resolved from 311 and 222; clusters of 55 atoms resolved 220 from its neighbors, but not 111; clusters of 379 atoms resolved 111 from 200, and 220 from the unresolved doublet 311 + 222. Many metals deposited on glass or on amorphous substrates yield diffraction patterns with such broad halos and unresolved lines in electron-diffraction transmission patterns that the number of

[1] G. I. Finch, A. G. Quarrell, and H. Wilman, *Trans. Faraday Soc.*, vol. 31, p. 1051, 1935.

[2] Small particles yield much sharper lines in electron diffraction patterns than in X-ray patterns because the electron wavelengths are shorter than the X-ray wavelengths.

[3] L. H. Germer and A. W. White, *Phys. Rev.*, vol. 60, p. 447, 1941.

atoms per grain cannot exceed one or two hundred, and the structure is commonly called amorphous (see page 267, Chap. XI and page 517, Chap. XX). With grain sizes this small, much of the material is in the "grain boundaries" and the structure would be best described in a statistical manner by radial-distribution plots of atomic density.

Germer found that vaporization of Cu, Ni, Au, and Pd on amorphous substrates produced crystallites—in the thinnest films—somewhat larger than the average thickness of the films; for example, a 3 A film of copper produces an electron-diffraction pattern characteristic of crystallites containing two or three hundred atoms.[1,2] Films of ionic compounds contain crystallites 50 to 100 A or more on a side in films of roughly 10 A average thickness.[2,3] It is therefore clear that there is considerable migration of atoms and molecules over the surface of the substrate, as has been concluded by resistivity, thermionic, photoelectric, and optical measurements,[1] and by electron-microscope observations.[4] Schulz points out[3] that this mobility is limited and does not approach that of a liquid state, for a liquid state would not account for the tipping of the fiber axis toward or away from the obliquely incident stream of vapor, or for the uniformly small size of the crystallites.

Films produced by sputtering, when the cathode in the sputtering chamber consists of gold and platinum wires twisted together, appeared to consist of mixtures of crystals of the two metals, without apparent alloying.[5]

Polished Surfaces. There has been much discussion of the nature of polished surfaces of metals. The discussion began with Sir George Beilby's suggestion that the polishing operation distorts the crystals until all crystallinity is lost and the amorphous state is reached. Much of the controversy about this amorphous-metal theory has arisen from the interpretation of certain electron-diffraction experiments.

Extremely diffuse electron-diffraction rings are given by reflection from a polished surface, as if the surface was amorphous or nearly so.[6] However, a film of metal may give diffuse rings by reflection and yet give sharp rings when examined by transmission, as Germer has shown with examples of the sort reproduced in Fig. 9,[7] and Kirchner has shown with certain

[1] L. H. Germer and A. H. White, *Phys. Rev.*, vol. 60, p. 447, 1941.

[2] L. H. Germer, *Phys. Rev.*, vol. 56, p. 58, 1939.

[3] L. G. Schulz, *J. Chem. Phys.*, vol. 17, p. 1153, 1949.

[4] R. C. Pickard and O. S. Duffendack, *J. Applied Phys.*, vol. 14, p. 291, 1943.

[5] G. I. Finch and S. Fordham, *J. Soc. Chem. Ind.*, vol. 56, p. 632, 1937.

[6] A summary of work on the subject—chiefly by surface reflection—together with a very emphatic statement of interpretations supporting the amorphous hypothesis and arguments attempting to discredit alternate theories is given by G. I. Finch and H. Wilman, *Ergeb. exakt. Naturw.*, vol. 16, p. 353, 1937.

[7] L. H. Germer, *Phys. Rev.*, vol. 43, p. 724, 1933; vol. 49, p. 163, 1936.

thin electrodeposited layers.[1]   The diffuseness in surface reflection patterns has been observed even with natural glassy smooth surfaces of carborundum crystals and of polycrystalline cuprous oxide.[2]   It arises at least in part from the effect of slight surface unevenness; for if the electrons enter and leave the surface at a small angle, the direction of the emerging rays will be affected by changes in the slope of the surface. This is because the angle through which the rays are bent by refraction is

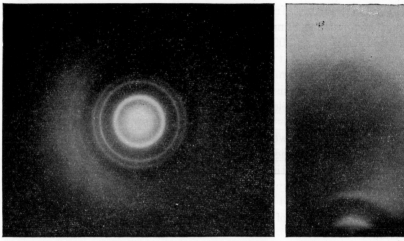

Fig. 9. A transparent film of zinc sulphide, 8×10^{-6} in. in thickness, gives a crystalline ring pattern by transmission (on the left) and a diffuse amorphous-type pattern by reflection (on the right). (*Germer.*)

sensitive to the angle at which the rays meet the surface, unless this angle is very large.[3]

It seems necessary, therefore, to base conclusions on transmission patterns rather than on reflection patterns, and to take precautions against the formation of oxides when a thin sheet is being deformed.   By the transmission method very diffuse rings are found in polished gold, provided that the patterns are made promptly after polishing.[4]   After standing 15 hr at room temperature the grains grow to a size giving sharp rings.   Diffuse patterns from severely hammered, rolled, and abraded

---

[1] F. Kirchner, *Nature*, vol. 129, p. 545, 1932; *Trans. Faraday Soc.*, vol. 31, p. 1114, 1935.

[2] L. H. Germer, *Phys. Rev.*, vol. 43, p. 724, 1933; vol. 49, p. 163, 1936.

[3] An electropolished single crystal produces a surface reflection pattern in which spots have tails extending toward the shadow of the specimen surface (toward smaller Bragg angles).   After the crystal is etched it produces sharp spots, for the beam enters and leaves the metal at large angles, as in Fig. 3.   W. Kranert, K. H. Leise, and H. Raether, *Z. Physik*, vol. 122, p. 248, 1944.

[4] W. Cochrane, *Proc. Roy. Soc. (London)*, vol. A166, p. 228, 1938.

copper and gold[1] indicate that crystallite size is reduced to the order of 50 A. When there are very few unit cells per crystallite there is not much difference between this structure and an amorphous state, provided that coordination numbers are substantially the same. For antimony, however, the amorphous state seems to have different coordination than the crystalline state; Hendus[2] concludes the amorphous state has 4 atoms at 2.87 A, 2 at 3.51, and 12 at 4.18, as compared with the crystalline state, which has 3 at 2.87, 3 at 3.37, 6 at 4.27, and 6 at 4.50. Therefore for Sb, and also for Se and Bi, the patterns of the amorphous state would not be the same as a blurred derivative of the polycrystalline pattern. Kranert and Raether[3] conclude from the positions of the diffuse rings that patterns for severely worked As, Se, and Bi resemble more closely the crystalline than the amorphous patterns of these metals. But the difference between the positions of the halos on these patterns is not great, and accurate radial-density-distribution curves would be required for an adequate description of the structure of the metal.

A polished layer is most severely distorted at the surface; the effective grain size increases as one goes to a depth of 100, 1000, or 10,000 A below the surface. A preferred orientation has been found at the surface of polished copper and gold, with (110) planes lying parallel to the surface;[4] and it has been suggested[5] that the melting which occurs at the surface of metals during polishing (Bowden and Ridler[6]) may produce recrystallization of the surface layers which affects the orientations.

Wulff and his collaborators have applied electron diffraction to the study of phase transformation induced in stainless steel (18% Ni, 8% Cr) by polishing, grinding, sanding, superfinishing, and cold rolling.[7] The surface layers resulting from dry or wet grinding are austenitic, indicating that they have been heated above 200°C. Below this austenitic layer is a layer that has been reduced to ferrite by cold work; the ferritic layer is about 6×10^{-4} cm below the surface in samples that have been ground. Samples that have received any type of polishing contain a ferritic layer at the surface 1.5×10^{-5} cm (1500 angstroms) or less in thickness. The ferrite layer in sheet reduced 50 per cent by cold rolling extends about 1×10^{-4} cm below the surface.

[1] W. Kranert and H. Raether, *Ann. phys.*, vol. 43, p. 520, 1943.

[2] G. Hendus, *Z. Physik*, vol. 119, p. 265, 1942.

[3] W. Kranert and H. Raether, *Z. Naturforsch.*, vol. 1, p. 512, 1946.

[4] H. G. Hopkins, *Trans. Faraday Soc.*, vol. 31, p. 1095, 1935. C. S. Lees, *Trans. Faraday Soc.*, vol. 31, p. 1102, 1935.

[5] G. I. Finch, *Sci. Progress*, vol. 31, p. 609, 1937.

[6] F. P. Bowden and K. E. W. Ridler, *Proc. Roy. Soc. (London)*, vol. A154, p. 640, 1936.

[7] J. Wulff, *Trans. AIME*, vol. 145, p. 295, 1941; J. T. Burwell and J. Wulff, *Trans. AIME*, vol. 135, p. 486, 1939.

Diffraction from Thin Crystals. The Laue equations must be satisfied for electrons to diffract, just as in the case of X-rays. The chief difference between the two cases lies in the fact that the electron wavelengths are much smaller than the X-ray wavelengths, and the interaction between the electrons and the atoms of the crystal is much greater, so that thinner layers are effective in diffraction.

Let us consider a small cubic crystal with an electron beam parallel to the *a* axis. The Laue conditions represent concentric sets of cones around *a*, *b*, and *c* axes. The cones around the *a* axis will intersect the photographic plate as circles much smaller than the circles for X-ray diffraction,

FIG. 10. Transmission through aluminum along a cube edge of a crystal. Polycrystalline aluminum also present, giving rings. (*Finch, Quarrell, and Wilman.*)

while the cones around *b* and *c* will be opened wide and intersect the plate nearly in straight lines. If the first Laue condition is relaxed, the second two will therefore produce two sets of nearly straight lines intersecting the photographic plate at the points of a square network. Figure 10 is a photograph of a single crystal of aluminum made with the beam parallel to the cube edge; the square array of reflections is very prominent.[1]

It can be shown by cleaving mica crystals to various thicknesses of the order of 10^{-6} to 10^{-7} cm that only the thinnest ones produce these regular point networks. As a thicker specimen is used, those spots of the network which satisfy the third Laue condition increase in intensity, while the others gradually disappear. The diffraction is best understood in terms of the reciprocal lattice. Each reciprocal lattice point becomes elongated in the direction of the thin dimension of the crystal; the extension of the region of intensity around each point can be computed from the equation for diffracted intensities from a parallelepiped formed of unit cells. If there are N_1, N_2, and N_3 cells along the three axes, respectively, and if the path differences between the waves scattered by the

[1] G. I. Finch, A. G. Quarrell, and H. Wilman, *Trans. Faraday Soc.*, vol. 31, p. 1051, 1935.

origin and the other extremities of the axes are A_1, A_2, and A_3 wavelengths, the intensity will be proportional to

$$\frac{\sin^2 (\pi N_1 A_1)}{\sin^2 \pi A_1} \cdot \frac{\sin^2 (\pi N_2 A_2)}{\sin^2 \pi A_2} \cdot \frac{\sin^2 (\pi N_3 A_3)}{\sin^2 \pi A_3}$$

Now the effect of reducing the number of cells along the a axis is to reduce N_1 in the first term. This first factor may become zero a number of times, and it will first reach zero when $A_1 = \pm 1/N_1$. Thus if the specimen is only two unit cells thick, its reciprocal lattice points are elongated halfway to the next reciprocal lattice point, while if it is four unit cells thick the first minimum is one-fourth of the way to the next point. A reciprocal lattice of elongated points is sketched in Fig. 11. Reflection occurs when the reflection sphere touches any part of the elongated points. When there is considerable elongation, the diffraction pattern shows the network of reflections that is characteristic of a two-dimensional grating. This network is the more evident because of the short wavelength of the electron waves, for in reciprocal space this corresponds to a reflection sphere of very large radius. The sphere is, in fact, almost a plane, as will be seen from the plot in Fig. 11, which is drawn to scale for a mica crystal 10^{-6} cm thick.

Slight imperfections in orientation, slight distortion of the crystal, or nonparallelism in the incident beam permit the reflection sphere to touch a large number of reciprocal lattice points and cause a network of reflections, even when

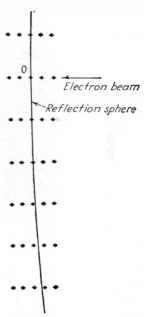

FIG. 11. Reciprocal lattice with elongated points and reflection sphere.

the points are not elongated by the thinness of the crystal. It will be found a great convenience in interpreting an electron diffraction pattern to remember that it is practically a plane section through the reciprocal lattice, a fact which makes the assignment of indices very simple.

Intensity of Scattering. The intensity of an electron beam scattered by a crystal is proportional to the efficiency of scattering of individual atoms. With X-ray scattering we use an atomic scattering factor, f, to take account of this efficiency; similarly with electrons we can use a factor E for the purpose. Both E and f are functions of the angle θ.* The value of f depends upon the number of electrons in the scattering

---

* W. L. Bragg, "The Crystalline State," vol. I, p. 254, G. Bell, London, 1939.

atom, Z, but E depends on the quantity $(Z - f)$ because of scattering of electrons by the nucleus as well as by the outer electrons in the atom. The factor E has the value

$$E = (Z - f) \left(\frac{\lambda}{\sin \theta}\right)^2 \cdot c$$

where λ is expressed in angstroms, and c is a constant involving the electronic charge and mass and Planck's constant $(c = e^2 m/2h^2)$. The value of E decreases with angle like f, though somewhat more abruptly, but the numerical value of E at small angles is about 10^4 times greater than f; hence, electrons scatter much more intensely than X-rays. This is the

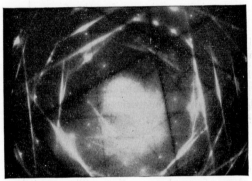

Fig. 12. Transmission pattern for a relatively thick graphite crystal, showing Kikuchi lines. (*Finch and Wilman.*)

reason electron diffraction can detect such minutely thin films of material. To compute the relative intensities of reflections from a crystal the usual X-ray formulas for $F(hkl)$ are used, with E substituted for F. (See, however, page 586 regarding anomolous intensities.)

Kikuchi Lines. A complex pattern of black and white lines appears when a mica crystal is too thick to give good patterns of the type illustrated above. The Kikuchi lines,[1] as they are called, are illustrated in Fig. 12.[2] The nature of these straight lines is adequately accounted for by assuming that electrons entering a crystal are scattered in various directions and that some of the scattered electrons find themselves going in exactly the right directions to reflect from some plane in the crystal. In Fig. 13, AB, $A'B'$ represent reflecting planes in a crystal. Diffusely scattered electrons that would have followed the path OP are reflected to P', while the scattered ray OQ is reflected to Q'. Now the intensity of the scattered ray in the direction OP is greater than in the direction OQ,

[1] S. Kikuchi, *Proc. Imp. Acad. (Tokyo)*, vol. 4, pp. 271, 354, 1928; *Japan. J. Phys.*, vol. 5, p. 83, 1928.

[2] G. I. Finch and H. Wilman, *Proc. Roy. Soc. (London)*, vol. A155, p. 345, 1936.

and so the energy robbed from the ray P is not fully returned by the reflected ray Q' and there is a net loss in the direction OP; similarly, there is a net gain in the direction OQ. Thus there will appear on the plate a white (weakened) line and a black (enhanced) line parallel to the projection of each crystal plane and equidistant from it. Sometimes there are so many lines at slight angles to each other, tangent along a curve, that the curved envelope of the lines becomes a prominent feature of the pattern.

Kikuchi lines are closely related to the Kossel lines seen with X-rays;[1] they are seen only with crystals of considerable perfection and disappear

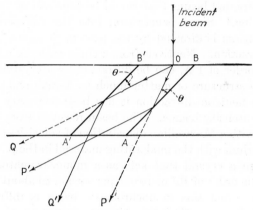

FIG. 13. Origin of Kikuchi lines.

when a crystal is distorted. They may be seen with both transmission and reflection experiments. They are also seen when crystals in the micron range of size are irradiated with an electron beam focused to a cross-section diameter of 100 to 200 A.[2] With this focused beam a pattern is obtained in which each spot is an enlarged image of the crystal; striations are obtained in the spots that agree with the predictions of the dynamical theory of diffraction as computed by MacGillavry.[3] Detailed theoretical treatments of Kikuchi lines, based on the dynamical theory of diffraction, have been published;[4] these are combined with a dynamical-

[1] Excellent reproductions of Kikuchi lines and Kossel lines, together with discussions of their geometry and indexing, will be found in *Ergeb. exakt. Naturw.*, vol. 16, pp. 296, 353, 1937.

[2] N. Davidson and J. Hillier, *J. Applied Phys.*, vol. 18, p. 499, 1947.

[3] C. H. MacGillavry, *Physica*, vol. 7, p. 329, 1940.

[4] K. Shinohara, *Sci. Pap. Phys. Chem. Res. Tokyo*, vol. 18, p. 223, 1932; vol. 18, p. 39, 1932; *Phys. Rev.*, vol. 47, p. 730, 1935. S. Kikuchi and S. Nakagawa, *Sci. Pap. Inst. Phys. Chem. Res. Tokyo*, vol. 21, p. 256, 1933. M. v. Laue, *Physik. Z.*, vol. 37, p. 544, 1936.

theory treatment of special features of single-crystal patterns that have been observed by Kossel and Möllenstedt[1] in the book by von Laue.[2]

Diffraction of Atoms and Molecules. Beams of atoms and molecules can also be diffracted by crystals, for the de Broglie relation, discussed in connection with electron diffraction, $\lambda = h/(mv)$, holds for any moving particle. The techniques, which are different from those used in other diffraction work, have been summarized by Estermann.[3] The source is an oven, which emits particles with a "continuous spectrum" of velocities. Monochromatization is possible either by sorting out definite velocities mechanically by the use of a rotating sector, or by a crystal monochromator. Beams of H, H_2, and He, when diffracted from cleaved ionic crystals, produce the diffracted beams that would be expected of diffraction from a crossed grating.[4] Since penetration into the diffracting crystal is negligible, the beam is directed by the pattern of atoms in the *surface*.

Neutron Diffraction. Neutrons from a chain-reacting pile, with wavelengths of the order of 1 A, can be diffracted by a crystal[5] and used for research on the structure of matter much as X-rays and electrons have been used. In neutron diffraction it has been necessary to work with extremely low intensity beams. The beam received from a reactor contains neutrons with a Maxwellian distribution of velocities that represents thermal equilibrium with the moderating material in the pile. When this is reflected from a crystal that acts as a monochromator the beam is reduced from the order of 10^7 neutrons per second to about 10^4, in a typical experiment; when this monochromatic beam is diffracted from a powdered crystalline sample into a Geiger counter set at the peak of a diffraction line the intensity is reduced to the order of 1 neutron per second, and the background intensity is, of course, much less than this. Nevertheless, a counter filled with BF_3 (in which the B is enriched in B^{10} for better absorption) can be used to map out the pattern if it is moved sufficiently slowly through the range of diffraction angles.[6]

[1] W. Kossel and G. Möllenstedt, *Naturwissenschaften*, vol. 26, p. 660, 1938; *Ann. phys.*, vol. 36, p. 113, 1939; vol. 42, p. 287, 1942. W. Kossel, I. Ackerman, and G. Möllenstedt, *Z. Physik*, vol. 120, p. 553, 1943.

[2] M. von Laue, "Materiewellen und ihre Interferenzen," Akademische Verlagsgesellschaft m.b.H., Leipzig, 1944, and Edwards Bros., Inc., Ann Arbor, Mich.

[3] I. Estermann, *Rev. Modern Phys.*, vol. 18, p. 300, 1946.

[4] I. Estermann and O. Stern, *Z. Physik*, vol. 61, p. 95, 1930. I. Estermann, R. Frisch, and O. Stern, *Z. Physik*, vol. 73, p. 348, 1931. T. H. Johnson, *J. Franklin Inst.*, vol. 210, p. 135, 1930.

[5] W. H. Zinn, *Phys. Rev.*, vol. 70, p. 102A, 1946; vol. 71, p. 752, 1947. L. B. Borst, A. J. Ulrich, C. L. Osborne, and B. Hasbrouck, *Phys. Rev.*, vol. 70, p. 108A, 1946; vol. 70, p. 557, 1946.

[6] E. O. Wollan and C. G. Shull, *Phys. Rev.*, vol. 73, p. 822, 1948. C. G. Shull, E. O. Wollan, G. A. Morton, and W. L. Davidson, *Phys. Rev.*, vol. 73, p. 830, 1948. A summary is given by E. O. Wollan and C. G. Shull in *Nucleonics*, vol. 3, July and August, 1948.

Neutrons are scattered chiefly by the atomic nuclei, rather than by the outer electrons that scatter X-rays and electrons. The scattering power of the elements does not vary with atomic number in the way that X-ray scattering power does; of particular importance is the fact that the light elements such as carbon and hydrogen scatter much more intensely relative to the heavier elements than is the case with X-rays, while the scattering powers of neighboring elements in the periodic table may differ much more than they do with X-rays; there is no regular increase with increasing atomic number; in fact, different isotopes of an element may differ markedly. The atomic scattering power does not fall with increasing angle as it does with X-rays, since the nucleus, which scatters neutrons, has a size of the order of 10^{-13} cm as contrasted with the size of the electron cloud that scatters X-rays, which has dimensions of the order of 10^{-8} cm. Neutrons scattered by some elements (*e.g.*, Mn, Li, Ti, and H) are 180° out of phase with the incident beam, the opposite of the phase that is found with the majority of the elements.[1] This must be recognized in interpreting the patterns of crystals containing the elements with "negative phase."

The positions of carbon and hydrogen atoms in crystalline compounds have been determined by neutron diffraction.[2] The superlattice lines from ordered FeCo and Ni_3Mn are readily detected by neutron diffraction, but only with difficulty by X-rays; yet the opposite is true for Cu_3Au. In the Ni_3Mn superlattice it is necessary to use a negative phase for the scattering from Mn in order to account for the observed intensities.[3] If the different isotopes of an element were arranged in an ordered way in a crystal this could be detected by neutron diffraction. However, superlattices of this kind cannot exist because the ordering forces are of negligible magnitude, and, instead, there is only a diffuse scattering from the random arrangement of dissimilar isotopes.

In addition to the nuclear scattering mentioned above there is a scattering from electrons outside of the nucleus. The magnetic moment of the neutron interacts with the magnetic moment resulting from the spins of the $3d$ electrons, the scattered intensity depending upon the parallelism or antiparallelism of the moments of the neutron and the scattering atom. Because of this extra-nuclear scattering (which is comparable in magnitude to the nuclear) neutron diffraction is a tool for investigating the alignment of magnetic moments in solids, *i.e.*, their magnetic structure. This characteristic is important when the neutron diffraction pattern of

[1] E. Fermi and L. Marshall, *Phys. Rev.*, vol. 71, p. 666, 1947; vol. 72, p. 408, 1947. The phase for isotype Li^7 is negative, but for Li^6 is positive, according to Shull and Wollan.

[2] C. G. Shull, E. O. Wollan, G. A. Morton, and W. L. Davidson, *Phys. Rev.*, vol. 73, p. 830, 1948 (NaH, NaD).

[3] C. G. Shull and E. O. Wollan, *Science*, vol. 108, p. 69, 1948.

a paramagnetic substance is compared with that of a ferromagnetic or an antiferromagnetic.   The randomly directed moments of a paramagnetic substance yield a broad diffuse background due to incoherent "magnetic" scattering, that is superimposed on the sharp peaks that are due to the coherent "nuclear" scattering.   This cause of incoherent scattering is absent with ferromagnetic substances, where atomic moments are in parallel alignment throughout a magnetic domain.   In antiferromagnetic substances there is an antiparallel alignment of moments of certain pairs

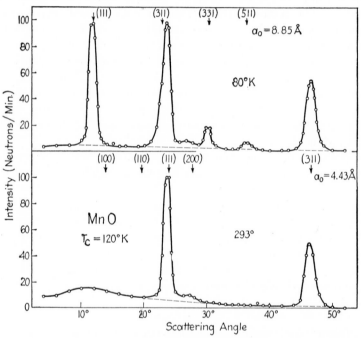

Fig. 14. Neutron diffraction pattern from the antiferromagnetic powder MnO at 80°K and 293°K, below and above the critical temperature for ordering, 120°K.   (*Shull.*)

of atoms; for example, in MnO, which has the NaCl-type structure, Mn atoms at positions 000 and 100 have oppositely directed magnetic moments and thus appear to the neutrons to be different atoms; similarly the atoms at 010 and 001 have spins directed oppositely to the one at 000. The result is that similarly oriented atoms form a unit cell with twice the linear dimensions of the NaCl-type structure and the corresponding superlattice lines appear in the neutron diffraction pattern.   The neutron diffraction pattern for the antiferromagnetic powder is reproduced in Fig. 14; the upper curve is for the sample at 80°K, below the Curie temperature of 120°K, and the lower curve is for the sample at 293°K, which is a temperature in the range where thermal agitation has destroyed the long-range ordering of the spins.[1]   It will be seen from the figure that some evidence of short-range order remains above the critical temperature.   The list of antiferromagnetic crystals, which is rapidly growing, includes

$Mn^{++}S$	FeF_2	FeO
$Mn^{++}F_2$	CoF_2	CoO
	NiF_2	NiO

In addition there appears to be a class of structures in which there is anti-parallel alignment of spins in neighboring atoms, just as in an antiferro-magnetic, but with the spins in one direction being unequal in magnitude to the spins in the other.   The result is a ferromagnetic alignment of the atoms with the stronger magnetic moment, such as to create ferromag-netism—but only a weak ferromagnetism because opposing spins partially cancel it.   An example is Fe_3O_4.   The term ferrimagnetism has been used by Néel for this property.[2]

In addition to the Geiger-counter spectrometer, the Laue method can be used in neutron diffraction[3] if a photographic film is covered by a sheet of indium or other activating material to increase the efficiency of recording the rays.   Beta particles emitted from the sheet during neutron capture are absorbed in the film.

The relations between crystal perfection and reflecting power must be modified from the form in which they apply to X-rays when they are extended to neutrons, because the much lower absorption coefficient of the neutrons makes secondary extinction a more important factor.[4]

[1] C. G. Shull and J. S. Smart, *Phys. Rev.*, vol. 76, p. 1256, 1949.
[2] L. Néel, *Ann. inst. Fourier*, vol. 1, p. 163, 1949.
[3] E. O. Wollan, C. G. Shull, and M. C. Marney, *Phys. Rev.*, vol. 73, p. 527, 1948
[4] G. E. Bacon and R. D. Lowde, *Acta Cryst.*, vol. 1, p. 303, 1948.

APPENDIX I

THE INTENSITY OF X-RAY REFLECTIONS

To determine the structure of a complex crystal a crystallographer must analyze the intensities of the reflections he observes, first computing true intensities from his films and then relating these intensities to the distribution of atoms in the unit cell. Several factors are involved in such analyses: the scattering power of individual electrons, of groups of electrons in atoms, of atoms in the unit cell, of crystals at different temperatures, and of crystals mounted in various X-ray cameras that require their individual geometrical correction factors. These have received only brief mention in Chaps. IV to VIII.

Scattering by an Electron. J. J. Thomson[1] derived the *classical-theory formula* for the intensity of X-rays that would be scattered by a free electron or by an electron that is held under negligible constraining forces. Consider a polarized beam of X-rays falling on an electron at e, Fig. 1. The electric field of the incident beam will accelerate the electron with a vibratory motion and cause it to radiate electromagnetic waves of the same wavelength as the original beam. The intensity, I_e, of this secondary radiation at the point P will be

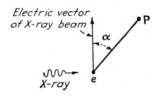

Fig. 1. Scattering from an electron.

related to the intensity of the primary beam, I_0, the distance r, and the angle α between the direction of observation and the direction of the electric vector of the incident radiation. The relation derived by Thomson is

$$I_e = \frac{I_0 e^4}{r^2 m^2 c^4} \sin^2 \alpha \tag{1}$$

where e and m are the charge and mass of the electron and c is the velocity of light.

We shall apply Thomson's formula to an electron at the origin of the coordinate axes of Fig. 2, with the incident beam proceeding along the X axis and the scattered rays observed at point P in the XZ plane. Let the angle between OP and the X axis be 2θ (since θ will then correspond

---

[1] J. J. Thomson, "Conduction of Electricity through Gases," 2d ed., p. 325, University Press, Cambridge, 1928, reviewed in A. H. Compton and S. K. Allison, "X-rays in Theory and Experiment," p. 117, Van Nostrand, New York, 1935.

to the angle in Bragg's law). If the electric vector of a polarized beam is parallel to Z and if the beam has intensity I_z, the intensity at P according to Eq. (1) will be

$$I_e = \frac{I_z e^4}{r^2 m^2 c^4} \cos^2 2\theta \tag{1a}$$

while if the electric vector of the polarized beam is parallel to Y and of intensity I_y, the intensity at P will be

$$I_e = \frac{I_y e^4}{r^2 m^2 c^4} \tag{1b}$$

Now under ordinary conditions the incident beam is unpolarized, and the electric vector E_0 of the primary ray may be resolved into components E_y along Y and E_z along Z such that

$$E_y^2 + E_z^2 = E_0^2$$

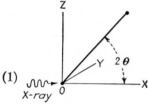

(1)

Fig. 2. Coordinates for scattered ray.

With unpolarized rays the electric vector occurs with equal probability at all angles; therefore, on the average, its component along Y is equal to its component along Z. On the average, therefore,

$$E_y^2 = E_z^2 = \tfrac{1}{2} E_0^2$$

and since the intensity is equal to the square of the amplitude, it follows that

$$I_y = I_z = \tfrac{1}{2} I_0$$

The intensity for an unpolarized beam is obtained by adding the contributions of the two components specified in (1a) and (1b), giving

$$I_e = \frac{e^4}{r^2 m^2 c^4} (I_y + I_z \cos^2 2\theta) = \frac{e^4}{r^2 m^2 c^4} \left(\frac{1}{2} I_0 + \frac{1}{2} I_0 \cos^2 2\theta \right)$$
$$= \frac{I_0 e^4}{r^2 m^2 c^4} \frac{(1 + \cos^2 2\theta)}{2} \tag{2}$$

The factor $\tfrac{1}{2}(1 + \cos^2 2\theta)$ in this equation appears in subsequent formulas for intensities of reflection from crystals and is known as the "polarization factor."

Scattering by an Atom. In an atom that is much smaller than the wavelength of the incident X-rays, the electrons oscillate back and forth together so that the atom acts as a unit of mass Zm and charge Ze, where Z is the number of electrons in the atom. Equation (2) then becomes

$$I_a = \frac{I_0 (Ze)^4}{r^2 (Zm)^2 c^4} \frac{(1 + \cos^2 2\theta)}{2} = Z^2 I_e \tag{3}$$

In X-ray diffraction work, however, the wavelengths used are of the same order of magnitude as the atomic diameters.   Consequently, the electrons within an atom do not scatter in phase and the intensity is less than the value predicted by Eq. (3).

It is customary to use a quantity f, the *atomic scattering factor*, by which the efficiency of the cooperation among the electrons in the atom may be expressed.   The definition of f is given by the relation

$$f^2 = \frac{I_a}{I_e} \tag{4}$$

or by the equivalent statement—since the intensity of a wave is the square of its amplitude—that *f is the ratio of the amplitude scattered by the atom to that scattered by an electron.*   When θ is very small, f approaches the atomic number Z, because the electrons scatter nearly in phase, as assumed in Eq. (3).   But f falls as θ increases because the waves from the individual electrons must traverse increasingly unequal paths.   Some of the radiation is scattered incoherently with a modified wavelength (Compton scattering); this forms an increasing fraction of the total intensity at the larger angles.

The atomic scattering factor is directly related to the distribution of electricity in the atom.   Every part of the electron cloud surrounding the nucleus of the atom scatters radiation in proportion to its density.   For the atom at rest (not "blurred" by thermal motion in the crystal) the formula for the atomic scattering factor is

$$f_0 = \int_0^\infty U(r) \frac{\sin kr}{kr} dr \tag{5}$$

where $k = 4\pi(\sin\theta)/\lambda$, λ is the wavelength of the radiation, and $U(r)$ represents the radial distribution of electric-charge density. $U(r)dr$ is the number of electrons between r and $r + dr$ from the center of the atom, which is assumed to be spherical,[1] and

$$\int_0^\infty U(r)\ dr = Z$$

[1] It is immaterial whether $U(r)$ is considered as the probability of finding an electron at a radius between r and $r + dr$ or whether it is assumed that a continuous charge is distributed in the atom with a density that varies as $U(r)$.   In the language of wave mechanics, the function ψ of Shrödinger's wave equation is such that $|\psi|^2\ dv$ is the probability of finding an electron in the element of volume dv at the point considered, and it has been shown that Eq. (5) gives the coherent scattering from an atom if we let $U(r) = 4\pi r^2|\psi|^2$.   Thus, wave mechanical models of an atom can predict f_0, and, conversely, experimental f_0 curves afford a test of atomic models.   By using a Fourier analysis of experimental f_0 curves it is possible to calculate directly the electric-charge density of atoms—thus *mathematically* to "see" the atoms with an "X-ray microscope."

It will be seen from Eq. (5) that f_0 is a function of (sin θ)/λ, so that a curve in which f_0 is plotted against (sin θ)/λ can be used for various wavelengths. The f_0 curve calculated for cesium by a method based on wave mechanics is plotted in this way in Fig. 3. These curves can also be determined by direct measurement in certain cases; this has been done by measuring the intensities of diffracted beams from crystals with simple structures (NaCl, MgO, KCl, Al, etc.) and in another way by measuring the intensity of scattering at different angles from the atoms of a gas.[1] It has been found that there is good agreement between f_0 values calculated by the method of Hartree (or in the case of heavy atoms by an approximate method of Thomas and Fermi) and the various experimental results. This gives confidence both in the theory of diffraction and in the atom models used. The tables of calculated f_0 values which are now available for nearly all atoms and some of the common ions are accurate enough to be highly useful in crystal analysis.[2]

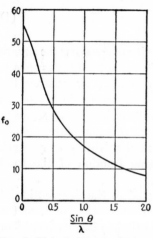

FIG. 3. Plot of structure factor for cesium.

The atomic scattering factors f_0 in Table XXX are given for a series of values of (sin θ)/λ and are therefore applicable to various wavelengths; they apply to atoms at rest and have not been modified by the temperature factor.

In using f_0 tables it must be remembered that they refer to atoms at rest and all values will be reduced by the thermal motions of the atoms in crystals. This correction, which will be discussed later, is often an important one. For example, it reduces the intensity of the tenth-order reflection from (100) planes in NaCl at room temperature to a third the intensity for atoms at rest. While f_0 is tabulated for different values of (sin θ)/λ so as to be applicable to all wavelengths, experiment shows that marked anomalies are introduced when λ is near an absorption edge of an

[1] For summaries of this field of physics see E. O. Wollen, *Rev. Modern Phys.*, vol. 4, p. 205, 1932; A. H. Compton and S. K. Allison, "X-rays in Theory and Experiment," Van Nostrand, New York, 1935; J. T. Randall, "Diffraction of X-rays and Electrons by Amorphous Solids, Liquids, and Gases," Wiley, New York, 1934; P. P. Ewald, "Handbuch der Physik," vol. XXIII/2, Springer, Berlin, 1933.

[2] R. W. James and G. W. Brindley, *Phil. Mag.*, vol. 12, pp. 81, 104, 1931; *Z. Krist.*, vol. 78, p. 490, 1931. W. L. Bragg and J. West, *Z. Krist.*, vol. 69, p. 118, 1928. Linus Pauling and J. Sherman, *Z. Krist.*, vol. 81, p. 1, 1932. A table designed for electron diffraction is given by H. Viervoll and O. Ögrim, *Acta Cryst.*, vol. 2, p. 277, 1949.

TABLE XXX. ATOMIC SCATTERING FACTORS*

$10^{-8} \times \frac{(\sin\theta)}{\lambda}$	0.0	0.1	0.2	0.3	0.4	0.5	0.6	0.7	0.8	0.9	1.0	1.1	1.2
H	1	0.81	0.48	0.25	0.13	0.07	0.04	0.3	0.02	0.01	0.00	0.00	
He	2	1.88	1.46	1.05	0.75	0.52	0.35	0.24	0.18	0.14	0.11	0.09	
Li+	2	1.96	1.8	1.5	1.3	1.0	0.8	0.6	0.5	0.4	0.3	0.3	
Li	3	2.2	1.8	1.5	1.3	1.0	0.8	0.6	0.5	0.4	0.3	0.3	
Be++	2	2.0	1.9	1.7	1.6	1.4	1.2	1.0	0.9	0.7	0.6	0.5	
Be	4	2.9	1.9	1.7	1.6	1.4	1.2	1.0	0.9	0.7	0.6	0.5	
B+3	2	1.99	1.9	1.8	1.7	1.6	1.4	1.3	1.2	1.0	0.9	0.7	
B	5	3.5	2.4	1.9	1.7	1.5	1.4	1.2	1.2	1.0	0.9	0.7	
C	6	4.6	3.0	2.2	1.9	1.7	1.6	1.4	1.3	1.16	1.0	0.9	
N+5	2	2.0	2.0	1.9	1.9	1.8	1.7	1.6	1.5	1.4	1.3	1.16	
N+3	4	3.7	3.0	2.4	2.0	1.8	1.66	1.56	1.49	1.39	1.28	1.17	
N	7	5.8	4.2	3.0	2.3	1.9	1.65	1.54	1.49	1.39	1.29	1.17	
O	8	7.1	5.3	3.9	2.9	2.2	1.8	1.6	1.5	1.4	1.35	1.26	
O-2	10	8.0	5.5	3.8	2.7	2.1	1.8	1.5	1.5	1.4	1.35	1.26	
F	9	7.8	6.2	4.45	3.35	2.65	2.15	1.9	1.7	1.6	1.5	1.35	
F-	10	8.7	6.7	4.8	3.5	2.8	2.2	1.9	1.7	1.55	1.5	1.35	
Ne	10	9.3	7.5	5.8	4.4	3.4	2.65	2.2	1.9	1.65	1.55	1.5	
Na+	10	9.5	8.2	6.7	5.25	4.05	3.2	2.65	2.25	1.95	1.75	1.6	
Na	11	9.65	8.2	6.7	5.25	4.05	3.2	2.65	2.25	1.95	1.75	1.6	
Mg+2	10	9.75	8.6	7.25	5.95	4.8	3.85	3.15	2.55	2.2	2.0	1.8	
Mg	12	10.5	8.6	7.25	5.95	4.8	3.85	3.15	2.55	2.2	2.0	1.8	
Al+3	10	9.7	8.9	7.8	6.65	5.5	4.45	3.65	3.1	2.65	2.3	2.0	
Al	13	11.0	8.95	7.75	6.6	5.5	4.5	3.7	3.1	2.65	2.3	2.0	
Si+4	10	9.75	9.15	8.25	7.15	6.05	5.05	4.2	3.4	2.95	2.6	2.3	
Si	14	11.35	9.4	8.2	7.15	6.1	5.1	4.2	3.4	2.95	2.6	2.3	
P+5	10	9.8	9.25	8.45	7.5	6.55	5.65	4.8	4.05	3.4	3.0	2.6	
P	15	12.4	10.0	8.45	7.45	6.5	5.65	4.8	4.05	3.4	3.0	2.6	
P-3	18	12.7	9.8	8.4	7.45	6.5	5.65	4.85	4.05	3.4	3.0	2.6	
S+6	10	9.85	9.4	8.7	7.85	6.85	6.05	5.25	4.5	3.9	3.35	2.9	
S	16	13.6	10.7	8.95	7.85	6.85	6.0	5.25	4.5	3.9	3.35	2.9	
S-2	18	14.3	10.7	8.9	7.85	6.85	6.0	5.25	4.5	3.9	3.35	2.9	
Cl	17	14.6	11.3	9.25	8.05	7.25	6.5	5.75	5.05	4.4	3.85	3.35	
Cl-	18	15.2	11.5	9.3	8.05	7.25	6.5	5.75	5.05	4.4	3.85	3.35	
A	18	15.9	12.6	10.4	8.7	7.8	7.0	6.2	5.4	4.7	4.1	3.6	
K+	18	16.5	13.3	10.8	8.85	7.75	7.05	6.44	5.9	5.3	4.8	4.2	
Ca++	18	16.8	14.0	11.5	9.3	8.1	7.35	6.7	6.2	5.7	5.1	4.6	
Sc+3	18	16.7	14.0	11.4	9.4	8.3	7.6	6.9	6.4	5.8	5.35	4.85	
Ti+4	18	17.0	14.4	11.9	9.9	8.5	7.85	7.3	6.7	6.15	5.65	5.05	
Rb+	36	33.6	28.7	24.6	21.4	18.9	16.7	14.6	12.8	11.2	9.9	8.9	
Sr	38	34.4	29.0	24.5	20.8	18.4	16.4	14.6	12.9	11.6	10.5	9.5	8.7
Y	39	35.4	29.9	25.3	21.5	19.0	17.0	15.1	13.4	12.0	10.9	9.9	9.0
Zr	40	36.3	30.8	26.0	22.1	19.7	17.5	15.6	13.8	12.4	11.2	10.2	9.3
Nb(Cb)	41	37.3	31.7	26.8	22.8	20.2	18.1	16.0	14.3	12.8	11.6	10.6	9.7
Mo	42	38.2	32.6	27.6	23.5	20.8	18.6	16.5	14.8	13.2	12.0	10.9	10.0
Ma	43	39.1	33.4	28.3	24.1	21.3	19.1	17.0	15.2	13.6	12.3	11.3	10.3
Ru	44	40.0	34.3	29.1	24.7	21.9	19.6	17.5	15.6	14.1	12.7	11.6	10.6
Rh	45	41.0	35.1	29.9	25.4	22.5	20.2	18.0	16.1	14.5	13.1	12.0	11.0
Pd	46	41.9	36.0	30.7	26.2	23.1	20.8	18.5	16.6	14.9	13.6	12.3	11.3
Ag	47	42.8	36.9	31.5	26.9	23.8	21.3	19.0	17.1	15.3	14.0	12.7	11.7
Cd	48	43.7	37.7	32.2	27.5	24.4	21.8	19.6	17.6	15.7	14.3	13.0	12.0
In	49	44.7	38.6	33.0	28.1	25.0	22.4	20.1	18.0	16.2	14.7	13.4	12.3
Sn	50	45.7	39.5	33.8	28.7	25.6	22.9	20.6	18.5	16.6	15.1	13.7	12.7
Sb	51	46.7	40.4	34.6	29.5	26.3	23.5	21.1	19.0	17.0	15.5	14.1	13.0
Te	52	47.7	41.3	35.4	30.3	26.9	24.0	21.7	19.5	17.5	16.0	14.5	13.3
I	53	48.6	42.1	36.1	31.0	27.5	24.6	22.2	20.0	17.9	16.4	14.8	13.6
Xe	54	49.6	43.0	36.8	31.6	28.0	25.2	22.7	20.4	18.4	16.7	15.2	13.9
Cs	55	50.7	43.8	37.6	32.4	28.7	25.8	23.2	20.8	18.8	17.0	15.6	14.5

TABLE XXX. ATOMIC SCATTERING FACTORS.*—(*Continued*)

$10^{-8} \times \frac{(\sin \theta)}{\lambda}$		0.0	0.1	0.2	0.3	0.4	0.5	0.6	0.7	0.8	0.9	1.0	1.1	1.2
Ba	56	51.7	44.7	38.4	33.1	29.3	26.4	23.7	21.3	19.2	17.4	16.0	14.7
La	57	52.6	45.6	39.3	33.8	29.8	26.9	24.3	21.9	19.7	17.9	16.4	15.0
Ce	58	53.6	46.5	40.1	34.5	30.4	27.4	24.8	22.4	20.2	18.4	16.6	15.3
Pr	59	54.5	47.4	40.9	35.2	31.1	28.0	25.4	22.9	20.6	18.8	17.1	15.7
Nd	60	55.4	48.3	41.6	35.9	31.8	28.6	25.9	23.4	21.1	19.2	17.5	16.1
Il	61	56.4	49.1	42.4	36.6	32.4	29.2	26.4	23.9	21.5	19.6	17.9	16.4
Sm	62	57.3	50.0	43.2	37.3	32.9	29.8	26.9	24.4	22.0	20.0	18.3	16.8
Eu	63	58.3	50.9	44.0	38.1	33.5	30.4	27.5	24.9	22.4	20.4	18.7	17.1
Gd	64	59.3	51.7	44.8	38.8	34.1	31.0	28.1	25.4	22.9	20.8	19.1	17.5
Tb	65	60.2	52.6	45.7	39.6	34.7	31.6	28.6	25.9	23.4	21.2	19.5	17.9
Dy	66	61.1	53.6	46.5	40.4	35.4	32.2	29.2	26.3	23.9	21.6	19.9	18.3
Ho	67	62.1	54.5	47.3	41.1	36.1	32.7	29.7	26.8	24.3	22.0	20.3	18.6
Er	68	63.0	55.3	48.1	41.7	36.7	33.3	30.2	27.3	24.7	22.4	20.7	18.9
Tu	69	64.0	56.2	48.9	42.4	37.4	33.9	30.8	27.9	25.2	22.9	21.0	19.3
Yb	70	64.9	57.0	49.7	43.2	38.0	34.4	31.3	28.4	25.7	23.3	21.4	19.7
Lu	71	65.9	57.8	50.4	43.9	38.7	35.0	31.8	28.9	26.2	23.8	21.8	20.0
Hf	72	66.8	58.6	51.2	44.5	39.3	35.6	32.3	29.3	26.7	24.2	22.3	20.4
Ta	73	67.8	59.5	52.0	45.3	39.9	36.2	32.9	29.8	27.1	24.7	22.6	20.9
W	74	68.8	60.4	52.8	46.1	40.5	36.8	33.5	30.4	27.6	25.2	23.0	21.3
Re	75	69.8	61.3	53.6	46.8	41.1	37.4	34.0	30.9	28.1	25.6	23.4	21.6
Os	76	70.8	62.2	54.4	47.5	41.7	38.0	34.6	31.4	28.6	26.0	23.9	22.0
Ir	77	71.7	63.1	55.3	48.2	42.4	38.6	35.1	32.0	29.0	26.5	24.3	22.3
Pt	78	72.6	64.0	56.2	48.9	43.1	39.2	35.6	32.5	29.5	27.0	24.7	22.7
Au	79	73.6	65.0	57.0	49.7	43.8	39.8	36.2	33.1	30.0	27.4	25.1	23.1
Hg	80	74.6	65.9	57.9	50.5	44.4	40.5	36.8	33.6	30.6	27.8	25.6	23.6
Tl	81	75.5	66.7	58.7	51.2	45.0	41.1	37.4	34.1	31.1	28.3	26.0	24.1
Pb	82	76.5	67.5	59.5	51.9	45.7	41.6	37.9	34.6	31.5	28.8	26.4	24.5
Bi	83	77.5	68.4	60.4	52.7	46.4	42.2	38.5	35.1	32.0	29.2	26.8	24.8
Po	84	78.4	69.4	61.3	53.5	47.1	42.8	39.1	35.6	32.6	29.7	27.2	25.2
—	85	79.4	70.3	62.1	54.2	47.7	43.4	39.6	36.2	33.1	30.1	27.6	25.6
Em (Rn, Nt)	86	80.3	71.3	63.0	55.1	48.4	44.0	40.2	36.8	33.5	30.5	28.0	26.0
—	87	81.3	72.2	63.8	55.8	49.1	44.5	40.7	37.3	34.0	31.0	28.4	26.4
Ra	88	82.2	73.2	64.6	56.5	49.8	45.1	41.3	37.8	34.6	31.5	28.8	26.7
Ac	89	83.2	74.1	65.5	57.3	50.4	45.8	41.8	38.3	35.1	32.0	29.2	27.1
Th	90	84.1	75.1	66.3	58.1	51.1	46.5	42.4	38.8	35.5	32.4	29.6	27.5
Pa	91	85.1	76.0	67.1	58.8	51.7	47.1	43.0	39.3	36.0	32.8	30.1	27.9
U	92	86.0	76.9	67.9	59.6	52.4	47.7	43.5	39.8	36.5	33.3	30.6	28.3

* Values are from R. W. James and G. W. Brindley (*Z. Krist.*, vol. 78, p. 470, 1931) and from "Internationale Tabellen zur Bestimmung von Kristallstrukturen," vol. II, Bornträger, Berlin, 1935; values for the lighter elements were computed by Hartree's method or by interpolation; elements heavier than rubidium were computed by the Thomas-Fermi method.

atom in the diffracting crystal; f_0 is decreased several units under these conditions.[1]

Scattering from a Unit Cell. Let us now consider the intensity of the diffracted beams that arise from the cooperation of the coherently scattered waves from each atom in the unit cell. Each atom scatters as a unit with an amplitude proportional to f and with a certain phase dependent upon its position. To compute the intensity of the diffracted beam it

[1] This has been made use of to increase the difference between scattering powers of Cu and Zn atoms in beta-brass in order to show up their distribution on the lattice points, a distribution otherwise masked by the great similarity in their scattering power (F. W. Jones and C. Sykes, *Proc. Roy. Soc. (London)*, vol. A161, p. 440, 1937).

is necessary to add sine waves of different amplitude and phase but of the same wavelength and to determine the amplitude of the sine wave that results. The intensity of the diffracted wave is the square of this amplitude. Differences in atomic scattering power lead to different amplitudes of the waves from individual atoms, while differing positions of the atoms along the path of the incident and diffracted beams determine the relative phases of these waves.

If the amplitude of each wave is represented by the length of a vector and its phase by the direction of the vector, the resultant diffracted beam will be represented by the vector sum of all the individual waves. This is indicated in Fig. 4 where four vectors of lengths f_1, f_2, f_3, and f_4 are drawn to represent the atomic scattering factors for four atoms of a unit

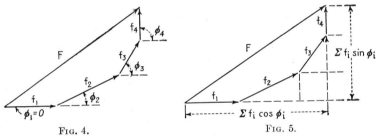

FIG. 4.   FIG. 5.

FIGS. 4 and 5. Vector addition of diffracted rays from individual atoms.

cell, and the angles ϕ_1, ϕ_2, ϕ_3, and ϕ_4 are drawn to represent the phases of the waves scattered by these individual atoms. The square of the length of the resultant vector, $|F|^2$, is proportional to the intensity that will be observed.

Reference to Fig. 5 shows that each vector may be resolved into a horizontal and a vertical component of lengths $f \cos \phi$ and $f \sin \phi$, respectively; these components when added give two sides of a right triangle whose hypotenuse is F. The square of the hypotenuse is given by the sum of the squares of the sides, and so we may write

$$|F|^2 = (f_1 \cos \phi_1 + f_2 \cos \phi_2 + \cdots)^2 + (f_1 \sin \phi_1 + f_2 \sin \phi_2 + \cdots)^2$$
$$= (\Sigma_i f_i \cos \phi_i)^2 + (\Sigma_i f_i \sin \phi_i)^2 \tag{6}$$

where the summation is to be carried out over all atoms in the unit cell, as indicated by the subscript $i = 1, 2, 3 \cdots$. Since f_i is the ratio of the amplitude of scattering by the ith atom to that scattered under the same conditions by an electron, the resultant intensity is proportional to $I_e|F|^2$. The quantity F is the *structure factor* or *structure amplitude* and is *the ratio of the amplitude of the wave scattered in a given direction by all the atoms in a unit cell to that scattered by a single electron under identical conditions.*

Relation of Phase, ϕ, to Atomic Position. A simple formula gives the value of the phase, ϕ, of Eq. (6) for an atom at the position uvw in a unit cell and for the hkl reflection. Consider first only the atoms on a simple lattice. A set of parallel planes in this lattice will produce diffracted beams going in directions (given by Bragg's law) such that neighboring planes of the set will contribute waves exactly in phase with one another. The phase difference between waves from adjacent planes of the simple lattice will thus be 2π in the first order and $2\pi n$ in the nth order. However, the nth-order reflection of a plane is conventionally treated as the first-order reflection from a fictitious set of planes of $1/n$th the spacing and having indices n times the Miller indices. The interplanar distance for these fictitious planes in a cubic crystal with a lattice constant a_0 is given by

$$d = \frac{a_0}{\sqrt{h^2 + k^2 + l^2}} \qquad \text{(cubic)} \qquad (7)$$

where h, k, l are the reflection indices. The phase difference between waves from neighboring planes of the set is proportional to the path difference for these rays and is equal to 2π.

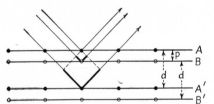

The path difference for the planes A, A' of spacing d is indicated in Fig. 6 by a heavy line. Consider a set of interleaved planes B, B' having the same spacing as these A planes. If the distance to the B plane is p, then the path difference to this plane is p/d of that to the A'

Fig. 6. Reflection from interleaved planes. Path differences are indicated by heavy lines.

plane, as will be seen from the heavy lines in the figure. Consequently, the phase difference between the ray reflected by the first A plane and the first B plane will be given by $2\pi p/d$. It can be shown geometrically that, with the same convention as used in formula (7), an atom at coordinates uvw in the unit cell will lie on a set of planes with indices (hkl) such that the plane next to the origin will be at a distance from the origin given by the equation

$$p = \frac{a_0(hu + kv + lw)}{\sqrt{h^2 + k^2 + l^2}} \qquad \text{(cubic)} \qquad (8)$$

Hence Eqs. (7) and (8) give the required expression for the phase of the wave from this atom,

$$\phi = \frac{2\pi p}{d} = 2\pi(hu + kv + lw)$$

Upon substituting in Eq. (6), the complete expression for the structure factor becomes

$$|F|^2 = [\Sigma_i f_i \cos 2\pi(hu_i + kv_i + lw_i)]^2 + [\Sigma_i f_i \sin 2\pi(hu_i + kv_i + lw_i)]^2 \quad (9)$$

where u_i, v_i, and w_i are the coordinates of the ith atom of the unit cell whose atomic scattering factor is f_i and where hkl are the indices of the reflection. The summation extends over all atoms in the unit cell.

The above discussion has been limited for simplicity to cubic crystals, but the same principles hold for other systems of axes, and *Eq.* (9) *is true for all crystal systems.* It is an equation of the utmost importance in crystallography, for the determination of atomic positions in crystals is always based on this relation between the coordinates of the atom in a unit cell and the intensity with which they will scatter X-rays in the different spectra. This equation has been applied to each of the 230 space groups, and the characteristic features of the reflections for each space group have been derived from it and tabulated.[1] There will be certain reflections absent from the diffraction pattern of a crystal because $|F|^2 = 0$ for these. By comparing a list of the missing reflections with the tables it is usually possible to determine to which one (or more) of the space groups the crystal might belong. When the space group has been determined, to find how the atoms are arranged in the unit cell it is necessary to employ the structure-factor equation either in the general form, Eq. (9), or more conveniently in a simplified form appropriate to the particular space group in question.

The equation will give one value of the structure factor of a reflection for each arrangement of atoms in the cell, and the problem is essentially one of choosing an arrangement such that the coordinates for all atoms, when inserted in the structure-factor equation, will predict the intensities actually observed for each of the reflections of the diffraction pattern. This extremely tedious procedure has been shortened and simplified in many ways, some of which are discussed in Chap. VIII, page 161, and in Appendix II.

Equation (9) reduces to a simpler form when the crystal has a center of symmetry and when this center is chosen as the origin of coordinates. The expression then becomes

$$|F|^2 = [\Sigma_i f_i \cos 2\pi(hu_i + kv_i + lw_i)]^2 \quad (10)$$

The Temperature Factor. In the section on the atomic scattering factor it was assumed that the atom was at rest. In crystals, however, the atoms are oscillating constantly and very rapidly about their mean

---

[1] "Internationale Tabellen zur Bestimmung von Kristallstrukturen," vol. I, Bornträger, Berlin, 1935. K. Lonsdale, "Simplified Structure Factor and Electron Density Formulae for the 230 Space Groups of Mathematical Crystallography," G. Bell, London, 1936.

position.   The effect of this thermal motion is to smear the electron distribution to larger radii and to decrease the scattering factor, f, below the value for the atom at rest, f_0.   The higher the temperature the more

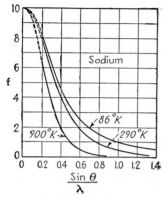

blurred the atom will appear and the more rapidly f will decrease with increasing angle, as will be seen from the curves of Fig. 7 for sodium atoms in crystals of rock salt at different temperatures.

It has been calculated that for an atom vibrating as a whole

$$f = f_0 e^{-M} \qquad (11)$$

where

$$M = 8\pi^2 \bar{U}^2 \left(\frac{\sin \theta}{\lambda} \right)^2$$

$\bar{U}^2$ being the mean square displacement of the atoms from their mean position measured at right angles to the reflecting planes.[1]

Since the atoms in a unit cell may have displacements that differ among themselves, the values of M may be different for each atom, and, strictly, Eq. (9) should be written

$$|F|^2 = [\Sigma f_0 e^{-M} \cos 2\pi(hu + kv + lw)]^2 \\ + [\Sigma f_0 e^{-M} \sin 2\pi(hu + kv + lw)]^2 \quad (12)$$

with the appropriate values of M inserted for each atom; furthermore, M may vary with the direction of the crystal planes, thus with the indices (hkl).   In practice, it is common to make the simplifying assumption that the mean displacement is the same for all atoms and all crystal planes; so Eq. (9) may be written

$$|F|^2 = |F_0|^2 e^{-2M} = e^{-2M} \{ [\Sigma f_0 \cos 2\pi(hu + kv + lw)]^2 \\ + [\Sigma f_0 \sin 2\pi(hu + kv + lw)]^2 \} \quad (13)$$

Figure 8 shows the values of the factor e^{-2M} for a number of common crystals, and it will be noticed that it is a function that falls slowly with increasing diffraction angle.   When the temperature factor is unknown or uncertain, it is best in comparing calculated and observed intensities of X-ray reflections to make all comparisons within groups of reflections having approximately similar θ values, since only small variations in e^{-2M} are to be expected within small ranges of θ.

[1] For detailed discussion of this factor see books on the theory of X-ray diffraction, and the current edition of "International Tables for Crystal Structure Determination."

Geometrical Factors Influencing Intensities of Diffracted X-rays. In the preceding sections it has been pointed out that the intensity of a diffracted beam depends on the structure factor, and this in turn on the temperature and also on the state of polarization of the primary beam. But additional factors belong in formulas giving diffracted beam intensities; these will now be presented. A summary at the end of this appendix lists the more important formulas. In practice, many structures have been determined without corrections for temperature, absorption, or extinction and with intensities estimated by eye with an error of some 25 per cent; the amount of effort that should be put on these correc-

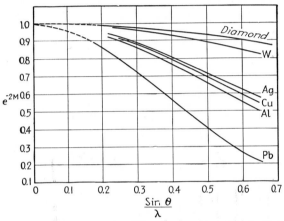

Fig. 8. Values of temperature factor for different elements. (*F. C. Blake, Rev. Modern Phys., vol. 5, p. 169, 1933.*)

tions depends on the difficulty to be encountered in a given structure determination.

1. THE LORENTZ FACTOR. A perfect crystallite can reflect a monochromatic beam of X-rays not only under the exact value of the glancing angle θ given by Bragg's law but also with smaller intensities at angles deviating some seconds of arc from this value. Darwin and others have calculated the total energy in the diffracted beam, taking into account this variable reflecting power near the angle θ.

The factor in the intensity equation that takes this into account differs for the different methods of diffraction (Laue, rotating crystal, powder, etc.), and a derivation would be too lengthy for presentation here. For our purposes it is sufficient to know the results. The total energy per second diffracted from a set of crystal planes (*hkl*) in the powder method is proportional to $1/\sin \theta$. This energy, however, spreads out along the generators of a cone and intersects the film to form a ring. In the powder method (Debye-Scherrer-Hull method) we observe only a fraction of the total circumference of this ring on a cylindrical film, and the blackening of the ring will depend not only upon the total energy contributing to the ring but also on the circumference over which this is spread.

If the radius of a cylindrical powder camera is R, Fig. 9, the film will intersect a circle of circumference $2\pi R \sin 2\theta$, from which it follows that the energy per centimeter along the circumference of this circle will be the product of the factor $1/\sin \theta$ mentioned in the preceding paragraph and the factor $1/(2\pi R \sin 2\theta)$, and the blackening of the powder diffraction line will thus be dependent upon this product, the so-called *Lorentz factor*, $1/(\sin 2\theta \sin \theta)$, which may also be written $1/(2 \sin^2 \theta \cos \theta)$. The various constants that go with these factors to make up the complete formula are of little interest to us in the usual crystallographic problems since they are the same for all lines on a given powder diffraction pattern

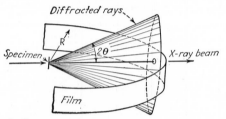

Fig. 9. Geometry of a Debye ring in a powder camera.

(as, for example, the radius of the camera, R) and do not influence the *relative* intensities of lines in the pattern.

Tables of the combined Lorentz and polarization factors for the more important X-ray diffraction methods have been published.[1] Buerger has shown that the Lorentz and polarization factor can be automatically corrected for in certain cameras by a high-speed rotating template in front of the film.[2]

2. THE MULTIPLICITY FACTOR, p. It is obvious that with several different sets of planes diffracting to a given spot on a photographic film the intensity at that spot will be greater than it would be with only one set of planes contributing. Since the reflections from the different sets are independent of one another, the intensity from p sets of equivalent planes contributing to the same area on the film will be p times the intensity from one set. In the powder method all planes of the same interplanar spacing will contribute to the same ring on the film, and p for any crystal will then be equal to the number of permutations of indices h, k, l that give identical values of $\sin^2 \theta$ in the quadratic form for the crystal.

[1] See "Internationale Tabellen zur Bestimmung von Kristallstrukturen," vol. II, pp. 556–568, Bornträger, Berlin, 1935, for discussion and tables of the Lorentz polarization factors. At the end of the present appendix will be found a list of the intensity formulas for each method.

[2] M. J. Buerger, *Proc. Natl. Acad. Sci.*, vol. 25, p. 383, 1939.

In cubic crystals of the most common classes, O_h, O, and T_d, the "multiplicity factor" p has the following values:

Planes............	{100}	{111}	{110}	{hk0}	{hhl}	{hkl}
Multiplicity.......	6	8	12	24	24	48

Any higher order reflections from these planes will have the same multiplicity factors as the listed ones. The multiplicity factor is determined by the crystal symmetry and for the powder method is tabulated in many crystallographic reference books.

Certain points should be kept in mind in connection with this factor. (1) It is only in the powder method that *all* planes of similar spacing can superpose their reflections, and so it is only for this method that the tabulated values of p hold. In the rotating-crystal or oscillating-crystal methods the orientation of the equivalent planes with respect to the axis of rotation will determine how many different sets give superimposed reflections, and p will usually be less than the values for the powder method.[1] (2) Planes of different forms may have the same interplanar spacings and superposed reflections; both sets of planes must then be taken into account. For example, in face-centered cubic crystals, {333} and {511} planes have identical spacings and contribute to the same Debye ring with different structure factors and multiplicity factors. (3) For the rotating- and oscillating-crystal methods the multiplicity factor depends on the orientation of the crystal in the camera; in the oscillating-crystal method, it also depends upon the range of oscillation.

3. THE ABSORPTION FACTOR, $A(\theta)$. The path of the reflected beam within the crystalline specimen varies with the angle of reflection and results in a reduction of intensity that changes with θ and with the shape of the specimen. The "absorption factor" that is inserted into intensity formulas to correct for this is one of the slowly varying factors that does not have an important influence on the relative intensities of *neighboring* reflections. It has been neglected by most experimenters, but Claassen,[2] Rusterholtz,[3] Blake,[4] and Bradley[5] have given detailed discussions of it

---

[1] Tables will be found in F. Halla and H. Mark, "Röntgenographische Untersuchung von Kristallen," p. 236, Barth, Leipzig, 1937; and for the powder method in R. W. G. Wyckoff, "Structure of Crystals," 2d ed., p. 177, Chemical Catalog Co., New York, 1931. For certain crystals of lower symmetry (with parallel-face hemihedrism) the structure factor of certain superposed reflections may differ from others, *i.e.*, the different faces of a form will not have equal reflecting powers. This should be taken into account in evaluating p.

[2] A. Claassen, *Phil. Mag.*, vol. 9, p. 57, 1930.

[3] A. Rusterholtz, *Helv. Phys. Acta*, vol. 4, p. 68, 1931.

[4] F. C. Blake, *Rev. Modern Phys.*, vol. 5, p. 169, 1933.

[5] A. J. Bradley, *Proc. Phys. Soc. (London)*, vol. 47, p. 879, 1935.

and have presented curves for predicting it from the known dimensions and absorption coefficient of the sample when the sample is a cylindrical rod in the powder method. While it is frequently an unimportant factor, as when molybdenum radiation is used on small specimens of low absorption coefficient, it may change manyfold when soft radiation is used. Calculations of the absorption factor, $A(\theta)$, by Blake are represented in Fig. 10, in which the ratio of the factor at angle θ compared with the factor at $\theta = 90°$ is plotted against θ for cylindrical samples. The radius of the

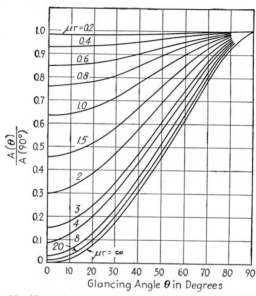

FIG. 10. Absorption factor for cylindrical specimens. (*Blake.*)

sample is assumed small compared with the radius of the cylindrical camera (*e.g.*, about 0.02-cm-diameter samples in ordinary Debye cameras). In this figure, r is the sample radius in centimeters and μ is the linear absorption coefficient for the rays in the powdered sample—not in the solid crystal—and the curves are plotted for different values of the product μr.*

The problem of absorption in powdered specimens when the particles are not so small that absorption within each is negligible is critically discussed by Brindley.[1] The question is of importance in quantitative analysis of mixed powders by diffraction; it involves not only the absorption of the specimen as a whole, but also the absorption coefficient in each

---

* Tables will be found in "Internationale Tabellen zur Bestimmung von Kristallstrukturen," vol. II, Bornträger, Berlin, 1935. For powders of 200 mesh or smaller, μr is perhaps 0.6 of the value for a homogeneous solid.

[1] G. W. Brindley, *Phil. Mag.*, vol. 36, p. 347, 1945.

substance individually and the effective size of the particles of each substance.

The absorption factor has been treated for rotating-crystal patterns,[1] Weissenberg patterns,[2] and others, but depends on the external shape of the crystal being used. The complications introduced by the crystal shape may be avoided by preparing a cylindrical crystal or a spherical one and employing the corrections worked out for these. A better solution, when it can be applied, is to use a crystal so small that absorption in the crystal is negligible.

4. THE VELOCITY FACTOR, $V(\theta)$, IN ROTATING- AND OSCILLATING-CRYSTAL METHODS. When a single crystal is turned about an axis with constant angular velocity, the crystal planes have various lengths of time in which to reflect, times that are inversely proportional to the rate of change of the glancing angle θ as the crystal rotates. Only for those planes which reflect to the equatorial line of spots (the planes whose zone axis coincides with the rotation axis) is $V(\theta)$, the velocity factor, equal to unity; it is less than unity for all spots above or below the equator and depends on the position of the spot in a way shown graphically in Fig. 11 for a cylindrical film.[3] If this figure is placed on a rotating- or oscillating-crystal pattern reduced to the same scale, the factor applicable to any spot can be read directly from the line that falls on that spot. Spots lying approximately above or below the direct beam at the center of the chart always give untrustworthy intensity data. The factor for Weissenberg photographs has been treated by Tunell[4] and by Warren and Fankuchen.[5]

5. EXTINCTION. A perfect crystal that is reflecting a strong beam acts as if it had a very high absorption coefficient. This effect, known as "primary extinction," results from the fact that within a perfect crystal if the Bragg-reflection condition is met for the primary ray it is also met for the reflected ray. A twice-reflected ray is therefore formed, which travels along with the primary and cancels a portion of the primary intensity. (This is because there is a shift of phase of 90° upon reflection, a shift of 180° with two reflections.) Reflecting power is also reduced by

[1] A. J. Bradley, *Proc. Phys. Soc. (London)*, vol. 47, p. 879, 1935.

[2] O. P. Hendershot, *Rev. Sci. Instruments*, vol. 8, p. 324, 1937.

[3] E. G. Cox and W. F. B. Shaw, *Proc. Roy. Soc. (London)*, vol. A127, p. 71, 1930. Other references are H. Ott, *Z. Physik*, vol. 88, p. 699, 1934; E. Schiebold, "Methoden der Kristallstrukturbestimmung mittels Röntgenstrahlen," vol. II, Die Drehkristallmethode, Akademische Verlagsgesellschaft m.b.H., Leipzig, 1932; H. Ott, "Handbuch der Experimentalphysik," Wien and Harms, vol. VII/2, Akademische Verlagsgesellschaft m.b.H., Leipzig, 1928; A. Hettich, *Z. Krist.*, vol. 90, p. 473, 1935. For Weissenberg photographs (inclined), see G. Tunell, *Am. Mineral.*, vol. 24, p. 448, 1939.

[4] G. Tunell, *Am. Mineral.*, vol. 24, p. 448, 1939.

[5] B. E. Warren and I. Fankuchen, *Rev. Sci. Instruments*, vol. 12, p. 90, 1941.

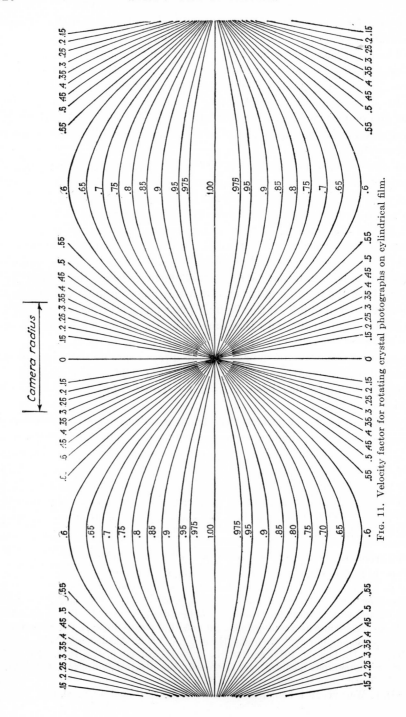

Fig. 11. Velocity factor for rotating crystal photographs on cylindrical film.

another effect, "secondary extinction," that is due to the upper blocks of a mosaic crystal, when they reflect, shielding the lower blocks. In precision measurements of integrated intensity both forms of extinction are important, for they may be very large for strong reflections and crystals of high perfection. The magnitudes of the effects vary from one sample to another of a given substance; so corrections are determined for each individual sample investigated. The effects may be minimized by reducing the perfection of the crystal—in effect reducing the size of the mosaic blocks within which the structure is perfect. The strains introduced into a crystal surface by grinding reduce extinction in the surface layers markedly; powdering a crystal is even more effective. Secondary extinction may be corrected for, to a good approximation, by assuming that the absorption coefficient is increased above normal by an amount that is proportional to the intensity of reflection.[1]

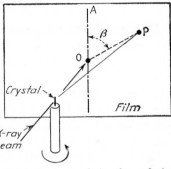

FIG. 12. Angle β in the velocity factor.

Summary of Formulas for Relative Intensities.

1. Powder method, cylindrical film (Debye-Scherrer-Hull cameras):

$$I \propto \frac{(1 + \cos^2 2\theta)}{\sin^2 \theta \cos \theta} \cdot p \cdot |F|^2 \cdot A(\theta) \tag{14}$$

2. Rotating- and oscillating-crystal method, assuming negligible absorption:

$$I \propto \frac{(1 + \cos^2 2\theta)}{\sin 2\theta} \cdot p' \cdot |F|^2 \cdot V(\theta) \tag{15}$$

For flat films, $V(\theta) = 1/\sin \beta$, where β is the angle in Fig. 12 between OP and OA, where O is the central spot, P the diffracted spot, and OA the projection on the film of the axis of rotation. For cylindrical films, see Fig. 10. The multiplicity factor p' must be calculated for each spot; in photogoniometers, such as the Weissenberg, p' is always unity.

3. Laue method:

$$I \propto \frac{(1 + \cos^2 2\theta)}{\sin^2 \theta} \cdot |F|^2 \cdot A'(\theta) \cdot f(\lambda) \tag{16}$$

where $f(\lambda)$ takes account of the variation with wavelength of the photographic efficiency and the incident intensity.

---

[1] For detailed treatments of extinction see books on diffraction theory; for example, R. W. James, "The Optical Principles of the Diffraction of X-rays," G. Bell, London, 1948.

APPENDIX II

DETERMINATION OF CRYSTAL STRUCTURE
WITH FOURIER SERIES

Electron Density Expressed by Fourier Series. The density of the diffracting material in a crystal (the electron density) varies periodically along any direction through the lattice, going through a complicated cycle of peaks and minima with the same spatial periodicity as the distribution of atoms of the lattice. Therefore, it is possible to describe the electron distribution by a Fourier series,[1] as can be done for any periodic function. Let us consider first the general case, which is not convenient to use in structure analysis, and then treat certain special cases and modifications.

Let $\rho(uvw)$ represent the electron density at a point whose coordinates in the unit cell are uvw. If a Fourier series for $\rho(uvw)$ is set up, each term in the series represents a stationary system of density waves. Each set of waves is capable of diffracting X-rays with a certain intensity, $|F(hkl)|^2$, for the successive parallel sheets of density act as reflecting planes. A set of standing waves parallel to the (hkl) plane in the crystal is represented by a Fourier term having $F(hkl)$ as a coefficient, and summing all terms gives the series

$$\rho(uvw) = \frac{1}{V} \sum_{h=-\infty}^{+\infty} \sum_{k=-\infty}^{+\infty} \sum_{l=-\infty}^{+\infty} F(hkl)e^{2\pi i(hu+kv+lw)} \qquad (1)$$

where V is the volume of the unit cell. Carrying out the summation is thus equivalent to superimposing the sheets of electron density, crossing each other in all directions, and also results in adding a constant term $F(000)$ which is equal to the total number of electrons in the unit cell. The relation is stated using the complex quantity $i = \sqrt{-1}$ because this is a convenient way to take account not only of the amplitude but also of the change of phase of the beam when it is scattered.[2]

---

[1] Reviews of this field will be found in W. L. Bragg and J. West, *Phil. Mag.*, vol. 10, p. 823, 1930. W. L. Bragg, "The Crystalline State," Macmillan, New York, 1934. A. H. Compton and S. K. Allison, "X-rays in Theory and Experiment," Van Nostrand, New York, 1935. J. M. Robertson, "Reports on Progress in Physics," vol. IV, pp. 332–367, Physical Society, London, 1938.

[2] Usually $|F(hkl)| = |F(\bar{h}\bar{k}\bar{l})|$ (Friedel's law) when the wavelength used is not near an absorption edge of any atom in the crystal and when the phase change on scattering is the same for all the electrons.

This expression takes a simple form when the crystal has a center of symmetry, for then the imaginary parts vanish and

$$\rho(uvw) = \frac{1}{V} \sum_{h=-\infty}^{+\infty} \sum_{k=-\infty}^{+\infty} \sum_{l=-\infty}^{+\infty} F(hkl) \cos 2\pi(hu + kv + lw) \qquad (2)$$

A direct determination of crystal structure is suggested by this relation: if one determines a great many $F(hkl)$ values for various planes and solves the series for different points (uvw) in the unit cell, a plot results that shows the distribution of electrons throughout the cell with peaks occurring at the position of atom centers. There are serious hindrances to this procedure, however. In the first place, there is an ambiguity as to the sign of each term, for the intensities are proportional to $|F(hkl)|^2$, not to $F(hkl)$. It requires an approximate knowledge of the structure of the crystal to determine these signs, for they are positive or negative depending on whether the diffracted waves have a phase the same as or opposite to that of a wave scattered by the origin. The second hindrance to the use of Eq. (2) is the tremendous number of calculations involved.

By projecting the electron density in the unit cell onto one of the principal planes of the crystal the number of terms to be calculated can be diminished from several thousand to several hundred. Suppose the electron density is projected parallel to the a axis so as to form a density pattern on the plane containing the b and c axes; Eq. (1) then reduces to

$$\rho(vw) = \frac{1}{A} \sum_{k=-\infty}^{+\infty} \sum_{l=-\infty}^{+\infty} F(0kl)e^{2\pi i(kv+lw)} \qquad (3)$$

or, if the projection has a center of symmetry at the origin,

$$\rho(vw) = \frac{1}{A} \sum_{k=-\infty}^{+\infty} \sum_{l=-\infty}^{+\infty} F(0kl) \cos 2\pi(kv + lw) \qquad (4)$$

where A is the area of the face of the unit cell on which the projection is made. It will be seen that the only data needed for this projection are the reflections from planes of the type $(0kl)$ (prism reflections), which belong to a single zone [100]. A plot of this function is shown in Fig. 1 for the crystal shown in a similar projection in Fig. 2.[1] The same uncertainty as to signs of the terms has to be dealt with by preliminary determinations of the structure.

This method has received considerable attention since its development by W. L. Bragg. Other types of projection somewhat analogous to this

[1] W. L. Bragg, Z. *Krist.* vol. 70, p. 475, 1929.

were devised earlier by A. H. Compton and others but are less used in structure analysis. Lonsdale[1] has published simplified electron-density formulas for each of the space groups; these speed the computations relating reflection intensities to atom positions.

FIG. 1. Electron density of diopside (calcium-magnesium silicate) projected upon (010) plane. (*W. L. Bragg.*)

It should be noticed that series which predict structure factors from an assumed distribution of atom positions [Chap. IV, page 78] are just the inverse of the series of this chapter, which deduce structures from observed F values.

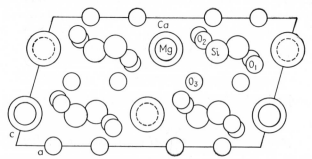

FIG. 2. Atom positions in diopside, projected as in Fig. 1. (*W. L. Bragg.*)

The F^2 Series of Patterson. A later development by Patterson[2] and its modification by Harker[3] stem from the same fundamental principles and will find wide usage in solving complex structures. It is possible to set up a Fourier series in which $|F(hkl)|^2$ occurs, and information about the atomic positions can be derived from it *without making assumptions as to*

[1] K. Lonsdale, "Simplified Structure Factor and Electron Density Formulae for the 230 Space Groups of Mathematical Crystallography," G. Bell, London, 1936.

[2] A. L. Patterson, *Z. Krist.*, vol. 90, pp. 517, 543, 1935; *Phys. Rev.*, vol. 46, p. 372, 1934.

[3] D. Harker, *J. Chem. Phys.*, vol. 4, p. 381, 1936.

the signs of the coefficients as is necessary in $F(hkl)$ series. Patterson's series for three dimensions is

$$P(uvw) = \sum_{h=-\infty}^{+\infty} \sum_{k=-\infty}^{+\infty} \sum_{l=-\infty}^{+\infty} |F(hkl)|^2 \, e^{2\pi i(hu+kv+lw)}$$

This reduces to the cosine form (either with or without a center of symmetry in the crystal),

$$P(uvw) = \sum_{h=-\infty}^{+\infty} \sum_{k=-\infty}^{+\infty} \sum_{l=-\infty}^{+\infty} |F(hkl)|^2 \cos 2\pi(hu + kv + lw) \quad (5)$$

The function $P(uvw)$ represents the product of the electron density at any point in the unit cell whose coordinates are xyz and the electron density at another point whose coordinates are $x + u$, $y + v$, $z + w$. Thus, if there is an atom in the crystal at xyz and another at $x + u$, $y + v$, $z + w$, there will be two peaks in the electron density $\rho(xyz)$, their distance apart will be given by the vector whose components are uvw, and there will be a maximum in $P(uvw)$ at the point uvw corresponding to this pair of atoms. In other words, Eq. (5) defines an electron-density product $P(uvw)$ that has maxima at distances and directions from the origin corresponding to the distances and directions between pairs of atoms in the crystal. The amplitudes of the peaks of $P(uvw)$ correspond to the products of the electron densities at the two points considered (roughly products of the two atomic numbers).

This triple Fourier series cannot be employed without a prohibitive amount of labor in calculation, but it becomes manageable if $P(uvw)$ is projected on one of the faces of the unit cell. With projection along the c axis onto the (001) plane, for instance, the projected function is

$$p(uv) = \int_0^1 P(uvw) \, dw = \sum_{h=-\infty}^{+\infty} \sum_{k=-\infty}^{+\infty} |F(hk0)|^2 \cos 2\pi(hu + kv) \quad (6)$$

A two-dimensional "Patterson plot" can then be made of the function $p(uv)$ with contours drawn to show the distribution of this function throughout the projection, as shown in Fig. 3.[1] A peak at uv on this plot corresponds to an interatomic distance in the crystal whose components along the x and y axes are u and v. It is to be noted that there is a certain ambiguity in interpreting the plot because it shows only the uv components of the interatomic vectors rather than the true vectors with components uvw; thus if there are two interatomic vectors with

---

[1] A. L. Patterson, *Z. Krist.*, vol. 90, pp. 517, 543, 1935. It is frequently unnecessary to plot more than a half or a quarter of a unit cell, if symmetry elements supply the rest.

u and v components the same but with the w component different, these will superpose on the $P(uv)$ plot.

In practice, the operations involved in using Eq. (6) are as follows: The intensities of all available reflections of the [001] zone are measured. This may be done by visual estimation of intensities from a film, using a set of graded exposures as a comparison standard. The intensities are then corrected by the Lorentz and polarization factors, and perhaps by additional factors, so as to yield $|F(hkl)|^2$ values. The series is then computed for a large number of values of u and v—perhaps 60 values of each variable—each value of $p(uv)$ being determined by some 20 to 200 values of $|F(hkl)|^2$. The computed values are plotted on a projection, and points of equal value are connected by contour lines as in Fig. 3.

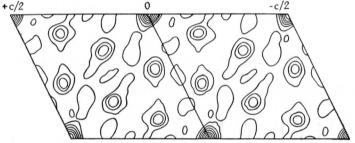

+c/2   0   -c/2

FIG. 3. Contour-line plot of F^2 series for C_6Cl_6. (*Patterson.*)

The Patterson-Harker F^2 Series.   Harker[1] has applied Eq. (5) in such a way as to make use of knowledge of the symmetry elements in crystals, thus simplifying the method.   When preliminary analysis has determined the space group to which a crystal belongs, a knowledge of the symmetry elements makes it possible to write down all the possible equivalent positions that atoms can occupy.   Suppose there is a *twofold axis* parallel to the b axis of the crystal; then an atom at xyz has an equivalent atom at $\bar{x}y\bar{z}$, and the vector between these two has components $2x$, 0, $2z$.   These values substituted in Eq. (5) will yield a maximum value of $P(uvw)$ at the point $u = 2x$, $v = 0$, $w = 2z$, which will be a point in the plane $v = 0$.   Every other atom will also be paired with an equivalent atom in the same way and will lead to maxima in the same plane.   Therefore, the u and w coordinates of every atom in the crystal can be found by evaluating $P(uvw)$ for the special case of $v = 0$.   Equation (5) then becomes

$$P(u0w) = \sum_{h=-\infty}^{+\infty} \sum_{k=-\infty}^{+\infty} \sum_{l=-\infty}^{+\infty} |F(hkl)|^2 \cos 2\pi(hu + lw)$$

$$= \sum_{h=-\infty}^{+\infty} \sum_{l=-\infty}^{+\infty} C_{hl} \cos 2\pi(hu + lw) \tag{7}$$

[1] D. Harker, *J. Chem. Phys.*, vol. 4, p. 381, 1936.

where

$$u = 2x, \qquad w = 2z, \qquad C_{hl} = \sum_{k=-\infty}^{+\infty} |F(hkl)|^2$$

On the two-dimensional plot of $P(u0w)$ there is now no confusion arising from interatomic vectors that are not parallel to the planes $y = $ a constant, for these vectors do not appear. The maxima on the plot will show directly the values of the parameters x and z of the atoms in the unit cell. A two-dimensional series $P(u0w)$ is used for all symmetry elements that are axes of rotation parallel to b, and similar ones with appropriate cyclic changes apply to rotation axes parallel to the other crystal axes.

With a *twofold screw axis* parallel to b an atom at xyz is equivalent to one at $\bar{x}, y + \frac{1}{2}, \bar{z}$, and interatomic vectors have components $2x, -\frac{1}{2}, 2z$. Thus $P(uvw)$ must be evaluated for $v = -\frac{1}{2}$ [or, since $P(uvw)$ has a center of symmetry, for $v = \frac{1}{2}$],

$$P(u\tfrac{1}{2}w) = \sum_{h=-\infty}^{+\infty} \sum_{k=-\infty}^{+\infty} \sum_{l=-\infty}^{+\infty} |F(hkl)|^2 \cos 2\pi \left(hu + \frac{k}{2} + lw \right)$$

$$= \sum_{h=-\infty}^{+\infty} \sum_{l=-\infty}^{+\infty} C_{hl} \cos 2\pi(hu + lw) \qquad (8)$$

where

$$C_{hl} = \sum_{k=-\infty}^{+\infty} (-1)^k |F(hkl)|^2 \qquad u = 2x \qquad w = 2z$$

The "Patterson-Harker plot" for a twofold screw axis parallel to b thus will be a two-dimensional plot having peaks from which the coordinates u and w of the interatomic vectors may be obtained. Other screw axes lead to related series.[1]

[1] The table below gives the form of series required for each type of symmetry axis parallel to b and for each type of symmetry plane perpendicular to b. Cyclic interchange will yield the corresponding cases for elements parallel and perpendicular to a and c axes.

Symmetry Element	Form of $P(uvw)$
(a) Axes parallel to b:	
$2, 4, 4_2, \bar{4}, 6, 6_2$	$P(u0w)$
$2_1, 4_1, 4_3, 6_1, 6_5$	$P(u\tfrac{1}{2}w)$
$3_1, 6_2, 6_4$	$P(u\tfrac{1}{3}w)$
(b) Planes perpendicular to b:	
Reflection plane	$P(0v0)$
Glide plane with glide of $\frac{1}{2}a_0$	$P(\tfrac{1}{2}v0)$
Glide plane with glide of $\frac{1}{2}c_0$	$P(0v\tfrac{1}{2})$
Glide plane with glide of $\frac{1}{2}(a_0 + c_0)$	$P(\tfrac{1}{2}v\tfrac{1}{2})$
Glide plane with glide of $\frac{1}{4}(a_0 + c_0)$	$P(\tfrac{1}{4}v\tfrac{1}{4})$
Glide plane with glide of $\frac{1}{4}(3a_0 + c_0)$	$P(\tfrac{3}{4}v\tfrac{1}{4})$

Whenever possible, a plane of symmetry or a glide plane is used as a basis for the series, since for these cases Eq. (5) can be reduced to a one-dimensional series that is quickly computed. For a *plane of symmetry* perpendicular to b, equivalent atoms are at xyz and $x\bar{y}z$ with interatomic vector components 0, $2y$, 0 giving maxima in $P(uvw)$ on the b axis only. Then

$$P(0v0) = \sum_{h=-\infty}^{+\infty} \sum_{k=-\infty}^{+\infty} \sum_{l=-\infty}^{+\infty} |F(hkl)|^2 \cos 2\pi kv$$

$$= \sum_{k=-\infty}^{+\infty} B_k \cos 2\pi kv$$

where

$$B_k = \sum_{h=-\infty}^{+\infty} \sum_{l=-\infty}^{+\infty} |F(hkl)|^2 \quad \text{and} \quad v = 2y$$

A Patterson-Harker plot effectively focuses all the diffraction data from a crystal on a certain feature in the structure, for instance, on the interatomic distances for atoms on a certain plane in the unit cell. The resolving power that results is correspondingly higher than is found in a two-dimensional Patterson plot which uses only reflections from planes of a single zone [*e.g.*, $(hk0)$ reflections in Eq. (6)]. Furthermore, this resolving power can be brought to focus on any plane the investigator believes will be most illuminating; or on a whole series of planes in turn that are spaced at intervals through the cell, giving a series of cross sections; or on a line that is run through the cell at any important position where a hint as to the structure might be found. The method thus can be an extremely powerful aid in solving complex crystal structures. The review by Robertson is recommended for a detailed discussion of the use of series of all types in structure determination.[1] The F^2 series method contains the ambiguity that results from the fact that it is not directly possible to decide which pair of atoms in the crystal belongs to a given interatomic vector. However, in some crystals there are only a few heavy atoms of large scattering power, and these can be identified readily.

Computing Aids for Series. The labor of computing any of the Fourier series mentioned above or any modifications of them is considerable, and much thought has been given lately to methods of shortening the work. Without short cuts, some crystal projections that have been published would require over 500,000 separate terms to be evaluated and summed. Robertson[2] has employed cards on which are printed appropriate sine and

---

[1] J. M. Robertson, "Reports on Progress in Physics," vol. IV, pp. 332–367, Physical Society, London, 1938.

[2] J. M. Robertson, *Phil. Mag.*, vol. 21, p. 176, 1936.

cosine functions. A semimechanical sorting device picks out the proper set to be added for a series summation. Lipson and Beevers[1] have made up sets of numbered strips or slide rules with some of the computations already performed on them, which, when placed on a board in proper positions, make visible a column of numbers that are the individual terms of the series to be summed. The same operations are accomplished in a different way by a smaller set of strips and templates devised by Patterson and Tunell.[2] By using one of these strip devices it is possible to compute a series in two or three days that would have required as many weeks by the older methods. Various mechanical, electronic, and punched-card computing machines are being used to an increasing extent when computations are lengthy.

Other Developments in Technique. Statistical studies of the intensity relations in groups of reflections can reveal much about the symmetry of a crystal, in favorable instances. It was recognized by Wilson[3] and his coworkers[4] and by Hughes[5] that the presence or absence of a center of symmetry could be determined by studying the average value of many intensities. Further development of the statistical method by Wilson[6] and by Rogers[7] has provided tests not only for centers of symmetry but also for mirror planes, rotation axes, rotation-inversion axes, screw axes, and glide planes; all 32 classes and nearly all of the 230 space groups can be distinguished by such methods, though morphological examination, pyro- and piezoelectric tests are more convenient in determining crystal class when the tests are applicable and not ambiguous.

Another line of approach to the solution of crystal structures has been through a better use of the information contained in Patterson projections. Buerger[8] has now shown that the space groups (with the exception of 11 enantiomorphous pairs) should be distinguishable by the appearance of Patterson syntheses, since it is possible—in theory, at least—to deduce a set of atomic positions when only the vectors connecting pairs of atoms are known.

Important advances have recently been made in Fourier synthesis techniques. The barrier to direct solution of structures by the Fourier

[1] H. Lipson and C. A. Beevers, *Proc. Phys. Soc. (London)*, vol. 48, p. 772, 1936; *Acta Cryst.*, vol. 2, p. 131, 1949.

[2] A. L. Patterson and G. Tunell, *Am. Mineral.*, vol. 27, p. 655, 1942.

[3] A. J. C. Wilson, *Research*, vol. 2, p. 246, 1949; vol. 4, p. 141, 1951.

[4] E. R. Howells, D. C. Phillips, and D. Rogers, *Research*, vol. 2, p. 342, 1949; vol. 3, p. 48, 1950; *Acta Cryst.*, vol. 3, p. 210, 1950.

[5] E. W. Hughes, *Acta Cryst.*, vol. 2, p. 34, 1949.

[6] A. J. C. Wilson, *Acta Cryst.*, vol. 3, p. 258, 1950.

[7] D. Rogers, *Acta Cryst.*, vol. 3, p. 455, 1950.

[8] J. M. Buerger, *Acta Cryst.*, vol. 3, pp. 87, 465; 1950; *Proc. Natl. Acad. Sci. (U.S.)*, vol. 36, p. 324, 1950.

method (plotting electron-density maps) has always been the fact that the signs of the Fourier terms are unknown and are not obvious from the intensity data. Intensities are related to the squares of amplitudes and are therefore always of positive sign regardless of the sign of the quantity that is squared. Yet it is possible to determine signs in many instances by studies of certain pairs of reflection intensities. Harker and Kasper[1] showed that certain inequalities must exist in these pairs because of the presence of symmetry elements, and that because of this the signs of certain F values can be deduced. One of the first applications of the method[2] was in the solution of decaborane ($B_{10}H_{14}$), on which the usual methods of structure analysis had been found ineffective. Subsequently, related methods of determining signs of coefficients in Fourier series have developed very rapidly, particularly as a result of research by J. Gillis, J. Karle, H. Hauptman, E. W. Hughes, D. Sayre, J. A. Goedkoop, R. Pepinsky, C. H. MacGillavry, W. Cochran, W. Zachariasen, and others in a series of papers appearing or to appear chiefly in *Acta Crystallographica*. The development of these methods was accelerated by the growing need for them in connection with the new high-speed calculating machines for Fourier synthesis.

A summary of the computing machines and computing techniques that have recently been developed for Fourier synthesis cannot be given here, although they are of tremendous value in solving complex inorganic and organic crystals. Outstanding among these, for the most complex crystals, is the electronic machine "XRAC" built by R. Pepinsky and his coworkers, a machine that automatically plots contour maps of electron density when its dials are set to correspond to the amplitude and sign of the Fourier coefficients.

The optical devices are interesting. The "Fly's Eye" yields a diffraction pattern of a proposed atomic arrangement that is to be tested in "trial-and-error" crystal structure determination.[3] It proved of great value in the determination of the structure of penicillin. A related device has been used to show, by optical diffraction patterns, the diffraction effects that result from various defects in ordering in a superlattice.[4] Optical methods have also been used for Fourier-series summation. Dark and light bands, corresponding to the waves represented by individual terms of a Fourier series, are projected upon a photographic paper;

[1] D. Harker and J. S. Kasper, *J. Chem. Phys.*, vol. 15, p. 882, 1947; *Acta Cryst.*, vol. 1, p. 70, 1948. See also J. Gillis, *Acta Cryst.*, vol. 1, pp. 76, 174, 1948.

[2] J. S. Kasper, C. M. Lucht, and D. Harker, *Acta Cryst.*, vol. 3, p. 436, 1950.

[3] W. L. Bragg, *Nature*, vol. 154, p. 69, 1944. A. R. Stokes, *Proc. Phys. Soc. (London)*, vol. 58, p. 306, 1946. P. J. G. de Vos, *Acta Cryst.*, vol. 1, p. 118, 1948.

[4] C. A. Taylor, R. M. Hinde, and H. Lipson, *Acta Cryst.*, vol. 4, p. 261, 1951. Devices related to this have also been constructed by M. J. Buerger, and by D. MacLaughlin.

summation is accomplished by successively projecting different sets of bands, each with its appropriate amplitude, phase, and wavelength,[1] each image contributing to the final developed picture of the distribution of electron density in the crystal. Early results obtained by M. L. Huggins are illustrated by Fig. 4 for fluorite (CaF_2).

Much excellent work has been done for a number of years by "heavy-atom" methods, in which one or more heavy atoms are inserted into crystals composed of light atoms and the resulting intensities of the reflections noted.

A very widely used method is first to obtain an approximate set of values of the atomic coordinates in a structure, and then to refine the

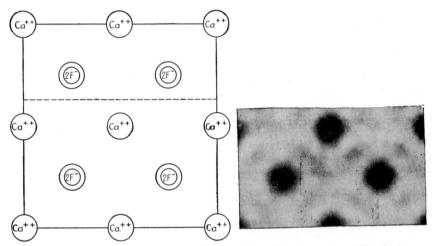

FIG. 4. Structure of CaF_2 by optical summation of Fourier series. (*Huggins.*)

structure, using the difference between calculated and observed F values both as a statistical test of the accuracy of the solution and as a basis for Fourier methods of eliminating the errors.

An attractive possibility for years has been to consider the solution of a crystal structure as the solution of a system of equations relating atomic positions to known intensities $|F_{hkl}|^2$, as pointed out by Avrami,[2] and Karle and Hauptman.[3] Because of the inexactness of the data, the multiplicities that would be encountered in some of the solutions,[3] and the complexity of the computations required, this approach to the problem has been considered impractical, though a statistical rather than exact method based on the same principles may ultimately prove useful.

[1] W. L. Bragg, *Z. Krist.*, vol. 70, p. 475, 1929. M. L. Huggins, *J. Am. Chem. Soc.*, vol. 63, p. 66, 1941. Modifications are being developed at the time of this writing.

[2] M. Avrami, *Phys. Rev.*, vol. 54, p. 300, 1938.

[3] J. Karle and H. Hauptman, *Acta Cryst.*, vol. 3, p. 478, 1950; vol. 4, p. 383, 1951; vol. 4, p. 188, 1951.

APPENDIX III

CRYSTAL GEOMETRY

Zone relationships, which apply to the Miller indices of all systems, are as follows:

1. The plane (hkl) belongs to the zone $[uvw]$ ($i.e.$, is parallel to the line $[uvw]$) if

$$hu + kv + lw = 0$$

2. The plane (hkl) belongs to the two zones $[u_1v_1w_1]$ and $[u_2v_2w_2]$ if $h:k:l = (v_1w_2 - v_2w_1):(w_1u_2 - w_2u_1):(u_1v_2 - u_2v_1)$.

This relation may be remembered by the following operation:

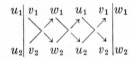

3. The zone $[uvw]$ contains the two planes $(h_1k_1l_1)$ and $(h_2k_2l_2)$ if $u:v:w = (k_1l_2 - k_2l_1):(l_1h_2 - l_2h_1):(h_1k_2 - h_2k_1)$. This is analogous to the preceding formula and may be remembered in the same way.

4. The plane $(h_3k_3l_3)$ will be among those belonging to the same zone as $(h_1k_1l_1)$ and $(h_2k_2l_2)$ if

$$h_3 = h_1 + h_2 \qquad k_3 = k_1 + k_2 \qquad \text{and} \qquad l_3 = l_1 + l_2$$

The same will be true if

$$h_3 = h_1 - h_2 \qquad k_3 = k_1 - k_2 \qquad \text{and} \qquad l_3 = l_1 - l_2$$

or if, in general,

$$h_3 = mh_1 \pm nh_2 \qquad k_3 = mk_1 \pm nk_2 \qquad \text{and} \qquad l_3 = ml_1 + nl_2$$

where m and n are integers.

These and other relations may be derived from the equations of planes and lines that pass through the origin.[1]

---

[1] J. D. H. Donnay, *Am. Mineral.*, vol. 19, p. 593, 1934. Consider, for example, the three planes $(h_1k_1l_1)$, $(h_2k_2l_2)$, $(h_3k_3l_3)$ which pass through the origin and intersect along the same straight line. This is equivalent to saying that the following three

The following formulas are useful in lattice computations:

1. The distance d_{hkl} between adjacent lattice planes in the simple space-lattices is most conveniently expressed in terms of $1/d_{hkl}^2$, given in the following formulas:

System:

Triclinic

$$\frac{1}{d^2} = \frac{1}{V^2} (S_{11}h^2 + S_{22}k^2 + S_{33}l^2 + 2S_{12}hk + 2S_{23}kl + 2S_{13}hl)$$

Monoclinic

$$\frac{1}{d^2} = \frac{h^2}{a^2 \sin^2 \beta} + \frac{k^2}{b^2} + \frac{l^2}{c^2 \sin^2 \beta} - \frac{2hl \cos \beta}{ac \sin^2 \beta}$$

Orthorhombic

$$\frac{1}{d^2} = \left(\frac{h}{a}\right)^2 + \left(\frac{k}{b}\right)^2 + \left(\frac{l}{c}\right)^2$$

---

equations for the planes have one system of solutions:

$$h_1 \frac{x}{a} + k_1 \frac{y}{b} + l_1 \frac{z}{c} = 0$$

$$h_2 \frac{x}{a} + k_2 \frac{y}{b} + l_2 \frac{z}{c} = 0$$

$$h_3 \frac{x}{a} + k_3 \frac{y}{b} + l_3 \frac{z}{c} = 0$$

This will be the case if the determinant of the coefficients is equal to zero,

$$\begin{vmatrix} h_1 & k_1 & l_1 \\ h_2 & k_2 & l_2 \\ h_3 & k_3 & l_3 \end{vmatrix} = 0$$

for when all the elements of a row are multiplied by the same factor, the determinant is multiplied by that factor. If this determinant is expanded by cofactors, the condition that the planes belong to the same zone may be written

$$\begin{vmatrix} k_2 & l_2 \\ k_3 & l_3 \end{vmatrix} h_1 + \begin{vmatrix} l_2 & h_2 \\ l_3 & h_3 \end{vmatrix} k_1 + \begin{vmatrix} h_2 & k_2 \\ h_3 & k_3 \end{vmatrix} l_1 = 0$$

which by expansion and substitution gives the formula under 1 above,

$$h_1 u + k_1 v + l_1 w = 0$$

where

$$u = k_2 l_3 - k_3 l_2 \qquad v = l_2 h_3 - l_3 h_2 \qquad w = h_2 k_3 - h_3 k_2$$

Hexagonal

$$\frac{1}{d^2} = \frac{4}{3} \cdot \frac{h^2 + hk + k^2}{a^2} + \left(\frac{1}{c}\right)^2$$

Rhombohedral (rhombohedral coordinates)

$$\frac{1}{d^2} = \frac{(h^2 + k^2 + l^2) \sin^2 \alpha + 2(hk + kl + hl)(\cos^2 \alpha - \cos \alpha)}{a^2(1 - 3 \cos^2 \alpha + 2 \cos^3 \alpha)}$$

Tetragonal

$$\frac{1}{d^2} = \frac{h^2 + k^2}{a^2} + \frac{l^2}{c^2}$$

Cubic

$$\frac{1}{d^2} = \frac{h^2 + k^2 + l^2}{a^2}$$

where

$$
\begin{aligned}
S_{11} &= b^2c^2 \sin^2 \alpha & S_{12} &= abc^2(\cos \alpha \cos \beta - \cos \gamma) \\
S_{22} &= a^2c^2 \sin^2 \beta & S_{23} &= a^2bc(\cos \beta \cos \gamma - \cos \alpha) \\
S_{33} &= a^2b^2 \sin^2 \gamma & S_{13} &= ab^2c(\cos \gamma \cos \alpha - \cos \beta) \\
\end{aligned}
$$

V = volume of the unit cell (see following paragraph)

2. The formulas for the volume of the unit cell, V, are as follows:

System:

Triclinic

$$V = abc \sqrt{1 - \cos^2 \alpha - \cos^2 \beta - \cos^2 \gamma + 2 \cos \alpha \cos \beta \cos \gamma}$$

Monoclinic

$$V = abc \sin \beta$$

Orthorhombic

$$V = abc$$

Hexagonal

$$V = \frac{\sqrt{3}}{2} a^2c = 0.866 \, a^2c$$

Rhombohedral (rhombohedral coordinates)

$$V = a^3 \sqrt{1 - 3 \cos^2 \alpha + 2 \cos^3 \alpha}$$

Tetragonal

$$V = a^2c$$

Cubic

$$V = a^3$$

3. The angle, ϕ, between two crystal planes $(h_1k_1l_1)$ and $(h_2k_2l_2)$ is determined by the following relations. [The quantities d and d' are the interplanar spacings for $(h_1k_1l_1)$ and $(h_2k_2l_2)$ planes from the formulas under 1 above; S_{11}, etc., are defined above.]

System:

Triclinic

$$\cos \phi = \frac{dd'}{V^2} \, [S_{11}h_1h_2 + S_{22}k_1k_2 + S_{33}l_1l_2 + S_{23}(k_1l_2 + k_2l_1)$$
$$+ S_{13}(l_1h_2 + l_2h_1) + S_{12}(h_1k_2 + h_2k_1)]$$

Hexagonal

$$\cos \phi = \frac{h_1h_2 + k_1k_2 + \frac{1}{2}(h_1k_2 + h_2k_1) + \frac{3}{4}\frac{a^2}{c^2}l_1l_2}{\sqrt{\left(h_1^2 + k_1^2 + h_1k_1 + \frac{3}{4}\frac{a^2}{c^2}l_1^2\right)\left(h_2^2 + k_2^2 + h_2k_2 + \frac{3}{4}\frac{a^2}{c^2}l_2^2\right)}}$$

Orthorhombic

$$\cos \phi = \frac{\frac{h_1h_2}{a^2} + \frac{k_1k_2}{b^2} + \frac{l_1l_2}{c^2}}{\sqrt{\left(\frac{h_1^2}{a^2} + \frac{k_1^2}{b^2} + \frac{l_1^2}{c^2}\right)\left(\frac{h_2^2}{a^2} + \frac{k_2^2}{b^2} + \frac{l_2^2}{c^2}\right)}}$$

The tetragonal equation is the same as the orthorhombic with $a = b$; the cubic is the same with $a = b = c$.

4. The shortest distance between identical points, the "identity distance," along a direction $[uvw]$ for the simple space-lattices is given by the following formulas:

General case:

$$I_{uvw} = \sqrt{a^2u^2 + b^2v^2 + c^2w^2 + 2bcvw \cos \alpha + 2cawu \cos \beta + 2abuv \cos \gamma}$$

Special cases:

Hexagonal

$$I_{uvw} = a\sqrt{u^2 + v^2 + \frac{w^2c^2}{a^2} - uv}$$

Orthorhombic

$$I_{uvw} = \sqrt{u^2a^2 + v^2b^2 + w^2c^2}$$

Cubic and tetragonal are special cases of the orthorhombic.

5. The area of the smallest unit parallelogram on the lattice plane (hkl) in simple space-lattices is

$$A_{hkl} = \sqrt{S_{11}h^2 + S_{22}k^2 + S_{33}l^2 + 2S_{12}hk + 2S_{13}hl + 2S_{23}kl}$$

for the triclinic lattice; others are special cases of this.

6. The angle between the direction $[uvw]$ and the plane (hkl) in terms of quantities defined above is, for the general case,

$$\sin \rho = \frac{abcP \sqrt{1 + 2 \cos \alpha \cos \beta \cos \gamma - \cos^2 \alpha - \cos^2 \beta - \cos^2 \gamma}}{A_{hkl} \cdot I_{uvw}}$$

where $P = (hu + kv + lw)$. The direction $[uvw]$ lies in the plane (hkl) or is parallel to the plane (hkl) when

$$hu + kv + lw = 0$$

and the direction is perpendicular to the plane when

$$hu + kv + lw = \frac{A_{hkl} \cdot I_{uvw}}{abc \sqrt{1 + 2 \cos \alpha \cos \beta \cos \gamma - \cos^2 \alpha - \cos^2 \beta - \cos^2 \gamma}}$$

7. The angle between the lattice directions $[u_1v_1w_1]$ and $[u_2v_2w_2]$ is given by

$$\cos \rho = \frac{\begin{aligned}a^2u_1u_2 + b^2v_1v_2 + c^2w_1w_2 + bc(v_1w_2 + v_2w_1) \cos \alpha \\ + ac(w_1u_2 + w_2u_1) \cos \beta + ab(u_1v_2 + u_2v_1) \cos \gamma\end{aligned}}{I_{u_1v_1w_1} \cdot I_{u_2v_2w_2}}$$

Special cases:

Hexagonal

$$\cos \rho = \frac{u_1u_2 + v_1v_2 + w_1w_2(c/a)^2 - \frac{1}{2}(u_1v_2 + u_2v_1)}{\sqrt{u_1^2 + v_1^2 - u_1v_1 + w_1^2(c/a)^2} \cdot \sqrt{u_2^2 + v_2^2 - u_2v_2 + w_2^2(c/a)^2}}$$

Orthorhombic

$$\cos \rho = \frac{u_1u_2a^2 + v_1v_2b^2 + w_1w_2c^2}{\sqrt{u_1^2a^2 + v_1^2b^2 + w_1^2c^2} \cdot \sqrt{u_2^2a^2 + v_2^2b^2 + w_2^2c^2}}$$

Tetragonal and cubic are special cases of this, the cubic formula being

$$\cos \rho = \frac{u_1u_2 + v_1v_2 + w_1w_2}{\sqrt{u_1^2 + v_1^2 + w_1^2} \cdot \sqrt{u_2^2 + v_2^2 + w_2^2}}$$

The directions $[u_1v_1w_1]$ and $[u_2v_2w_2]$ are mutually perpendicular when the numerators in these expressions are zero; for example, in the cubic case

$$u_1u_2 + v_1v_2 + w_1w_2 = 0$$

APPENDIX IV

ABSORPTION COEFFICIENTS

Absorber	Z	Radiation						
		Ag $K\alpha$	Rh $K\alpha$	Mo $K\alpha$	Cu $K\alpha$	Ni $K\alpha$	Fe $K\alpha$	Cr $K\alpha$
He	2	0.16	0.16	0.18				
Li	3	0.18	0.20	0.22				
Be	4	0.22	0.25	0.30	1.35	1.80	3.24	4.74
B	5	0.30	0.35	0.45	3.06	3.79	5.80	9.37
C	6	0.42	0.51	0.70	5.50	6.76	10.73	17.9
N	7	0.60	0.70	1.10	8.51	10.7	17.3	27.7
O	8	0.80	1.00	1.50	12.7	16.2	25.2	40.1
F	9	1.00	1.32	1.93	17.5	21.5	33.0	51.6
Ne	10	1.41	1.80	2.67	24.6	30.2	46.0	72.7
Na	11	1.75	2.25	3.36	30.9	37.9	56.9	92.5
Mg	12	2.27	2.93	4.38	40.6	47.9	75.7	120.1
Al	13	2.74	3.60	5.30	48.7	58.4	92.8	149
Si	14	3.44	4.52	6.70	60.3	75.8	116.3	192
P	15	4.20	5.36	7.98	73.0	90.5	141.1	223
S	16	5.15	6.65	10.03	91.3	111.5	175	273
Cl	17	5.86	7.50	11.62	103.4	125.6	199	308
A	18	6.40	8.00	12.55	112.9	141	217	341
K	19	8.05	10.7	16.7	143	179	269	425
Ca	20	9.66	12.8	19.8	172	210	317	508
Sc	21	10.5	13.8	21.1	185	222	338	545
Ti	22	11.8	15.8	23.7	204	247	377	603
Va	23	13.3	17.7	26.5	227	275	422	77.3
Cr	24	15.7	20.4	30.4	259	316	490	89.9
Mn	25	17.4	22.6	33.5	284	348	63.6	99.4
Fe	26	19.9	25.8	38.3	324	397	72.8	114.6
Co	27	21.8	28.1	41.6	354	54.4	80.6	125.8
Ni	28	25.0	32.3	47.4	49.2	61.0	93.1	145
Cu	29	26.4	34.0	49.7	52.7	65.0	98.8	154
Zn	30	28.2	37.7	54.8	59.0	72.1	109.4	169
Ga	31	30.8	39.7	57.3	63.3	76.9	116.5	179
Ge	32	33.5	42.8	63.4	69.4	84.2	128.4	196
As	33	36.5	46.0	69.5	76.5	93.8	142	218
Se	34	38.5	49.0	74.0	82.8	100.6	152	235
Br	35	42.3	53.5	82.2	92.6	112.4	169	264
Kr	36	45.0	57.5	88.1	100.4	121.9	182	285
Rb	37	48.2	62.8	94.4	109.1	132.9	197	309
Sr	38	52.1	68.3	101.2	119	145	214	334
Y	39	55.5	74.0	108.9	129	158	235	360
Zr	40	61.1	80.9	17.2	143	173	260	391

[1] Values are from "Internationale Tabellen zur Bestimmung von Kristallstrukturen," vol. II, Bornträger, Berlin, 1935.

Mass Absorption Coefficients (μ/ρ) of Elements, Including Scattering.[1]—
(*Continued*)

Absorber	Z	Radiation						
		Ag $K\alpha$	Rh $K\alpha$	Mo $K\alpha$	Cu $K\alpha$	Ni $K\alpha$	Fe $K\alpha$	Cr $K\alpha$
Nb	41	65.8	86.0	18.7	153	183	279	415
Mo	42	70.7	91.6	20.2	164	197	299	439
Ru	44	$\begin{cases} \alpha_1 79.9 \\ \alpha_2 12.2 \end{cases}$	15.4	23.4	185	221	337	488
Rh	45	13.1	16.6	25.3	198	240	361	522
Pd	46	13.8	17.6	26.7	207	254	376	545
Ag	47	14.8	19.1	28.6	223	276	402	585
Cd	48	15.5	20.1	29.9	234	289	417	608
In	49	16.5	21.7	31.8	252	307	440	648
Sn	50	17.4	22.9	33.3	265	322	457	681
Sb	51	18.6	24.6	35.3	284	342	482	727
Te	52	19.1	25.0	36.1	289	347	488	742
I	53	20.9	27.3	39.2	314	375	527	808
Xe	54	22.1	28.5	41.3	330	392	552	852
Cs	55	23.6	30.0	43.3	347	410	579	844
Ba	56	24.5	31.1	45.2	359	423	599	819
La	57	26.0	33.0	47.9	378	444	632	218
Ce	58	28.4	35.8	52.0	407	476	636	235
Pr	59	29.4	37.2	54.5	422	493	624	251
Nd	60	30.5	38.8	57.0	437	510	651	263
Sm	62	33.1	41.2	62.3	467	519	183	289
Eu	63	35.0	44.5	65.9	461	498	193	306
Gd	64	35.8	45.7	68.0	470	509	199	316
Tb	65	37.5	47.9	71.7	435	140	211	333
Dy	66	39.1	49.9	75.0	462	146	220	345
Ho	67	41.3	52.7	79.3	128	153	232	361
Er	68	42.6	54.6	82.0	133	159	242	370
Tm	69	44.8	57.6	86.3	139	168	257	387
Yb	70	46.1	59.4	88.7	144	174	265	396
Lu	71	48.4	62.6	93.2	151	184	281	414
Hf	72	50.6	65.0	96.9	157	191	291	426
Ta	73	52.2	67.7	100.7	164	200	305	440
W	74	54.6	70.7	105.4	171	209	320	456
Os	76	58.6	76.3	112.9	186	226	346	480
Ir	77	61.2	80.0	117.9	194	237	362	498
Pt	78	64.2	83.8	123	205	248	376	518
Au	79	66.7	87.1	128	214	260	390	537
Hg	80	69.3	90.1	132	223	272	404	552
Tl	81	71.7	92.4	136	231	282	416	568
Pb	82	74.4	95.8	141	241	294	429	585
Bi	83	78.1	100.4	145	253	310	448	612
Nt	86	84.7	109.1	159	278	341	476	657
Ra	88	91.1	117	172	304	371	509	708
Th	90	97.0	119	143	327	399	536	755
U	92	104.2	129	153	352	423	566	805

[1] Values are from "Internationale Tabellen zur Bestimmung von Kristallstrukturen," vol. II, Bornträger, Berlin, 1935.

INTERNATIONAL ATOMIC WEIGHTS[1]

Element	Symbol	Atomic number	Atomic weight*	Element	Symbol	Atomic number	Atomic weight*
Actinium	Ac	89	227	Neodymium	Nd	60	144.27
Aluminum	Al	13	26.97	Neon	Ne	10	20.183
Americium	Am	95	[241]	Neptunium	Np	93	[237]
Antimony	Sb	51	121.76	Nickel	Ni	28	58.69
Argon	A	18	39.944	Niobium (columbium)	Nb	41	92.91
Arsenic	As	33	74.91	Nitrogen	N	7	14.008
Astatine	At	85	[210]	Osmium	Os	76	190.2
Barium	Ba	56	137.36	Oxygen	O	8	16.0000
Beryllium	Be	4	9.013	Palladium	Pd	46	106.7
Bismuth	Bi	83	209.00	Phosphorus	P	15	30.98
Boron	B	5	10.82	Platinum	Pt	78	195.23
Bromine	Br	35	79.916	Plutonium	Pu	94	[239]
Cadmium	Cd	48	112.41	Polonium	Po	84	210
Calcium	Ca	20	40.08	Potassium	K	19	39.096
Carbon	C	6	12.010	Praseodymium	Pr	59	140.92
Cerium	Ce	58	140.13	Promethium	Pm	61	[147]
Cesium	Cs	55	132.91	Protoactinium	Pa	91	231
Chlorine	Cl	17	35.457	Radium	Ra	88	226.05
Chromium	Cr	24	52.01	Radon	Rn	86	222
Cobalt	Co	27	58.94	Rhenium	Re	75	186.31
Copper	Cu	29	63.54	Rhodium	Rh	45	102.91
Curium	Cm	96	[242]	Rubidium	Rb	37	85.48
Dysprosium	Dy	66	162.46	Ruthenium	Ru	44	101.7
Erbium	Er	68	167.2	Samarium	Sm	62	150.43
Europium	Eu	63	152.0	Scandium	Sc	21	45.10
Fluorine	F	9	19.00	Selenium	Se	34	78.96
Francium	Fr	87	[223]	Silicon	Si	14	28.06
Gadolinium	Gd	64	156.9	Silver	Ag	47	107.880
Gallium	Ga	31	69.72	Sodium	Na	11	22.997
Germanium	Ge	32	72.60	Strontium	Sr	38	87.63
Gold	Au	79	197.2	Sulfur	S	16	32.006
Hafnium	Hf	72	178.6	Tantalum	Ta	73	180.88
Helium	He	2	4.003	Technetium	Tc	43	[99]
Holmium	Ho	67	164.94	Tellurium	Te	52	127.61
Hydrogen	H	1	1.0080	Terbium	Tb	65	159.2
Indium	In	49	114.76	Thallium	Tl	81	204.39
Iodine	I	53	126.92	Thorium	Th	90	232.12
Iridium	Ir	77	193.1	Thulium	Tm	69	169.4
Iron	Fe	26	55.85	Tin	Sn	50	118.70
Krypton	Kr	36	83.7	Titanium	Ti	22	47.90
Lanthanum	La	57	138.92	Uranium	U	92	238.07
Lead	Pb	82	207.21	Vanadium	V	23	50.95
Lithium	Li	3	6.940	Wolfram (tungsten)	W	74	183.92
Lutetium	Lu	71	174.99	Xenon	Xe	54	131.3
Magnesium	Mg	12	24.32	Ytterbium	Yb	70	173.04
Manganese	Mn	25	54.93	Yttrium	Y	39	88.92
Mercury	Hg	80	200.61	Zinc	Zn	30	65.38
Molybdenum	Mo	42	95.95	Zirconium	Zr	40	91.22

[1] As published in *J. Am. Chem. Soc.*, April, 1950.

* A value given in brackets denotes the mass number of the most stable known isotope.

APPENDIX VI

PHYSICAL CONSTANTS[1] AND NUMERICAL FACTORS

N, Avogadro's number $(6.0235 \pm 0.0004) \times 10^{23}$ (chemical scale, for use with International atomic weights)

h, Planck's constant $6.6234 \pm 0.0011 \times 10^{-27}$ erg-sec

m, electron mass $9.1055 \pm 0.0012 \times 10^{-28}$ g

e, electronic charge $(4.8024 \pm 0.0005) \times 10^{-10}$ esu

$\qquad (1.60199 \pm 0.00016) \times 10^{-20}$ emu

F, Faraday, 9649.6 ± 0.7 emu equivalent^{-1} (chemical scale)

λ_0, X-ray wavelength associated with 1 ev $(12394.2 \pm 0.9) \times 10^{-8}$ cm

e/m, $(1.75936 \pm 0.00018) \times 10^7$ emu g^{-1}

$\qquad (5.2741 \pm 0.0005) \times 10^{17}$ esu g^{-1}

h/e, $(1.37920 \pm 0.00009) \times 10^{-17}$ erg-sec esu^{-1}

c, velocity of light $(2.99776 \pm 0.00004) \times 10^{10}$ cm sec^{-1}

n_0, Loschmidt's number $(2.68731 \pm 0.00019) \times 10^{19}$ cm^{-1}

k, Boltzmann's constant $(1.38032 \pm 0.00011 \times 10^{-16}$ erg deg^{-1}

R_0, gas constant per mole $(8.31436 \pm 0.00038 \times 10^7$ erg mole^{-1} deg^{-1}

V_0, standard volume of perfect gas $(22.4146 \pm 0.0006) \times 10^3$ cm^3 mole^{-1}

λ_g/λ_s ratio, grating wavelengths to Siegbahn wavelengths of X-rays, 1.002030 ± 0.000020 (Note: by international agreement of 1947 Siegbahn's values are converted to angstroms by multiplying by 1.00202)

d_{20}, grating space of calcite (20°C) $(3.03567 \pm 0.00005) \times 10^{-8}$ cm

$\qquad$ Density of calcite 20°C (2.71030 ± 0.00003) g cm^{-3}

Ice point, $T_0 = 273.15°$K

1 electron volt $= 1.602 \times 10^{-12}$ erg

1 electron volt per molecule $= 23.05$ kcal per mole

1 kcal $= 4.185 \times 10^{10}$ ergs

1 electron volt $= 11,500k$

1 cal (15°C) $= 4.182$ joules

---

[1] Least-square fitted values of the atomic constants are from J. W. M. DuMond and E. R. Cohen, *Rev. Modern Phys.*, vol. 20, p. 82, 1948. Accuracy figures are given as $\pm 0.6745\sigma$ with the standard deviation, σ, computed by the relation

$$\sigma^2 = \Sigma p_i v_i^2 / (N - 1) \Sigma p_i$$

where p_i are the weights assigned to each observation and v_i are the deviations of each observation from the weighted mean of the set. The quantity 0.6745σ is the "probable error" and expresses the range that, with a Gaussian distribution, corresponds to a probability of 0.5 that the correct value lies in the range.

1 volt = $\frac{1}{300}$ esu = 10^8 emu

1 radian = 57.29578 deg

1 in. = 2.5400 cm

1 A = 10^{-8} cm

1 micron = 10^{-3} mm = 10^4 A

1 psi = 1.422 kg per sq mm

ln x = $\log_e x$ = 2.302585 $\log_{10} x$

The base of natural logarithms, e = **2.718**

APPENDIX VII

REFLECTING PLANES OF CUBIC CRYSTALS

The quadratic form for the cubic system can be written

$$\log \sin^2 \theta = 2 \log \lambda - \log 4 - 2 \log a + \log (h^2 + k^2 + l^2)$$

The following table gives values of $\log (h^2 + k^2 + l^2)$ and indicates the reflections that are possible from face-centered (F), body-centered (B), and diamond cubic (D) lattices. All entries are possible reflections for simple cubic space-lattices.

$h^2 + k^2 + l^2$	$\log (h^2 + k^2 + l^2)$	Lattice	hkl
1	0.00000	....	100
2	0.30103	B	110
3	0.47712	FD	111
4	0.60206	BF	200
5	0.69897	....	210
6	0.77815	B	211
7			
8	0.90309	BFD	220
9	0.95424	....	300, 221
10	1.00000	B	310
11	1.04139	FD	311
12	1.07918	BF	222
13	1.11394	....	320
14	1.14613	B	321
15			
16	1.20412	BFD	400
17	1.23045	....	410, 322
18	1.25527	B	411, 330
19	1.27875	FD	331
20	1.30103	BF	420
21	1.32222	....	421
22	1.34242	B	332
23			
24	1.38021	BFD	422
25	1.39794	....	500, 430
26	1.41497	B	510, 431

$h^2 + k^2 + l^2$	$\log (h^2 + k^2 + l^2)$	Lattice	hkl
27	1.43136	*FD*	511, 333
28			
29	1.46240	....	520, 432
30	1.47712	*B*	521
31			
32	1.50515	*BFD*	440
33	1.51851	....	522, 441
34	1.53148	*B*	530, 433
35	1.54407	*FD*	531
36	1.55630	*BF*	600, 442
37	1.56820	....	610
38	1.57978	*B*	611, 532
39			
40	1.60206	*BFD*	620
41	1.61278	....	621, 540, 443
42	1.62325	*B*	541
43	1.63347	*FD*	533
44	1.65321	*BF*	622
45	1.66276	....	630, 542
46	1.67210	*B*	631
47			
48	1.68124	*BFD*	444
49	1.69020	....	700, 632
50	1.69897	*B*	710, 550, 543
51	1.70757	*FD*	711, 551
52	1.71600	*BF*	640
53	1.72428	....	720, 641
54	1.73239	*B*	721, 633, 552
55			
56	1.74819	*BFD*	642
57	1.75587	....	722, 544
58	1.76343	*B*	730
59	1.77084	*FD*	731, 553

APPENDIX VIII

EMISSION AND ABSORPTION WAVELENGTHS

Table XXXI. Principal K Emission Lines and K Absorption Edges,[1] Converted to Angstroms

Element	Atomic number	α_2 strong	α_1 very strong	β_3	β_1 weak	β_5^{II}	β_5^{I}	β_2^{II}	β_2^{I}	β_{4z}	β_4	$KO_{II,III}$	K absorption edge
Sodium	11	11.909	11.909		11.617								
Magnesium	12	9.8889	9.8889		9.558								9.5117
Aluminum	13	8.33916	8.33669		7.981								7.9511
Silicon	14	7.12773	7.12528		6.7681								6.7446
Phosphorus	15	6.1549	6.1549		5.8038								5.7866
Sulfur	16	5.37472	5.37196		5.03169								5.0182
Chlorine	17	4.73050	4.72760		4.4031								4.3969
Argon	18	4.19456	4.19162										3.87068
Potassium	19	3.74462	3.74122		3.4538	3.4414							3.43645
Calcium	20	3.36159	3.35825		3.0896	3.0742							3.07016
Scandium	21	3.03452	3.03114		2.7795	2.7636							2.7572
Titanium	22	2.75207	2.74841		2.51381	2.4980							2.4973_0
Vanadium	23	2.50729	2.50348		2.28434	2.26942							2.2696_2
Chromium	24	2.29351	2.28962		2.08480	2.07070							2.070_{12}
Manganese	25	2.10568	2.10175		1.91015	1.89698							1.896_{36}
Iron	26	1.93991	1.93597		1.75653	1.74406							1.743_{34}
Cobalt	27	1.79278	1.78892		1.62075	1.60882							1.608_{11}
Nickel	28	1.66169	1.65784		1.50010	1.48853		1.48861					1.488_{62}
Copper	29	1.54433	1.54050	1.39255	1.39217	1.38146		1.38102					1.380_{43}
Zinc	30	1.43894	1.43511		1.29522	1.28450		1.28366					1.283_5
Gallium	31	1.34394	1.34003	1.20830	1.20784	1.19778		1.19595					1.195_{67}
Germanium	32	1.25796	1.25401	1.12932	1.12890	1.11937		1.11682					1.116_{62}
Arsenic	33	1.17981	1.17581	1.05777	1.05726	1.0487		1.04498					1.044_{97}
Selenium	34	1.10876	1.10471	0.99262	0.99212	0.9843		0.97986					0.979_{78}
Bromine	35	1.04376	1.03968	0.93322	0.93273	0.9255		0.92064					0.91994
Krypton	36	0.9841	0.9801	0.87896	0.87845	0.87080		0.86608		0.86521			0.86546
Rubidium	37	0.92963	0.92550	0.82916	0.82863	0.82183		0.81640		0.81527			0.81549
Strontium	38	0.87938	0.87521	0.78341	0.78288	0.77636		0.77076		0.76985			0.76969
Yttrium	39	0.83300	0.82879	0.74121	0.74068	0.73449		0.72874		0.72766			0.72762
Zirconium	40	0.79010	0.78588	0.70224	0.70169	0.69587		0.68989		0.68895			0.68877
Niobium	41	0.75040	0.74615	0.66630	0.66572	0.66000		0.65412		0.65316			0.65291
Molybdenum	42	0.713543	0.709261	0.632819	0.632252	0.62704	0.62688	0.62103	0.620950	0.62020	0.61998		0.61977
Technetium	43	0.676	0.673		0.602								

Element	Z													
Ruthenium	44	0.64736	0.64304	0.57308	0.57246	0.56797	0.56782	0.56164	0.53514	0.53504	0.56087	0.53425	0.54404	0.560_{47}
Rhodium	45	0.617610	0.613245	0.54619	0.54559	0.54118	0.54101	....	....	....	....	....	....	0.533_{78}
Palladium	46	0.589801	0.585415	0.52114	0.52052	0.51669	....	0.51021	....	....	0.48701	....	....	0.509_{15}
Silver	47	0.563774	0.559363	0.49765	0.49701	0.493069	0.493001	0.465312	0.48597	0.48637	....	0.44390	0.44371	0.4858_{2}
Cadmium	48	0.53941	0.53498	0.475705	0.454514	0.45096	0.45084	0.444963	0.44963	0.45900	0.44436	0.42493	0.42465	0.46408
Indium	49	0.51652	0.51209	0.455150	0.435216	0.43183	0.43174	0.425900	0.425900	....	0.42529	0.42493	....	0.44397
Tin	50	0.49502	0.49056	0.435859	0.417060	0.41385	0.41375	0.407950	0.407950	....	0.40744	0.40700	0.40664	0.42468
Antimony	51	0.474791	0.470322	0.417713	0.399972	....	....	0.391080	0.37547	....	....	....	0.38972	0.40663
Tellurium	52	0.455751	0.451263	0.400637	0.383884	....	....	0.37547	....	....	....	....	....	0.38972
Iodine	53	0.437804	0.433293	0.384542	0.36846	....	....	0.35989	....	....	....	....	....	0.373_{79}
Xenon	54	0.42043	0.41596	....	....	....	....	0.346084	....	....	....	....	....	0.35849
Cesium	55	0.404812	0.400268	0.355033	0.354347	0.340789	0.33832	0.332745	0.33226	0.33124	....	0.31928	0.33124	0.34473
Barium	56	0.389646	0.385089	0.341485	0.340789	0.327959	0.32561	0.32038	0.320091	0.31965	0.31928	....	0.31861	0.33137
Lanthanum	57	0.375278	0.370709	0.328662	0.327959	0.315792	0.31354	0.30839	0.308135	0.30734	0.30734	....	0.306648	0.31842
Cerium	58	0.361665	0.357075	0.316495	0.315792	0.304238	....	0.29703	0.296766	....	....	....	....	0.30647
Praseodymium	59	0.348728	0.344122	0.304932	0.304238	0.293274	....	0.28631	....	....	....	....	....	0.29517
Neodymium	60	0.336446	0.331822	0.294003	0.293274	0.28209	....	....	....	....	....	....	....	0.28451
Promethium	61	0.3248	0.3207	....	....	....	....	....	....	....	....	....	....	....
Samarium	62	0.31365	0.30850	0.27380	0.27305	0.26360	....	0.26629	....	....	....	....	....	0.26462
Europium	63	0.30326	0.29850	0.26439	0.26360	0.25445	....	0.25697	....	....	....	....	....	0.25552
Gadolinium	64	0.29320	0.28840	0.25522	0.25445	0.24600	....	0.24812	....	....	....	....	....	0.24680
Terbium	65	0.28343	0.27876	0.24679	0.24600	0.23835	....	0.23960	....	....	....	....	....	0.23840
Dysprosium	66	0.27430	0.26957	0.23835	0.23758	....	....	0.23175	....	....	....	....	....	0.23046
Holmium	67	0.26552	0.26082	0.22345	0.22260	....	....	....	....	....	....	....	....	0.22290
Erbium	68	0.25716	0.25248	0.21602	0.21530	....	....	0.21715	....	....	....	....	....	0.21565
Thulium	69	0.24911	0.24436	0.20958	0.20876	....	....	....	....	....	....	....	....	0.2089
Ytterbium	70	0.24147	0.23676	0.20293	0.20212	....	....	0.20363	....	....	....	....	....	0.20223
Lutetium	71	0.23405	0.22928	0.19622	0.19554	....	....	0.19689	....	....	....	....	....	0.19584
Hafnium	72	0.22699	0.22218	0.190877	0.190076	....	....	0.19080	....	....	....	....	....	0.18981
Tantalum	73	0.220290	0.215484	0.185168	0.184363	0.188907	0.188743	0.185175	0.184998	0.184019	0.18449	....	0.184019	0.18393
Wolfram	74	0.213813	0.208992	0.179685	0.178870	0.183251	0.183080	0.179594	0.179411	0.178433	0.17891	....	0.178433	0.17837
Rhenium	75	0.207598	0.202778	0.174424	0.173607	0.177870	....	0.174250	0.174049	....	....	....	0.17311	0.17311
Osmium	76	0.201626	0.196783	0.169357	0.168533	0.173607	....	0.169097	0.168898	....	....	....	....	0.16780
Iridium	77	0.195889	0.191033	0.164488	0.163664	0.168533	0.167571	0.164139	0.163943	0.163007	0.16351	....	0.163007	0.16286
Platinum	78	0.190372	0.185504	0.159799	0.158871	0.163664	0.162692	0.159374	0.159184	0.158241	0.15880	....	0.158241	0.15817
Gold	79	0.185064	0.180185	0.159799	0.158871	0.158052	0.157869	0.154817	0.154607	0.153684	0.15421	....	0.153684	0.15344
Mercury	80	....	....	0.150970	0.150133	....	....	....	....	....	....	....	....	0.14923
Thallium	81	0.175028	0.170131	0.146802	0.145962	0.14511	0.14494	0.14212	0.14154	0.141906	0.14154	....	0.141004	0.14470
Thallium	81													0.14077
Lead	82	0.170285	0.165364	0.142772	0.141941	....	....	0.13817	0.13797	0.13797	....	....	0.13706	0.13706
Bismuth	83	0.165704	0.160777	0.142772	0.141941	0.117389	0.11666	0.11428	0.11404	0.11404	....	....	0.11321	0.11293
Thorium	90	0.137820	0.132806	0.118260	0.117389	0.111386	....	0.10864	....	....	....	....	....	....
Uranium	92	0.130962	0.125940	0.112288	0.111386	....	....	....	....	....	....	....	....	0.10680

¹ Y. Cauchois and H. Hulubei, Longueur d'onde des émissions X et les discontinuité d'absorption X, Hermann, Paris, 1947. All lines are very weak except α1, α2, and β1; satellites are not listed.

CRYSTAL STRUCTURES OF THE ELEMENTS

Element and modification	Type of structure	Lattice constants converted to A		c or axial angle	Temperature for which constants apply	Distance of closest approach, A
		a	b			
Actinium						
Alabamine	See Francium					
Aluminum	F.c.c. A1	4.0490	......	....	20°C	2.862
Americium						
Antimony	Rhombohedral A7	4.5064	......	57°6.5′	20°C	2.903
Argon	F.c.c. A1	5.43	......	....	−233°C	3.84
Arsenic	Rhombohedral A7	4.159	......	53°49′	20°C	2.51
Astatine						
Barium	B.c.c. A2	5.025	......	....	20°C	4.35
Beryllium, α*	C.p.h. A8	2.2854	......	3.5841	20°C	2.225
β (doubtful)	Hexagonal	7.1	.....	10.8	Room	
Bismuth	Rhombohedral A7	4.7356	......	57°14.2′	20°C	3.111
Boron	Rhombohedral	9.45	......	23.8	Room	
Bromine	Orthorhombic	4.49	6.68	8.74	−150°C	2.27
Cadmium	C.p.h. A3	2.9787	......	5.617	20°C	2.979
Calcium, α	F.c.c. A1	5.57	......	....	20°C	3.94
β (300–450°C)					20°C	
γ (> 450°C)	C.p.h. A3	3.99	......	6.53	460°C	3.95
Carbon, diamond*	Diamond cubic A4	3.568	......		18°C	1.544
Graphite, α*	Hexagonal A9	2.4614	......	6.7014	20°C	1.42
Graphite, β	Rhombohedral, D^5_{3d}	2.461	......	10.064		
Cerium*	F.c.c. A1	5.140	......	....	Room	3.64
	F.c.c. A1	4.82	......	....	−180°C	3.40
At 15,000 atm	F.c.c. A1	4.84	......	....	Room	3.42
Cesium	B.c.c. A2	6.06	......		−173°C	5.25
Chlorine, α	Tetragonal	8.58	......	6.13	−110°C	1.88
Chromium	B.c.c. A2	2.8845	......	....	20°C	2.498
(Transit. at 37°C).	B.c.c. A2	2.8851	......		38°C	
Cobalt, α*	C.p.h. A3	2.507	......	4.069	20°C	2.506
β	F.c.c. A1	3.552	......	....	Room	2.511
Columbium	See Niobium					
Copper	F.c.c. A1	3.6153	......	....	20°C	2.556
Dysprosium	C.p.h. A3	3.585	......	5.659	20°C	3.506
Erbium	C.p.h. A3	3.539	......	5.601	20°C	3.466
Europium	B.c.c. A2	4.582	......	....	20°C	2.968
Francium	(Formerly Alabamine)					
Gadolinium	C.p.h. A3	3.629	.....	5.759	20°C	3.561
Gallium	One f.c. orthorhombic A11	3.526	4.520	7.660	20°C	2.442
Germanium	Diamond cubic A4	5.658	......	....	20°C	2.450
Gold	F.c.c. A1	4.0783	......	....	20°C	2.884
Hafnium	C.p.h., A3	3.206	......	5.087	20°C	3.15
Helium	C.p.h. A3 (?)	3.58	......	5.84	−271.5°C	3.58
Holmium	C.p.h. A3	3.564	......	5.631	20°C	3.487
Hydrogen, para	Hexagonal	3.76	......	6.13	−271°C	
Illinium	See Promethium					
Indium	F.c. tetragonal A6	4.594	......	4.951	20°C	3.25
Iodine	Orthorhombic	4.787	7.266	9.793	20°C	2.71
Iridium	F.c.c. A1	3.8389	......	....	20°C	2.714

APPENDIX IX.—(Continued)

Element and modification	Type of structure	Lattice constants converted to A		c or axial angle	Temperature for which constants apply	Distance of closest approach, A
		a	b			
Iron, α*...............	B.c.c. $A2$	2.8664	......	....	20°C	2.481
γ (extrapolated)......	F.c.c. $A1$	3.571	......	....	20°C	2.525
γ (908–1403°C)......		3.656	......	....	950°C	2.585
δ (> 1403°C).........	B.c.c. $A2$	2.94	......	....	1425°C	2.54
Krypton...............	F.c.c. $A1$	5.69	......	....	−191°C	4.03
Lanthanum, α*.........	C.p.h. $A3$	3.762	......	6.075	20°C	3.74
β....................	F.c.c. $A1$	5.307	......	....	Room	3.762
Lead..................	F.c.c. $A1$	4.9495	......	....	20°C	3.499
Lithium...............	B.c.c. $A2$	3.5089	......	....	20°C	3.039
(cold worked).........	F.c.c. $A1$	4.40	......	....	−195°C	3.11
	C.p.h. $A3$ (?)	3.08	......	4.82	−195°C	3.08
Lutecium..............	C.p.h. $A3$	3.516	......	5.570	20°C	3.446
Magnesium............	C.p.h. $A3$	3.2092	......	5.2103	20°C	3.196
Manganese, α*.........	Cubic $A12$	8.912	......	....	20°C	2.24
β (727–1095°C)......	Cubic $A13$	6.313	......	....	Room	2.373
γ (1095–1133°C)......	F.c. tetragonal $A6$	3.782	......	3.533	Room	2.587
δ (> 1133°C)						
Masurium..............	(Technetium)					
Mercury...............	Rhombohedral $A11$	2.006	......	70°31.7′	−46°C	3.006
Molybdenum...........	B.c.c. $A2$	3.1466	......	....	20°C	2.725
Neodymium, α*........	C.p.h. $A3$(?)	3.657	......	....	20°C	5.902
Neon..................	F.c.c. $A1$	4.51	......	....	−268°C	3.21
Neptunium						
Nickel*...............	F.c.c. $A1$	3.5238	......	....	20°C	2.491
(unstable, with H_2 or N_2?)...............	C.p.h. $A3$	2.66	......	4.32	Room	
(unstable)(?)........	Tetragonal D^{17}_{4h}	4.00	......	3.77	Room	
Niobium...............	B.c.c. $A2$	3.3007	......	....	....	2.859
Nitrogen, α............	Cubic	5.67	......	....	−252°C	1.06
β....................	Hexagonal	4.04	......	6.60	−234°C	
Osmium...............	C.p.h. $A3$	2.7333	......	4.3191	....	2.675
Oxygen, α.............	Orthorhombic	5.51	3.83	3.45	−252°C	
β....................	Rhombohedral	6.20	......	99.1°	−238°C	
γ....................	Cubic	6.84	......	....	−225°C	
Palladium.............	F.c.c. $A1$	3.8902	......	....	20°C	2.750
Phosphorus, white.......	Cubic	7.18	......	....	−35°C	
Black*...............	Orthorhombic $A16$	3.32	4.39	10.52	Room	2.17
Platinum..............	F.c.c. $A1$	3.9237	......	....	20°C	2.775
Plutonium						
Polonium, α............	Simple cubic	3.345	......	....	....	3.35
β (above 75°C).......	Simple rhombohedral	3.359	......	98°13′	....	4.40
Potassium.............	B.c.c. $A2$	5.344	......	....	20°C	4.627
Praseodymium, α*......	C.p.h. $A3$(?)	3.669	......	5.920	20°C	3.640
β....................	F.c.c. $A1$	5.161	......	....	Room	3.649
Promethium						
Protoactinium						
Radium						
Radon						
Rhenium...............	C.p.h. $A3$	2.7609	......	4.4583	20°C	2.740
Rhodium, β*..........	F.c.c. $A1$	3.8034	......	....	20°C	2.689
α (electrolytic)........	Cubic	9.230	......	....	Room	

APPENDIX IX.—(Continued)

Element and modification	Type of structure	Lattice constants converted to A		c or axial angle	Temperature for which constants apply	Distance of closest approach A
		a	b			
Rubidium.............	B.c.c. A2	5.63	......	....	−173°C	4.88
Ruthenium, α*........	C.p.h. A3	2.7038	......	4.2816	20°C	2.649
Samarium............	F.c. tetragonal(?)					
Scandium, α*..........	F.c.c. A1	4.541	......		20°C	3.2110
β.................	C.p.h. A3	3.3ĩ	......	5.24	Room	3.24
Selenium* (gray, stable, metallic)............	Hexagonal, A8	4.3640	......	4.9594	20°C	2.32
α (red, metastable)....	Monoclinic, P2₁/n	9.05	9.07	$\begin{cases} \beta = 90°46' \\ 11.61 \end{cases}$	Room	2.34
β (red, metastable)....	Monoclinic, C^5_{2h} or C^4_{2h} or C^2_5	12.76	8.06	$\begin{cases} \beta = 93°4' \\ 9.27 \end{cases}$	Room	
Silicon..............	Diamond cubic A4	5.4282	......	....	20°C	2.351
Silver...............	F.c.c. A1	4.0856	......	....	20°C	2.888
Sodium..............	B.c.c. A2	4.2906	......	....	20°C	3.715
Strontium............	F.c.c. A1	6.087	......		20°C	4.31
Sulfur, α, yellow*......	Orthorhombic A17	10.50	12.94	24.60	20°C	2.12
β.................	Monoclinic	10.92	11.04	$\begin{cases} \beta = 83°16' \\ 10.98 \end{cases}$	103°C	
Tantalum............	B.c.c. A2	3.3026	......	....	20°C	2.860
Tellurium............	Hexagonal A8	4.4559	......	5.9268	20°C	2.87
Terbium.............	C.p.h. A3	3.592	......	5.675	20°C	3.515
Thallium, α*..........	C.p.h. A3	3.4564	......	5.531	Room	3.407
β.................	B.c.c. A2	3.882	......		262°C	3.362
Thorium.............	F.c.c. A1	5.088	......	....	20°C	3.60
Thulium.............	C.p.h.	3.530	......	5.575	20°C	3.453
Tin, α, gray..........	Diamond cubic A4	6.47	......	....	18°C	2.81
β, white*............	Tetragonal A5	5.8311	......	3.1817	20°C	3.022
Titanium, α*..........	C.p.h. A3	2.9504	......	4.6833	25°C	2.89
β.................	B.c.c. A2	3.33	......		900°C	2.89
Tungsten (wolfram), α*..	B.c.c. A2	3.1648	......	....	20°C	2.739
β (unstable).........	Cubic A15	5.049	......		20°C	2.524
Uranium, α* (< 665°C).	Orthorhombic A20	2.858	5.877	4.955	20°C	2.77
β (665–775°C).......	Low symmetry					
γ (775–1130°C).......	B.c.c. A2	3.49	......	....	800°C	3.02
Vanadium............	B.c.c. A2	3.039	......		20°C	2.632
Virginium............	See Astatine					
Wolfram.............	See Tungsten					
Xenon...............	F.c.c. A1	6.25	......	....	−185°C	4.42
Ytterbium............	F.c.c. A1	5.488	......		....	3.874
Yttrium.............	C.p.h. A3	3.670	......	5.826	....	3.60
Zinc................	C.p.h. A3	2.664	......	4.945	....	2.664
Zirconium, α*.........	C.p.h. A3	3.230	......	5.133	....	3.17
β.................	B.c.c.	3.62	......	....	867°C	3.13

* Ordinary form of an element that exists (or is thought to exist) in more than one form.

INDEX

DATE DUE